Collins

Student Book, **Higher 1**

Approved by AQA

NEW GCSE MATHS
AQA Modular

Matches the 2010 GCSE Specification

Brian Speed • Keith Gordon • Kevin Evans • Trevor Senior • Chris Pearce

CONTENTS

CORE

UNIT 1: Statistics and Number

Remember: You will not be allowed the use of a calculator in your Unit 2 exam.

UNIT 2: Number and Algebra

INTRODUCTION

Welcome to Collins New GCSE Maths for AQA Modular Higher Book 1. The first part of this book covers all the Core content you need for your Unit 1 and Unit 2 exams. The second part covers the content that is specific for Unit 1 and Unit 2, divided into separate sections.

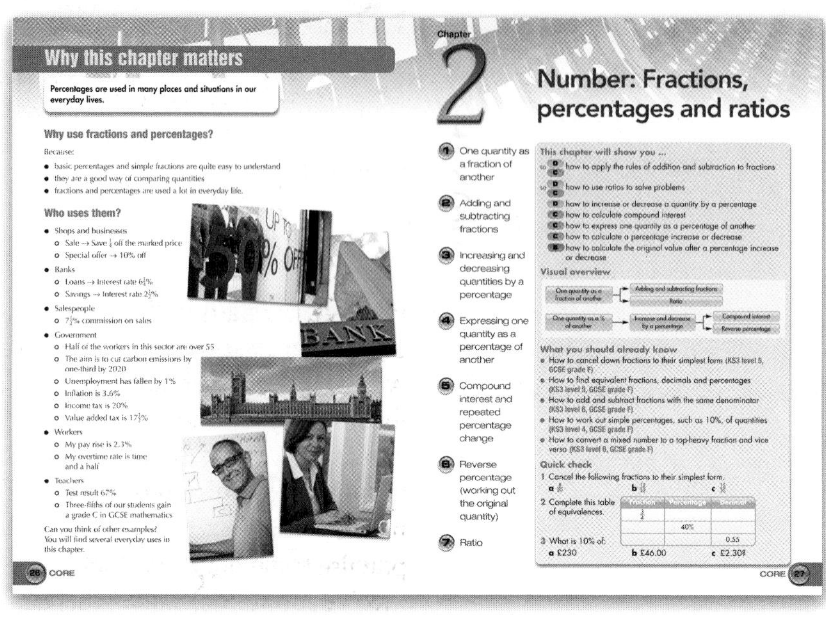

Why this chapter matters

Percentages are used in many places and situations in our everyday lives.

Why use fractions and percentages?

Because:

- basic percentages and simple fractions are quite easy to understand
- they are a good way of comparing quantities
- fractions and percentages are used a lot in everyday life.

Who uses them?

- Shops and businesses
  - Sale → Save $\frac{1}{4}$ off the marked price
  - Special offer → 10% off
- Banks
  - Loans → Interest rate $6\frac{3}{4}$%
  - Savings → Interest rate $2\frac{1}{2}$%
- Salespeople
  - $7\frac{1}{2}$% commission on sales
- Government
  - Half of the workers in this sector are over 55
  - The aim is to cut carbon emissions by one-third by 2020
  - Unemployment has fallen by 1%
  - Inflation is 3.6%
  - Income tax is 20%
  - Value added tax is $17\frac{1}{2}$%
- Workers
  - My pay rise is 2.3%
  - My overtime rate is time and a half
- Teachers
  - Test result 67%
  - Three-fifths of our students gain a grade C in GCSE mathematics

Can you think of other examples? You will find several everyday uses in this chapter.

26 CORE

Chapter 2

Number: Fractions, percentages and ratios

1. One quantity as a fraction of another
2. Adding and subtracting fractions
3. Increasing and decreasing quantities by a percentage
4. Expressing one quantity as a percentage of another
5. Compound interest and repeated percentage change
6. Reverse percentage (working out the original quantity)
7. Ratio

This chapter will show you ...

- D to C how to apply the rules of addition and subtraction to fractions
- D to C how to use ratios to solve problems
- D how to increase or decrease a quantity by a percentage
- C how to calculate compound interest
- C how to express one quantity as a percentage of another
- C how to calculate a percentage increase or decrease
- B how to calculate the original value after a percentage increase or decrease

Visual overview

One quantity as a fraction of another → Adding and subtracting fractions; Ratio

One quantity as a % of another → Increase and decrease by a percentage → Compound interest; Reverse percentage

What you should already know

- How to cancel down fractions to their simplest form (KS3 level 5, GCSE grade F)
- How to find equivalent fractions, decimals and percentages (KS3 level 5, GCSE grade F)
- How to add and subtract fractions with the same denominator (KS3 level 6, GCSE grade F)
- How to work out simple percentages, such as 10%, of quantities (KS3 level 4, GCSE grade F)
- How to convert a mixed number to a top-heavy fraction and vice versa (KS3 level 6, GCSE grade F)

Quick check

1 Cancel the following fractions to their simplest form.

a [illegible] **b** [illegible] **c** [illegible]

2 Complete this table of equivalences.

Fraction	Percentage	Decimal
$\frac{3}{4}$		
	40%	
		0.55

3 What is 10% of:

a £230 **b** £46.00 **c** £2.30?

CORE 27

Why this chapter matters

Find out why each chapter is important through the history of maths, seeing how maths links to other subjects and cultures, and how maths is related to real life.

Chapter overviews

Look ahead to see what maths you will be doing and how you can build on what you already know.

Colour-coded grades

Know what target grade you are working at and track your progress with the colour-coded grade panels at the side of the page.

Use of calculators

Questions where you must or could use your calculator are marked with icon.

Explanations involving calculators are based on *CASIO fx–83ES*.

Grade booster

Review what you have learnt and how to get to the next grade with the Grade booster at the end of each chapter.

Worked examples

Understand the topic before you start the exercise by reading the examples in blue boxes. These take you through questions step by step.

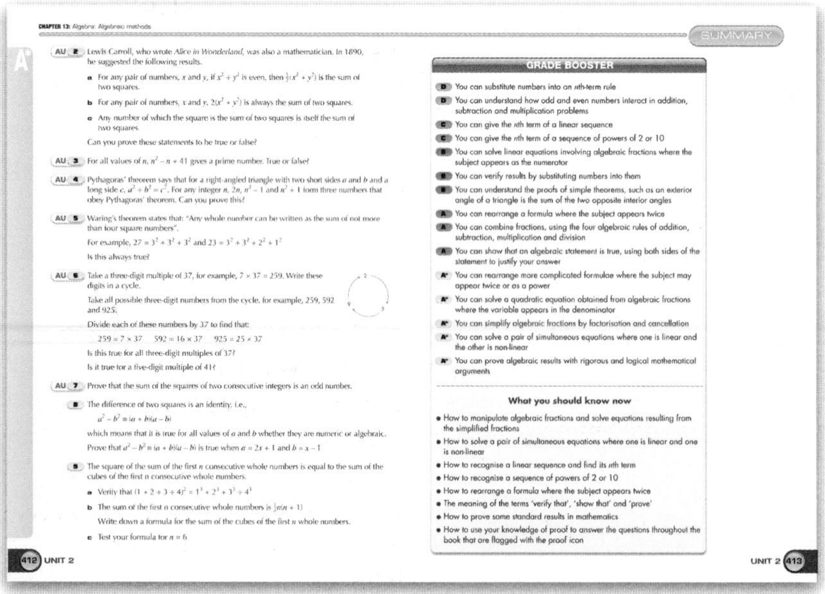

CHAPTER 13: Algebra: Algebraic methods

A*

AU **2** Lewis Carroll, who wrote *Alice in Wonderland*, was also a mathematician. In 1890, he suggested the following results.

a For any pair of numbers, x and y, if $x^2 + y^2$ is even, then $\frac{1}{2}(x^2 + y^2)$ is the sum of two squares.

b For any pair of numbers, x and y, $2(x^2 + y^2)$ is always the sum of two squares.

c Any number of which the square is the sum of two squares is itself the sum of two squares.

Can you prove these statements to be true or false?

AU **3** For all values of n, $n^2 - n + 41$ gives a prime number. True or false?

AU **4** Pythagoras' theorem says that for a right-angled triangle with two short sides a and b and a long side c, $a^2 + b^2 = c^2$. For any integer n, $2n$, $n^2 - 1$ and $n^2 + 1$ form three numbers that obey Pythagoras' theorem. Can you prove this?

AU **5** Waring's theorem states that: "Any whole number can be written as the sum of not more than four square numbers".

For example, $27 = 3^2 + 3^2 + 3^2$ and $23 = 3^2 + 3^2 + 2^2 + 1^2$

Is this always true?

AU **6** Take a three-digit multiple of 37, for example, $7 \times 37 = 259$. Write these digits in a cycle.

Take all possible three-digit numbers from the cycle, for example, 259, 592 and 925.

Divide each of these numbers by 37 to find that:

$259 = 7 \times 37$ $592 = 16 \times 37$ $925 = 25 \times 37$

Is this true for all three-digit multiples of 37?

Is it true for a five-digit multiple of 41?

AU **7** Prove that the sum of the squares of two consecutive integers is an odd number.

8 The difference of two squares is an identity, i.e.,

$a^2 - b^2 \equiv (a + b)(a - b)$

which means that it is true for all values of a and b whether they are numeric or algebraic. Prove that $a^2 - b^2 \equiv (a + b)(a - b)$ is true when $a = 2x + 1$ and $b = x - 1$

9 The square of the sum of the first n consecutive whole numbers is equal to the sum of the cubes of the first n consecutive whole numbers.

a Verify that $(1 + 2 + 3 + 4)^2 = 1^3 + 2^3 + 3^3 + 4^3$

b The sum of the first n consecutive whole numbers is $\frac{1}{2}n(n + 1)$

Write down a formula for the sum of the cubes of the first n whole numbers.

c Test your formula for $n = 6$

412 UNIT 2

SUMMARY

GRADE BOOSTER

- D You can substitute numbers into an nth-term rule
- D You can understand how odd and even numbers interact in addition, subtraction and multiplication problems
- C You can give the nth term of a linear sequence
- C You can give the nth term of a sequence of powers of 2 or 10
- B You can solve linear equations involving algebraic fractions where the subject appears as the numerator
- B You can verify results by substituting numbers into them
- B You can understand the proofs of simple theorems, such as an exterior angle of a triangle is the sum of the two opposite interior angles
- A You can rearrange a formula where the subject appears twice
- A You can combine fractions, using the four algebraic rules of addition, subtraction, multiplication and division
- A You can show that an algebraic statement is true, using both sides of the statement to justify your answer
- A* You can rearrange more complicated formulae where the subject may appear twice or as a power
- A* You can solve a quadratic equation obtained from algebraic fractions where the variable appears in the denominator
- A* You can simplify algebraic fractions by factorisation and cancellation
- A* You can solve a pair of simultaneous equations where one is linear and the other is non-linear
- A* You can prove algebraic results with rigorous and logical mathematical arguments

What you should know now

- How to manipulate algebraic fractions and solve equations resulting from the simplified fractions
- How to solve a pair of simultaneous equations where one is linear and one is non-linear
- How to recognise a linear sequence and find its nth term
- How to recognise a sequence of powers of 2 or 10
- How to rearrange a formula where the subject appears twice
- The meaning of the terms 'verify that', 'show that' and 'prove'
- How to prove some standard results in mathematics
- How to use your knowledge of proof to answer the questions throughout the book that are flagged with the proof icon

UNIT 2 413

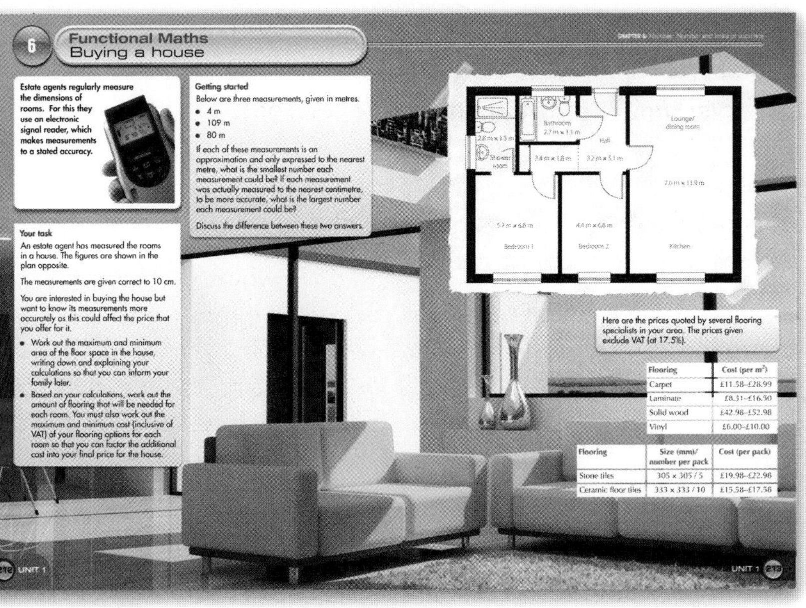

6 Functional Maths
Buying a house

Estate agents regularly measure the dimensions of rooms. For this they use an electronic signal reader, which makes measurements to a stated accuracy.

Getting started

Below are three measurements, given in metres.

- 4 m
- 109 m
- 80 m

If each of these measurements is an approximation and only expressed to the nearest metre, what is the smallest number each measurement could be? If each measurement was actually measured to the nearest centimetre, to be more accurate, what is the largest number each measurement could be?

Discuss the difference between these two answers.

Your task

An estate agent has measured the rooms in a house. The figures are shown in the plan opposite.

The measurements are given correct to 10 cm.

You are interested in buying the house but want to know its measurements more accurately as this could affect the price that you offer for it.

- Work out the maximum and minimum area of the floor space in the house, writing down and explaining your calculations so that you can inform your family later.
- Based on your calculations, work out the amount of flooring that will be needed for each room. You must also work out the maximum and minimum cost (inclusive of VAT) of your flooring options for each room so that you can factor the additional cost into your final price for the house.

Here are the prices quoted by several flooring specialists in your area. The prices given exclude VAT (at 17.5%).

Flooring	Cost (per m²)
Carpet	£11.58–£28.99
Laminate	£8.31–£16.50
Solid wood	£42.98–£52.98
Vinyl	£6.00–£10.00

Flooring	Size (mm)/ number per pack	Cost (per pack)
Stone tiles	305 × 305 / 5	£19.98–£22.98
Ceramic floor tiles	333 × 333 / 10	£15.58–£17.56

212 UNIT 1 UNIT 1 213

Functional maths

Practise functional maths skills to see how people use maths in everyday life. Look out for practice questions marked **FM**. There are also extra functional-maths and problem-solving activities at the end of every chapter to build and apply your skills.

New Assessment Objectives

Practise new parts of the curriculum (Assessment Objectives AO2 and AO3) with questions that assess your understanding marked **AU** and questions that test if you can solve problems marked **PS**. You will also practise some questions that involve several steps and where you have to choose which method to use; these also test AO2. There are also plenty of straightforward questions (AO1) that test if you can do the maths.

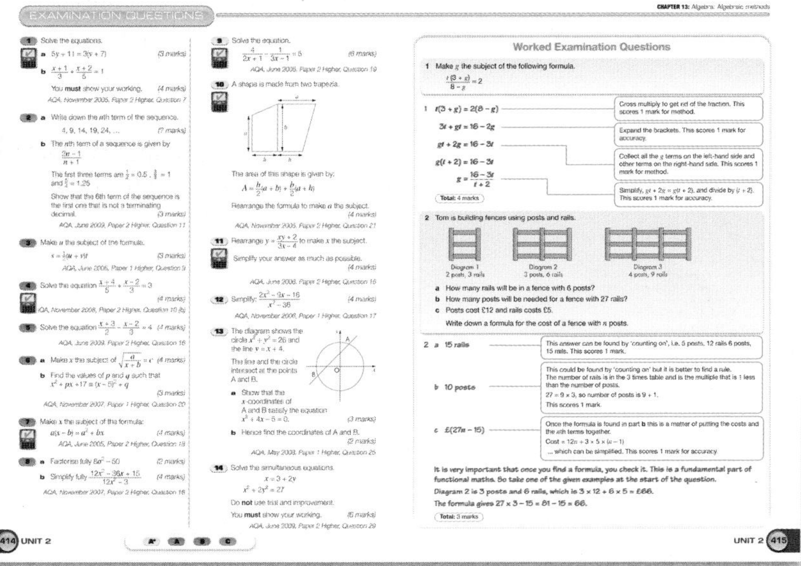

EXAMINATION QUESTIONS

CHAPTER 13: Algebra: Algebraic methods

Worked Examination Questions

1 Make g the subject of the following formula.

$$\frac{t(3+g)}{8-g} = 2$$

1 $t(3+g) = 2(8-g)$ — Cross multiply to get rid of the fraction. This scores 1 mark for method.

$3t + gt = 16 - 2g$ — Expand the brackets. This scores 1 mark for accuracy.

$gt + 2g = 16 - 3t$

$g(t+2) = 16 - 3t$ — Collect all the g terms on the left-hand side and other terms on the right-hand side. This scores 1 mark for method.

$g = \frac{16-3t}{t+2}$ — Simplify, $gt + 2g = g(t+2)$, and divide by $(t+2)$. This scores 1 mark for accuracy.

Total: 4 marks

2 Tom is building fences using posts and rails.

Diagram 1: 2 posts, 3 rails — Diagram 2: 3 posts, 6 rails — Diagram 3: 4 posts, 9 rails

a How many rails will be in a fence with 6 posts?

b How many posts will be needed for a fence with 27 rails?

c Posts cost £12 and rails costs £5.

Write down a formula for the cost of a fence with n posts.

2 a 15 rails — This answer can be found by 'counting on', i.e. 5 posts, 12 rails 6 posts, 15 rails. This scores 1 mark.

b 10 posts — This could be found by 'counting on' but it is better to find a rule. The number of rails is in the 3 times table and is the multiple that is 1 less than the number of posts. $27 = 9 \times 3$, so number of posts is $9 + 1$. This scores 1 mark.

c £(27n − 15) — Once the formula is found in part **b** this is a matter of putting the costs and the nth terms together. Cost $= 12n + 3 \times 5 \times (n-1)$ ... which can be simplified. This scores 1 mark for accuracy.

It is very important that once you find a formula, you check it. This is a fundamental part of functional maths. So take one of the given examples at the start of the question.

Diagram 2 is 3 posts and 6 rails, which is $3 \times 12 + 6 \times 5 = £66$.

The formula gives $27 \times 3 - 15 = 81 - 15 = 66$.

Total: 3 marks

414 UNIT 2 UNIT 2 415

Exam practice

Prepare for your exams with past exam questions and detailed worked exam questions with examiner comments to help you score maximum marks.

Quality of Written Communication (QWC)

Practise using accurate mathematical vocabulary and writing logical answers to questions to ensure you get your QWC (Quality of Written Communication) marks in the exams. The Glossary and worked exam questions will help you with this.

Why this chapter matters

Most jobs require some knowledge of mathematics. You should be competent in the basic number skills of addition, subtraction, multiplication and division using whole numbers, fractions and decimals. You should know when it is sensible to use estimation or approximation and when it is important to have exact answers.

You need to be able to identify the skills required when questions are set in real-life situations in preparation for the world of work.

Jobs or careers using mathematics

How many jobs can you think of that require some mathematics?

Here are a few job ideas.

Pilot
How much fuel do I need?

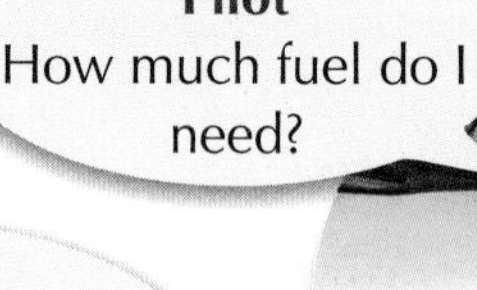

Engineer
What measurements do I need to take?

Doctor
How much medicine should I prescribe?

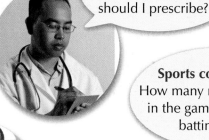

Cashier
What coins do I need to give change?

Sports commentator
How many minutes are left in the game? What is his batting average?

Baker
What quantity of flour should I order?

Delivery driver
What is the best route?

Accountant
How much profit has she made?

If you have chosen a job you would like to do, think of the questions you will need to ask and the mathematics you will require.

Chapter

Number: Number skills

1 Solving real-life problems

2 Multiplication and division with decimals

3 Approximation of calculations

This chapter will show you ...

D how to calculate with integers and decimals

D how to round numbers to a given number of significant figures

Visual overview

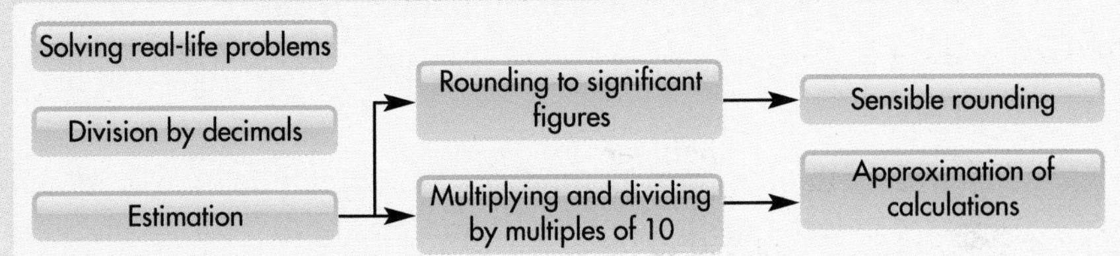

What you should already know

- How to add, subtract, multiply and divide with integers **(KS3 level 4, GCSE grade G)**
- The BIDMAS/BODMAS rule and how to substitute values into simple algebraic expressions **(KS3 level 5, GCSE grade F)**

Quick check

1 Work out the following.

a 6×78 **b** 3×122 **c** $432 \div 8$

d $3 \times 5 \times 20$ **e** $6 \times 34 \div 2$ **f** $5 \times (12 + 7)$

2 Work out the following.

a 23×167 **b** $984 \div 24$ **c** $(16 + 9)^2$

3 Work out the following.

a $2 + 3 \times 5$ **b** $(2 + 3) \times 5$ **c** $2 + 3^2 - 6$

1.1 Solving real-life problems

This section will show you how to:

- solve problems set in a real-life context

Key words
column method (or traditional method)
grid method (or box method)
long division
long multiplication
problem
strategy

In your GCSE examination, you will be given *real-life* **problems** that you have to *read carefully, think about* and then plan a **strategy** without using a calculator. These may involve arithmetical skills such as **long multiplication** and **long division**.

There are several ways to do these, so make sure you are familiar with and confident with at least one of them.

The **grid method** (or **box method**) for long multiplication is shown in the first example and the standard **column method** (or **traditional method**) for long division is shown in the second example. In this type of problem it is important to show your working as you will get marks for correct methods.

EXAMPLE 1

A supermarket receives a delivery of 235 cases of tins of beans. Each case contains 24 tins.

a How many tins of beans does the supermarket receive altogether?

b 5% of the tins were damaged. These were thrown away. The supermarket knows that it sells, on average, 250 tins of beans a day. How many days will the delivery of beans last before a new delivery is needed?

a The number of tins is worked out by the multiplication 235 × 24.

Using the grid method:

×	200	30	5
20	4000	600	100
4	800	120	20

$$\begin{array}{r} 4000 \\ 600 \\ 100 \\ +\ 800 \\ 120 \\ 20 \\ \hline 5640 \end{array}$$

Using the column method:

$$\begin{array}{r} 235 \\ \times\ \ 24 \\ \hline 940 \\ 4700 \\ \hline 5640 \end{array}$$

So the answer is 5640 tins.

FM Functional Maths **AU** (AO2) Assessing Understanding **PS** (AO3) Problem Solving

b 10% of 5640 is 564, so 5% is 564 ÷ 2 = 282

This leaves 5640 – 282 = 5358 tins to be sold.

There are 21 lots of 250 in 5358 (you should know that 4 × 250 = 1000), so the beans will last for 21 days before another delivery is needed.

EXAMPLE 2

A party of 613 children and 59 adults are going on a day out to a theme park.

a How many coaches, each holding 53 people, will be needed?

b One adult gets into the theme park free for every 15 children. How many adults will have to pay to get in?

a Altogether there are 613 + 59 = 672 people.

So the number of coaches needed is 672 ÷ 53 (number of seats on each coach).

$$\begin{array}{r} 12 \\ 53\overline{)672} \\ \underline{530} \\ 142 \\ \underline{106} \\ 36 \end{array}$$

The answer is 12 remainder 36. So, there will be 12 full coaches and one coach with 36 people on it. So, they would have to book 13 coaches.

b This is also a division, 613 ÷ 15. This can be done quite easily if you know the 15 times table as 4 × 15 = 60, so 40 × 15 = 600. This leaves a remainder of 13. So 40 adults get in free and 59 – 40 = 19 adults will have to pay.

EXERCISE 1A

1 There are 48 cans of soup in a crate. A supermarket had a delivery of 125 crates of soup.

a How many cans of soup were in this delivery?

b The supermarket is running a promotion on soup. If you buy five cans you get one free. Each can costs 39p. How much will it cost to get 32 cans of soup?

2 Greystones Primary School has 12 classes, each of which has 24 students.

a How many students are there at Greystones Primary School?

b The student–teacher ratio is 18 to 1. That means there is one teacher for every 18 students. How many teachers are there at the school?

3 Barnsley Football Club is organising travel for an away game. 1300 adults and 500 juniors want to go. Each coach holds 48 people and costs £320 to hire. Tickets to the match are £18 for adults and £10 for juniors.

a How many coaches will be needed?

b The club is charging adults £26 and juniors £14 for travel and a ticket. How much profit does the club make out of the trip?

D

D

4 A first-class letter costs 39p to post and a second-class letter costs 30p. How much will it cost to send 20 first-class and 90 second-class letters?

PS 5 Kirsty collects small models of animals. Each one costs 45p. She saves enough to buy 23 models but when she goes to the shop she finds that the price has gone up to 55p. How many can she buy now?

PS 6 Eunice wanted to save up for a mountain bike that costs £250. She baby-sits each week for 6 hours for £2.75 an hour, and does a Saturday job that pays £27.50. She saves three-quarters of her weekly earnings. How many weeks will it take her to save enough to buy the bike?

PS 7 The magazine *Teen Dance* comes out every month. In a newsagent the magazine costs £2.45. The annual (yearly) subscription for the magazine is £21. How much cheaper is each magazine when bought on subscription?

AU 8 Paula buys a sofa. She pays a deposit of 10% of the cash price and then 36 monthly payments of £12.50. In total she pays £495. How much was the cash price of the sofa?

FM 9 There are 125 people at a wedding. They need to get to the reception.

52 people are going by coach and the rest are travelling in cars. Each car can take up to five people.

What is the least number of cars needed to take everyone to the reception?

C

PS 10 A fish pond in a shop contains 240 fish.

Each week the manager has a delivery from one supplier of 45 new fish that he adds to the pond.

On average he sells 62 fish each week. When his stock falls below 200 fish, he buys in extra fish from a different supplier. After how many weeks will he need to buy in extra fish?

AU 11 A baker supplies bread rolls to a catering company.

The bread rolls are sold in packs of 24 for £1.99 per pack. The catering company want 500 fresh rolls each day. How much will the bill be for one week, assuming they do not work on Sundays?

FM 12 Gavin's car does 8 miles to each litre of petrol. He does 12 600 miles a year of which 4 600 is on company business.

Petrol costs 95p per litre.

Insurance and servicing costs £800 a year.

Gavin's company gives him an allowance of 40p for each mile he drives on company business.

How much does Gavin pay towards running his car each year?

1.2 Multiplication and division with decimals

This section will show you how to:
- multiply a decimal number by another decimal number
- divide by decimals by changing the calculation to division by an integer

Key words
decimal places
decimal point
integer

Multiplying two decimal numbers together

Follow these steps to multiply one decimal number by another decimal number.

- First, complete the whole calculation as if the **decimal points** were not there.
- Then, count the total number of **decimal places** in the two decimal numbers. This gives the number of decimal places in the answer.

EXAMPLE 3

Work out: 3.42 × 2.7

Ignoring the decimal points gives the following calculation.

Now, 3.42 has two decimal places (.42) and 2.7 has one decimal place (.7). So, the total number of decimal places in the answer is three.

$$\begin{array}{r} 342 \\ \times \quad 27 \\ \hline 2394 \\ 6840 \\ \hline 9234 \\ \hline \end{array}$$

So 3.42 × 2.7 = 9.234

Dividing by a decimal

EXAMPLE 4

Work out the following. **a** 42 ÷ 0.2 **b** 19.8 ÷ 0.55

a The calculation is 42 ÷ 0.2 which can be rewritten as 420 ÷ 2 . In this case both values have been multiplied by 10 to make the divisor into a whole number or **integer**. This is then a straightforward division to which the answer is 210.

Another way to view this is as a fraction problem.

$$\frac{42}{0.2} = \frac{42}{0.2} \times \frac{10}{10} = \frac{420}{2} = \frac{210}{1} = 210$$

b 19.8 ÷ 0.55 = 198 ÷ 5.5 = 1980 ÷ 55

This then becomes a long division problem.

This has been solved by the method of repeated subtraction.

$$\begin{array}{rr} 1980 & \\ -\ 1100 & 20 \times 55 \\ \hline 880 & \\ -\ 440 & 8 \times 55 \\ \hline 440 & \\ -\ 440 & 8 \times 55 \\ \hline 0 & 36 \times 55 \end{array}$$

So 19.8 ÷ 0.55 = 36

EXERCISE 1B

D

1 Work out each of these.

a 0.14×0.2 **b** 0.3×0.3 **c** 0.24×0.8 **d** 5.82×0.52

e 5.8×1.23 **f** 5.6×9.1 **g** 0.875×3.5 **h** 9.12×5.1

2 For each of the following:

i estimate the answer by first rounding each number to the nearest whole number

ii calculate the exact answer and then calculate the difference between this and your answers to part **i**.

a 4.8×7.3 **b** 2.4×7.6 **c** 15.3×3.9 **d** 20.1×8.6

e 4.35×2.8 **f** 8.13×3.2 **g** 7.82×5.2 **h** 19.8×7.1

AU 3 **a** Use any method to work out: 26×22

b Use your answer to part **a** to work out the following.

i 2.6×2.2 **ii** 1.3×1.1 **iii** 2.6×8.8

AU 4 Lee is trying to work out the answer to 8.6×4.7. His answer is 40.24.

a Without working it out, can you tell whether his answer is correct?

b Tracy says the answer is 46.42.
Without working out the answer can you tell whether her answer is correct?
In each part, show how you decided.

PS 5 Here are three calculations. $26.66 \div 3.1$ $17.15 \div 3.5$ $55.04 \div 8.6$

Which has the largest answer? Show how you know.

6 Work out each of these.

a $3.6 \div 0.2$ **b** $56 \div 0.4$ **c** $0.42 \div 0.3$ **d** $8.4 \div 0.7$ **e** $4.26 \div 0.2$

f $3.45 \div 0.5$ **g** $83.7 \div 0.03$ **h** $0.968 \div 0.08$ **i** $7.56 \div 0.4$

7 Work out each of these.

a $67.2 \div 0.24$ **b** $6.36 \div 0.53$ **c** $0.936 \div 5.2$ **d** $162 \div 0.36$ **e** $2.17 \div 3.5$

f $98.8 \div 0.26$ **g** $0.468 \div 1.8$ **h** $132 \div 0.55$ **i** $0.984 \div 0.082$

8 A pile of paper is 6 cm high. Each sheet is 0.008 cm thick. How many sheets are in the pile of paper?

9 Doris buys a big bag of safety pins. The bag weighs 180 g. Each safety pin weighs 0.6 g. How many safety pins are in the bag?

AU 10 **a** Use any method to work out: $81 \div 3$

b Use your answer to part **a** to work these out.

i $8.1 \div 0.3$ **ii** $0.81 \div 30$ **iii** $0.081 \div 0.3$

D

FM **11** A party of 24 scouts and their leader went to a zoo. The cost of a ticket for each scout was £2.15, and the cost of a ticket for the leader was £2.60. What was the total cost of entering the zoo?

PS **12** Mark went shopping.
He went into three stores and bought one item from each store.

Music Store		**Clothes Store**		**Book Store**	
CDs	£5.98	Shirt	£12.50	Magazine	£2.25
DVDs	£7.99	Jeans	£32.00	Pen	£3.98

In total he spent £43.97. What did he buy?

1.3 Approximation of calculations

This section will show you how to:

- round to a given number of significant figures
- approximate the result before multiplying two numbers together
- approximate the result before dividing two numbers
- round a calculation, at the end of a problem, to give what is considered to be a sensible answer

Key words
approximate
estimation
round
significant figures

Rounding to significant figures

We often use **significant figures** when we want to **approximate** a number with quite a few digits in it. We use this technique in **estimations**.

Look at this table which shows some numbers rounded to one, two and three significant figures (sf).

One sf	8	50	200	90 000	0.000 07	0.003	0.4
Two sf	67	4.8	0.76	45 000	730	0.0067	0.40
Three sf	312	65.9	40.3	0.0761	7.05	0.003 01	0.400

The steps taken to round a number to a given number of significant figures are very similar to those used for rounding to a given number of decimal places.

- From the left, count the digits. If you are rounding to 2 sf, count two digits, for 3 sf count three digits, and so on. When the original number is less than 1, start counting from the first non-zero digit.
- Look at the next digit to the right. When the value of this next digit is less than 5, leave the digit you counted to the same. However if the value of this next digit is equal to or greater than 5, add 1 to the digit you counted to.
- Ignore all the other digits, but put in enough zeros to keep the number the right size (value).

For example, look at the following table, which shows some numbers rounded to one, two and three significant figures, respectively.

Number	Rounded to 1 sf	Rounded to 2 sf	Rounded to 3 sf
45 281	50 000	45 000	45 300
568.54	600	570	569
7.3782	7	7.4	7.38
8054	8000	8100	8050
99.8721	100	100	99.9
0.7002	0.7	0.70	0.700

EXERCISE 1C

D

1 Round each of the following numbers to 1 significant figure.

a 46 313 **b** 57 123 **c** 30 569 **d** 94 558 **e** 85 299

f 0.5388 **g** 0.2823 **h** 0.005 84 **i** 0.047 85 **j** 0.000 876

k 9.9 **l** 89.5 **m** 90.78 **n** 199 **o** 999.99

2 Round each of the following numbers to 2 significant figures.

a 56 147 **b** 26 813 **c** 79 611 **d** 30 578 **e** 14 009

f 1.689 **g** 4.0854 **h** 2.658 **i** 8.0089 **j** 41.564

k 0.8006 **l** 0.458 **m** 0.0658 **n** 0.9996 **o** 0.009 82

3 Round each of the following to the number of significant figures (sf) indicated.

a 57 402 (1 sf) **b** 5288 (2 sf) **c** 89.67 (3 sf) **d** 105.6 (2 sf)

e 8.69 (1 sf) **f** 1.087 (2 sf) **g** 0.261 (1 sf) **h** 0.732 (1 sf)

i 0.42 (1 sf) **j** 0.758 (1 sf) **k** 0.185 (1 sf) **l** 0.682 (1 sf)

4 What are the least and the greatest numbers of sweets that can be found in these jars?

a

b

c

5 3000 × 400 = 1 200 000

Write down four multiplication problems for which that answer is 1 200 000.

C

6 What are the least and the greatest numbers of people that live in these towns?

Elsecar population 800 (to 1 significant figure)
Hoyland population 1200 (to 2 significant figures)
Barnsley population 165 000 (to 3 significant figures)

PS 7 A joiner estimates that he has 20 pieces of skirting board in stock. This is correct to 1 sf.

He uses three pieces and now has 10 left, to 1 sf. How many pieces could he have had to start with? Work out all possible answers.

PS 8 There are 500 fish in a pond, to 1 sf. What is the least possible number of fish that could be taken from the pond so that there are 400 fish in the pond to 1 sf?

AU 9 Karen says that the population of Preston is 132 000 to the nearest thousand. Donte says that the population of Preston is 130 000. Explain why Donte could also be correct.

Multiplying and dividing by multiples of 10

Questions often involve multiplication of multiples of 10, 100 and so on. This method is used in estimation. You should have the skill to do this mentally so that you can check that your answers to calculations are about right. (Approximation of calculations is covered in the next section.)

Use a calculator to work out the following.

a $300 \times 200 =$ **b** $100 \times 40 =$ **c** $2000 \times 0.3 =$

d $0.2 \times 50 =$ **e** $0.2 \times 0.5 =$ **f** $0.3 \times 0.04 =$

Can you see a way of doing these without using a calculator or pencil and paper? Basically, you multiply the non-zero digits and then work out the number of zeros or the position of the decimal point by combining the zeros or decimal places in the original calculation.

Dividing is almost as simple. Try doing the following on your calculator.

a $400 \div 20 =$ **b** $200 \div 50 =$ **c** $1000 \div 0.2 =$

d $300 \div 0.3 =$ **e** $250 \div 0.05 =$ **f** $30\,000 \div 0.6 =$

Once again, there is an easy way of doing these 'in your head'. Look at these examples.

$300 \times 4000 = 1\,200\,000$ $5000 \div 200 = 25$ $20 \times 0.5 = 10$

$0.6 \times 5000 = 3000$ $400 \div 0.02 = 20\,000$ $800 \div 0.2 = 4000$

Can you see a connection between the digits, the number of zeros and the position of the decimal point, and the way in which these calculations are worked out?

EXERCISE 1D

D

1 Without using a calculator, write down the answers to these.

a 200×300 **b** 30×4000 **c** 50×200 **d** 0.3×50 **e** 200×0.7

f 200×0.5 **g** 0.1×2000 **h** 0.2×0.14 **i** 0.3×0.3 **j** $(20)^2$

k $(20)^3$ **l** $(0.4)^2$ **m** 0.3×150 **n** 0.4×0.2 **o** 0.5×0.5

p $20 \times 40 \times 5000$ **q** $20 \times 20 \times 900$

D

2 Without using a calculator, write down the answers to these.

a 2000 ÷ 400 **b** 3000 ÷ 60 **c** 5000 ÷ 200

d 300 ÷ 0.5 **e** 2100 ÷ 0.7 **f** 2000 ÷ 0.4

g 3000 ÷ 1.5 **h** 400 ÷ 0.2 **i** 2000 × 40 ÷ 200

j 200 × 20 ÷ 0.5 **k** 200 × 6000 ÷ 0.3 **l** 20 × 80 × 60 ÷ 0.03

AU 3 You are given that 16 × 34 = 544
Write down the value of:

a 160 × 340 **b** 544 000 ÷ 34

PS 4 Match each calculation to its answer and then write out the calculations in order, starting with the smallest answer.

5000 × 4000	600 × 8000	200 000 × 700	30 × 90 000
140 000 000	4 800 000	2 700 000	20 000 000

5 In 2009 there were £28 000 million worth of £20 notes in circulation.
How many notes is this?

Approximation of calculations

How do you approximate the value of a calculation?

What do you actually do when you try to approximate an answer to a problem?

For example, what is the approximate answer to 35.1 × 6.58?

To approximate the answer in this and many other similar cases, you simply round each number to 1 significant figure, then work out the calculation.

So in this case, the approximation is:

35.1 × 6.58 ≈ 40 × 7 = 280

Note: ≈ symbol means 'approximately equal to'.

For the division 89.1 ÷ 2.98, the approximate answer is 90 ÷ 3 = 30

Sometimes when dividing it can be sensible to round to 2 significant figures instead of 1 significant figure. For example:

24.3 ÷ 3.87 using 24 ÷ 4 gives an approximate answer of 6

whereas

24.3 ÷ 3.87 using 20 ÷ 4 gives an approximate answer of 5

Both of these answers would be acceptable in the GCSE examination as they are both sensible answers, but generally rounding to 1 significant figure is easier.

If you are using a calculator, whenever you see a calculation with a numerator and denominator *always* put brackets around the top and the bottom. This is to remind you that the numerator and denominator must be worked out separately before the division. You can work out the numerator and denominator separately but most calculators will work out the answer straight away if you use brackets. You are expected to use a calculator *efficiently*; doing the calculation in stages is not efficient.

EXAMPLE 5

a Find approximate answers to these calculations.

i $\frac{213 \times 69}{42}$ **ii** $\frac{78 \times 397}{0.38}$

b Use a calculator to work out the answer. Round this to 3 significant figures.

a i Round each number to 1 significant figure. $\frac{200 \times 70}{40}$

Work out the numerator. $= \frac{14\,000}{40}$

Divide by the denominator. $= 350$

ii Round each value to 1 significant figure. $\frac{80 \times 400}{0.4}$

Work out the numerator. $= \frac{32\,000}{0.4}$

$= \frac{320\,000}{4}$

Divide by the denominator. $= 80\,000$

b Use a calculator to check your approximate answers.

i $\frac{213 \times 69}{42} = \frac{(213 \times 69)}{(42)}$

So key in

(2 1 3 × 6 9) ÷ (4 2) =

The display should say 349.9285714 which rounds to 350. This agrees exactly with the estimate.

Note that you do not have to put brackets around the 42 but it is a good habit to get into.

ii $\frac{78 \times 397}{0.38} = \frac{(78 \times 397)}{(0.38)}$

So key in

(7 8 × 3 9 7) ÷ (0 • 3 8) =

The display should say 81489.47368 which rounds to 81 500. This agrees with the estimate.

EXERCISE 1E

1 Find approximate answers to the following.

a 5435×7.31 **b** 5280×3.211 **c** $63.24 \times 3.514 \times 4.2$

d $354 \div 79.8$ **e** $5974 \div 5.29$ **f** $208 \div 0.378$

D

D

2 Use a calculator to work out the answers to question **1**. Round your answers to 3 significant figures and compare them with the estimates you made.

3 By rounding, find approximate answers to these.

a $\dfrac{573 \times 783}{107}$ **b** $\dfrac{783 - 572}{24}$ **c** $\dfrac{352 + 657}{999}$

d $\dfrac{78.3 - 22.6}{2.69}$ **e** $\dfrac{3.82 \times 7.95}{9.9}$ **f** $\dfrac{11.78 \times 61.8}{39.4}$

4 Use a calculator to work out the answers to question **3**. Round your answers to 3 significant figures and compare them with the estimates you made.

5 Find the approximate monthly pay of the following people, whose annual salaries are given.

a Paul £35 200 **b** Michael £25 600 **c** Jennifer £18 125 **d** Ross £8420

6 Find the approximate annual pay of the following people, whose earnings are shown.

a Kevin £270 a week **b** Malcolm £1528 a month **c** David £347 a week

AU **7** A farmer bought 2713 kg seed at a cost of £7.34 per kg. Find the approximate total cost of this seed.

8 A greengrocer sold a box of 450 oranges for £37. Approximately how much did each orange sell for?

9 Gold bars weigh 400 ounces (12.44 kg). On 6 October 2009, one gold bar was worth $413 080.

Approximately how much is one ounce of gold worth, in dollars?

C

FM **10** It took me 6 hours 40 minutes to drive from Sheffield to Bude, a distance of 295 miles. My car uses petrol at the rate of about 32 miles per gallon. The petrol cost £3.51 per gallon.

a Approximately how many miles did I travel each hour?

b Approximately how many gallons of petrol did I use in going from Sheffield to Bude?

c What was the approximate cost of all the petrol I used in the journey to Bude and back again?

11 By rounding, find an approximate answer to each of the following.

a $\dfrac{462 \times 79}{0.42}$ **b** $\dfrac{583 - 213}{0.21}$ **c** $\dfrac{252 + 551}{0.78}$ **d** $\dfrac{296 \times 32}{0.325}$

e $\dfrac{297 + 712}{0.578 - 0.321}$ **f** $\dfrac{893 \times 87}{0.698 \times 0.47}$ **g** $\dfrac{38.3 + 27.5}{0.776}$ **h** $\dfrac{29.7 + 12.6}{0.26}$

i $\dfrac{4.93 \times 3.81}{0.38 \times 0.51}$ **j** $\dfrac{12.31 \times 16.9}{0.394 \times 0.216}$

12 Use a calculator to work out the answers to question **11**. Round your answers to 3 significant figures and compare them with the estimates you made.

C

13 A sheet of paper is 0.012 cm thick. Approximately how many sheets will there be in a pile of paper that is 6.35 cm deep?

PS 14 Kirsty arranges for magazines to be put into envelopes. She sorts out 178 magazines between 10.00 am and 1.00 pm. Approximately how many magazines will she be able to sort in a week in which she works for 17 hours?

AU 15 A box full of magazines weighs 8 kg. One magazine weighs about 15 g. Approximately how many magazines are there in the box?

16 Use your calculator to work out the following. In each case:

i write down the full calculator display of the answer

ii round your answer to 3 significant figures.

a $\dfrac{12.3 + 64.9}{6.9 - 4.1}$ **b** $\dfrac{13.8 \times 23.9}{3.2 \times 6.1}$ **c** $\dfrac{48.2 + 58.9}{3.62 \times 0.042}$

Sensible rounding

Sensible rounding is simply writing or saying answers to questions that have a real-life context so that the answer makes sense and is the sort of thing someone might say in a normal conversation.

For example:

'The distance from Rotherham to Sheffield is 9 miles,' is a sensible statement.
'The distance from Rotherham to Sheffield is 8.7864 miles,' is not sensible.

'Painting a house takes 6 tins of paint,' is sensible.
'Painting a house takes 5.91 tins of paint,' is not sensible.

As a general rule, if it sounds sensible it will be acceptable.

In a question for which you are asked to give an answer to a sensible or appropriate degree of accuracy, use the following rule. Give the answer to the same accuracy as the numbers in the question. So, for example, if the numbers in the question are given to 2 significant figures give your answer to 2 significant figures but remember, unless working out an approximation, do all the working to at least 4 significant figures or use the calculator display.

EXERCISE 1F

D

1 Round each of the figures in these statements to a suitable degree of accuracy.

a I am 1.7359 metres tall.

b It took me 5 minutes 44.83 seconds to mend the television.

c My kitten weighs 237.97 grams.

d The correct temperature at which to drink Earl Grey tea is 82.739 °C.

e There were 34 827 people at the test match yesterday.

f The distance from Wath to Sheffield is 15.528 miles.

g The area of the floor is 13.673 m^2.

D

FM 2 Rewrite the following article, using sensible numbers.

It was a hot day; the temperature was 81.699 °F and still rising. I had now walked 5.3289 km in just over 113.98 minutes. But I didn't care since I knew that the 43 275 people watching the race were cheering me on. I won by clipping 6.2 seconds off the record time. This was the 67th time it had happened since records first began in 1788. Well, next year I will only have 15 practice walks beforehand as I strive to beat the record by at least another 4.9 seconds.

3 1 litre = 1000 cm^3

About how many test tubes, each holding 24 cm^3 of water, can be filled from a 1 litre flask?

FM 4 A light aircraft cruises at 104 mph. It travels for 2 hours 50 minutes.

Approximately how long is the flight?

AU 5 A lorry load of scrap metal weighs 39.715 tonnes. It is worth £20.35 per tonne.

Approximately how much is the load worth?

C

6 If I walk at an average speed of 70 metres per minute, approximately how long will it take me to walk a distance of 3 km?

7 About how many stamps at 21p each can I buy for £12?

8 At Manchester United, it takes 160 minutes for 43 500 fans to get into the ground. On average, about how many fans are let into the ground every minute?

9 A 5p coin weighs 4.2 g. Approximately how much will one million pounds worth of 5p pieces weigh?

PS 10 The accurate temperature is 18.2 °C. David rounds the temperature to the nearest 5 °C.

David says the temperature is about 20 °C.

How much would the temperature need to rise for David to say that the temperature is about 25 °C?

AU 11 The distance from the Sun to Earth is approximately 149 000 000 km. The speed of light is approximately 300 000 km per second.

Use your calculator to work out how many seconds it takes for light to travel from the Sun to Earth.

Give your answer to a sensible degree of accuracy.

AU 12 The population density of a country is measured by dividing the population by the area. For example the population of the United Kingdom is 61 700 000 and the area is 243 000 km^2. So the population density is approximately 250 people per square kilometre.

The most densely populated country is Macau with a population of 541 200 and an area of 29.2 km^2.

The least densely populated country is Greenland with a population of 57 000 and an area of 2 176 000 km^2.

How many times is the population density of Macau greater than the population density of Greenland?

Give your answer to a suitable degree of accuracy.

GRADE BOOSTER

- **D** You can recognise and work out multiples, factors and primes
- **D** You can multiply and divide with negative numbers
- **D** You can estimate the values of calculations involving positive numbers bigger than one
- **D** You can round numbers to a given number of significant figures
- **C** You can estimate the values of calculations involving positive numbers between zero and one
- **C** You can write a number as the product of its prime factors
- **C** You can work out the LCM and HCF of pairs of numbers
- **C** You can use a calculator efficiently and know how to give answers to an appropriate degree of accuracy
- **B** You can work out the square roots of some decimal numbers
- **B** You can estimate answers involving the square roots of decimals

What you should know now

- How to solve complex real-life problems without a calculator
- How to divide by decimals with up to two decimal places
- How to estimate the values of calculations including those with decimal fractions, and use a calculator efficiently
- How to write a number in prime factor form and find LCMs and HCFs
- How to find the square roots of some decimal numbers

EXAMINATION QUESTIONS

1 Frank earns £12 per hour. He works for 40 hours per week. He saves $\frac{1}{5}$ of his earnings each week. *(1 mark)*

How many weeks will it take him to save £500? *(1 mark)*

AQA, June 2009, Module 3 Higher, Question 4

2 A floor measures 4.75 metres by 3.5 metres. It is to be covered with square tiles of side 25 centimetres.

Tiles are sold in boxes of 16. How many boxes are needed?

3 Gianni wants to tile the wall behind his bath. The total area measures 3.45 metres by 1.85 metres. He is going to use square tiles of side 15 centimetres. Tiles are sold in boxes of 24. How many boxes of tiles does he need?

4 Work out:

$$\frac{21.6 \times 64}{35.1 + 9.57}$$

a Write down your full calculator display. *(1 mark)*

b Write your answer to two decimal places. *(1 mark)*

AQA, June 2009, Module 3 Higher, Question 1

5 Work out as a decimal:

$$\frac{4.6^2}{8.6 - 2.7}$$

a Write down your full calculator display. *(1 mark)*

b Write your answer to three significant figures. *(1 mark)*

AQA, March 2008, Module 3 Higher, Question 4

6 Use approximations to estimate the value of:

$$\frac{212 \times 7.88}{0.365}$$

7 Ahmed, Briony and Carl used calculators to find the value of:

$$\frac{56.94}{7.16 \times 0.83}$$

Ahmed's answer was 6.5797, Briony had 9.581 and Carl made it 95.81.

Use approximations to find out which one was correct.

Worked Examination Questions

1 Estimate the result of the calculation

$$\frac{195.71 - 53.62}{\sqrt{0.0375}}$$

Show the estimates you make.

1 $\frac{200 - 50}{\sqrt{0.04}}$ — First round each number to 1 significant figure. Rounding the two numbers in the numerator to 1sf gets 1 mark for method.

$\frac{150}{0.2}$ — Working out the numerator and taking out the square root in the denominator gets 1 mark.

$\frac{150}{0.2} = \frac{1500}{2} = 750$ — Change the problem so it becomes division by an integer 750 gets 1 mark for accuracy.

Total: 3 marks

FM **2** I earn £30 000 in 12 months.

Half of this is spent on tax.

How much do I have left each month?

2 30 000 ÷ 2 or £15 000 — Work out how much I spend on tax or how much I have left. This is the same calculation as it is half of £30 000 and gets 1 mark for method. Note the answer of £15 000 does not need to be worked out at this stage.

30 000 ÷ 2 ÷ 12 — The next step is to calculate one twelfth of £30 000 ÷ 2. This gets 1 mark for method.

= £1250 — This gets 1 mark for accuracy.

Total: 3 marks

PS **3** Two numbers have been rounded.
The first number is 360 to two significant figures.
The second number is 500 to one significant figure.

What is the smallest sum of the two original numbers?

3 The smallest that the first number could be is 355.
The smallest that the second number could be is 450. — Realising that each number needs to be the smallest possible gets 1 mark for method. Either value 355 or 450 gets 1 mark for accuracy.

Smallest sum = 355 + 450 = 805 — Correctly adding the two smallest numbers gets 1 mark for accuracy.

Total: 3 marks

1 Functional Maths
Planning a dinner party

You are planning a dinner party but have not finalised your guest list or menu.

You have decided to make your dessert from scratch because it will be cheaper than buying it from the local shop. Your Aunt Mildred has helped you by giving you four recipes for desserts that all your friends will like: crème caramel, blueberry and lime cheesecake, mango sorbet and chocolate brownies. You have already researched the prices of the ingredients required to make these desserts and are now ready to plan which ones to make!

Getting started

Consider the questions below to get you started.

- How many 150 g portions can I get from 1 kg?
- How many 75-g bars of chocolate would I need to buy if I wanted 0.5 kg of chocolate?
- What is cheaper, three 330-ml cans of lemonade at 59p per can, or a litre bottle of lemonade at £1.80?
- In a meeting one packet of biscuits is bought per three people attending. How many packets would be needed if 20 people attend the meeting?

Your task

You have £50 to spend on your desserts.

Working in pairs, decide on several different numbers of guests that you might have at your dinner party. For each potential number of guests, plan three different combinations of desserts to make, and work out how much these combinations would cost overall and per person.

Ingredient costs

Item	Amount	Cost
Butter	500 g	£2.40
Eggs	6	£1.10
Lime	1	20p
Mango	1	£1.50
Milk	2.272 litres	£1.53
Plain chocolate	200 g	£1.09
Plain flour	1.5 kg	75p
Caster sugar	1 kg	£1.25
Granulated sugar	2 kg	£1.90
Walnuts	200 g	£2.50
Vanilla extract	30 ml	£1.55
Baking powder	50 g	£1.25
Biscuits	275 g	89p
Blueberries	500 g	£3.99
Quark	10 oz	£2.49
Double cream	284 ml	£1.89
Sour cream	284 ml	£1.39
Gelatine sachet	25 g	99p

(Ingredients can only be bought in these amounts or multiples of these amounts.)

Recipes

Crème Caramel – serves 6

500 ml milk
2 eggs
4 egg yolks
225 g caster sugar
1 teaspoon of vanilla extract

Blueberry and Lime Cheesecake – serves 8

10 oz sweet oaty biscuits
4 oz butter
1 lb 2 oz blueberries
$8\frac{1}{2}$ oz caster sugar
Grated zest and juice of two limes
20 oz of quark
$\frac{1}{2}$ pint of double cream
4 tsp powdered gelatine
$\frac{1}{2}$ pint sour cream

Mango Sorbet – serves 8

4 large ripe mangos
Juice of 2 large limes
450 ml sugar syrup
(150 g granulated sugar and
300 ml water)

Chocolate Brownies – serves 15

50 g plain flour
110 g butter
2 eggs
225 g granulated sugar
175 g walnuts
1 level teaspoon of baking powder

Extend your task

1 Find a recipe for your favourite dessert and research the cost of its ingredients. Work out the cost of the dessert per person for each number of guests.

2 You are going to create table decorations for your dinner party. The basic outlines of these decorations can be seen below.

Find the missing lengths required to make these decorations. How much card would you need in order to make enough decorations for each of your guests?

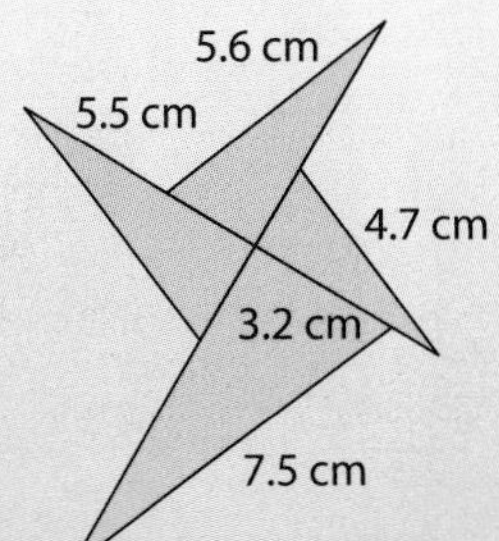

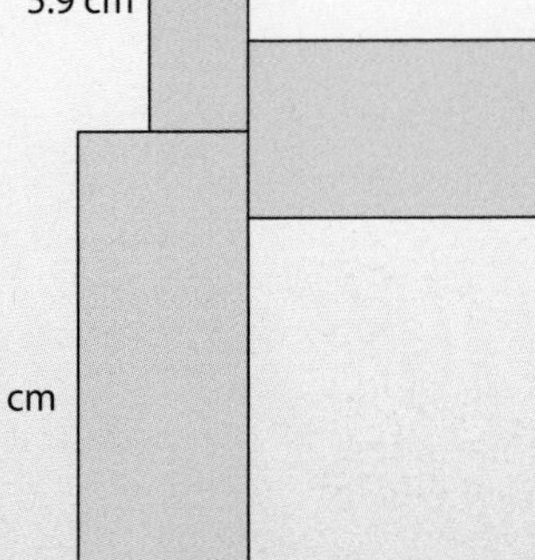

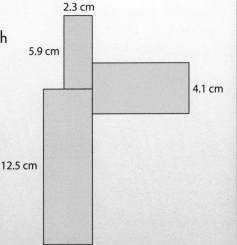

Why this chapter matters

Percentages are used in many places and situations in our everyday lives.

Why use fractions and percentages?

Because:

- basic percentages and simple fractions are quite easy to understand
- they are a good way of comparing quantities
- fractions and percentages are used a lot in everyday life.

Who uses them?

- Shops and businesses
  - Sale → Save $\frac{1}{4}$ off the marked price
  - Special offer → 10% off
- Banks
  - Loans → Interest rate $6\frac{1}{4}$%
  - Savings → Interest rate $2\frac{1}{2}$%
- Salespeople
  - $7\frac{1}{2}$% commission on sales
- Government
  - Half of the workers in this sector are over 55
  - The aim is to cut carbon emissions by one-third by 2020
  - Unemployment has fallen by 1%
  - Inflation is 3.6%
  - Income tax is 20%
  - Value added tax is $17\frac{1}{2}$%
- Workers
  - My pay rise is 2.3%
  - My overtime rate is time and a half
- Teachers
  - Test result 67%
  - Three-fifths of our students gain a grade C in GCSE mathematics

Can you think of other examples? You will find several everyday uses in this chapter.

Chapter

Number: Fractions, percentages and ratios

1. One quantity as a fraction of another
2. Adding and subtracting fractions
3. Increasing and decreasing quantities by a percentage
4. Expressing one quantity as a percentage of another
5. Compound interest and repeated percentage change
6. Reverse percentage (working out the original quantity)
7. Ratio

This chapter will show you ...

- **D to C** how to apply the rules of addition and subtraction to fractions
- **D to C** how to use ratios to solve problems
- **D** how to increase or decrease a quantity by a percentage
- **C** how to calculate compound interest
- **C** how to express one quantity as a percentage of another
- **C** how to calculate a percentage increase or decrease
- **B** how to calculate the original value after a percentage increase or decrease

Visual overview

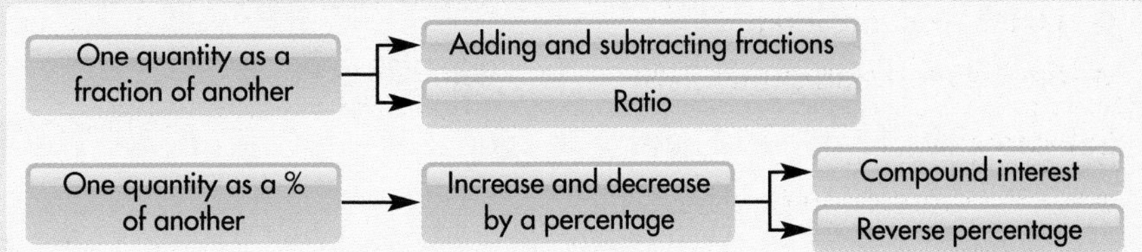

What you should already know

- How to cancel down fractions to their simplest form **(KS3 level 5, GCSE grade F)**
- How to find equivalent fractions, decimals and percentages **(KS3 level 5, GCSE grade F)**
- How to add and subtract fractions with the same denominator **(KS3 level 6, GCSE grade F)**
- How to work out simple percentages, such as 10%, of quantities **(KS3 level 4, GCSE grade F)**
- How to convert a mixed number to a top-heavy fraction and vice versa **(KS3 level 6, GCSE grade F)**

Quick check

1 Cancel the following fractions to their simplest form.

a $\frac{8}{20}$ **b** $\frac{12}{32}$ **c** $\frac{15}{35}$

2 Complete this table of equivalences.

Fraction	Percentage	Decimal
$\frac{3}{4}$		
	40%	
		0.55

3 What is 10% of:

a £230 **b** £46.00 **c** £2.30?

2.1 One quantity as a fraction of another

This section will show you how to:
- find one **quantity** as a fraction of another

Key words
fraction
quantity

An amount often needs to be given as a **fraction** of another amount.

EXAMPLE 1

Write £5 as a fraction of £20.

As a fraction this is written $\frac{5}{20}$. This cancels to $\frac{1}{4}$.

So £5 is one-quarter of £20.

EXERCISE 2A

D

1 Write the first quantity as a fraction of the second.

a 2 cm, 6 cm **b** 4 kg, 20 kg **c** £8, £20 **d** 5 hours, 24 hours

e 12 days, 30 days **f** 50p, £3 **g** 4 days, 2 weeks **h** 40 minutes, 2 hours

2 In a form of 30 students, 18 are boys. What fraction of the form are boys?

3 During March, it rained on 12 days. For what fraction of the month did it rain?

FM **4** Linda earns £120 a week. She saves $\frac{1}{4}$ of her earnings. She is saving for the deposit on a car of £600. How many weeks will it take until she has saved enough?

AU **5** Jon earns £90 and saves £30 of it. Matt earns £100 and saves £35 of it.

Who is saving the greater proportion of their earnings?

AU **6** In two tests Harry gets 13 out of 20 and 16 out of 25. Which is the better mark? Explain your answer.

C

7 Frank gets a pay rise from £120 a week to £135 a week. What fraction of his original pay was his pay rise?

8 When she was born Alice weighed 3 kg. After a month she weighed 4 kg 250 g. By what fraction of what she originally weighed had she increased?

9 After the breeding season a bat colony increased in size from 90 bats to 108 bats. What fraction had the size of the colony increased?

10 After dieting Bart went from 80 kg to 68 kg. What fraction did his weight decrease by?

FM Functional Maths AU (AO2) Assessing Understanding PS (AO3) Problem Solving

C

AU 11 In a class of 30 students, 18 are boys. Half of the boys study French.

What fraction of the class are boys who study French?

Give your answer in its simplest form.

PS 12 The manager of a small company claims that three out of every four of her workers are women.

She employs between 30 and 40 workers altogether.

If her statement is true, how many workers could she have altogether? Write down all possible answers.

2.2 Adding and subtracting fractions

This section will show you how to:

- add and subtract fractions with different denominators

Key words

denominator
equivalent fraction
lowest common denominator

Fractions can only be added or subtracted after they have been changed to **equivalent fractions** with the same **denominator**.

EXAMPLE 2

Work out: $\frac{5}{6} - \frac{3}{4}$

The **lowest common denominator** (LCM of 4 and 6) is 12.

The problem becomes $\frac{5}{6} - \frac{3}{4} = \frac{5}{6} \times \frac{2}{2} - \frac{3}{4} \times \frac{3}{3} = \frac{10}{12} - \frac{9}{12} = \frac{1}{12}$

EXAMPLE 3

Work out: **a** $2\frac{1}{3} + 3\frac{5}{7}$ **b** $3\frac{1}{4} - 1\frac{3}{5}$

The best way to deal with addition and subtraction of mixed numbers is to deal with the whole numbers and the fractions separately.

a $2\frac{1}{3} + 3\frac{5}{7} = 2 + 3 + \frac{1}{3} + \frac{5}{7} = 5 + \frac{7}{21} + \frac{15}{21} = 5 + \frac{22}{21} = 5 + 1\frac{1}{21} = 6\frac{1}{21}$

b $3\frac{1}{4} - 1\frac{3}{5} = 3 - 1 + \frac{1}{4} - \frac{3}{5} = 2 + \frac{5}{20} - \frac{12}{20} = 2 - \frac{7}{20} = 1\frac{13}{20}$

EXERCISE 2B

D

1 Work out the following.

a $\frac{1}{3}+\frac{1}{5}$ **b** $\frac{1}{3}+\frac{1}{4}$ **c** $\frac{1}{5}+\frac{1}{10}$ **d** $\frac{2}{3}+\frac{1}{4}$ **e** $\frac{1}{5}-\frac{1}{10}$ **f** $\frac{7}{8}-\frac{3}{4}$

g $\frac{5}{6}-\frac{3}{4}$ **h** $\frac{5}{6}-\frac{1}{2}$ **i** $\frac{1}{3}+\frac{4}{9}$ **j** $\frac{1}{4}+\frac{3}{8}$ **k** $\frac{7}{8}-\frac{1}{2}$ **l** $\frac{3}{5}-\frac{8}{15}$

2 Work out the following.

a $1\frac{7}{18}+2\frac{3}{10}$ **b** $3\frac{1}{3}+1\frac{9}{20}$ **c** $1\frac{1}{8}-\frac{5}{9}$ **d** $1\frac{3}{16}-\frac{7}{12}$

e $\frac{5}{6}+\frac{7}{16}+\frac{5}{8}$ **f** $\frac{7}{10}+\frac{3}{8}+\frac{5}{6}$ **g** $1\frac{1}{3}+\frac{7}{10}-\frac{4}{15}$ **h** $\frac{5}{14}+1\frac{3}{7}-\frac{5}{12}$

C

3 In a class of children, three-quarters are Chinese, one-fifth are Malay and the rest are Indian. What fraction of the class are Indian?

4 **a** In a class election, half of the students voted for Aminah, one-third voted for Janet and the rest voted for Peter. What fraction of the class voted for Peter?

PS **b** One of the following is the number of students in the class.

25 28 30 32

How many students are in the class?

FM **5** A one-litre bottle of milk is used to fill three glasses with a capacity of an eighth of a litre and one glass with a capacity of a half a litre.

Priya likes milky coffee so has at least 10 cl of milk in each cup. Is there enough milk left for Priya to have two cups of coffee?

6 Because of illness, $\frac{2}{5}$ of a school was absent one day. If the school had 650 students on the register, how many were absent that day?

AU **7** Which is the biggest: half of 96, one-third of 141, two-fifths of 120, or three-quarters of 68?

AU **8** Mick says that $1\frac{1}{3}+2\frac{1}{4}=3\frac{2}{7}$

He is incorrect. What is the mistake that he has made? Work out the correct answer.

AU **9** Here is a calculation.

$\frac{1}{4}+\frac{2}{5}$

Imagine that you are trying to explain to someone over the telephone how to do this calculation.

Write down what you would say.

10 To increase sales, a shop reduced the price of a car stereo set by $\frac{2}{5}$. If the original price was £85, what was the new price?

PS **11** At a burger-eating competition, Lionel ate 34 burgers in 20 minutes while Brian ate 26 burgers in 20 minutes. How long after the start of the competition would they have consumed a total of 30 burgers between them?

2.3 Increasing and decreasing quantities by a percentage

This section will show you how to:
- increase and decrease quantities by a percentage

Key words
multiplier
percentage

Increasing by a percentage

There are two methods for increasing a quantity by a **percentage**.

Method 1

Work out the increase and add it on to the original amount.

EXAMPLE 4

Increase £6 by 5%.

Work out 5% of £6: (5 ÷ 100) × 6 = £0.30

Add the £0.30 to the original amount: £6 + £0.30 = £6.30

Method 2

Use a **multiplier**. An increase of 6% is equivalent to the original 100% plus the extra 6%. This is a total of 106% ($\frac{106}{100}$) and is equivalent to the multiplier 1.06.

EXAMPLE 5

Increase £6.80 by 5%.

A 5% increase is a multiplier of 1.05.

So £6.80 increased by 5% is £6.80 × 1.05 = £7.14

EXERCISE 2C

1 What multiplier is used to increase a quantity by:

a 10% **b** 3% **c** 20% **d** 7% **e** 12%?

2 Increase each of the following by the given percentage. (Use any method you like.)

a £60 by 4% **b** 12 kg by 8% **c** 450 g by 5%

d 545 m by 10% **e** £34 by 12% **f** £75 by 20%

g 340 kg by 15% **h** 670 cm by 23% **i** 130 g by 95%

j £82 by 75% **k** 640 m by 15% **l** £28 by 8%

D

D

FM **3** Kevin is on a salary of £27 500. He is offered a pay rise of 7% or an extra £150 per month. Which should he accept? Show how you decided.

4 In 2005 the population of Melchester was 1 565 000. By 2010 it had increased by 8%. What was the population of Melchester in 2010?

5 A small firm made the same pay increase of 5% for all its employees.

a Calculate the new pay of each employee listed below. Each of their salaries before the increase is given.

Bob, caretaker, £16 500

Anne, tea lady, £17 300

Jean, supervisor, £19 500

Brian, manager, £25 300

AU **b** Explain why the actual pay increases are different for each employee.

6 A bank pays 7% interest on the money that each saver keeps in the bank for a year. Allison keeps £385 in the bank for a year. How much will she have in the bank after the year?

7 In 1980 the number of cars on the roads of Sheffield was about 102 000. Since then it has increased by 90%. Approximately how many cars are there on the roads of Sheffield now?

8 An advertisement for a breakfast cereal states that a special-offer packet contains 15% more cereal for the same price as a normal 500 g packet. How much breakfast cereal is in a special-offer packet?

9 A headteacher was proud to point out that, since he had arrived at the school, the number of students had increased by 35%. How many students are now in the school, if there were 680 when the headteacher started at the school?

10 At a school disco there are always about 20% more girls than boys. If at one disco there were 50 boys, how many girls were there?

FM **11** The Government adds a tax called VAT to the price of most goods in shops. At the moment, it is 17.5% on all electrical equipment.

Calculate the price of the following electrical equipment after VAT of 17.5% has been added.

Equipment	*Pre-VAT price*
TV set	£245
Microwave oven	£72
CD player	£115
Personal stereo	£29.50

PS **12** A television costs £400 before VAT at 17.5% is added.

If the rate of VAT goes up from 17.5% to 20%, how much will the cost of the television increase?

C

AU **13** Bookshop BookWorms increased its prices by 5%, then increased them by 3%. Bookshop Books Galore increased its prices by 3%, then increased them by 5%.

Which shop's prices increased by the greatest percentage?

a BookWorms **b** Books Galore **c** Both same **d** Cannot tell

Justify your choice.

AU **14** Shop A increased its prices by 4% and then by another 4%. Shop B increased its prices by 8%.

Which shop's prices increased by the greatest percentage?

a Shop A **b** Shop B **c** Both same **d** Cannot tell

Justify your choice.

AU **15** A hi-fi system was priced at £420 at the start of 2008. At the start of 2009, it was 12% more expensive. At the start of 2010, it was 15% more expensive than the price at the start of 2009. What is the price of the hi-fi at the start of 2010?

B

FM **16** A quick way to work out VAT is to divide the pre-VAT price by 6. For example, the VAT on an item costing £120 is approximately £120 ÷ 6 = £20. Show that this approximate method gives the VAT correct to within £5 for pre-VAT prices up to £600.

Decreasing by a percentage

There are two methods for decreasing by a percentage.

Method 1

Work out the decrease and subtract it from the original amount.

EXAMPLE 6

Decrease £8 by 4%.

Work out 4% of £8: (4 ÷ 100) × 8 = £0.32

Subtract the £0.32 from the original amount: £8 – £0.32 = £7.68

Method 2

Use a multiplier. A 7% decrease is equivalent to 7% less than the original 100%, so it represents 100% – 7% = 93% of the original. This is a multiplier of 0.93.

EXAMPLE 7

Decrease £8.60 by 5%.

A decrease of 5% is a multiplier of 0.95.

So £8.60 decreased by 5% is £8.60 × 0.95 = £8.17

EXERCISE 2D 

D

1 What multiplier is used to decrease a quantity by:

a 8% **b** 15% **c** 25% **d** 9% **e** 12%?

2 Decrease each of the following by the given percentage. (Use any method you like.)

a £10 by 6% **b** 25 kg by 8% **c** 236 g by 10%

d 350 m by 3% **e** £5 by 2% **f** 45 m by 12%

g 860 m by 15% **h** 96 g by 13% **i** 480 cm by 25%

j 180 minutes by 35% **k** 86 kg by 5% **l** £65 by 42%

3 A car valued at £6500 last year is now worth 15% less. What is its value now?

4 A new P-plan diet guarantees that you will lose 12% of your weight in the first month. How much should the following people weigh after one month on the diet?

a Gillian, who started at 60 kg **b** Peter, who started at 75 kg

c Margaret, who started at 52 kg

FM **5** A motor insurance firm offers no-claims discounts off the full premium, as follows.

1 year no claims 15% discount off the full premium
2 years no claims 25% discount off the full premium
3 years no claims 45% discount off the full premium
4 years no claims 60% discount off the full premium

Mr Speed and his family are all offered motor insurance from this firm.

Mr Speed has four years' no-claims discount and the full premium would be £440.
Mrs Speed has one year's no-claims discount and the full premium would be £350.
James has three years' no-claims discount and the full premium would be £620.
John has two years' no-claims discount and the full premium would be £750.

Calculate the actual amount each member of the family has to pay for the motor insurance.

6 A large factory employed 640 people. It had to streamline its workforce and lose 30% of the workers. How big is the workforce now?

7 On the last day of the Christmas term, a school expects to have an absence rate of 6%. If the school population is 750 students, how many students will the school expect to see on the last day of the Christmas term?

8 A charity called *Young Ones* said that since the start of the National Lottery they have had a decrease of 45% in the amount of money raised by scratch cards. If before the start of the National Lottery the charity had an annual income of £34 500 from their scratch cards, how much do they collect now?

9 Most speedometers in cars have an error of about 5% from the true reading. When my speedometer says I am driving at 70 mph,

a what is the lowest speed I could be doing

b what is the highest speed I could be doing?

FM **10** Kerry wants to buy a sweatshirt (£19), a tracksuit (£26) and some running shoes (£56). If she joins the store's premium club which costs £25 to join she can get 20% off the cost of the goods.

Should she join or not? Give figures to support your answer.

FM **11** **a** I read an advertisement in my local newspaper last week which stated: "By lagging your roof and hot water system you will use 18% less fuel." Since I was using an average of 640 units of gas a year, I thought I would lag my roof and my hot water system. How much gas would I expect to use now?

AU **b** I actually used 18% more gas than I expected to use.

Did I use less gas than last year, more gas than last year or the same amount of gas as last year?

Show how you work out your answer.

12 Shops add VAT to the basic price of goods to find the selling price that customers will be asked to pay. In a sale, a shop reduces the selling price by a certain percentage to set the sale price. Calculate the sale price of each of these items.

Item	Basic price	VAT rate	Sale discount	Sale price
TV	£220	17.5%	14%	
DVD player	£180	17.5%	20%	

AU PS **13** A shop advertises garden ornaments at £50 but with 10% off in a sale. It then advertises an extra 10% off the sale price.

Show that this is not a decrease in price of 20%.

AU **14** A computer system was priced at £1000 at the start of 2008. At the start of 2009, it was 10% cheaper. At the start of 2010, it was 15% cheaper than the price at the start of 2009. What is the price of the computer system at the start of 2010?

PS **15** Show that a 10% decrease followed by a 10% increase is equivalent to a 1% decrease overall.

HINTS AND TIPS

Choose an amount to start with.

PS **16** A cereal packet normally contains 300 g of cereal and costs £1.40.

There are two special offers.

Offer A: 20% more for the same price

Offer B: Same amount for 20% off the normal price

Which is the better offer?

a Offer A **b** Offer B **c** Both same **d** Cannot tell

Justify your choice.

2.4 Expressing one quantity as a percentage of another

This section will show you how to:
- express one quantity as a percentage of another
- work out percentage change

Key words
percentage change
percentage decrease
percentage increase
percentage loss
percentage profit

You express one quantity as a percentage of another by setting up the first quantity as a fraction of the second, making sure that the *units of each are the same*. Then you convert the fraction into a percentage by multiplying by 100%.

EXAMPLE 8

Express £6 as a percentage of £40.

Set up the fraction and multiply by 100%.

$\frac{6}{40} \times 100\% = 15\%$

EXAMPLE 9

Express 75 cm as a percentage of 2.5 m.

First, change 2.5 m to 250 cm to get a common unit.

So, the problem now becomes: Express 75 cm as a percentage of 250 cm.

Set up the fraction and multiply by 100%.

$\frac{75}{250} \times 100\% = 30\%$

Percentage change

A **percentage change** may be a **percentage increase** or a **percentage decrease**.

$$\text{Percentage change} = \frac{\text{change}}{\text{original amount}} \times 100$$

Use this to calculate **percentage profit** or **percentage loss** in a financial transaction.

EXAMPLE 10

Jake buys a car for £1500 and sells it for £1800. What is Jake's percentage profit?

Jake's profit is £300, so his percentage profit is:

$$\text{percentage profit} = \frac{\text{profit}}{\text{original amount}} \times 100 = \frac{300}{1500} \times 100\% = 20$$

Using a multiplier (or decimal)

To use a multiplier, divide the increase by the original quantity and change the resulting decimal to a percentage.

EXAMPLE 11

Express 5 as a percentage of 40.

Set up the fraction or decimal: $5 \div 40 = 0.125$

Convert the decimal to a percentage: $0.125 = 12.5\%$

EXERCISE 2E

D

1 Express each of the following as a percentage. Give suitably rounded figures where necessary.

a £5 of £20 **b** £4 of £6.60 **c** 241 kg of 520 kg

d 3 hours of 1 day **e** 25 minutes of 1 hour **f** 12 m of 20 m

g 125 g of 600 g **h** 12 minutes of 2 hours **i** 1 week of a year

j 1 month of 1 year **k** 25 cm of 55 cm **l** 105 g of 1 kg

2 Liam went to school with his pocket money of £2.50. He spent 80p at the tuck shop. What percentage of his pocket money had he spent?

3 In Greece, there are 3 654 000 acres of agricultural land. Olives are grown on 237 000 acres of this land. What percentage of the agricultural land is used for olives?

4 During the wet year of 1981, it rained in Manchester on 123 days of the year. What percentage of days were wet?

C

5 Find the percentage profit on the following. Give your answers to one decimal place.

	Item	*Retail price* (selling price)	*Wholesale price* (price the shop paid)
a	CD player	£89.50	£60
b	TV set	£345.50	£210
c	Computer	£829.50	£750

6 Before Anton started to diet, he weighed 95 kg. He now weighs 78 kg. What percentage of his original weight has he lost?

7 In 2009 the Melchester County Council raised £14 870 000 in council tax. In 2010 it raised £15 597 000 in council tax. What was the percentage increase?

8 When Blackburn Rovers won the championship in 1995, they lost only four of their 42 league games. What percentage of games did they *not* lose?

C

AU **9** In the year 1900 Britain's imports were as follows.

British Commonwealth	£109 530 000
USA	£138 790 000
France	£53 620 000
Other countries	£221 140 000

a What percentage of the total imports came from each source? Give your answers to 1 decimal place.

b Add up your answers to part **a**. What do you notice? Explain your answer.

AU **10** Calum and Stacey take the same tests. Both tests are out of the same mark.

Here are their results.

	Test A	Test B
Calum	12	17
Stacey	14	20

Whose result has the greater percentage increase from test A to test B? Show your working.

FM **11** A supermarket advertises its cat food as shown.

8 out of 10 cat owners choose our cat food.

Trading standards are checking the claim.

They observe that over one hour, 46 people buy cat food and 38 buy the store's own brand.

Based on these figures is the store's claim correct?

2.5 Compound interest and repeated percentage change

This section will show you how to:

- calculate compound interest
- solve problems involving repeated percentage change

Key words

annual rate
compound interest
multiplier
principal

Banks and building societies usually pay **compound interest** on savings accounts.

When compound interest is used, the interest earned each year is added to the original amount (**principal**) and the new total then earns interest at the **annual rate** in the following year. This pattern is then repeated each year while the money is in the account.

The most efficient way to calculate the total amount in the account after several years is to use a **multiplier**.

EXAMPLE 12

Elizabeth invests £400 in a savings account. The account pays compound interest at 6% each year. How much will she have in the account after three years?

The amount in the account increases by 6% each year, so the multiplier is 1.06.

After 1 year she will have £400 × 1.06 = £424
After 1 year she will have £424 × 1.06 = £449.44
After 1 year she will have £449.44 × 1.06 = £476.41 (rounded)

If you calculate the differences, you can see that the amount of interest increases each year (£24, £25.44 and £26.97).

From this example, you should see that you could have used £400 × $(1.06)^3$ to find the amount after three years. That is, you could have used the following formula for calculating the total amount due at any time:

$$\text{total amount} = P \times \text{multiplier raised to the power } n = P \times (1 + \frac{r}{100})^n$$

or $A = P(1 + r)^n$ where P is the original amount invested, r is the percentage interest rate, giving a multiple of $(1 + r)$, and n is the number of years for which the money is invested.

So, in Example 11, P = £400, $r = 0.06$ and $n = 3$,

and the total amount = £400 × $(1.06)^3$

Using your calculator

You may have noticed that you can do the above calculation on your calculator without having to write down all the intermediate steps.

To add on the 6% each time, just multiply by 1.06 each time. So you can do the calculation as:

4 0 0 × 1 • 0 6 × 1 • 0 6 × 1 • 0 6 =

or

4 0 0 × 1 • 0 6 x■ 3 =

or

4 0 0 × 1 0 6 % x■ 3 =

You need to find the method with which you are comfortable and which you understand.

The idea of compound interest does not only concern money. It can be about, for example, the growth in population, increases in salaries, or increases in body weight or height. Also, the idea can involve regular reduction by a fixed percentage: for example, car depreciation, population losses and even water losses. The next exercise shows the extent to which compound interest ideas are used.

EXERCISE 2F

C

1 A baby octopus increases its body weight by 5% each day for the first month of its life. In a safe ocean zoo, a baby octopus was born weighing 10 g.

a What was its weight after:

i 1 day **ii** 2 days **iii** 4 days **iv** 1 week?

b After how many days will the octopus first weigh over 15 g?

2 A certain type of conifer hedging increases in height by 17% each year for the first 20 years. When I bought some of this hedging, it was all about 50 cm tall. How long will it take to grow 3 m tall?

3 The manager of a small family business offered his staff an annual pay increase of 4% for every year they stayed with the firm.

a Gareth started work at the business on a salary of £12 200. What salary will he be on after 4 years?

PS **b** Julie started work at the business on a salary of £9350. How many years will it be until she is earning a salary of over £20 000?

4 Scientists have been studying the shores of Scotland and estimate that due to pollution the seal population of those shores will decline at the rate of 15% each year. In 2006 they counted about 3000 seals on those shores.

a If nothing is done about pollution, how many seals did they expect to be there in

i 2007 **ii** 2008 **iii** 2011?

PS **b** How long will it take for the seal population to be less than 1000?

5 I am told that if I buy a new car its value will depreciate at the rate of 20% each year. If I bought a car in 2009 priced at £8500, what would be the value of the car in:

a 2010 **b** 2011 **c** 2013?

6 At the peak of a drought during the summer, a reservoir in Derbyshire was losing water at the rate of 8% each day. On 1 August this reservoir held 2.1 million litres of water.

a At this rate of losing water, how much would have been in the reservoir on the following days?

i 2 August **ii** 4 August **iii** 8 August

FM **b** The danger point is when the water drops below 1 million litres. When would this have been if things had continued as they were?

7 The population of a small country, Yebon, was only 46 000 in 2001, but it steadily increased by about 13% each year during the 2000s.

a Calculate the population in:

i 2002 **ii** 2006 **iii** 2010.

PS **b** If the population keeps growing at this rate, when will it be half a million?

B

PS **8** How long will it take to accumulate one million pounds in the following situations?

a An investment of £100 000 at a rate of 12% compound interest

b An investment of £50 000 at a rate of 16% compound interest

PS **9** An oak tree is 60 cm tall. It grows at a rate of 8% per year. A conifer is 50 cm tall. It grows at a rate of 15% per year. How many years does it take before the conifer is taller than the oak?

PS **10** A tree increases in height by 18% per year. When it is 1 year old, it is 8 cm tall. How long will it take the tree to grow to 10 m?

PS **11** Show that a 10% increase followed by a 10% increase is equivalent to a 21% increase overall.

FM AU **12** Here are two advertisements for savings accounts.

Bradley Bank

Invest £1000 for two years and earn 3.2% interest overall.

Monastery Building Society

Invest £1000. Interest rate 1.3% compound per annum. Bonus of 0.5% on balance after 2 years.

Which account is worth more after 2 years?

You **must** show your working.

PS **13** A fish weighs 3 kg and increases in weight by 10% each month. A crab weighs 6 kg but decreases in weight by 10% each month. After how many months will the fish weigh more than the crab?

FM **14** There is a bread shortage.

Each week during the shortage a shop increases its price of bread by 20% of the price the week before.

After how many weeks would the price of the bread have doubled?

PS **15** In a survey exactly 35% of the people surveyed wanted a new supermarket.

What is the least number that could have been surveyed?

2.6 Reverse percentage (working out the original quantity)

This section will show you how to:

- calculate the original amount, given the final amount, after a known percentage increase or decrease

Key words
final amount
multiplier
original amount
unitary method

Reverse percentage questions involve working backwards from the **final amount** to find the **original amount** when you know, or can work out, the final amount as a percentage of the original amount.

Method 1: The unitary method

The **unitary method** has three steps.

Step 1: Equate the final percentage to the final value.

Step 2: Use this to calculate the value of 1%.

Step 3: Multiply by 100 to work out 100% (the original value).

EXAMPLE 13

In a factory, 70 workers were given a pay rise. This was 20% of all the workers. How many workers are there altogether?

20% represents 70 workers.

Divide by 20.
1% represents 70 ÷ 20 workers. (There is no need to work out this calculation yet.)

Multiply by 100.
100% represents all the workers: 70 ÷ 20 × 100 = 350

So there are 350 workers altogether.

EXAMPLE 14

The price of a car increased by 6% to £9116. Work out the price before the increase.

106% represents £9116.

Divide by 106.
1% represents £9116 ÷ 106

Multiply by 100.
100% represents original price: £9116 ÷ 106 × 100 = £8600

So the price before the increase was £8600.

Method 2: The multiplier method

The **multiplier** method involves fewer steps.

Step 1: Write down the multiplier.

Step 2: Divide the final value by the multiplier to give the original value.

EXAMPLE 15

In a sale the price of a freezer is reduced by 12%. The sale price is £220. What was the price before the sale?

A decrease of 12% gives a multiplier of 0.88.

Dividing the sale price by the multiplier gives £220 ÷ 0.88 = £250

So the price before the sale was £250.

EXERCISE 2G 

1 Find what 100% represents in these situations.

- **a** 40% represents 320 g
- **b** 14% represents 35 m
- **c** 45% represents 27 cm
- **d** 4% represents £123
- **e** 2.5% represents £5
- **f** 8.5% represents £34

2 On a gruelling army training session, only 28 youngsters survived the whole day. This represented 35% of the original group. How large was the original group?

3 VAT is a government tax added to goods and services. With VAT at 17.5%, what is the pre-VAT price of the following priced goods?

T-shirt	£9.87	Tights	£1.41
Shorts	£6.11	Sweater	£12.62
Trainers	£29.14	Boots	£38.07

4 Howard spends £200 a month on food. This represents 24% of his monthly take-home pay. How much is his monthly take-home pay?

5 Tina's weekly pay is increased by 5% to £315. What was Tina's pay before the increase?

6 The number of workers in a factory fell by 5% to 228. How many workers were there originally?

7 In a sale the price of a TV is reduced to £325.50. This is a 7% reduction on the original price. What was the original price?

C

B

B

8 If 38% of plastic bottles in a production line are blue and the remaining 7750 plastic bottles are brown, how many plastic bottles are blue?

9 I received £3.85 back from the tax office, which represented the 17.5% VAT on a piece of equipment. How much did I pay for this equipment in the first place?

A

FM 10 A company is in financial trouble. The workers are asked to take a 10% pay cut for each of the next two years.

a Rob works out that his pay in two years' time will be £1296 per month. How much is his pay now?

b Instead he offers to take an immediate pay cut of 14% and have his pay frozen at that level for two years. Has he made the correct decision?

AU 11 The population in a village is 30% of the size of the population in a neighbouring town.

a If both populations double, what is the population of the village as a percentage of the population of the town?

b If the population of the village stays the same but the population of the town doubles, what is the population of the village as a percentage of the population of the town?

PS 12 A man's salary was increased by 5% in one year and reduced by 5% in the next year. Is his final salary greater or less than the original one and by how many per cent?

PS 13 A woman's salary increased by 5% in one year and then increased the following year by 5% again.

Her new salary was £19 845.

How much was the increase, in pounds, in the first year?

PS 14 A quick way of estimating the pre-VAT price of an item with VAT added is to divide by 6 and then multiply by 5. For example, if an item costs £360 including VAT, it cost approximately (360 ÷ 6) × 5 = £300 before VAT. Show that this gives an estimate to within £5 of the pre-VAT price for items costing up to £280.

PS 15 After a 6% increase followed by an 8% increase, the monthly salary of a chef was £1431. What was the original salary?

PS 16 Cassie invests some money at 4% interest per annum for five years. After five years, she had £1520.82 in the bank. How much did she invest originally?

AU 17 A teacher asked her class to work out the original price of a cooker that after a 12% increase the price was £291.20.

This is Baz's answer: 12% of 291.20 = £34.94

Original price = 291.20 – 34.94 = 256.26 ≈ £260

When the teacher read out the answer Baz ticked his work as correct.

What errors has he made?

2.7 Ratio

This section will show you how to:

- simplify a ratio
- express a ratio as a fraction
- divide amounts into given ratios
- complete calculations from a given ratio and partial information

Key words
cancel
common units
ratio
simplest form

A **ratio** is a way of comparing the sizes of two or more quantities.

A ratio can be expressed in a number of ways. For example, if Joy is five years old and James is 20 years old, the ratio of their ages is:

	Joy's age : James's age	
which is:	5 : 20	
which simplifies to:	1 : 4	(dividing both sides by 5)

A ratio is usually given in one of these three ways.

Joy's age : James's age	or	5 : 20	or	1 : 4
Joy's age to James's age	or	5 to 20	or	1 to 4
$\frac{\text{Joy's age}}{\text{James's age}}$	or	$\frac{5}{20}$	or	$\frac{1}{4}$

Common units

When working with a ratio involving different units, *always convert them to a* **common unit**. A ratio can be simplified only when the units of each quantity are the same, because the ratio itself has no units. Once the units are the same, the ratio can be simplified or **cancelled**.

For example, the ratio of 125 g to 2 kg must be converted to the ratio of 125 g to 2000 g, so that you can simplify it.

	125 : 2000	
Divide both sides by 25:	5 : 80	
Divide both sides by 5:	1 : 16	The ratio 125 : 2000 can be simplified to 1 : 16.

EXAMPLE 16

Express 25 minutes : 1 hour as a ratio in its simplest form.

The units must be the same, so change 1 hour into 60 minutes.

25 minutes : 1 hour = 25 minutes : 60 minutes
= 25 : 60 Cancel the units (minutes).
= 5 : 12 Divide both sides by 5.

So 25 minutes : 1 hour simplifies to 5 : 12

Ratios as fractions

A ratio in its **simplest form** can be expressed as portions by expressing the whole numbers in the ratio as fractions with the same denominator (bottom number).

EXAMPLE 17

A garden is divided into lawn and shrubs in the ratio 3 : 2.

What fraction of the garden is covered by **a** lawn, **b** shrubs?

The denominator (bottom number) of the fraction comes from *adding the numbers in the ratio* (that is, 2 + 3 = 5).

a The lawn covers $\frac{3}{5}$ of the garden.

b The shrubs cover $\frac{2}{5}$ of the garden.

EXERCISE 2H

D

1 A length of wood is cut into two pieces in the ratio 3 : 7. What fraction of the original length is the longer piece?

2 Jack and Thomas find a bag of marbles which they divide between them in the ratio of their ages. Jack is 10 years old and Thomas is 15 years old. What fraction of the marbles did Jack get?

3 Dave and Sue share a pizza in the ratio of 2 : 3. They eat it all.

a What fraction of the pizza did Dave eat?

b What fraction of the pizza did Sue eat?

4 A camp site allocates space to caravans and tents in the ratio 7 : 3. What fraction of the total space is given to:

a the caravans **b** the tents?

5 Two sisters, Amy and Katie, share a packet of sweets in the ratio of their ages. Amy is 15 and Katie is 10. What fraction of the sweets does each sister get?

6 **a** The recipe for a fruit punch is 1.25 litres of fruit crush to 6.75 litres of lemonade. What fraction of the punch is each ingredient?

FM **b** A different recipe for fruit punch is 1 litre of fruit crush to 5 litres of lemonade.

Roy wants to make the fruit punch with the biggest proportion of fruit crush. Which recipe should he use?

PS **7** Three cows, Gertrude, Gladys and Henrietta produced milk in the ratio 2 : 3 : 4. Henrietta produced $1\frac{1}{2}$ more litres than Gladys. How much milk did the three cows produce altogether?

D

8 In a safari park at feeding time, the elephants, the lions and the chimpanzees are given food in the ratio 10 to 7 to 3. What fraction of the total food is given to:

a the elephants **b** the lions **c** the chimpanzees?

9 Three brothers, James, John and Joseph, share a huge block of chocolate in the ratio of their ages.

James is 20, John is 12 and Joseph is 8.

What fraction of the bar of chocolate does each brother get?

10 The recipe for a pudding is 125 g of sugar, 150 g of flour, 100 g of margarine and 175 g of fruit. What fraction of the pudding is each ingredient?

C

AU 11 June wins three-quarters of her bowls matches. She loses the rest.

What is the ratio of wins to losses?

PS 12 Three brothers share some cash.

The ratio of Mark's and David's share is 1 : 2.

The ratio of David's and Paul's share is 1 : 2.

What is the ratio of Mark's share to Paul's share?

PS 13 In a garden, the area is divided into lawn, vegetables and flowers in the ratio 3 : 2 : 1.

If one-third of the lawn is dug up and replaced by flowers what is the ratio of lawn : vegetables : flowers now?

Give your answer as a ratio in its simplest form.

Dividing amounts in a given ratio

To divide an amount in a given ratio, you first look at the ratio to see how many parts there are altogether.

For example 4 : 3 has four parts and three parts giving seven parts altogether. Seven parts is the whole amount.

One part can then be found by dividing the whole amount by 7. Three parts and four parts can then be worked out from one part.

EXAMPLE 18

Divide £28 in the ratio 4 : 3.

4 + 3 = 7 parts altogether
So 7 parts = £28
Divide by 7
1 part = £4
4 parts = 4 × £4 = £16 and 3 parts = 3 × £4 = £12

So £28 divided in the ratio 4 : 3 gives £16 and £12.

To divide an amount in a given ratio you can also use fractions.

Express the whole numbers in the ratio as fractions with the same common denominator.

Then multiply the amount by each fraction.

EXAMPLE 19

Divide £40 between Peter and Hitan in the ratio 2 : 3.

Changing the ratio to fractions gives:

$$\text{Peter's share} = \frac{2}{(2+3)} = \frac{2}{5}$$

$$\text{Hitan's share} = \frac{3}{(2+3)} = \frac{3}{5}$$

So, Peter receives £40 × $\frac{2}{5}$ = £16 and Hitan receives £40 × $\frac{3}{5}$ = £24

Note that whichever method you use, you should always check that the final values add up to the original amount: £16 + £12 = £28 and £16 + £24 = £40.

EXERCISE 2I

C

1 Divide the following amounts in the given ratios.

- **a** 400 g in the ratio 2 : 3
- **b** 280 kg in the ratio 2 : 5
- **c** 500 in the ratio 3 : 7
- **d** 1 km in the ratio 19 : 1
- **e** 5 hours in the ratio 7 : 5
- **f** £100 in the ratio 2 : 3 : 5
- **g** £240 in the ratio 3 : 5 : 12
- **h** 600 g in the ratio 1 : 5 : 6

2 The ratio of female to male members of Lakeside Gardening Club is 7 : 3.

The total number of members of the club is 250.

- **a** How many members are female?
- PS **b** What percentage of members are male?

3 A supermarket aims to stock branded goods and their own goods in the ratio 2 : 3.

They stock 500 kg of breakfast cereal.

- **a** What percentage of the cereal stock is branded?
- **b** How much of the cereal stock is their own?

4 The Illinois Department of Health reported that, for the years 1981 to 1992, when it tested a total of 357 horses for rabies, the ratio of horses with rabies to those without was 1 : 16.

How many of these horses had rabies?

5 Being overweight increases the chances of an adult suffering from heart disease. A way to test whether an adult has an increased risk is shown below.

W and *H* refer to waist and hip measurements.

For women, there is increased risk when $W/H > 0.8$

For men, there is increased risk when $W/H > 1.0$

a Find whether the following people have an increased risk of heart disease.

Miss Mott: waist 26 inches, hips: 35 inches
Mrs Wright: waist 32 inches, hips: 37 inches
Mr Brennan: waist 32 inches, hips: 34 inches
Ms Smith: waist 31 inches, hips: 40 inches
Mr Kaye: waist 34 inches, hips: 33 inches

b Give three examples of waist and hip measurements that would suggest no risk of heart disease for a man, but would suggest a risk for a woman.

6 Rewrite the following scales as ratios, as simply as possible.

a 1 cm to 4 km **b** 4 cm to 5 km **c** 2 cm to 5 km

d 4 cm to 1 km **e** 5 cm to 1 km **f** 2.5 cm to 1 km

7 A map has a scale of 1 cm to 10 km.

a Rewrite the scale as a ratio in its simplest form.

b What is the actual length of a lake that is 4.7 cm long on the map?

c How long will a road be on the map if its actual length is 8 km?

8 A map has a scale of 2 cm to 5 km.

a Rewrite the scale as a ratio in its simplest form.

b How long is a path that measures 0.8 cm on the map?

c How long should a 12 km road be on the map?

9 The scale of a map is 5 cm to 1 km.

a Rewrite the scale as a ratio in its simplest form.

b How long is a wall that is shown as 2.7 cm on the map?

c The distance between two points is 8 km; how far will this be on the map?

10 A car is 240 miles from Manchester. A lorry is 180 miles from Manchester.

a Work out the ratio of the distances, giving your answer in its simplest form.

b Two hours later the ratio of the distances is exactly the same.
The car is 120 miles from Manchester.

How far is the lorry from Manchester?

PS **c** If the ratio of the distances stays the same for the entire journeys to Manchester, which vehicle, if either, arrives first?

C

AU **11** A piece of wood is 5 m long. It is cut into pieces.
The lengths of the pieces are in the ratio 4 : 3 : 2 : 1.
The biggest piece is then cut in the ratio 4 : 1 so that there are now five pieces.

How long is the smallest piece?

12 You can simplify a ratio by changing it into the form 1 : n.

For example, 5 : 7 can be rewritten as $\frac{5}{5} : \frac{7}{5} = 1 : 1.4$

Rewrite each of the following in the form 1 : n.

a 5 : 8 **b** 4 : 13

c 8 : 9 **d** 25 : 36

e 5 : 27 **f** 12 : 18

g 5 hours : 1 day **h** 4 hours : 1 week

i £4 : £5

Calculating with ratios when only part of the information is known

EXAMPLE 20

A fruit drink is made by mixing orange squash with water in the ratio 2 : 3.
How much water needs to be added to 5 litres of orange squash to make the drink?

2 parts are 5 litres.
Divide by 2.
1 part is 2.5 litres
3 parts = 2.5 litres × 3 = 7.5 litres

So 7.5 litres of water are needed to make the drink.

EXAMPLE 21

Two business partners, John and Ben, divided their total profit in the ratio 3 : 5.
John received £2100. How much did Ben get?

John's £2100 was $\frac{3}{8}$ of the total profit. (Check you know why.)

$\frac{1}{8}$ of the total profit = £2100 ÷ 3 = £700

So, Ben's share, which was $\frac{5}{8}$ of the total, amounted to £700 × 5 = £3500

EXERCISE 2J

1 Derek, aged 15, and Ricki, aged 10, shared all the conkers they found in the woods in the same ratio as their ages. Derek had 48 conkers.

- **a** Simplify the ratio of their ages.
- **b** How many conkers did Ricki have?
- **c** How many conkers did they find altogether?

2 Two types of crisps, plain and salt 'n' vinegar, were bought for a school party in the ratio 5 : 3. The school bought 60 packets of salt 'n' vinegar crisps.

- **a** How many packets of plain crisps did they buy?
- **b** How many packets of crisps altogether did they buy?

3 Robin is making a drink from orange juice and lemon juice in the ratio 9 : 1. If Robin has only 3.6 litres of orange juice, how much lemon juice does he need to make the drink?

4 When I picked my strawberries, I found some had been spoilt by snails. The rest were good. These were in the ratio 3 : 17. Eighteen of my strawberries had been spoilt by snails. How many good strawberries did I find?

5 A blend of tea is made by mixing Lapsang with Assam in the ratio 3 : 5. I have a lot of Assam tea but only 600 g of Lapsang. How much Assam do I need to make the blend using all the Lapsang?

FM 6 An old recipe to make pancakes says, "For every four ounces of flour, add two eggs and half a pint milk. This is enough for 10 pancakes".

Jamie wants to make two pancakes each for 15 people. He has 1 litre of milk.

Will he have enough milk? Explain how you decide.

7 The ratio of male to female spectators at ice hockey games is 4 : 5. At the Steelers' last match, 4500 men watched the match. What was the total attendance at the game?

8 'Proper tea' is made by putting milk and tea together in the ratio 2 : 9. How much proper tea can be made if you have 1 litre of milk?

9 A teacher always arranged the content of each of his lessons to Year 10 as 'teaching' and 'practising learnt skills' in the ratio 2 : 3.

- **a** If a lesson lasted 35 minutes, how much teaching would he do?
- **b** If he decided to teach for 30 minutes, how long would the lesson be?

10 A 'good' children's book is supposed to have pictures and text in the ratio 17 : 8. In a book I have just looked at, the pictures occupy 23 pages.

- **a** Approximately how many pages of text should this book have to be deemed a 'good' children's book?
- **b** What percentage of a 'good' children's book will be text?

11 Three business partners, Kevin, John and Margaret, put money into a business in the ratio 3 : 4 : 5. They shared any profits in the same ratio. Last year, Margaret made £3400 out of the profits. How much did Kevin and John make last year?

AU 12 The ratio of daffodils to tulips in a flower bed is 3 : 7.

Which of the following statements is true (T), false (F) or could be true (C). The first one has been done for you.

- **a** There are 25 daffodils in the flower bed. **F**
- **b** There are 140 flowers altogether in the flower bed
- **c** The fraction of daffodils in the flower bed is $\frac{3}{7}$.
- **d** The percentage of tulips in the flower bed is 70%.
- **e** If half of the daffodils were dug up the ratio of daffodils to tulips would now be 3 : 14.

PS 13 In a factory, the ratio of female employees to male employees is 3 : 8. There are 85 more males than females.

How many females work in the factory?

PS 14 There is a group of boys and girls waiting for school buses. 25 girls get on the first bus. The ratio of boys to girls at the stop is now 3 : 2. 15 boys get on the second bus. There are now the same number of boys and girls at the bus stop.

How many students altogether were originally at the bus stop?

PS 15 A jar contains 100 cc of a mixture of oil and water in the ratio 1 : 4. Enough oil is added to make the ratio of oil to water 1 : 2.

How much water needs to be added to make the ratio of oil to water 1 : 3?

16 The soft drinks Cola, Orange Fizz and Zesto were bought for the school disco in the ratio 10 : 5 : 3. The school bought 80 cans of Orange Fizz.

- **a** How much Cola did they buy?
- **b** How much Zesto did they buy?

17 **a** Iqra is making a drink from lemonade, orange juice and ginger ale in the ratio 40 : 9 : 1. If Iqra has only 4.5 litres of orange juice, how much of the other two ingredients does she need to make the drink?

AU **b** Another drink made from lemonade, orange juice and ginger ale uses the ratio 10 : 2 : 1.

Which drink has a larger proportion of ginger ale, Iqra's or this one? Show how you work out your answer.

18 Bob is making concrete, using sand and cement in the ratio 3 : 1. He has three 25 kg bags of cement. How much sand will he need if he is to use all his cement?

PS 19 The ratio of my sister's age to my age is 10 : 9.
The ratio of my brother's age to my age is 29 : 27.
I am over 40 years old but under 70 years old.

What is my age?

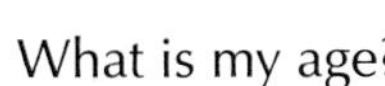

GRADE BOOSTER

- **D** You can add and subtract fractions
- **C** You can calculate percentage increases and decreases
- **C** You can calculate with mixed numbers
- **C** You can work out compound interest problems
- **C** You can solve problems using ratio in appropriate situations
- **B** You can do reverse percentage problems
- **A** You can solve complex problems involving percentage increases and percentage decreases

What you should know now

- How to calculate with fractions
- How to do percentage problems
- How to divide any amount in a given ratio

1 Mrs Senior earns £320 per week. She is awarded a pay rise of 4%.

How much does she earn each week after the pay rise?

2 Five girls run a 100 metre race.

Their times are shown in the table.

Name	Amy	Bavna	Charlotte	Di	Ellie
Time (seconds)	49.0	45.5	51.3	44.7	48.1

a Write down the median time.

b The five girls run another 100 metre race.

They all reduce their times by 10%.

i Calculate Amy's new time.

ii Who won this race?

iii Who improved her time by the least amount of time?

3 Mr Shaw's bill for new tyres is £120 plus VAT. VAT is charged at 17.5%. What is his total bill?

4 Andy's salary is £24 000 per year.

He is paid the same amount each month. He is given a pay rise of 10%.

Calculate his new **monthly** salary.

You **must** show your working. *(4 marks)*

AQA, November 2008, Paper 1 Higher, Question 3

5 Mr and Mrs Jones are buying a tumble dryer that normally costs £250. They save 12% in a sale. How much do they pay for the tumble dryer?

6 Work out the value of $\frac{3}{5} - \frac{3}{8}$

7 On Monday Joe drinks $2\frac{1}{3}$ pints of milk. On Tuesday he drinks $1\frac{3}{4}$ pints of milk.

Work out the total amount of milk that Joe drinks on Monday and Tuesday. *(3 marks)*

AQA, June 2005, Paper 1 Intermediate, Question 13

8 Andy uses $\frac{3}{8}$ of a tin of creosote to creosote 2 m of fencing. What is the least number of tins he needs to creosote 10 m of fencing?

9 Pythagoras made a number of calculations trying to find an approximation for π.

Here are a few of the closest approximations

$$\frac{22}{7} \quad \frac{54}{17} \quad \frac{221}{71} \quad \frac{312}{77}$$

a Put these approximations into order of size, largest on the left, smallest of the right.

b Use your calculator to find which of the above is the closest approximation to π.

10 John has £2000 to invest.

He sees this advert.

SureFire Investments

Don't see your money go up in smoke!

Double your money in 10 years!

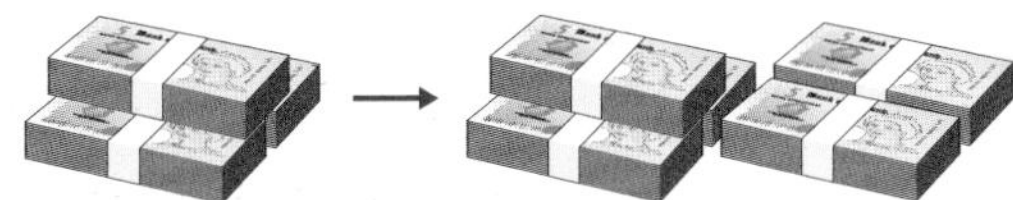

The average annual growth of our investment account is **7.2%**

Will John double his money in ten years with SureFire Investments?

You **must** show your working. *(4 marks)*

AQA, June 2006, Paper 2 Higher, Question 9

11 During 2003 the number of unemployed people in Barnsley fell from 2800 to 2576. What was the percentage decrease?

12 A painter has 50 litres of paint. Each litre covers 2.5 m^2.

The area to be painted is 98 m^2.

Estimate the percentage of paint used.

13 **a** Poppy the dog has two meals a day.

At each meal Poppy eats $\frac{2}{5}$ of a tin of dog food.

On Monday morning there are 5 tins of dog food in the cupboard. Is this enough dog food to feed Poppy for one week?

You must show your working.

b Work out $4\frac{2}{3} \div 1\frac{3}{4}$ *(3 marks)*

AQA, November 2006, Paper 1 Higher, Question 4

14 Zoe invests £6000 in a savings account that pays 3.5% compound interest per year.

How much does she have in the account after 6 years?

15 Simon weighed 3.7 kg when he was born.

One year later he weighed 10.9 kg.

Calculate the percentage increase in his weight. *(3 marks)*

AQA, November 2005, Module 3, Question 2

16 The house price index for a flat in Leeds was 190 in August 2006, compared with a base of 100 in April 2000.

a Write down the percentage increase in the price of flats in Leeds in that period. *(1 mark)*

b A flat cost £80 000 in April 2000.

What was its likely value in August 2006? *(2 marks)*

AQA, June 2008, Paper 1 Higher, Question 12

17 There are 126 people at a party.

The ratio of adults to children at the party is 1 : 6.

a How many adults and children are there? *(3 marks)*

b Nine more adults arrive.

Including these adults, what is the new ratio of adults to children?

Give your answer in the form 1 : k, where k is to be found. *(3 marks)*

AQA, June 2008, Module 3, Question 3

18 A bag contains 6 blue balls and 8 red balls.

Some more red balls are added. The ratio of blue balls to red balls can now be written in the form 1 : n, where n is an integer.

What is the smallest number of red balls that can be added? *(2 marks)*

AQA, Question 10, Specification A, Paper 2, June 2008

19 Helen weighed 100 kg. Her target was to weigh 70 kg or less.

Her weight decreased by 4% each month. Has she achieved her target after nine months?

You **must** show your working. *(3 marks)*

AQA, June 2008, Module 3 Higher, Question 7

20 Gotland is an island which forms part of Sweden. The area of Gotland is 3140 square kilometres.

This area is 0.8% of the total area of Sweden.

What is the total area of Sweden? *(3 marks)*

AQA, November 2005, Module 3 Higher, Question 4

21 Jack and Jill want to buy some towels.

A store displays the following signs.

January Sales
All towels 60% off
Normally £10
January sale price £4

Today Only
EXTRA
25% off the
January sale price

Jack: That is 85% off the original price

Jill: No, it is only 70% off the original price

Who is correct?

Explain your answer fully. *(2 marks)*

AQA, June 2006, Paper 2 Higher, Question 5

22 A leaking water tank loses 36% of its contents each day.

Isobel says that the tank will have lost over 90% of its original contents by the end of the fifth day.

Is Isobel correct?

You **must** explain your answer. *(3 marks)*

AQA, November 2007, Module 3 Higher, Question 9

23 The cost of bananas increased by 25% one week but then fell the following week back to the original price.

By what percentage did the cost of bananas fall in the following week?

24 110 men and women visit a cinema. There are 20% more men than women.

How many men are at the cinema?

Worked Examination Questions

FM **1** Kelly bought a television set. After a reduction of 15% in a sale, the one she bought cost her £319.60. What was the original price of the television set?

1 Multiplier is 0.85 or 85% is equivalent to £319.60

A 15% reduction is a multiplier of 0.85, or realising the sale price is 85% scores 1 mark for method.

£319.60 ÷ 0.85, or 100% is equivalent to £319.60 ÷ 85 × 100

Showing the correct calculation that will lead to the correct answer scores 1 mark for method.

= £376

£376 gets 1 mark for accuracy.

Total: 3 marks

PS **2** A plant in a greenhouse is 10 cm high. It increases its height by 15% each day. How many days does it take to double in height?

2 1.15 is the multiplier

Recognising the multiplier scores 1 mark.

$10 \times 1.15 = 11.5$ (one day)

10×1.15^2 (or 11.5×1.15) $= 13.225$

Getting to this stage scores 1 mark for method.

$10 \times 1.15^3 = 15.2$

$10 \times 1.15^4 = 17.5$

$10 \times 1.15^5 = 20.1$ and therefore it takes 5 days to double its height

Reaching the correct solution gets 1 mark for accuracy.

Total: 3 marks

PS AU **3** Decide whether $\frac{2}{3} + \frac{4}{5}$ is greater or less than $1\frac{7}{9}$. Show clearly how you decide.

3 The answer to part a is less than $1(\frac{33}{40})$ so the numerator $(\frac{2}{3} + \frac{4}{5})$ must be smaller than the denominator $(1\frac{7}{9})$.

or

$\frac{2}{3} + \frac{4}{5} = \frac{22}{15}$ from part a

$= \frac{198}{135}$

and $1\frac{7}{9} = \frac{240}{135}$

Any valid reason would be acceptable and scores 1 mark.

Total: 3 marks

2 Functional Maths
Understanding VAT

VAT means 'Value Added Tax'. You pay it when you buy goods or services and it is normally included in the price of the goods or services. The rate of VAT can vary from country-to-country and even product-to-product (for example, some goods are exempt from VAT, such as food and children's clothes).

In the economic recession of 2009, the British government reduced the VAT rate from 17.5% to 15%, to help stimulate economic recovery. This had practical implications for shops, which had to find the best way to include the VAT reduction in the price labels in their shops.

Your task

To accommodate the reduced VAT rate, many shops had to change their price labels overnight.

Write a report advising shops on how best to accommodate the change in VAT. Use mathematical evidence to support your advice.

Consider the points below in your report:

- Some shops took 2.5% from their displayed prices. Was this the correct thing to do? Use evidence to support your answer.
- Is there a quick calculation that shops could use to work out the new price at the till?
- Does the change in VAT rate affect shops' overall profit?
- Does the change in VAT have an effect on the prices displayed in the annual 'January sales'?

On 1st January 2010, the government reversed the VAT reduction.

- What should shopkeepers do now to come into line with the increased VAT rate?

Getting started

The price of a TV is £420 + VAT. What is its final price if VAT is charged at:

- 15%
- 17.5%
- 20%?

The price of a TV is £450 including VAT. What would the pre-VAT price have been if VAT is charged at:

- 15%
- 17.5%
- 20%?

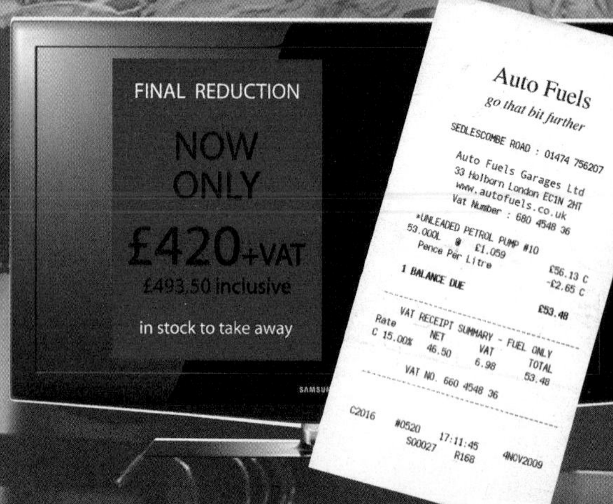

FINAL REDUCTION
NOW ONLY
£420+VAT
£493.50 inclusive
in stock to take away
Auto Fuels
go that bit further

Extension

Research two case studies to find out how shops actually dealt with the changes in VAT. Identify the mathematics that the shops used and evaluate the approach that they took.

Why this chapter matters

In Britain today, taking the pulse of the nation is an involved affair. Does the teacher in London have the same views as the banker in Sheffield? Will a milkman in Cornwall agree with an IT specialist in Scotland? And if not, how can the opinions of all the people be sought?

Opinion polls

Opinion polls have been used by politicians for centuries.

The Greeks and Romans used opinion polls years ago. At the time of Plato, Athens only had a population of around 30 000 people who could vote (all men!) and if an Ancient Greek wanted to know the opinions of his townsfolk he would simply ask a question in a public forum.

The politicians didn't see rival groups as an important section of society. These groups were small, for example, small groups of farmers, of old men, of wine makers.

Plato

Straw polls

Polling, as we know it, began in Pennsylvania, USA. In 1824, the *Harrisburg Pennsylvanian* newspaper surveyed about 500 potential voters and found that Andrew Jackson held a commanding lead over John Quincy Adams (70% vs. 23%). Jackson went on to win the election by 38 000, so the poll was accurate.

This type of poll is called a 'straw poll' – it involves no analysis of statistical trends but is just a vote.

Gallup polls

For the next 100 years, straw polling was used but it was not always very accurate. Eventually a change was made to the way polls were taken. In 1936, the USA Presidential election between Franklin Roosevelt and Alf Landon was about to take place. A popular newspaper mailed over 10 million questionnaires. They received about two million responses and, a few days before election day, they predicted an overwhelming win for Alf Landon. The results of the straw poll were:

Landon	1 293 669 (57%)
Roosevelt	972 897 (43%)

At this time, George Gallup had created a new type of poll—one that used a much smaller sample but involved some statistical analysis. Gallup's polls showed a victory for Roosevelt. Roosevelt won a huge victory, gaining 63% of the vote.

George Gallup

The American public asked how the newspaper could be so wrong. The questionnaires were sent to their own subscribers, so the poll was biased from the start. Then only those who were interested replied, so another bias. The Gallup polls did not have this same bias as they used a representative, stratified sampling.

George Gallup went from strength to strength and, to this day, his firm are responsible for finding out opinions for a whole range of people from politicians to farmers, from trade union leaders to football clubs.

Sampling is used frequently today. We are regularly being asked our opinions in the street. However, they don't ask everyone; they select particular people so that their sample is truly representative.

Statistics: Data handling

This chapter will show you …

- D to C how to calculate and use the mode, median, mean and range from frequency tables of discrete data
- D to C how to decide which is the best average for different types of data
- D to C how to recognise the modal class and calculate an estimate of the mean from frequency tables of grouped data
- C to B how to use the data-handling cycle
- A to A* how to draw frequency polygons and histograms
- A to A* how to design questions for questionnaires and surveys

Visual overview

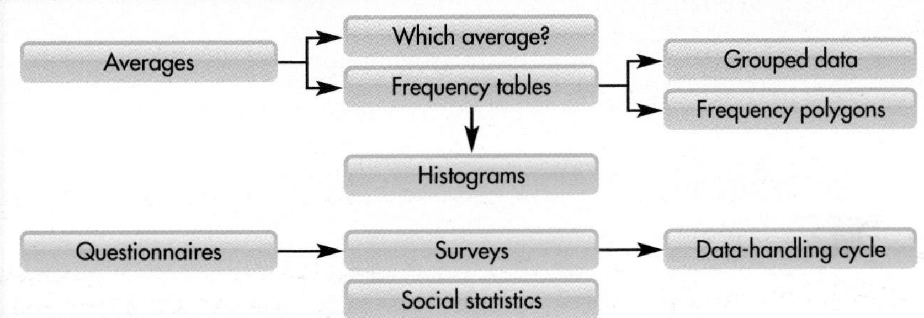

What you should already know

- How to work out the mean, mode, median and range of small sets of discrete data **(KS3 level 4, GCSE grade F)**
- How to extract information from tables and diagrams **(KS3 level 4, GCSE grade F)**

Quick check

1 The marks for 15 students in a maths test are as follows

2, 3, 4, 5, 5, 6, 6, 6, 7, 7, 7, 7, 7, 8, 10

a What is the modal mark?

b What is the median mark?

c What is the range of the marks?

d What is the mean mark?

3.1 Averages

This section will show you how to:

- use averages
- solve more complex problems using averages
- identify the advantages and disadvantages of each type of average and learn which one to use in different situations

Key words

mean
measure of location
median
mode

Average is a term you will often use when describing or comparing sets of data. The average is also known as a **measure of location**. For example, you may refer to the average rainfall in Britain, the average score of a batsman, an average weekly wage, the average mark in an examination. In each of these examples, you are representing the whole set of many values by just one single, typical value, called the average.

The idea of an average is extremely useful, because it enables you to compare one set of data with another set by comparing just two values—their averages.

There are several ways of expressing an average, but the most commonly used averages are the **mode**, the **median** and the **mean**.

An average must be truly representative of a set of data. So, when you have to find an average, it is crucial to choose the *correct type of average* for this particular set of data. If you use the wrong average, your results will be distorted and give misleading information.

This table, which compares the advantages and disadvantages of each type of average, will help you to make the correct decision.

	Mode	Median	Mean
Advantages	Very easy to find Not affected by extreme values Can be used for non-numerical data	Easy to find for ungrouped data Not affected by extreme values	Easy to find Uses all the values The total for a given number of values can be calculated from it
Disadvantages	Doesn't use all the values May not exist	Doesn't use all the values Often not understood	Extreme values can distort it Has to be calculated
Used for	Non-numerical data For finding the most likely value	Data with extreme values	Data with values that are spread in a balanced way

EXAMPLE 1

The ages of 20 people attending a conference are as follows.

23, 25, 26, 28, 28, 34, 34, 34, 37, 45, 47, 48, 52, 53, 56, 63, 67, 70, 73, 77

a Find **i** the mode **ii** the median **iii** the mean of the data.

b Which average best represents the age of the people at the conference?

a **i** The mode is 34 **ii** the median is 46 **iii** the mean is $920 \div 20 = 46$

b The mean is distorted because of the few very old people at the conference. The median is also distorted by the larger values, so in this case the mode would be the most representative average.

EXERCISE 3A

FM **1** Shopkeepers always want to keep the most popular items in stock. Which average do you think is often known as the shopkeeper's average?

2 A list contains seven even numbers. The largest number is 24. The smallest number is half the largest. The mode is 14 and the median is 16. Two of the numbers add up to 42. What are the seven numbers?

3 The marks of 25 students in an English examination are as follows.

55, 63, 24, 47, 60, 45, 50, 89, 39, 47, 38, 42, 69, 73, 38, 47, 53, 64, 58, 71, 41, 48, 68, 64, 75

Find the median.

AU **4** Decide which average you would use for each of the following. Give a reason for your answer.

a The average mark in an examination.

b The average pocket money for a group of 16-year-old students.

c The average shoe size for all the girls in Year 10.

d The average height for all the artistes on tour with a circus.

e The average hair colour for students in your school.

f The average weight of all newborn babies in a hospital's maternity ward.

AU **5** A pack of matches consists of 12 boxes. The contents of each box are as follows.

34 31 29 35 33 30 31 28 29 35 32 31

On the box it states that the average contents is 32 matches. Is this correct?

Explain your answer.

D

D

FM **6** This table shows the annual salaries for a firm's employees.

Chairman	£83 000
Managing director	£65 000
Floor manager	£34 000
Skilled worker 1	£28 000
Skilled worker 2	£28 000
Machinist	£20 000
Computer engineer	£20 000
Secretary	£20 000
Office junior	£8 000

a What is the **i** modal salary **ii** median salary and **iii** mean salary?

b The management has suggested a pay rise for all of 6%. The shopfloor workers want a pay rise for all of £1500. What difference to the mean salary would each suggestion make?

AU **7** Mr Brennan, a caring maths teacher, told each student their individual test mark and only gave the test statistics to the whole class. He gave the class the modal mark, the median mark and the mean mark.

a Which average would tell a student whether he/she was in the top half or the bottom half of the class?

b Which average tells the students nothing really?

c Which average allows a student to gauge how well he/she has done compared with everyone else?

FM **8** Three players were hoping to be chosen for the basketball team.

The table shows their scores for the last few games they played.

Tom	16, 10, 12, 10, 13, 8, 10
David	16, 8, 15, 25, 8
Mohammed	15, 2, 15, 3, 5

The teacher said they would be selected by their best average score.

By which average would each boy choose to be selected?

C

9 A list of nine numbers has a mean of 7.6. What number must be added to the list to give a new mean of 8?

10 A dance group of 17 teenagers had a mean weight of 44.5 kg. To enter a competition, there needs to be 18 people in the group with an average weight of 44.4 kg or less. What is the maximum weight that the 18th person could be?

11 The mean age of a group of eight walkers is 42. Joanne joins the group and the mean age changes to 40. How old is Joanne?

PS **12** **a** Find five numbers that have **both** the properties below.

i A range of 5 **ii** A mean of 5

b Find five numbers that have **all** the properties below.

i A range of 5 **ii** A median of 5 **iii** A mean of 5

FM AU **13** What is the average pay at a factory with 10 employees?

The boss said, "£43 295." A worker said, "£18 210."

They were both correct. Explain how this can be.

3.2 Frequency tables

This section will show you how to:
- calculate the mode and median from a frequency table
- calculate the mean from a frequency table

Key words
frequency table

When a lot of information has been gathered, it is often convenient to put it together in a **frequency table**. From this table, you can then find the values of the mode, median, mean and range of the data.

EXAMPLE 2

A survey was done on the number of people in each car leaving the Meadowhall Shopping Centre, in Sheffield. The results are summarised in the table.

Calculate **a** the mode, **b** the median, **c** the mean number of people in a car.

Number of people in each car	1	2	3	4	5	6
Frequency	45	198	121	76	52	13

a The modal number of people in a car is easy to spot. It is the number with the largest frequency (198). Hence, the modal number of people in a car is 2.

b The median number of people in a car is found by working out where the middle of the set of numbers is located. First, add up frequencies to get the total number of cars surveyed, which comes to 505. Next, calculate the middle position.

$(505 + 1) \div 2 = 253$

You now need to add the frequencies across the table to find which group contains the 253rd item. The 243rd item is the end of the group with 2 in a car. Therefore, the 253rd item must be in the group with 3 in a car. Hence, the median number of people in a car is 3.

c The mean number of people in a car is found by calculating the total number of people, and then dividing this total by the number of cars surveyed.

Number in car	Frequency	Number in these cars
1	45	$1 \times 45 = 45$
2	198	$2 \times 198 = 396$
3	121	$3 \times 121 = 363$
4	76	$4 \times 76 = 304$
5	52	$5 \times 52 = 260$
6	13	$6 \times 13 = 78$
Totals	505	1446

Hence, the mean number of people in a car is $1446 \div 505 = 2.9$ (2 significant figures)

Using your calculator

The previous example can also be done by using the statistical mode which is available on some calculators. However, not all calculators are the same, so you will either have to read your instruction manual or experiment with the statistical keys on your calculator.

You may find one labelled

DATA or M+ or Σ+ or $\bar{x}$ where $\bar{x}$ is printed in blue.

Try the following key strokes.

1 × 4 5 DATA 2 × 1 9 8 DATA …

1 × 4 5 DATA $\bar{x}$

EXERCISE 3B

D

1 Find **i** the mode, **ii** the median and **iii** the mean from each frequency table below.

a A survey of the shoe sizes of all the Year 10 boys in a school gave these results.

Shoe size	4	5	6	7	8	9	10
No. of students	12	30	34	35	23	8	3

b This is a record of the number of babies born each week over one year in a small maternity unit.

No. of babies	0	1	2	3	4	5	6	7	8	9	10	11	12	13	14
Frequency	1	1	1	2	2	2	3	5	9	8	6	4	5	2	1

2 A survey of the number of children in each family of a school's intake gave these results.

No. of children	1	2	3	4	5
Frequency	214	328	97	26	3

a Assuming each child at the school is shown in the data, how many children are at the school?

b Calculate the mean number of children in a family.

c How many families have this mean number of children?

FM **d** How many families would consider themselves average from this survey?

3 A dentist kept records of how many teeth he extracted from his patients.

In 1989 he extracted 598 teeth from 271 patients.

In 1999 he extracted 332 teeth from 196 patients.

In 2009 he extracted 374 teeth from 288 patients.

a Calculate the average number of teeth taken from each patient in each year.

AU **b** Explain why you think the average number of teeth extracted falls each year.

D

4 The teachers in a school were asked to indicate the average number of hours they spent each day marking. The table summarises their replies.

No. of hours spent marking	1	2	3	4	5	6
No. of teachers	10	13	12	8	6	1

a How many teachers are at the school?

b What is the modal number of hours spent marking?

c What is the mean number of hours spent marking?

5 Two friends often played golf together. They recorded their scores for each hole over five games to determine who was more consistent and who was the better player. The results are summarised in the table.

No. of shots to hole ball	1	2	3	4	5	6	7	8	9
Roger	0	0	0	14	37	27	12	0	0
Brian	5	12	15	18	14	8	8	8	2

a What is the modal score for each player?

b What is the range of scores for each player?

c What is the median score for each player?

d What is the mean score for each player?

e Which player is the more consistent? Explain why.

AU **f** Who would you say is the better player. State why.

C

6 The number of league goals scored by a football team over a season is given in the table.

No. of goals scored	0	1	2	3	4	5	6	7
No. of matches	3	8	10	11	4	2	1	1

a How many games were played that season?

b What is the range of goals scored?

c What is the modal number of goals scored?

d What is the median number of goals scored?

e What is the mean number of goals scored?

FM **f** Which average do you think the team's supporters would say is the average number of goals scored by the team that season?

g If the team also scored 20 goals in 10 cup matches that season, what was the mean number of goals the team scored throughout the whole season?

C

7 A survey of the number of children in each family of a school's intake gave these results.

No. of children	1	2	3	4	5
Frequency	214	328	97	26	3

a State the median number of children per family.

b Calculate the mean number of children in a family.

FM c What percentage of families could consider themselves average from this survey?

FM PS 8 The number of sweets in some tubes is shown in the table below, but a coffee stain has deleted one of the figures.

No. of sweets	Frequency
32	4
33	[illegible]
34	9
35	1
36	1

The mean number of sweets in a tube is known to be 33.5.

Find out what the missing number is in the table.

FM AU 9 I have been given a frequency table by Corrin. She says, "I can calculate the mean to be an integer but not the median. Why is that?"

Can you give a possible explanation?

B

10 The table shows the number of passengers in each of 100 taxis leaving London Heathrow Airport one day.

No. of passengers in a taxi	1	2	3	4
No. of taxis	x	40	y	26

a Find the value of $x + y$.

b If the mean number of passengers per taxi is 2.66, show that $x + 3y = 82$.

c Find the values of x and y by solving appropriate equations.

d State the median of the number of passengers per taxi.

FM 11 Sam, a farmer, thinks that the amount of rain fall is decreasing each year.

He records the amount of rain that falls each month for a year. The table shows the results (in mm).

Months	Jan	Feb	Mar	Apr	May	Jun	Jul	Aug	Sep	Oct	Nov	Dec
Rainfall (mm)	27	43	30	37	54	20	16	21	32	36	41	39

From the internet Sam finds that the mean rainfall for 2008 is 36 mm with a range of 34. Investigate the hypothesis:

'The amount of rainfall is decreasing each year.'

3.3 Grouped data

This section will show you how to:
- identify the modal group
- calculate and estimate the mean from a grouped table

Key words
continuous data
discrete data
estimated mean
group
modal group

Sometimes the information you are given is grouped in some way, as in the table in Example 3, which shows the range of weekly pocket money given to Year 10 students in a particular class.

EXAMPLE 3

From the data in the table:

a write down the **modal group**

b calculate an estimate of the mean weekly pocket money.

Pocket money, p, (£)	$0 < p \leqslant 1$	$1 < p \leqslant 2$	$2 < p \leqslant 3$	$3 < p \leqslant 4$	$4 < p \leqslant 5$
No. of students	2	5	5	9	15

a The modal group is still easy to pick out, since it is simply the one with the largest frequency. Here the modal group is £4 to £5.

b The mean can only be estimated, since you do not have all the information.
To estimate the mean, you simply assume that each person in each **group** has the midway amount, then you can proceed to build up the table as before.
To find the midway value. Add the two end values and divide the total by two.

Pocket money, p, (£)	**Frequency (f)**	**Midway (m)**	$f \times m$
$0 < p \leqslant 1$	2	0.50	1.00
$1 < p \leqslant 2$	5	1.50	7.50
$2 < p \leqslant 3$	5	2.50	12.50
$3 < p \leqslant 4$	9	3.50	31.50
$4 < p \leqslant 5$	15	4.50	67.50
Totals	36		120

The **estimated mean** is £120 ÷ 36 = £3.33 (rounded)

Note the notation used for the groups.

$0 < p \leqslant 1$ means any amount above 0p up to and including £1.

$1 < p \leqslant 2$ means any amount above £1 up to and including £2.

If you had written 0.01 – 1.00, 1.01 – 2.00, … for the groups, the midway values would have been 0.505, 1.505, … Although technically correct, this makes the calculation of the mean harder and does not have a significant effect on the final answer, which is an estimate anyway.

This issue only arises because money is **discrete data**, which is data that consists of separate numbers, such as goals scored, marks in a test, number of children and shoe sizes. Normally, grouped tables use **continuous data**, which is data that can have an infinite number of different values, such as height, weight, time, area and capacity. It is always rounded information.

Whatever the type of data, remember to find the midway value by adding the two end values of the group and dividing by 2.

EXERCISE 3C

C

1 For each table of values, find the following.

i The modal group **ii** An estimate for the mean

a

x	$0 < x \leqslant 10$	$10 < x \leqslant 20$	$20 < x \leqslant 30$	$30 < x \leqslant 40$	$40 < x \leqslant 50$
Frequency	4	6	11	17	9

b

y	$0 < y \leqslant 100$	$100 < y \leqslant 200$	$200 < y \leqslant 300$	$300 < y \leqslant 400$	$400 < y \leqslant 500$	$500 < y \leqslant 600$
Frequency	95	56	32	21	9	3

c

z	$0 < z \leqslant 5$	$5 < z \leqslant 10$	$10 < z \leqslant 15$	$15 < z \leqslant 20$
Frequency	16	27	19	13

d

Weeks	1–3	4–6	7–9	10–12	13–15
Frequency	5	8	14	10	7

HINTS AND TIPS

When you copy the tables, draw them vertically, as in Example 3.

2 Jason brought 100 pebbles back from the beach and weighed them all, to the nearest gram. His results are summarised in this table.

Weight, w (grams)	$40 < w \leqslant 60$	$60 < w \leqslant 80$	$80 < w \leqslant 100$	$100 < w \leqslant 120$	$120 < w \leqslant 140$	$140 < w \leqslant 160$
Frequency	5	9	22	27	26	11

Find the following.

a The modal weight of the pebbles **b** An estimate of the total weight of all the pebbles

c An estimate of the mean weight of the pebbles

3 One hundred light bulbs were tested by their manufacturer to see whether the average life span of the bulbs was over 200 hours. The table summarises the results.

Life span, h (hours)	$150 < h \leqslant 175$	$175 < h \leqslant 200$	$200 < h \leqslant 225$	$225 < h \leqslant 250$	$250 < h \leqslant 275$
Frequency	24	45	18	10	3

a What is the modal length of time a bulb lasts?

b What percentage of bulbs last longer than 200 hours?

FM **c** Estimate the mean life span of the light bulbs.

FM **d** Do you think the test shows that the average life span is over 200 hours? Explain your answer fully.

FM **4** The table shows the distances run by an athlete who is training for a marathon.

Distance, *d*, (miles)	$0 < d \leqslant 5$	$5 < d \leqslant 10$	$10 < d \leqslant 15$	$15 < d \leqslant 20$	$20 < d \leqslant 25$
Frequency	3	8	13	5	2

a It is recommended that an athlete's daily average mileage should be at least one-third of the distance of the race being trained for. A marathon is 26.2 miles. Is this athlete doing enough training?

b The athlete records the times of some runs and calculates that her average pace for all runs is $6\frac{1}{2}$ minutes for a mile. Explain why she is wrong to expect a finishing time of $26.2 \times 6\frac{1}{2}$ minutes ≈ 170 minutes for the marathon.

c The athlete claims that the difference between her shortest and longest run is 21 miles. Could this be correct? Explain your answer.

FM **5** The owners of a boutique did a survey to find the average age of people using the boutique. The table summarises the results.

Age (years)	14–18	19–20	21–26	27–35	36–50
Frequency	26	24	19	16	11

What do you think is the average age of the people using the boutique?

FM AU **6** Three supermarkets each claimed to have the lowest average price increase over the year. The table summarises their average price increases.

Price increase (p)	1–5	6–10	11–15	16–20	21–25	26–30	31–35
Soundbuy	4	10	14	23	19	8	2
Springfields	5	11	12	19	25	9	6
Setco	3	8	15	31	21	7	3

Using their average price increases, make a comparison of the supermarkets and write a report on which supermarket, in your opinion, has the lowest price increases over the year. Don't forget to justify your answers.

7 A survey was conducted to see how quickly the AOne attended calls that were not on a motorway.

The following table summarises the results.

Time (min)	1–15	16–30	31–45	46–60	61–75	76–90	91–105
Frequency	2	23	48	31	27	18	11

a How many calls were used in the survey?

b Estimate the mean time taken per call.

FM **c** Which average would the AOne use for the average call-out time?

d What percentage of calls do the AOne get to within the hour?

C

PS **8** In a cricket competition, the table shows the runs scored by all the batsmen.

Runs	0–9	10–19	20–29	30–39	40–49
Frequency	8	5	10	5	2

Helen noticed that two numbers were in the wrong part of the table and that this made a difference of 1.7 to the arithmetic mean.

Which two numbers were the wrong way round?

AU **9** The profit made each week by a charity shop is shown in the table below.

Profit (£)	0–500	501–1000	1001–1500	1501–2000
Frequency	15	26	8	3

Explain how you would estimate the mean profit made each week.

AU **10** The table shows the number of members of 100 football clubs.

Weight	20–29	30–39	40–49	50–59	60–69
Frequency	16	34	27	18	5

a Roger claims that the median number of members is 39.5.

Is he correct? Explain your answer

b He also says that the range of the number of members is 34.

Could he be correct? Explain your answer.

3.4 Frequency diagrams

This section will show you how to:

- draw frequency polygons for discrete and continuous data
- draw histograms for continuous data with equal intervals
- draw pie charts

Key words

continuous data
discrete data
frequency density
frequency polygon
grouped data
histogram
pie chart
sector

Pie charts

Bar charts and line graphs are easy to draw but they can be difficult to interpret when there is a big difference between the frequencies or there are only a few categories. In these cases, it is often more convenient to illustrate the data on a **pie chart.**

In a pie chart, the whole of the data is represented by a circle (the 'pie') and each category is represented by a **sector** of the circle (a 'slice of the pie'). The angle of each sector is proportional to the frequency of the category it represents.

A pie chart cannot show individual frequencies, like a bar chart can, for example. It can only show proportions.

Sometimes the pie chart will be marked off in equal sections rather than angles. In these cases, the numbers are always easy to work with.

EXAMPLE 4

In a survey on holidays, 120 people were asked to state which type of transport they used on their last holiday. This table shows the results of the survey. Draw a pie chart to illustrate the data.

Type of transport	Train	Coach	Car	Ship	Plane
Frequency	24	12	59	11	14

You need to find the angle for the fraction of 360° that represents each type of transport. This is usually done in a table, as shown below.

Types of transport	**Frequency**	**Calculation**	**Angle**
Train	24	$\frac{24}{120} \times 360° = 72°$	72°
Coach	12	$\frac{12}{120} \times 360° = 36°$	36°
Car	59	$\frac{59}{120} \times 360° = 177°$	177°
Ship	11	$\frac{11}{120} \times 360° = 33°$	33°
Plane	14	$\frac{14}{120} \times 360° = 42°$	42°
Totals	120		360°

Draw the pie chart, using the calculated angle for each sector.

Note:

- Use the frequency total (120 in this case) to calculate each fraction.
- Check that the sum of all the angles is 360°.
- Label each sector.
- The angles or frequencies do not have to be shown on the pie chart.

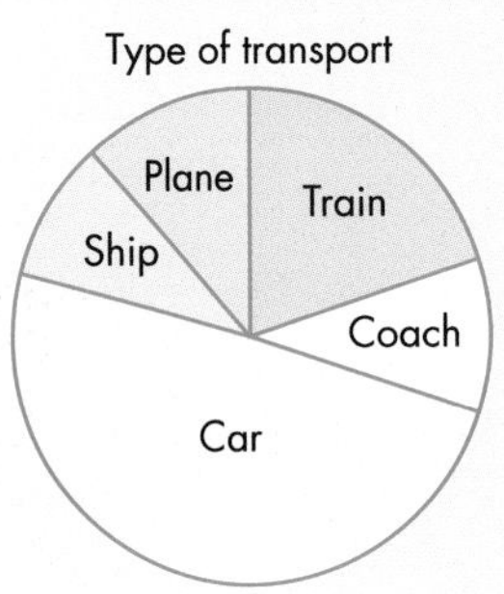

EXERCISE 3D 

D

1 Andy wrote down the number of lessons he had per week in each subject on his school timetable.

Mathematics 5	English 5	Science 8	Languages 6
Humanities 6	Arts 4	Games 2	

a How many lessons did Andy have on his timetable?

b Draw a pie chart to show the data.

c Draw a bar chart to show the data.

d Which diagram better illustrates the data? Give a reason for your answer.

2 In the run up to an election, 720 people were asked in a poll which political party they would vote for. The results are given in the table.

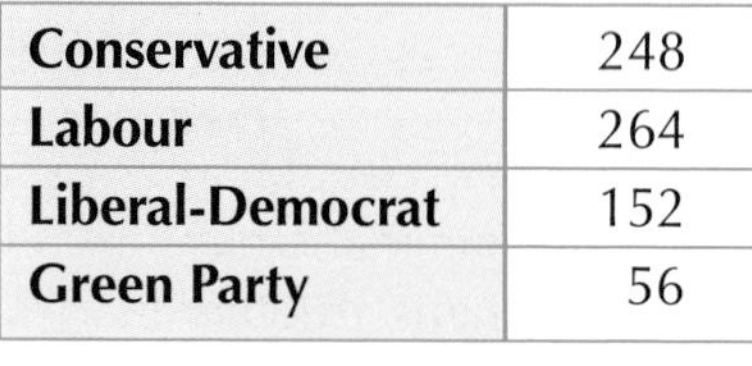

Conservative	248
Labour	264
Liberal-Democrat	152
Green Party	56

a Draw a pie chart to illustrate the data.

b Why do you think pie charts are used to show this sort of information during elections?

3 This pie chart shows the proportions of the different shoe sizes worn by 144 students in Year 11 in a London school.

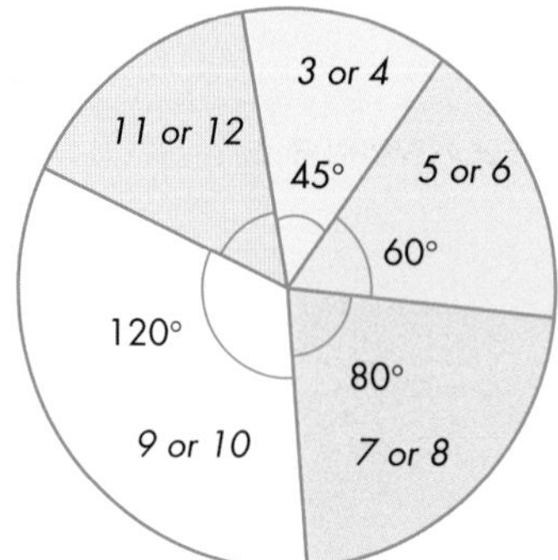

a What is the angle of the sector representing shoe sizes 11 and 12?

b How many students had a shoe size of 11 or 12?

c What percentage of students wore the modal size?

FM 4 The table below shows the numbers of candidates, at each grade, taking music examinations in Strings and Brass.

	Grades					Total no. of candidates
	3	4	5	6	7	
Strings	200	980	1050	600	70	3000
Brass	250	360	300	120	70	1100

a Draw a pie chart to represent each of the two examinations.

b Compare the pie charts to decide which group of candidates, Strings or Brass, did better overall. Give reasons to justify your answer.

D

PS 5 In a survey, a rail company asked passengers whether their service had improved.

What is the probability that a person picked at random from this survey answered "Don't know"?

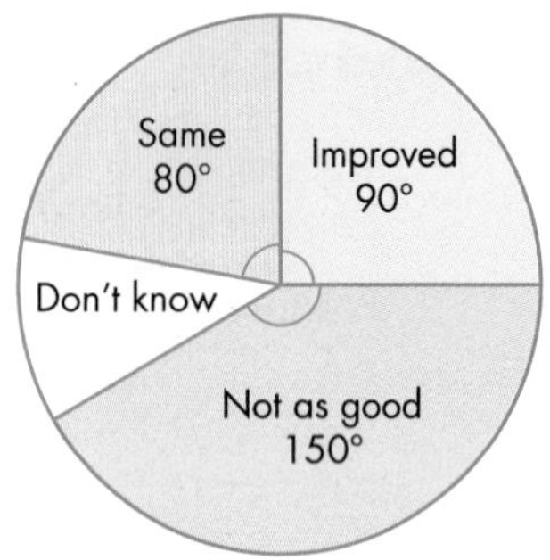

AU 6 You have been asked to draw a pie chart representing the different ways in which students come to school one morning.

What data would you collect, to do this?

Frequency polygons

To help people understand it, statistical information is often presented in pictorial or diagrammatic form. For example, you should have seen pie charts, bar charts and stem-and-leaf diagrams. Another method of showing data is by **frequency polygons**.

Frequency polygons can be used to represent both ungrouped data and **grouped data**, as shown in Example 5 and Example 6 respectively. They are useful to show the shapes of distributions, and can be used to compare distributions.

EXAMPLE 5

No. of children	0	1	2	3	4	5
Frequency	12	23	36	28	16	11

This is the frequency polygon for the ungrouped data in the table.

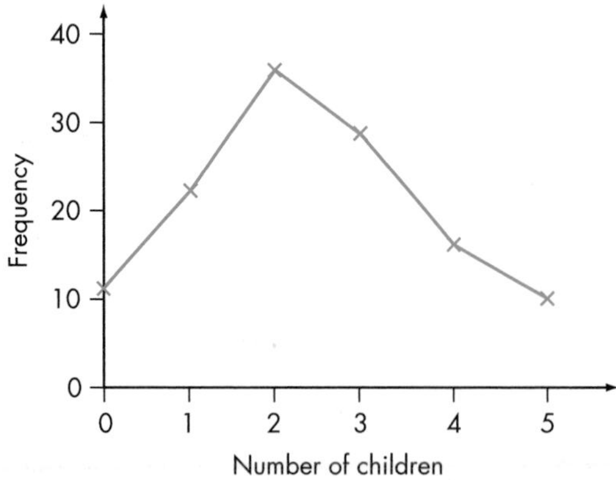

- You simply plot the coordinates from each ordered pair in the table.
- You complete the polygon by joining up the plotted points with straight lines.

EXAMPLE 6

Weight, w (kilograms)	$0 < w \leqslant 5$	$5 < w \leqslant 10$	$10 < w \leqslant 15$	$15 < w \leqslant 20$	$20 < w \leqslant 25$	$25 < w \leqslant 30$
Frequency	4	13	25	32	17	9

This is the frequency polygon for the grouped data in the table.

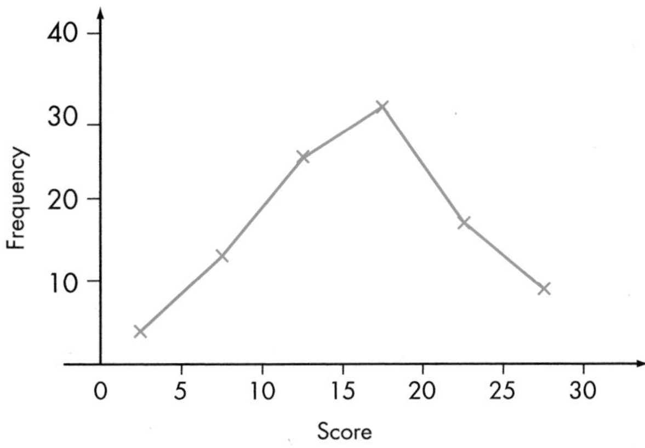

- You use the midway value of each group, just as in estimating the mean.
- You plot the ordered pairs of midway values with frequency, namely,
  (2.5, 4), (7.5, 13), (12.5, 25), (17.5, 32), (22.5, 17), (27.5, 9)
- You do not know what happens above and below the groups in the table, so do not draw lines before (2.5, 4) or after (27.5, 9). The diagram shows the shape of the distribution.

Bar charts and histograms

You should already be familiar with the bar chart in which the vertical axis represents frequency, and the horizontal axis represents the type of data. (Sometimes it is more convenient to have the axes the other way.)

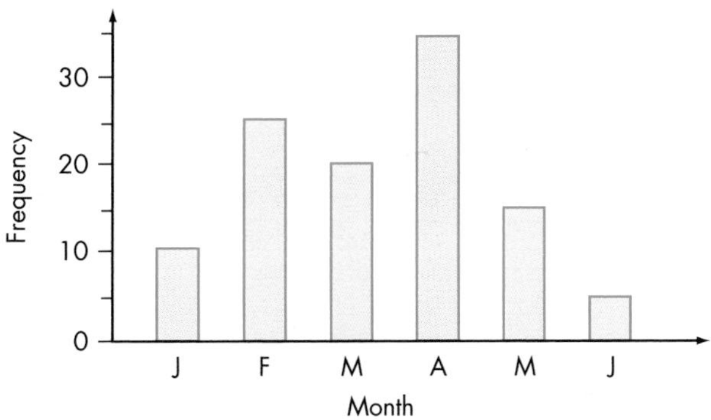

You should also recognise a composite bar chart, which can be used to compare two sets of related data.

EXAMPLE 7

This dual bar chart shows the average daily maximum temperatures for England and Turkey over a five-month period.

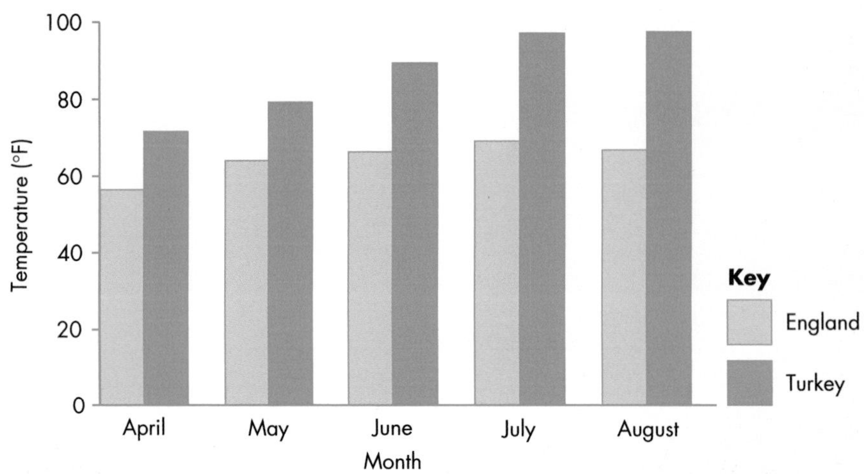

In which month was the difference between temperatures in England and Turkey the greatest?

The largest difference can be seen in August.

A **histogram** looks similar to a bar chart, but there are four fundamental differences.

- There are no gaps between the bars.
- The horizontal axis has a continuous scale since it represents **continuous data**, such as time, weight or length.
- The area of each bar represents the class or group frequency of the bar.
- The vertical axis is labelled '**frequency density**', where

$$\text{frequency density} = \frac{\text{frequency of class interval}}{\text{width of class interval}}$$

When the data is not continuous, a simple bar chart is used. For example, you would use a bar chart to represent the runs scored in a test match or the goals scored by a hockey team since these are integer values and are **discrete data**.

The histogram below has been drawn from this table of times it takes people to walk to work.

Time, t (min)	$0 < t \leqslant 4$	$4 < t \leqslant 8$	$8 < t \leqslant 12$	$12 < t \leqslant 16$
Frequency	8	12	10	7
Frequency density	2	3	2.5	1.75

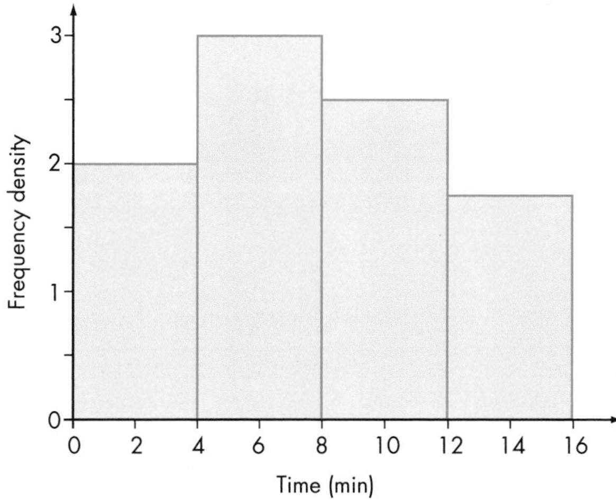

Notice that each histogram bar starts at the *least possible* time and finishes at the *greatest possible* time for its group.

Using your calculator

Histograms can also be drawn on graphics calculators or by using computer software packages. If you have access to either of these, try to use them.

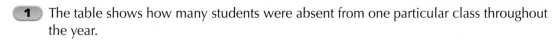

EXERCISE 3E

D

1 The table shows how many students were absent from one particular class throughout the year.

Students absent	1	2	3	4	5
Frequency	48	32	12	3	1

a Draw a frequency polygon to illustrate the data.

b Calculate the mean number of absences each lesson.

2 The table shows the number of goals scored by a hockey team in one season.

Goals	1	2	3	4	5
Frequency	3	9	7	5	2

a Draw the frequency polygon for this data.

b Calculate the mean number of goals scored per game in the season.

3 The frequency polygon shows the amount of money spent in a corner shop by the first 40 customers on one day.

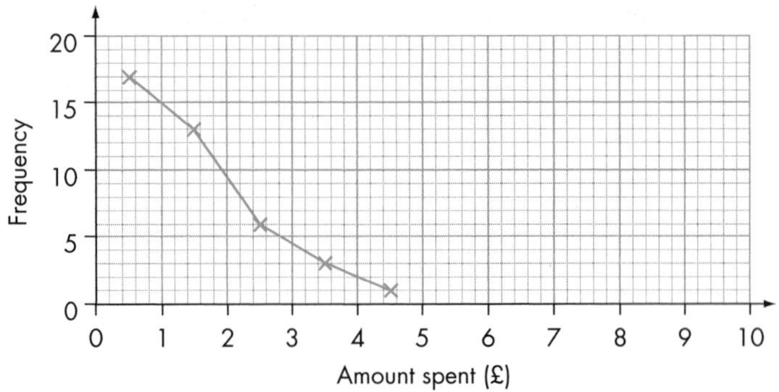

a **i** Use the frequency polygon to complete the table for the amounts spent by the first 40 customers.

Amount spent, *m* (£)	$0 < m \leqslant 1$	$1 < m \leqslant 2$	$2 < m \leqslant 3$	$3 < m \leqslant 4$	$4 < m \leqslant 5$
Frequency					

ii Work out the mean amount of money spent by these 40 customers.

b Mid-morning the shopkeeper records the amount spent by another 40 customers. The table below shows the data.

Amount spent, *m* (£)	$0 < m \leqslant 2$	$2 < m \leqslant 4$	$4 < m \leqslant 6$	$6 < m \leqslant 8$	$8 < m \leqslant 10$
Frequency	3	5	18	10	4

i On a copy of the graph above, draw the frequency polygon to show this data.

ii Calculate the mean amount spent by the 40 mid-morning customers.

FM **c** Comment on the differences between the frequency polygons and the average amounts spent by the different sets of customers.

4 The table shows the range of heights of the girls in Year 11 at a London school.

Height, *h* (cm)	$120 < h \leqslant 130$	$130 < h \leqslant 140$	$140 < h \leqslant 150$	$150 < h \leqslant 160$	$160 < h \leqslant 170$
Frequency	15	37	25	13	5

a Draw a frequency polygon for this data.

b Draw a histogram for this data.

c Estimate the mean height of the girls.

5 A doctor was concerned at the length of time her patients had to wait to see her when they came to the morning surgery. The survey she did gave her these results.

Time, *m* (minutes)	$0 < m \leqslant 10$	$10 < m \leqslant 20$	$20 < m \leqslant 30$	$30 < m \leqslant 40$	$40 < m \leqslant 50$	$50 < m \leqslant 60$
Monday	5	8	17	9	7	4
Tuesday	9	8	16	3	2	1
Wednesday	7	6	18	2	1	1

a On the same pair of axes draw a frequency polygon for each day.

b What is the average amount of time spent waiting each day?

FM **c** Why might the average time for each day be different?

C

6 After a spelling test, all the results were collated for girls and boys separately as below.

Number correct, N	$1 \leqslant N \leqslant 4$	$5 \leqslant N \leqslant 8$	$9 \leqslant N \leqslant 12$	$13 \leqslant N \leqslant 16$	$17 \leqslant N \leqslant 20$
Boys	3	7	21	26	15
Girls	4	8	17	23	20

a Draw frequency polygons to illustrate the differences between the boys' scores and the girls' scores.

b Estimate the mean scores for boys and girls separately, then comment on your results.

FM PS **7** The frequency polygon shows the lengths of time that students spent on homework one weekend.

Calculate an estimate of the mean time spent on homework by the students.

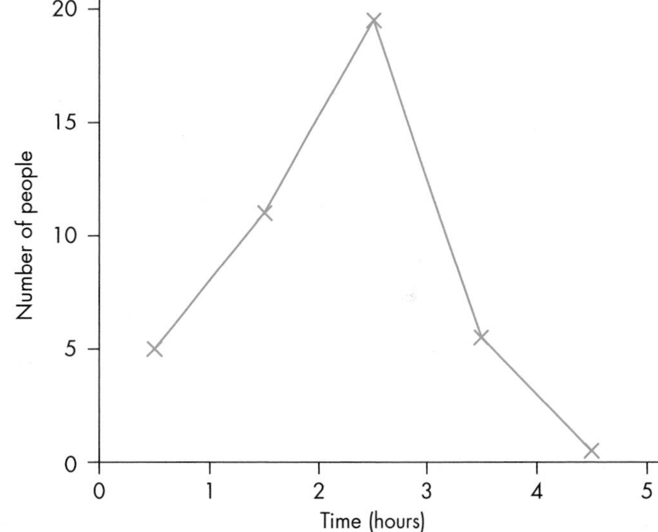

FM AU **8** The frequency polygon shows the times that a number of people waited at a Post Office before being served one morning.

Julie said, "Most people spent 30 seconds waiting."

Explain why this might be wrong.

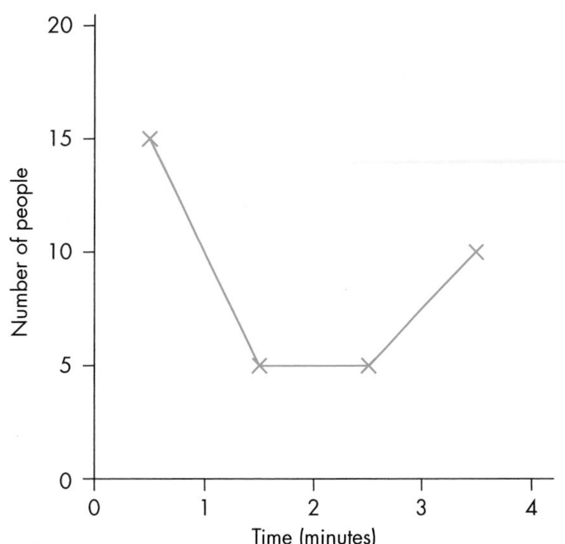

3.5 Histograms with bars of unequal width

This section will show you how to:

- draw and read histograms where the bars are of unequal width
- find the median, quartiles and interquartile range from a histogram

Key words

class interval
interquartile range
lower quartile
median
upper quartile

Sometimes the data in a frequency distribution are grouped into classes with intervals that are different. In this case, the resulting histogram has bars of unequal width.

The key fact that you should always remember is that the area of a bar in a histogram represents the class frequency of the bar. So, in the case of an unequal-width histogram, you find the height to draw each bar by dividing its class frequency by its **class interval** width (bar width), which is the difference between the lower and upper bounds for each interval. Conversely, given a histogram, you can find any of its class frequencies by multiplying the height of the corresponding bar by its width.

It is for this reason that the scale on the vertical axes of histograms is nearly always labelled 'frequency density', where

$$\text{frequency density} = \frac{\text{frequency of class interval}}{\text{width of class interval}}$$

EXAMPLE 8

The heights of a group of girls were measured. The results were classified as shown in the table.

Height, h (cm)	$151 \leqslant h < 153$	$153 \leqslant h < 154$	$154 \leqslant h < 155$	$155 \leqslant h < 159$	$159 \leqslant h < 160$
Frequency	64	43	47	96	12

It is convenient to write the table vertically and add two columns, class width and frequency density.

The class width is found by subtracting the lower class boundary from the upper class boundary. The frequency density is found by dividing the frequency by the class width.

Height, h (cm)	Frequency	Class width	Frequency density
$151 \leqslant h < 153$	64	2	32
$153 \leqslant h < 154$	43	1	43
$154 \leqslant h < 155$	47	1	47
$155 \leqslant h < 159$	96	4	24
$159 \leqslant h < 160$	12	1	12

The histogram can now be drawn. The horizontal scale should be marked off as normal, from a value below the lowest value in the table to a value above the largest value in the table. In this case, mark the scale from 150 cm to 160 cm. The vertical scale is always frequency density and is marked up to at least the largest frequency density in the table. In this case, 50 is a sensible value.

continued

EXAMPLE 8 continued

Each bar is drawn between the lower class interval and the upper class interval horizontally, and up to the frequency density vertically.

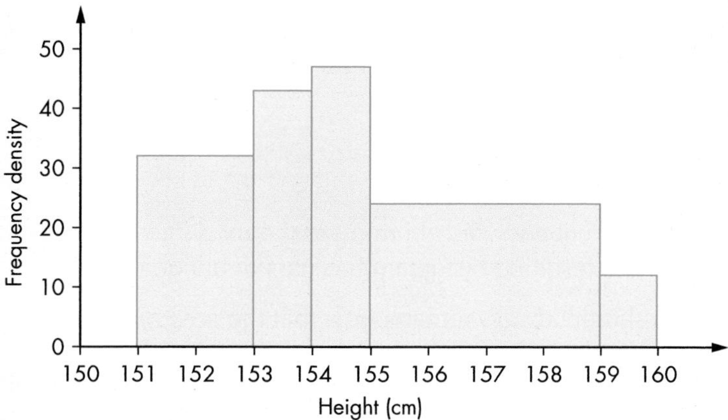

EXAMPLE 9

This histogram shows the distribution of heights of daffodils in a greenhouse.

a Complete a frequency table for the heights of the daffodils, and show the cumulative frequency.

b Find the **median** height.

c Find the **interquartile range** of the heights.

d Estimate the mean of the distribution.

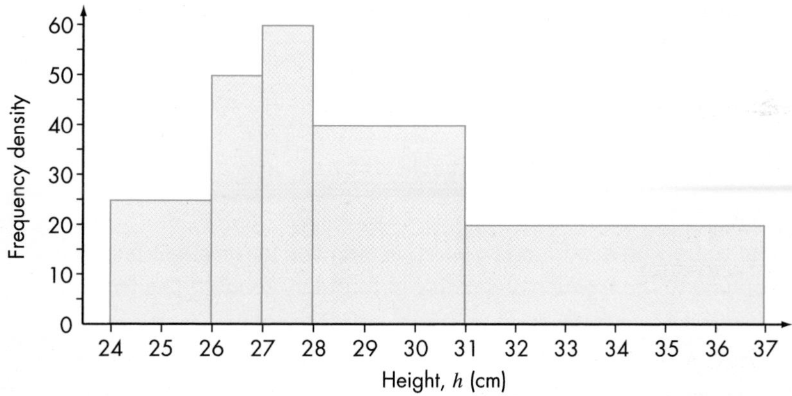

a The frequency table will have groups of $24 \leqslant h < 26$, $26 \leqslant h < 27$, etc. These are read from the height axis. The frequencies will be found by multiplying the width of each bar by the frequency density. Remember that the value on the vertical axis is not the frequency.

Height, h (cm)	$24 \leqslant h < 26$	$26 \leqslant h < 27$	$27 \leqslant h < 28$	$28 \leqslant h < 31$	$31 \leqslant h < 37$
Frequency	50	50	60	120	120
Cumulative frequency	50	100	160	280	400

b There are 400 values so the median will be the 200th value. Counting up the frequencies from the beginning you reach the third row of the table above.

The median occurs in the $28 \leq h < 31$ group. There are 160 values before this group and 120 in it. To get to the 200th value you need to go 40 more values into this group. 40 out of 120 is one-third. One-third of the way through this group is the value 29 cm. Hence the median is 29 cm.

c The interquartile range is the difference between the **upper quartile** and the **lower quartile**, the quarter and three-quarter values respectively. In this case, the lower quartile is the 100th value (found by dividing 400, the total number of values, by 4) and the upper quartile is the 300th value. So, in the same way that you found the median, you can find the lower (100th value) and upper (300th value) quartiles. The 100th value is at 27 cm and the 300th value is at 32 cm. The interquartile range is 32 cm – 27 cm = 5 cm.

d To estimate the mean, use the table to get the midway values of the groups and multiply these by the frequencies. The sum of these divided by 400 will give the estimated mean.

So, the mean is:

$$(25 \times 50 + 26.5 \times 50 + 27.5 \times 60 + 29.5 \times 120 + 34 \times 120) \div 400$$
$$= 11\,845 \div 400 = 29.6 \text{ cm (3 significant figures)}$$

EXERCISE 3F

1 Draw histograms for these grouped frequency distributions.

a

Temperature, t (°C)	$8 \leq t < 10$	$10 \leq t < 12$	$12 \leq t < 15$	$15 \leq t < 17$	$17 \leq t < 20$	$20 \leq t < 24$
Frequency	5	13	18	4	3	6

b

Wage, w (£1000)	$6 \leq w < 10$	$10 \leq w < 12$	$12 \leq w < 16$	$16 \leq w < 24$
Frequency	16	54	60	24

c

Age, a (nearest year)	$11 \leq a < 14$	$14 \leq a < 16$	$16 \leq a < 17$	$17 \leq a < 20$
Frequency	51	36	12	20

d

Pressure, p (mm)	$745 \leq p < 755$	$755 \leq p < 760$	$760 \leq p < 765$	$765 \leq p < 775$
Frequency	4	6	14	10

e

Time, t (min)	$0 \leq t < 8$	$8 \leq t < 12$	$12 \leq t < 16$	$16 \leq t < 20$
Frequency	72	84	54	36

A

A

FM 2 The following information was gathered about the weekly pocket money given to 14-year-olds.

Pocket money, p (£)	$0 \leqslant p < 2$	$2 \leqslant p < 4$	$4 \leqslant p < 5$	$5 \leqslant p < 8$	$8 \leqslant p < 10$
Girls	8	15	22	12	4
Boys	6	11	25	15	6

a Represent the information about the boys on a histogram.

b Represent both sets of data with a frequency polygon, using the same pair of axes.

c What is the mean amount of pocket money given to each sex? Comment on your answer.

3 The sales of the *Star* newspaper over 70 years are recorded in this table.

Years	1940–60	1961–80	1981–90	1991–2000	2001–05	2006–2010
Copies	62 000	68 000	71 000	75 000	63 000	52 000

Illustrate this information on a histogram. Take the class boundaries as 1940, 1960, 1980, 1990, 2000, 2005, 2010.

4 The London trains were always late, so one month a survey was undertaken to find how many trains were late, and by how many minutes (to the nearest minute). The results are illustrated by this histogram.

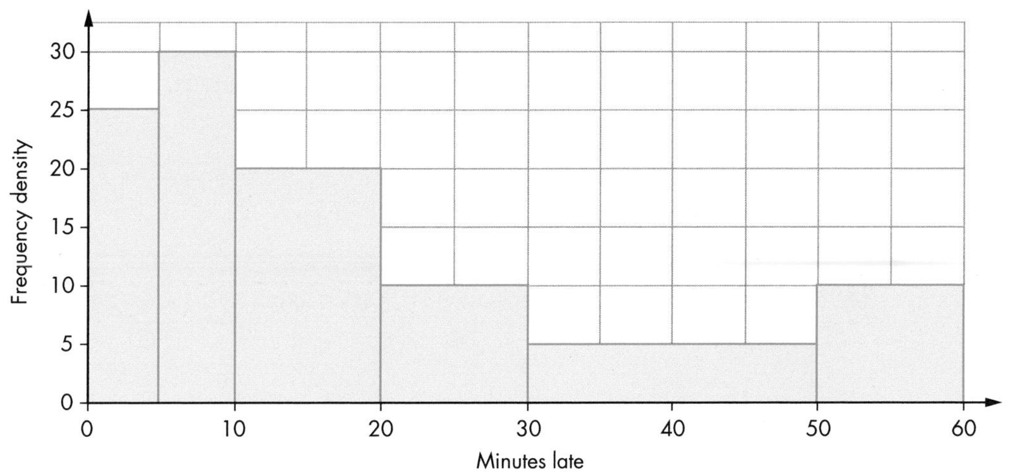

a How many trains were in the survey?

b How many trains were delayed for longer than 15 minutes?

AU 5 Hannah was asked to create a histogram.

Explain how Hannah will find the height of each bar on the frequency density scale.

A*

6 For each of the frequency distributions illustrated in the histograms:

i write down the grouped frequency table

ii state the modal group

iii estimate the median

iv find the lower and upper quartiles and the interquartile range

v estimate the mean of the distribution.

a

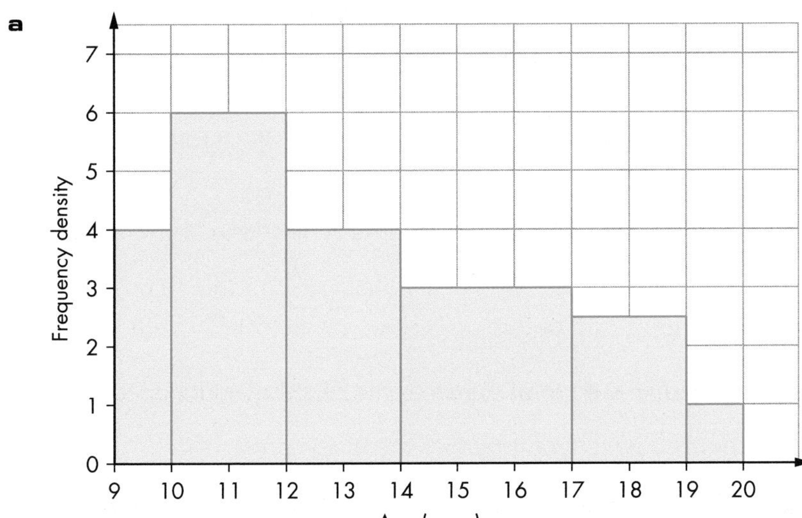

b

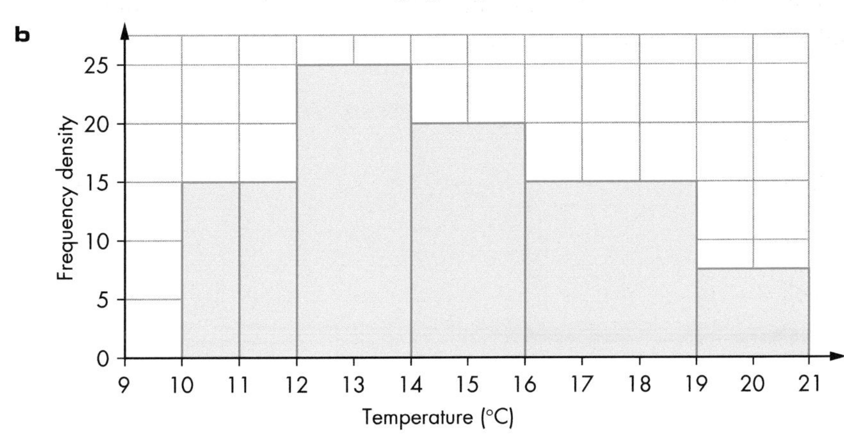

c

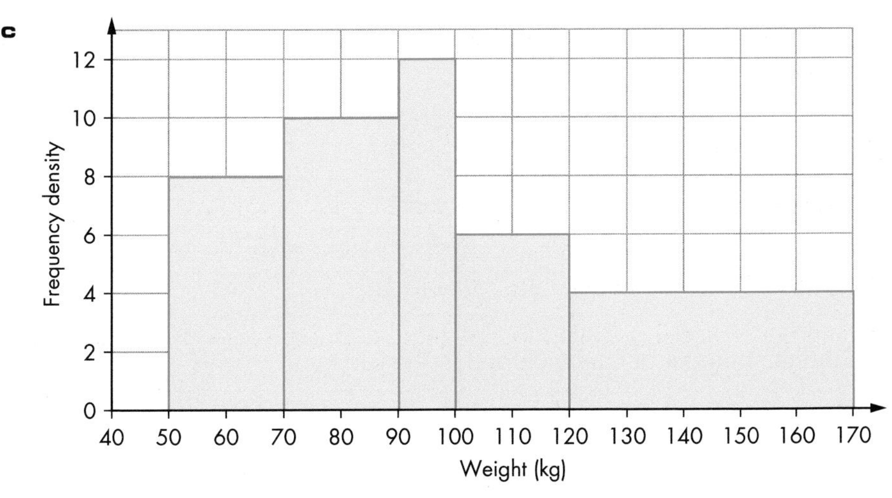

7 All the patients in a hospital were asked how long it was since they last saw a doctor. The results are shown in the table.

Hours, h	$0 \leqslant h < 2$	$2 \leqslant h < 4$	$4 \leqslant h < 6$	$6 \leqslant h < 10$	$10 \leqslant h < 16$	$16 \leqslant h < 24$
Frequency	8	12	20	30	20	10

a Find the median time since a patient last saw a doctor.

b Estimate the mean time since a patient last saw a doctor.

c Find the interquartile range of the times.

8 One summer, Albert monitored the weight of the tomatoes grown on each of his plants. His results are summarised in this table.

Weight, w (kg)	$6 \leqslant w < 10$	$10 \leqslant w < 12$	$12 \leqslant w < 16$	$16 \leqslant w < 20$	$20 \leqslant w < 25$
Frequency	8	15	28	16	10

a Draw a histogram for this distribution.

b Estimate the median weight of tomatoes the plants produced.

c Estimate the mean weight of tomatoes the plants produced.

d How many plants produced more than 15 kg?

9 A survey was carried out to find the speeds of cars passing a particular point on the M1. The histogram illustrates the results of the survey.

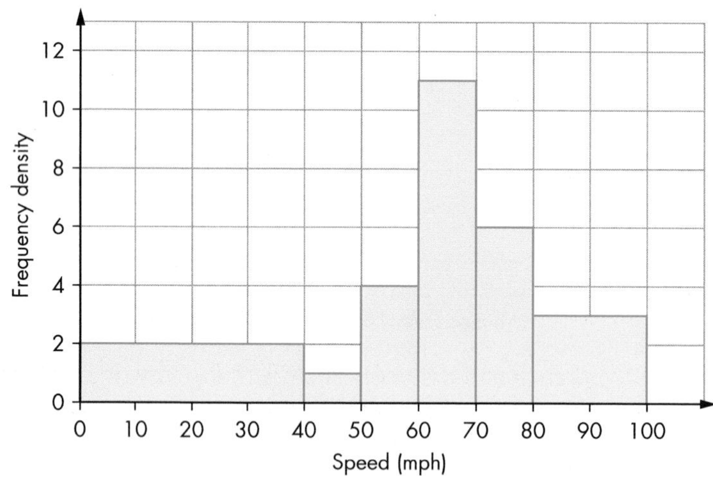

a Copy and complete this table.

Speed, v (mph)	$0 < v \leqslant 40$	$40 < v \leqslant 50$	$50 < v \leqslant 60$	$60 < v \leqslant 70$	$70 < v \leqslant 80$	$80 < v \leqslant 100$
Frequency		10	40	110		

b Find the number of cars included in the survey.

c Work out an estimate of the median speed of the cars on this part of the M1.

d Work out an estimate of the mean speed of the cars on this part of the M1.

A*

10 The histogram shows the test scores for 320 students in a school.

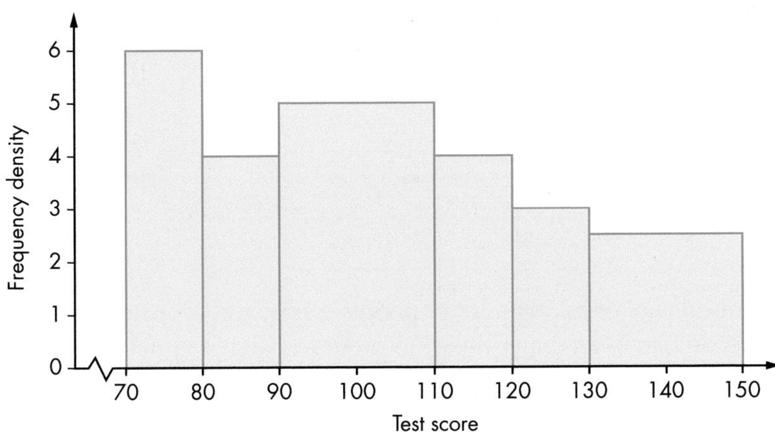

a Find the median score.

b Find the interquartile range of the scores.

c Find an estimate for the mean score.

FM **d** What was the pass score if 90% of the students passed this test?

FM PS **11** The distances employees of a company travel to work are shown in the histogram below.

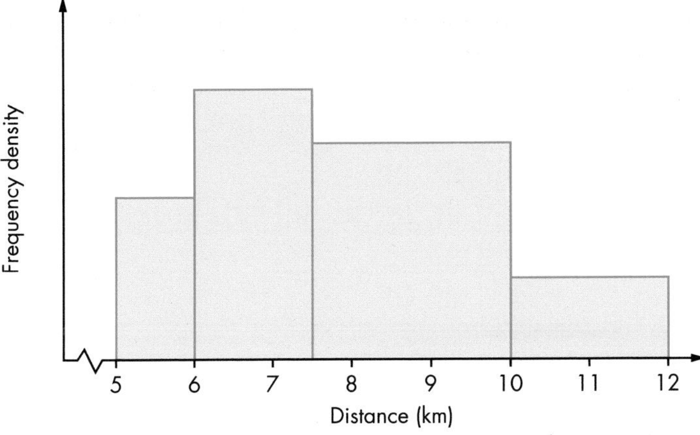

It is known that 18 workers travel between 10 and 12 km to work. What is the probability of choosing a worker at random who travels less than 7.5 km to work?

3.6 Surveys

This section will show you how to:
- conduct surveys

Key words
data collection sheet
hypothesis
survey

A **survey** is an organised way of asking a lot of people a few, well-constructed questions, or of making a lot of observations in an experiment, in order to reach a conclusion about something.

Surveys are used to test out people's opinions or to test a **hypothesis**.

Simple data collection sheet

If you just need to collect some data to analyse, you will have to design a simple **data collection sheet**. This section will show you how to design a clear, easy-to-fill-in data collection sheet.

For example, if you want to find out Year 10 students' preferences for the end-of-term trip from four options you could ask:

Where do you want to go for the Year 10 trip at the end of term — Blackpool, Alton Towers, The Great Western Show or London?

You would put this question, on the same day, to a lot of Year 10 students, and enter their answers straight onto a data collection sheet, as below.

Place	Tally	Frequency
Blackpool	~~IIII~~ ~~IIII~~ ~~IIII~~ ~~IIII~~ III	23
Alton Towers	~~IIII~~ ~~IIII~~ ~~IIII~~ ~~IIII~~ ~~IIII~~ ~~IIII~~ ~~IIII~~ ~~IIII~~ ~~IIII~~ I	46
The Great Western Show	~~IIII~~ ~~IIII~~ IIII	14
London	~~IIII~~ ~~IIII~~ ~~IIII~~ ~~IIII~~ II	22

Notice how plenty of space is available for the tally marks, and how the tallies are gated in groups of five to make counting easier when the survey is complete.

This is a good, simple data collection sheet because:

- only one question *(Where do you want to go?)* has to be asked
- all the four possible venues are listed
- the answer from each interviewee can be easily and quickly tallied, then on to the next interviewee.

Notice, too, that since the question listed specific places, they must appear on the data collection sheet.

You would lose many marks in an examination if you just asked the open question: *Where do you want to go?*

Data sometimes needs to be collected to obtain responses for two different categories. The data collection sheet is then in the form of a two-way table.

EXAMPLE 10

The head of a school carries out a survey to find out how much time students in different year groups spend on their homework during a particular week. He asks a sample of 60 students and fills in a two-way table with headings as follows.

	0–5 hours	0–10 hours	10–20 hours	More than 20 hours
Year 7				

This is not a good table as the headings overlap. A student who does 10 hours' work a week could tick either of two columns. Response sections should not overlap, so that there is only one possible place to put a tick.

A better table would be like this.

	0 up to 5 hours	More than 5 and up to 10 hours	More than 10 and up to 15 hours	More than 15 hours
Year 7	卌 ||	卌		
Year 8	卌	卌 ||		
Year 9	|||	卌 ||	||	
Year 10	|||	卌	|||	|
Year 11	||	||||	||||	||

This gives a clearer picture of the amount of homework done in each year group.

EXERCISE 3G

FM 1 'People like the supermarket to open on Sundays.'

a To see whether this statement is true, design a data collection sheet that will allow you to capture data while standing outside a supermarket.

b Does it matter on which day you collect data outside the supermarket?

FM 2 The school tuck shop wants to know which types of chocolate it should get in to sell — plain, milk, fruit and nut, wholenut or white chocolate.

a Design a data collection sheet that you could use to ask students in your school which of these chocolate types are their favourite.

b Invent the first 30 entries on the chart.

HINTS AND TIPS

Include space for tallies.

D

D

3 When you throw two dice together, what number are you most likely to get?

a Design a data collection sheet on which you can record the data from an experiment in which two dice are thrown together and note the sum of the two numbers shown on the dice.

b Carry out this experiment for at least 100 throws.

c Which sums are most likely to occur?

d Illustrate your results on a frequency polygon.

FM **4** Who uses the buses the most in the mornings? Is it pensioners, mums, schoolchildren, the unemployed or some other group? Design a data collection sheet to be used in a survey of bus passengers.

HINTS AND TIPS

Make sure all possible responses are covered.

C

FM **5** Design two-way tables to show:

a how students in different year groups travel to school in the morning

b the types of programme that different age groups prefer to watch on TV

c the favourite sports of boys and girls

d the amount of time students in different year groups spend on the computer in the evening.

Invent about 40 entries for each one.

FM **6** Hassan wanted to find out who eats healthy food.

He decided to investigate the hypothesis:

'Boys are less likely to eat healthy food than girls are.'

a Design a data collection sheet that Hassan could use to help him do this.

b Hassan records information from a sample of 40 boys and 25 girls. He finds that 17 boys and 15 girls eat healthy food.

Based on this sample, is the hypothesis correct? Explain your answer.

7 What kind of tariffs do your classmates use on their mobile phones?

Design a data collection sheet to help you find this out.

FM AU **8** You are asked to find out what shops the parents of the students at your school like to use.

When creating a data collection sheet for this information what two things must you include on the collection sheet?

3.7 Questionnaires

This section will show you how to:

- ask good questions in order to collect reliable and valid data

Key words

data collection sheet
hypothesis
leading question
questionnaire
survey

This section will show you how to put together a clear, easy-to-use **questionnaire**.

When you are putting together a questionnaire for a **survey**, you must think very carefully about the sorts of question you are going to ask. Here are five rules that you should always follow.

- Never ask a **leading question** designed to get a particular response.
- Never ask a personal, irrelevant question.
- Keep each question as simple as possible.
- Include questions that will get a response from whomever is asked.
- Make sure the responses do not overlap and keep the number of choices to a reasonable number (six at the most).

The following questions are badly constructed and should *never* appear in any questionnaire.

What is your age? This is personal. Many people will not want to answer. It is always better to give a range of ages.

☐ Under 15 ☐ 16–20 ☐ 21–30 ☐ 31–40 ☐ Over 40

Slaughtering animals for food is cruel to the poor defenceless animals. Don't you agree? This is a leading question, designed to get a 'yes' response. It is better to ask an impersonal question.

Are you a vegetarian? ☐ Yes ☐ No

Do you go to discos when abroad? This can be answered only by people who have been abroad. It is better to ask a starter question, with a follow-up question.

Have you been abroad for a holiday? ☐ Yes ☐ No

If yes, did you go to a disco whilst you were away? ☐ Yes ☐ No

When you first get up in a morning and decide to have some sort of breakfast that might be made by somebody else, do you feel obliged to eat it all or not? This question is too complicated. It is better to ask a series of shorter questions.

What time do you get up for school? ☐ Before 7 ☐ Between 7 and 8 ☐ After 8

Do you have breakfast every day? ☐ Yes ☐ No

If No, on how many school days do you have breakfast? ☐ 0 ☐ 1 ☐ 2 ☐ 3 ☐ 4 ☐ 5

A questionnaire is usually a specialised **data collection sheet**, put together to test a **hypothesis** or a statement. For example, a questionnaire might be constructed to test this statement.

People buy cheaper milk from the supermarket as they don't mind not getting it on their doorstep. They'd rather go out to buy it.

A questionnaire designed to test whether this statement is true or not should include these questions.

Do you have milk delivered to your doorstep?

Do you buy cheaper milk from the supermarket?

Would you buy your milk only from the supermarket?

Once these questions have been answered, the responses can be checked to see whether the majority of people hold views that agree with the statement.

EXERCISE 3H

1 These are questions from a questionnaire on healthy eating.

a

Fast food is bad for you. Don't you agree?		
☐ Strongly agree	☐ Agree	☐ Don't know

Give two criticisms of the question.

b

Do you eat fast food?	☐ Yes	☐ No	
If yes, how many times on average do you eat fast food a week?			
☐ Once or less	☐ 2 or 3 times	☐ 4 or 5 times	☐ More than 5 times

Give two reasons why these are good questions.

2 This is a question from a survey on pocket money.

How much pocket money do you get each week?			
☐ £0–£2	☐ £0–£5	☐ £5–£10	☐ £10 or more

a Give a reason why this is not a good question.

b Rewrite the question to make it a good question.

3 Design a questionnaire to test this statement.

'People under 16 do not know what is meant by all the jargon used in the business news on TV, but the over-twenties do.'

C

FM PS **4** Design a questionnaire to test this statement.

'The under-twenties feel quite at ease with computers, while the over-forties would rather not bother with them. The 20–40s are all able to use computers effectively.'

FM PS **5** Design a questionnaire to test this hypothesis.

'The older you get, the less sleep you need.'

FM PS **6** A headteacher wants to find out if her students think they have too much, too little or just the right amount of homework. She also wants to know the parents' views about homework.

Design a questionnaire that could be used to find the data that the headteacher needs to look at.

7 Anja and Andrew are doing a survey on the type of music people buy.

a This is one question from Anja's survey.

> Folk music is just for country people.
>
> Don't you agree?
>
> ☐ Strongly agree ☐ Agree ☐ Don't know

Give two criticisms of Anja's question.

b This is a question from Andrew's survey.

> How many CDs do you buy each month?
>
> ☐ 2 or fewer ☐ 3 or 4 ☐ more than 4

Give two reasons why this is a good question.

c Make up another good question with responses that could be added to this survey.

PS **8** Design a questionnaire to test this hypothesis.

'People with back problems do not sit properly.'

AU **9** As each customer left a store, an assistant gave them a questionnaire containing the following question.

> Question: How much do you normally spend in this shop?
>
> Response: ☐ Less than £15 ☐ More than £25
>
> ☐ Less than £25 ☐ More than £50

Explain why the response section of this questionnaire is poor.

3.8 The data-handling cycle

This section will show you how to:

- use the data-handling cycle

Key words
hypothesis
primary data
secondary data

The data-handling cycle

Testing out a **hypothesis** involves a cycle of planning, collecting data, evaluating the significance of the data and then interpreting the results, which may or may not show the hypothesis to be true. This cycle often leads to a refinement of the problem, which starts the cycle all over again.

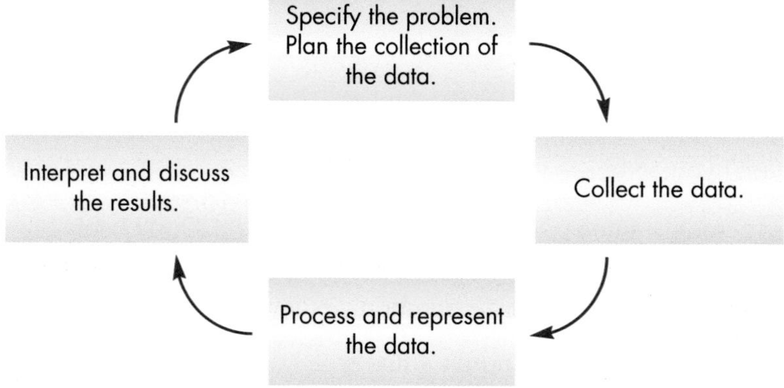

There are four parts to the data-handling cycle.

1. State the hypothesis, which is the idea being tested, outlining the problem and planning what needs to be done.
2. Plan the data collection and collect the data.
3. Choose the best way to process and represent the data. This will normally mean calculating averages (mean, median, mode) and measures of spread, then representing data in suitable diagrams.
4. Interpret the data and make conclusions.

Then the hypothesis can be refined or changes can be made in respect to the data, whether in the type to be studied or in method of collection, and the process becomes a cycle of improving reliability.

EXAMPLE 11

A gardener grows tomatoes, both in a greenhouse and outside.

He wants to investigate whether tomato plants grown in the greenhouse produce more tomatoes than those grown outside.

Describe the data-handling cycle that may be applied to this problem.

State the hypothesis: 'Tomato plants grown in the greenhouse produce more tomatoes than those grown outside.'

Plan the data collection and collect the data. Consider 10 tomato plants grown in the greenhouse, and 10 plants grown outside. Count the tomatoes on each plant. Record the numbers of tomatoes collected from the plants between June and September. Only count those that are 'fit for purpose'.

Choose the best way to process and represent the data. Calculate the mean number collected per plant as well as the range.

Interpret the data and make conclusions. Look at the statistics. *What do they show? Is there a clear conclusion or do you need to alter the hypothesis in any way?* Discuss results, refine the method and continue the cycle.

As you see, in describing the data-handling cycle, you must refer to each of the four parts.

Data collection

Data that you collect yourself is called **primary data**. You control it, in terms of accuracy and amount.

Data collected by someone else is called **secondary data**. Generally, there is a lot of this type of data available on the internet or in newspapers. This provides a huge volume of data but you have to rely on the sources being reliable, for accuracy.

EXERCISE 3I

C

1 Use the data-handling cycle to describe how you would test each of the following statements or scenarios. Write your own hypothesis to suit the situation. In each case state whether you would use primary or secondary data.

- **a** Oliver is investigating which month of the year is the hottest.
- **b** Andrew wants to compare how good boys and girls are at estimating distances.
- **c** Joy thinks that more men than women go to football matches.
- **d** Sheehab wants to know if tennis is watched by more women than men.
- **e** A headteacher said that the more revision you do, the better your examination results.
- **f** A newspaper suggested that the older you are, the more likely you are to shop at Marks and Spencers.

FM **2** You are asked to compare the number of news programmes on different TV channels.

- **a** Write down a suitable hypothesis that you could test.
- **b** Design a suitable observation sheet to record the data.
- **c** Show how the data-handling cycle would be used in this investigation.

AU **3** Kath thinks that girls are better at mental arithmetic than boys.

Explain how Kath could test this. Use the stages of the data-handling cycle in your answer.

3.9 Other uses of statistics

This section will show you how to:
- apply statistics in everyday situations

Key words
margin of error
national census
polls
Retail Price Index
social statistics
time series

Many situations occur in daily life where statistical techniques are used to produce data. The results of surveys appear in newspapers every day. There are many on-line **polls** and phone-ins to vote in reality TV shows, for example.

Results for these polls are usually given as a percentage with a **margin of error**, which is a measure of how accurate the information is.

Here are some common **social statistics** in daily use.

General Index of Retail Prices

This is also know as the **Retail Price Index** (RPI). It measures how much the daily cost of living increases (or decreases). One year is chosen as the base year and given an index number, usually 100. The costs of subsequent years are compared to this and given a number proportional to the base year, say 103, etc.

Note the numbers do not represent actual values but just compare current prices to the base year.

Time series

Like the RPI, a **time series** measures changes in a quantity over time. Unlike the RPI, the actual values of the quantity are used. This might measure how the exchange rate between the pound and the dollar changes over time.

National census

A **national census** is a survey of all people and households in a country. Data about age, gender, religion, employment status, etc. is collected to enable governments to plan where to allocate resources in the future. In Britain, a national census is taken every 10 years. The last census was in 2001.

EXERCISE 3J 

D

FM **1** In 2000, the cost of a litre of petrol was 78p. Using 2000 as a base year, the price index of petrol for the next five years is shown in this table.

Year	2000	2001	2002	2003	2004	2005
Index	100	103	108	109	112	120
Price	78p					

Work out the price of petrol in each subsequent year. Give your answers to 1 decimal place.

FM **2** The graph shows the exchange rate for the dollar against the pound for each month in one year.

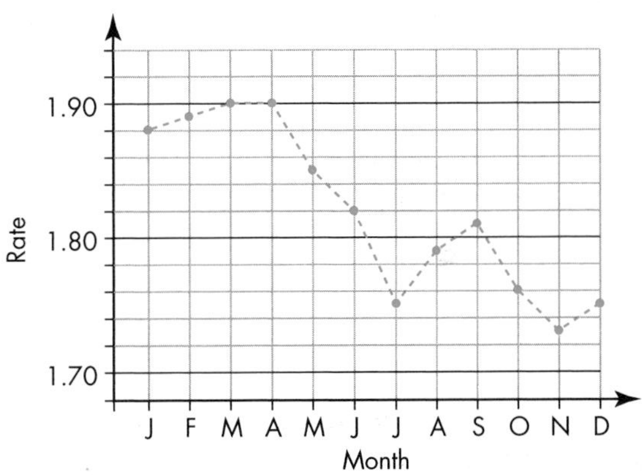

a What was the exchange rate in January?

b Between which two months did the exchange rate fall the most?

c Explain why you could not use the graph to predict the exchange rate in January of the next year.

FM **3** The following is taken from the UK government statistics website.

> In mid-2004 the UK was home to 59.8 million people, of which 50.1 million lived in England. The average age was 38.6 years, an increase on 1971 when it was 34.1 years. In mid-2004 approximately one in five people in the UK were aged under 16 and one in six people were aged 65 or over.

Use this extract to answer these questions.

a How many of the population of the UK do *not* live in England?

b By how much has the average age increased since 1971?

c Approximately how many of the population are under 16?

d Approximately how many of the population are over 65?

FM **4** The General Index of Retail Prices started in January 1987 when it was given a base number of 100. In January 2006 the index number was 194.1.

If the 'standard weekly shopping basket' cost £38.50 in January 1987, how much would it be in January 2006?

C

FM AU **5** The Retail Price Index measures how much the daily cost of living increases or decreases. If 2008 is given a base index number of 100, then 2009 is given 98. What does this mean?

B

FM 6 This time series shows car production in Britain from November 2004 to November 2005.

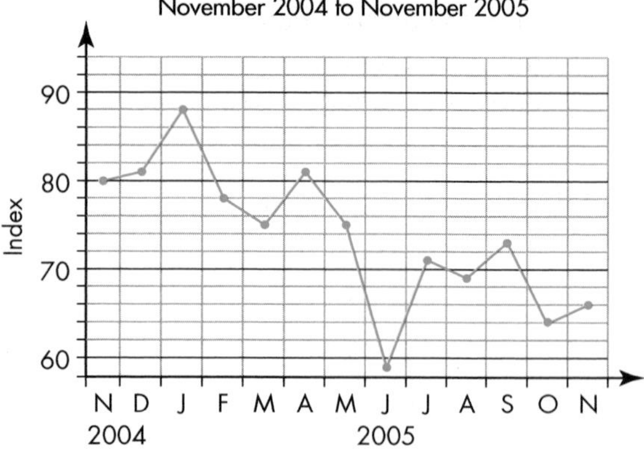

a Why was there a sharp drop in production in July?

b The average production over the first three months shown was 172 thousand cars.

i Work out an approximate number for the average production over the last three months shown.

ii The base month for the index is January 2000 when the index was 100. What was the approximate production in January 2000?

3.10 Sampling

This section will show you how to:
- understand different methods of sampling
- collect unbiased reliable data

Key words
population
random
sample
stratified
unbiased

Statisticians often have to carry out surveys to collect information and test hypotheses about the **population** for a wide variety of purposes. (In statistics, population does not only mean a group of people, it also means a group of objects or events.)

It is seldom possible to survey a whole population, mainly because such a survey would cost too much and take a long time. Also, there are populations for which it would be physically impossible to survey every member. For example, if you wanted to find the average length of eels in the North Sea, it would be impossible to find and measure every eel. So a statistician chooses a small part of the population to survey and assumes that the results for this **sample** are representative of the whole population.

Therefore, to ensure the accuracy of a survey, you must consider two questions.

- Will the sample be representative of the whole population and thereby eliminate bias?
- How large should the sample be to give results that are valid for the whole population?

Sampling methods

There are two main types of sample: **random** and **stratified**.

In a random sample, every member of the population has an equal chance of being chosen. For example, it may be the first 100 people met in a survey, or 100 names picked from a hat, or 100 names taken at random from the electoral register or a telephone directory.

In a stratified sample, the population is first divided into categories and the number of members in each category determined. The sample is then made up of members from these categories in the same proportions as they are in the population. The required sample in each category is chosen by random sampling.

EXAMPLE 12

A school's student numbers are given in the table. The headteacher wants to take a stratified sample of 100 students for a survey.

a Calculate the number of boys and girls in each year that should be interviewed.

b Explain how the students could then be chosen to give a random sample.

School year	Boys	Girls	Total
7	52	68	120
8	46	51	97
9	62	59	121
10	47	61	108
11	39	55	94
Total number in school			540

a To get the correct number in each category, say, boys in Year 7, the calculation is done as follows.

$\frac{52}{540} \times 100 = 9.6$ (1 decimal place)

After all calculations are done, you should get the values in this table.

School year	Boys	Girls
7	9.6	12.6
8	8.5	9.4
9	11.5	10.9
10	8.7	11.3
11	7.2	10.2

Obviously you cannot have a decimal fraction of a student, so round all values and make sure that the total is 100. This gives the final table.

School year	Boys	Girls	Total
7	10	13	23
8	8	9	17
9	12	11	23
10	9	11	20
11	7	10	17

b Within each category, choose students to survey at random. For example, all the Year 7 girls could have their names put into a hat and 13 names drawn out or they could be listed alphabetically and a random number generator used to pick out 13 names from 68.

Sample size

Before the sampling of a population can begin, it is necessary to determine how much data needs to be collected to ensure that the sample is representative of the population. This is called the sample size.

Two factors determine sample size:

- the desired precision with which the sample represents the population
- the amount of money available to meet the cost of collecting the sample data.

The greater the precision desired, the larger the sample size needs to be. But the larger the sample size, the higher the cost will be. Therefore, the benefit of achieving high accuracy in a sample will always have to be set against the cost of achieving it.

There are statistical procedures for determining the most suitable sample size, but these are beyond the scope of the GCSE syllabus.

The next example addresses some of the problems associated with obtaining an **unbiased** sample.

EXAMPLE 13

You are going to conduct a survey among an audience of 30 000 people at a rock concert. How would you choose the sample?

1. You would not want to question all of them, so you might settle for a sample size of 2%, which is 600 people.
2. Assuming that there will be as many men at the concert as women, you would need the sample to contain the same proportion of each, namely, 300 men and 300 women.
3. Assuming that about 20% of the audience will be aged under 20, you would also need the sample to contain 120 people aged under 20 (20% of 600) and 480 people aged 20 and over (600 – 120 or 80% of 600).
4. You would also need to select people from different parts of the auditorium in equal proportions so as to get a balanced view. Say this breaks down into three equal groups of people, taken respectively from the front, the back and the middle of the auditorium. So, you would further need the sample to consist of 200 people at the front, 200 at the back and 200 in the middle.
5. If you now assume that one researcher can survey 40 concert-goers, you would arrive at this sampling strategy

   $600 \div 40 = 15$ researchers to conduct the survey

   $15 \div 3 = 5$ researchers in each part of the auditorium

   Each researcher would need to question four men aged under 20, 16 men aged 20 and over, four women aged under 20 and 16 women aged 20 and over.

EXERCISE 3K

FM 1 Comment on the reliability of the following ways of finding a sample.

- **a** Find out about smoking by asking 50 people in a non-smoking part of a restaurant.
- **b** Find out how many homes have video recorders by asking 100 people outside a video hire shop.
- **c** Find the most popular make of car by counting 100 cars in a city car park.
- **d** Find a year representative on a school's council by picking a name out of a hat.
- **e** Decide whether the potatoes have cooked properly by testing one with a fork.

FM 2 Comment on the way the following samples have been taken. For those that are not satisfactory, suggest a better way to find a more reliable sample.

- **a** Joseph had a discussion with his dad about pocket money. To get some information, he asked 15 of his friends how much pocket money they each received.
- **b** Douglas wanted to find out what proportion of his school went abroad for holidays, so he asked the first 20 people he came across in the school yard.
- **c** A teacher wanted to know which lesson his students enjoyed most. So he asked them all.
- **d** It has been suggested that more females than males go to church. So Ruth did a survey in her church that Sunday and counted the number of females there.
- **e** A group of local people asked for a crossing on a busy road. The council conducted a survey by asking 100 randomly-selected people in the neighbourhood.

FM 3 For a school project you have been asked to do a presentation of the social activities of the students in your school. You decide to interview a sample of students. Explain how you will choose the students you wish to interview if you want your results to be:

a reliable **b** unbiased **c** representative **d** random.

FM 4 A fast-food pizza chain attempted to estimate the number of people in a certain town who eat pizzas. One evening they telephoned 50 people living in the town and asked: "Have you eaten a pizza in the last month?" Eleven people said "Yes." The pizza chain stated that 22% of the town's population eat pizzas. Give three criticisms of this method of estimation.

5 Mr Charlton, the deputy head at High Storrs School, wanted to find out how often the upper-school students in his school visited a fast-food outlet. The numbers of students in each upper-school year are given in the table.

	Boys	Girls
Y9	119	85
Y10	107	118
Y11	104	110

- **a** Create a questionnaire that Mr Charlton could use to sample the school.
- **b** Mr Charlton wanted to do a stratified sample using 60 students. To how many of each group should he give the questionnaire?

C

PS 6 Naysha belonged to a school of 1850 students. She was in a class of 30 students. She noticed one day that the school was doing a survey over the whole school. Four boys and five girls in her class were involved in the survey.

Estimate how many students in the whole school were involved in the sample.

AU 7 You are asked to conduct a survey at a football match where the attendance is approximately 20 000.

Explain how you could create a stratified sample of the crowd.

FM 8 **a** Adam is writing a questionnaire for a survey about the Meadowhall shopping centre in Cambridge. He is told that fewer local people than people from further away visit Meadowhall. He is also told that the local people spend less money per visit. Write two questions that would help him to test these ideas. Each question should include at least three options for a response. People are asked to choose one of these options.

b For another survey, Adam investigates how much is spent at the chocolate machines by students at his school. The numbers of students in each year group are shown in the table. Explain, with calculations, how Adam should obtain a stratified random sample of 100 students for his survey.

Year group	7	8	9	10	11
No. of students	143	132	156	131	108

9 Claire made a survey of students in her school. She wanted to find out their opinions on the eating facilities in the school. The size of each year group in the school is shown in the table.

Year group	Boys	Girls	Total
8	96	78	174
9	84	86	170
10	84	91	175
11	82	85	167
6th form	83	117	200
			886

Claire took a sample of 90 students.

a Explain why she should not have sampled equal numbers of boys and girls in the sixth form.

b Calculate the number of students she should have sampled in the sixth form.

Using the internet

Through the internet you have access to a vast amount of data on many topics, which you can use to carry out statistical investigations. This data will enable you to draw statistical diagrams, answer a variety of questions and test all manner of hypotheses.

Here are some examples of hypotheses you can test.

- Football teams are most likely to win when they are playing at home.
- Boys do better than girls at GCSE mathematics.
- The number 3 gets drawn more often than the number 49 in the National Lottery.
- The literacy rate in a country is linked to that country's average income.
- People in the north of England have larger families than people who live in the south.

The following websites are a useful source of data for some of the above.

www.statistics.gov.uk

www.national-lottery.co.uk

www.cia.gov/cia/publications/the-world-factbook/index.html

GRADE BOOSTER

- **D** You can draw and interpret pie charts
- **D** You can find the mean from a frequency table of discrete data and also draw a frequency polygon for such data
- **C** You can find an estimate of the mean from a grouped table of continuous data and draw a frequency polygon for continuous data
- **C** You can design questionnaires and surveys
- **C** You can use the data-handling cycle
- **A** You can draw histograms from frequency tables with unequal class intervals
- **A** You can calculate the numbers to be surveyed for a stratified sample
- **A*** You can find the median, quartiles and the interquartile range from a histogram

What you should know now

- Which average to use in different situations
- How to find the modal class and an estimated mean for continuous data
- How to draw and interpet pie charts
- How to draw frequency polygons and histograms for discrete and continuous data
- How to design questionnaires and surveys
- How to use the data-handling cycle to test and refine a hypothesis

1 **a** The two-way table shows the number of televisions and radios in 50 households.

		Televisions			
		0	**1**	**2**	**3**
Radios	**0**	0	3	0	0
	1	2	5	8	3
	2	1	6	12	5
	3	0	0	3	2

i How many households have two televisions and one radio? *(1 mark)*

ii How many households have two televisions? *(2 marks)*

iii How many households have the same number of televisions as radios? *(2 marks)*

b Louise wanted to find out the number of hours of television watched last Sunday.

This is her question and response section.

Question: How many hours of television did you watch last Sunday?
Response: Tick a box

☐ 1 to 3 hours ☐ 4 to 6 hours ☐ 6 to 8 hours ☐ more than 8 hours

Write down two criticisms of the response section. *(2 marks)*

AQA, June 2008, Module 1 Higher, Question 6

2 A factory manager surveys the owners of the cars parked in the car park.
One of the questions is:
When you drive to work how many people, including yourself, are in your car?
The responses are summarised in the table below.

Number of people	Number of cars
1	42
2	26
3	12
4	2
5	0
6	1
Total	83

a Calculate the mean number of people per car. *(3 marks)*

b The manager wants to find out if car owners are prepared to car-share.

Write a suitable question with a response section to find out which days from Monday to Friday the owners will car-share. *(2 marks)*

AQA, March 2008, Module 1 Higher, Question 2

3 A student recorded the time, in minutes, that 50 people spent in the library.

Time, t (minutes)	Frequency
$0 < t \leqslant 10$	2
$10 < t \leqslant 20$	8
$20 < t \leqslant 30$	20
$30 < t \leqslant 40$	12
$40 < t \leqslant 50$	8

Calculate an estimate of the mean number of minutes spent in the library. *(4 marks)*

AQA, March 2007, Module 1 Higher, Question 2

4 **a** The table shows the frequency of the variable, x, for various values.

x	Frequency
25	16
35	38
45	26
55	14
65	6
Total	100

Show that the mean of x is 40.6 *(3 marks)*

b The table shows the heights, h (in centimetres), of 100 girls in year 10.

Height, h (cm)	Frequency
$120 < h \leqslant 130$	16
$130 < h \leqslant 140$	38
$140 < h \leqslant 150$	26
$150 < h \leqslant 160$	14
$160 < h \leqslant 170$	6
Total	100

i What is the midpoint of the group $120 < h \leqslant 130$? *(1 mark)*

ii Using the mean value of x from part **a**, write down an estimate for the mean height of the 100 girls. *(1 mark)*

c The frequency diagram shows the distribution of the heights of 100 boys in Y10.

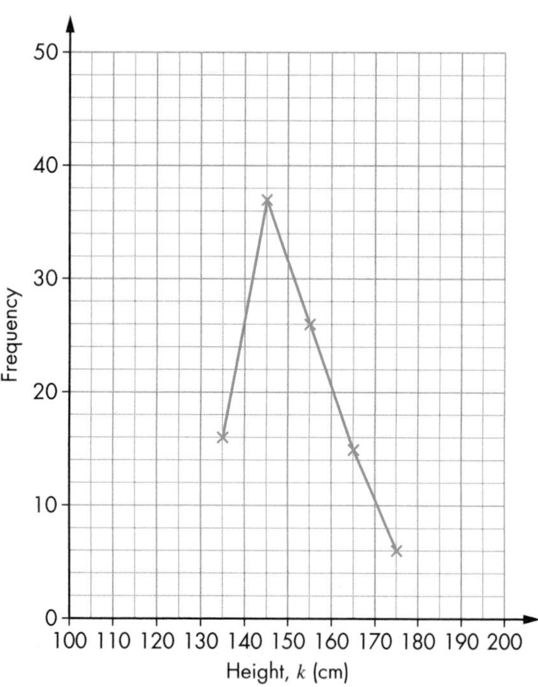

i On a copy of the same grid, draw a frequency diagram for the heights of the girls in Y10. *(2 marks)*

ii Make two comments to compare the heights of the boys and the girls. *(2 marks)*

AQA, June 2008, Paper 2 Higher, Question 13

5 The headteacher of a school sends a questionnaire to each head of department.

One of the questions is:

How many hours do you think you are working each week?

The results are shown in the table.

Hours worked each week, t	Number of heads of department
$25 \leq t < 30$	0
$30 \leq t < 35$	2
$35 \leq t < 40$	3
$40 \leq t < 45$	8
$45 \leq t < 50$	6
$50 \leq t < 55$	1

a Draw a frequency diagram to represent this data. *(3 marks)*

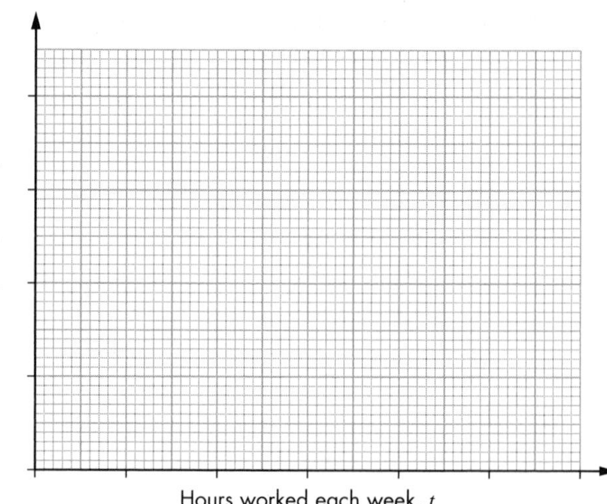

b There are 80 teachers in the school.

Use the figures in the table to calculate an estimate of how many teachers in the school are working 40 or more hours each week. *(3 marks)*

c Explain why the answer to part **b** is likely to be unrealistic. *(1 mark)*

AQA, March 2008, Module 1 Higher, Question 5

6  n Year 9 there are 30 students who study both German and French. Their National Curriculum levels in these subjects are shown in the two-way table.

		Level in French					
		1	2	3	4	5	6
Level in German	1	0	0	0	0	0	0
	2	1	0	0	0	0	0
	3	2	1	1	0	0	0
	4	0	3	4	1	0	0
	5	0	1	2	3	2	0
	6	0	0	3	3	2	1

a What is the median level for German?

b What is the mean level for French?

c The teacher claims that the students are better at German than at French. How can you tell from the table that this is true?

7 The weekly pocket money of one class is shown in the table below.

Pocket money	£0–£5	£5–£10	£10–£15	£15–£20
Frequency	4	6	12	8

Sean says that he has estimated the mean amount of pocket money as £9.50.

Explain how you can tell Sean must be wrong without having to calculate the estimated mean.

8 Reya knew that the cost of living price index was set at 100 for 2007, 104 for 2008 and 105 for 2009. She bought some sausages for £2.10 in 2009. How much would you have expected them to have cost a year earlier?

9 The house price index for a flat in Leeds was 190 in August 2006, compared with a base of 100 in April 2000.

a Write down the percentage increase in the price of flats in Leeds in that period. *(1 mark)*

b A flat cost £80 000 in April 2000.

What was its likely value in August 2006? *(2 marks)*

AQA, May 2008, Paper 1 Higher, Question 12

10 The histogram shows the distribution of ages of 100 members of a chess club.

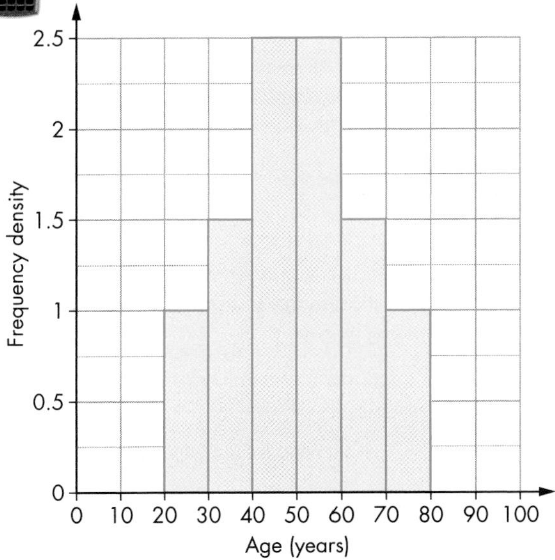

a How many members of the club were less than 40 years old? *(1 mark)*

b How many members of the club are between 40 and 60 years old? *(1 mark)*

c Work out the interquartile range of the ages. *(2 marks)*

AQA, November 2008, Paper 2 Higher, Question 16

11 The histogram represents the times that a number of runners took to complete a cross-country race.

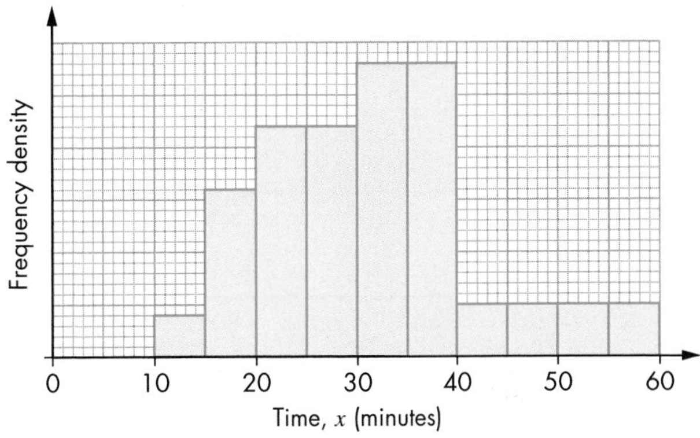

Ten runners completed the race in under 20 minutes.

How many runners completed the race? *(3 marks)*

AQA, June 2008, Module 1 Higher, Question 9

12 A mobile speed camera recorded the speed of some vehicles on a motorway.

The table shows the results.

Speed, s (mph)	Frequency
$0 < s \leqslant 30$	42
$30 < s \leqslant 50$	54
$50 < s \leqslant 60$	82
$60 < s \leqslant 70$	116
$70 < s \leqslant 80$	70
$80 < s \leqslant 120$	36
Total	400

a Draw a histogram to illustrate the data. *(3 marks)*

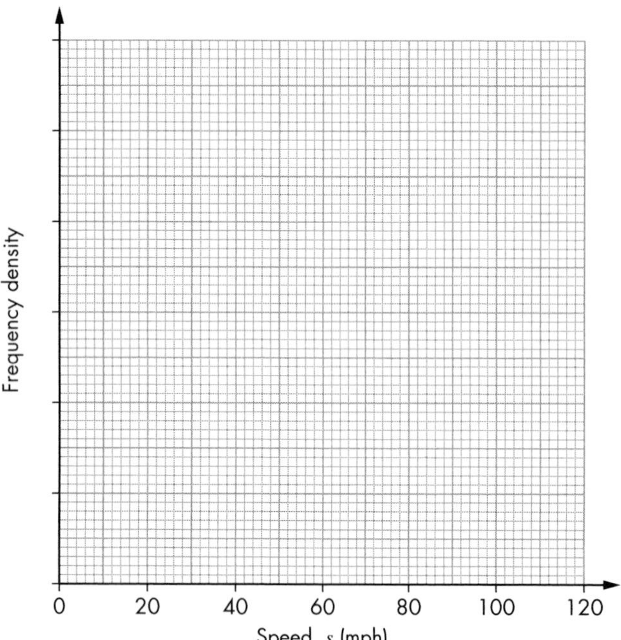

b Drivers of vehicles doing more than 77 miles per hour were given a speeding ticket.

Estimate the number of drivers who receive a ticket. *(1 mark)*

AQA, June 2008, Paper 2 Higher, Question 22

13 The examination scores of a group of students are summarised in the table.

Examination score, s	Frequency
$0 \leqslant s < 20$	10
$20 \leqslant s < 40$	18
$40 \leqslant s < 50$	25
$50 \leqslant s < 60$	20
$60 \leqslant s < 80$	16
$80 \leqslant s < 100$	2

a Draw a histogram for this data. *(3 marks)*

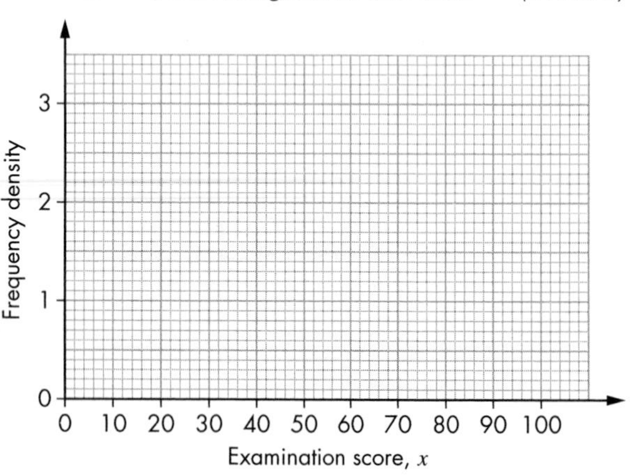

b A Merit is awarded for a mark between 48 and 75.

Calculate an estimate of the number of students awarded a Merit. *(2 marks)*

AQA, November 2008, Module 1 Higher, Question 8

14 A company wants to obtain a stratified sample of total size 2000 from the members of three teaching unions.

The table shows the number of members, in thousands, of the three unions.

Union	No. of members in thousands
NUT	260
ATL	170
NATFHE	70

Calculate the number of members of each union selected for the stratified sample.

15 The table shows the number of students in each year group of a junior school.

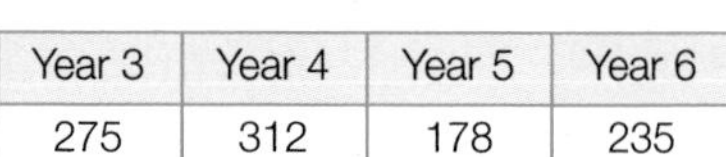

Year 3	Year 4	Year 5	Year 6
275	312	178	235

There are 1000 students in the school.

The headteacher wants to take a stratified sample of 50 children to carry out a survey.

How many more year 6 students than year 5 students would be chosen? *(3 marks)*

AQA, June 2008, Module 1 Higher, Question 4

16 The table shows the bookings at a hotel for one month.

Single person	Couple	Family
27	70	103

The hotel manager wants to send questionnaires to a stratified sample of 30 of these bookings.

Calculate the number of each type of booking he should include. *(3 marks)*

AQA, March 2009, Module 1 Higher, Question 4

Worked Examination Questions

1 The distances travelled by 100 cars using 10 litres of petrol is shown in the histogram and table.

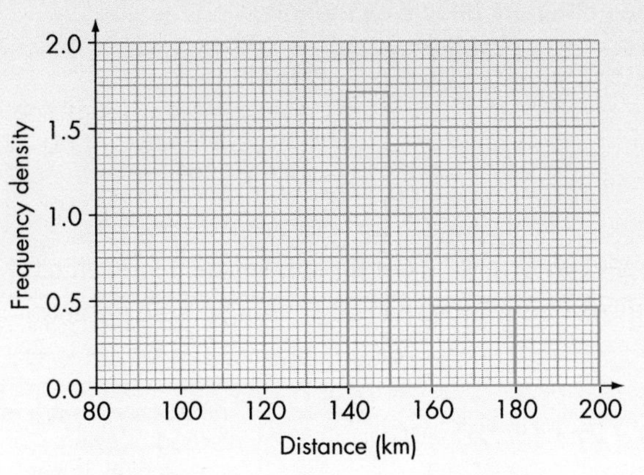

a Complete the histogram and the table.

b Estimate the number of cars that travel between 155 km and 185 km using 10 litres of petrol.

Distance (km)	80–110	110–130	130–140	140–150	150–160	160–200
Frequency	9	22	20			

1 a Set up the table with columns for class width and frequency density and fill in the given information, reading frequency densities from the graph (be careful with scales).

Now fill in the rest of the information using $\text{f.d.} = \frac{\text{frequency}}{\text{class width}}$ and

frequency = f.d. × class width

These values are shown in red.

Distance (km)	Frequency	Class width	Frequency density
80–110	9	30	0.3
110–130	22	20	1.1
130–140	20	10	2
140–150	17	10	1.7
150–160	14	10	1.4
160–200	18	40	0.45

This scores 1 mark for accuracy in completing the frequency column from the information in the histogram. This scores 1 mark for method in creating the frequency density column. This scores 2 marks for accuracy of completing the frequency density column – 1 mark lost for each error.

Complete the graph.

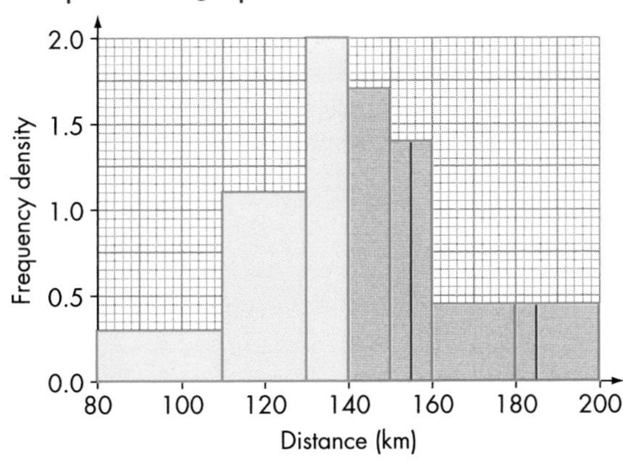

This scores 3 marks for accurately drawing the three columns.

b Draw lines at 155 and 185. The number of cars is represented by the area between these lines.
In the 150–160 bar the area is $\frac{1}{2}$ of the total.
In the 160–200 bar the area is $\frac{5}{8}$ of the total.

This scores 1 mark for method of attempting to find area between the two lines.

Number of cars = $\frac{1}{2} \times 14 + \frac{5}{8} \times 18 = 18.25 \approx 18$ cars

This scores 1 mark for method and 1 mark for accuracy.

Total: 10 marks

Worked Examination Questions

FM **2** A survey was taken to find how many days people had to wait to get a dental appointment. One hundred people were surveyed in three different cities with the following results.

Days, d	$0 < d \leqslant 2$	$2 < d \leqslant 5$	$5 < d \leqslant 10$	$10 < d \leqslant 15$	$15 < d \leqslant 20$
London	25	47	20	7	1
Sheffield	13	44	35	6	2
York	8	37	41	10	4

a What is the average number of days spent waiting for a dental appointment in each city?

b Give two reasons why the average number of days for each city might be so different.

2 a London

[(1 × 25) + (3.5 × 47) + (7.5 × 20) + (12.5 × 7) + (17.5)] ÷ 100

= 444.5 ÷ 100 = 4.445

London = 4.4 days

Sheffield

[(1 × 13) + (3.5 × 44) + (7.5 × 35) + (12.5 × 6) + (17.5 × 2)] ÷ 100

= 539.5 ÷ 100 = 5.395

Sheffield = 5.4 days

York

[(1 × 8) + (3.5 × 37) + (7.5 × 41) + (12.5 × 10) + (17.5 × 4] ÷ 100

= 640 ÷ 100 = 6.4

York = 6.4 days

> This scores 1 mark for method of using midpoints in at least one city.
>
> This scores 1 mark for method of multiplying the midpoints by each frequency in at least one city.
>
> This scores 3 marks for accuracy for the mean in each city.

b There might be more dentists in London, or there might be more people with problem teeth in York.

> This scores 1 mark for each valid reason, to a maximum of two marks.

Total: 7 marks

PS **3** The mean speed of each member of a cycling club over a long-distance race was recorded and a frequency polygon was drawn.

From the frequency polygon, estimate the mean speed.

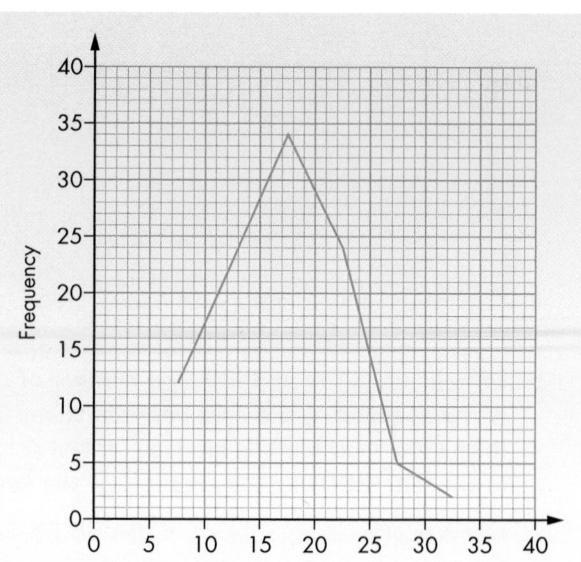

Worked Examination Questions

3 Create a grouped frequency table.

Speed, s (mph)	Frequency, f	Midpoint, m	$f \times m$
5–10	12	7.5	90
10–15	23	12.5	287.5
15–20	34	17.5	595
20–25	24	22.5	540
25–30	5	27.5	137.5
30–35	2	32.5	65
	100		1715

The table must include the midpoint values, the frequency and $f \times m$.

This gets 1 method mark for giving the frequencies and showing a total.

This gets 1 method mark for working out the midpoints.

This gets 1 method mark for attempting to work out $f \times m$ and showing a total.

An estimate of the mean is 1715 ÷ 100 = 17.15 mph

This gets 1 method mark for dividing the total $f \times m$ by the total f.

This gets 1 mark for accuracy.

Total: 5 marks

4 An inspector visits a large company to check their vehicles. The company has large-load vehicles, light vans and cars. The inspector decides to sample 100 vehicles. Each type of vehicle is to be represented in the sample.

a What is this kind of sampling procedure called?

b How will the inspector decide how many of each type of vehicle he should inspect?

4 a Stratified sampling

This gets 1 mark.

b Find the total number of vehicles and the numbers of each type.

This gets 1 mark for stating he needs to find the numbers of each type of vehicle.

Work out the proportion of each type of vehicle in the total number.

Multiply each proportion by 100.

This gets 1 mark.

This will give the number of each type of vehicle to inspect.

This gets 1 mark for stating he needs to multiply the proportions by 100.

Total: 4 marks

3 Functional Maths
Fishing competition on the Avon

Averages are used to compare data collected through surveys and investigations. They are used every day for a wide variety of purposes, from describing the weather to analysing the economy. In this activity surveys and averages will be looked at in the context of a sporting event.

Your task

Every summer, Kath's family runs a fishing competition on their land by the river Avon. Kath plans to use this year's fishing competition to learn more about competitive fishing and the 'average' angler.

- Show how Kath could collect information on competitive fishing.
- Kath collects this data during the first four weeks in July:

	Week 1	Week 2	Week 3	Week 4	Week 5
Mean number of fish caught	12.1	12.3	7.2	11.8	
Mean time spent fishing (h)	6.1	5.6	4.5	5.4	
Mean weight of fish caught (g)	1576.0	1728.0	1635.0	1437.0	
Mean length of longest fish caught (cm)	21.7	17.6	21.6	19.2	

In the fifth week of July she collects this information (given on the right) from each angler.

- What conclusions can Kath draw from this data about fishing and the 'average' angler? Is it possible for Kath to apply her conclusions to competitive fishing in general?

Support your ideas with figures and diagrams.

Number of fish caught per angler
Up to 5: 6
Between 6 and 10: 11
Between 11 and 15: 8
Between 16 and 20: 5

Weight of largest fish caught (g)
Up to 500: 1
Between 501 and 1000: 8
Between 1001 and 1500: 18
Between 1501 and 2000: 3
Over 2000: 0

Time spent fishing per angler (h/min)
Up to 4: 2
Between 4 and 4.59: 14
Between 5 and 5.59: 6
Between 6 and 6.59: 8
7 and over: 0

Length of longest fish caught (cm)
Up to 10: 2
Between 10.1 and 15: 6
Between 15.1 and 20: 12
Between 20.1 and 25: 10

Getting started

Use the questions below to get you started in thinking about averages and the organisation of data.

- Start by thinking about how averages are calculated.
  - What do the mean, median, mode and range show when applied to sets of data? How do they apply to frequency tables?
  - What are the mean, median, mode and range for this set of data?
    3, 4, 8, 3, 2, 4, 5, 3, 4, 6, 8, 4, 2, 9, 1
  - Which averages might you need in your presentation? How could you represent these averages graphically?
- Think about how data can be ordered.
  - Write down a number smaller than five. Are you sure that you have written down the smallest number possible?
  - Write down the largest number that is smaller than five. Are you sure that you've written down the largest possible number?
  - Write this set of numbers using inequalities.

Handy hints

Inequalities can be used to accurately represent ranges in data.

> means 'greater than' (for example, $5 > 2$)

< means 'less than' (for example, $2 < 5$)

≥ means 'greater than or equal to'

≤ means 'less than or equal to'

Try to make use of these signs when representing your data.

Why this chapter matters

Statistical distributions can help us to understand our society and the world we live in. There are many different sorts of distribution, two of which are described here.

Population distribution

Where on Earth do people live?

Population distribution is the number of people living in a square mile (or kilometre). Calculating this over the whole planet shows that it is far from uniform.

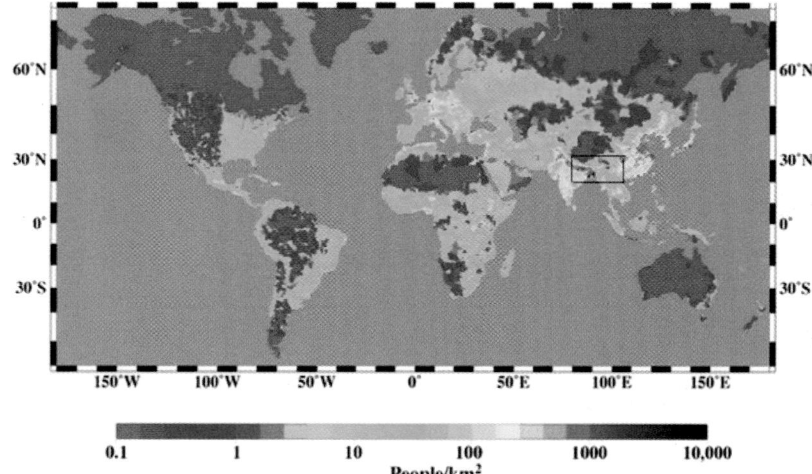

The map shows areas of the world that are densely populated and areas where very few people live. In some areas it is easy to understand the distribution of the population. For example, central regions of Australia are so hot and so thickly covered in scrubland that very few people would want to live there, hence they are thinly populated. However, coastal regions that enjoy good climate are much more thickly populated.

The south-east part of the UK is far more densely populated than the rest of the UK and much of Europe. In fact, the southern part of England has a very similar population density to India and Pakistan.

The normal distribution

This can be a confusing description of a distribution, as it often tells us little about what is normal. For example, the bar chart shows the normal distribution of IQ scores amongst the UK population.

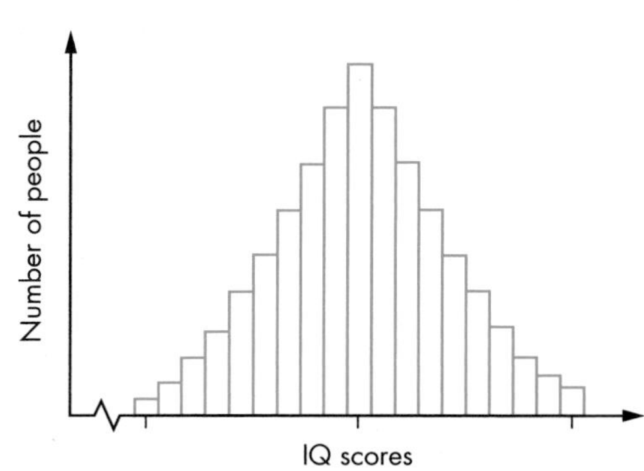

Although this shows there are more people with the 'average' score of 100 than any other score, there is no such thing as a normal IQ since there are many more people who score higher than 100 and less than 100.

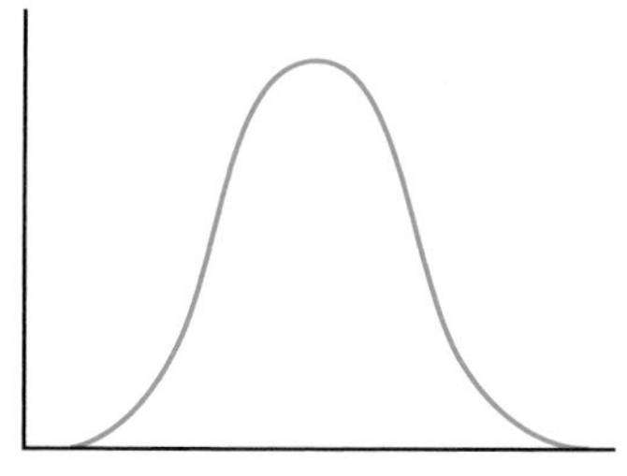

So what is normal?

What is normal is that none of us is normal! It is normal for some of us to be clever and others not to be so clever, but no particular IQ can be considered normal. And it is normal that this causes confusion, so it is not covered in your GCSE (you'll be pleased to know).

In this chapter we examine ways of looking at distributions of sets of people or data in order to compare them with each other.

Chapter

Statistics: Statistical representation

This chapter will show you ...

D how to interpret and draw line graphs and stem-and-leaf diagrams

D to C how to draw scatter diagrams and lines of best fit

D to C how to interpret scatter diagrams and the different types of correlation

B how to draw and interpret cumulative frequency diagrams

B to A how to draw and interpret box plots

Visual overview

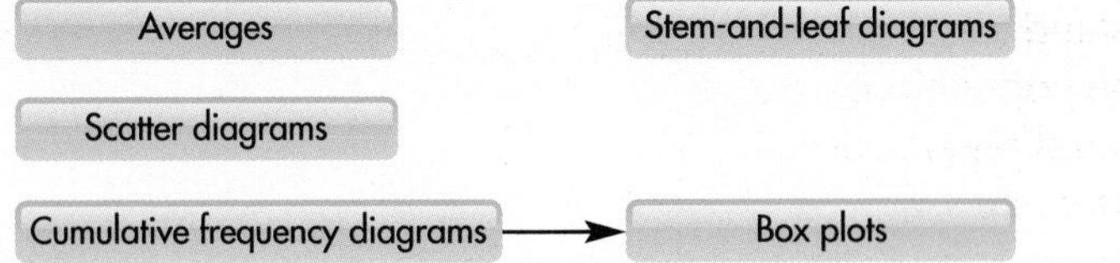

What you should already know

- How to plot coordinate points **(KS3 level 4, GCSE grade F)**
- How to read information from charts and tables **(KS3 level 4, GCSE grade F)**
- How to calculate the mean of a set of data from a frequency table **(KS3 level 5, GCSE grade E)**
- How to recognise a positive or negative gradient **(KS3 level 6, GCSE grade D)**

Quick check

The table shows the numbers of children in 10 classes in a primary school.

Calculate the mean number of children in each class.

Number of children	27	28	29	30	31
Frequency	1	2	4	2	1

4.1 Line graphs

This section will show you how to:

- draw a line graph to show trends in data

Key words
line graphs
trends

Line graphs are usually used in statistics to show how data changes over a period of time. One use is to indicate **trends**: for example, line graphs can be used to show whether the Earth's temperature is increasing as the concentration of carbon dioxide builds up in the atmosphere, or whether a firm's profit margin is falling year on year.

Line graphs are best drawn on graph paper.

EXAMPLE 1

This line graph shows the outside temperature one day in November.

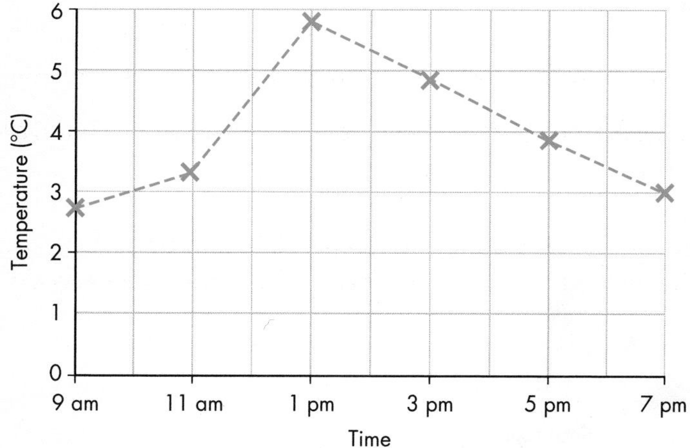

For this graph, the values between the plotted points have no true meaning because only the temperatures at the plotted points are known. However, by joining the points with a dashed line, as shown, you can estimate the temperatures at points in between. Although the graph shows the temperature falling in the early evening, it would not be sensible to try to predict what will happen after 7 pm that night.

EXERCISE 4A

D

1 The table shows the estimated numbers of tourists worldwide.

Year	1975	1980	1985	1990	1995	2000	2005	2010
No. of tourists (millions)	100	150	220	280	290	320	340	345

a Draw a line graph for the data.

b Use your graph to estimate the number of tourists in 2002.

c In which five-year period did tourism increase the most?

FM **d** Explain the trend in tourism. What reasons can you give to explain this trend?

2 The table shows the maximum and minimum daily temperatures for London over a week.

Day	Sunday	Monday	Tuesday	Wednesday	Thursday	Friday	Saturday
Maximum (°C)	12	14	16	15	16	14	10
Minimum (°C)	4	5	7	8	7	4	3

a Draw line graphs on the *same axes* to show the maximum and minimum temperatures.

b Find the smallest and greatest differences between the maximum and minimum temperatures.

3 Maria opened a coffee shop. She was interested in how trade was picking up over the first few weeks. The table shows the number of coffees sold in these weeks.

Week	1	2	3	4	5
Coffees sold	46	71	89	103	113

a Draw a line graph for this data.

b From your graph, estimate the number of coffees Maria hopes to sell in week 6.

FM **c** Give a possible reason for the way in which the number of coffees sold increased.

PS **4** A puppy is weighed at the end of each week.

Week	1	2	3	4	5
Weight (g)	850	920	940	980	1000

Estimate how much the puppy would weigh after eight weeks.

AU **5** When plotting a graph to show the summer midday temperatures in Spain, Abbass decided to start his graph at the temperature 20 °C.

Explain why he might have done that.

4.2 Stem-and-leaf diagrams

This section will show you how to:
- draw and read information from an ordered stem-and-leaf diagram

Key words
discrete data
ordered
raw data
unordered

Raw data

If you are recording the ages of the first 20 people who line up at a bus stop in the morning, the **raw data** might look like this.

23, 13, 34, 44, 26, 12, 41, 31, 20, 18, 19, 31, 48, 32, 45, 14, 12, 27, 31, 19

This data is **unordered** and is difficult to read and analyse. When the data is **ordered**, it looks like this.

12, 12, 13, 14, 18, 19, 19, 20, 23, 26, 27, 31, 31, 31, 32, 34, 41, 44, 45, 48

This is easier to read and analyse.

Another method for displaying **discrete data**, such as this, is a stem-and-leaf diagram. The tens values will be the 'stem' and the units values will be the 'leaves'.

Key: 1 | 2 represents 12

1	2	2	3	4	8	9	9
2	0	3	6	7			
3	1	1	1	2	4		
4	1	4	5	8			

This is called an ordered stem-and-leaf diagram. It gives a better idea of how the data is distributed.

A stem-and-leaf diagram should always have a key.

EXAMPLE 2

Put the following data into an ordered stem-and-leaf diagram.

45, 62, 58, 58, 61, 49, 61, 47, 52, 58, 48, 56, 65, 46, 54

a What is the modal value?

b What is the median value?

c What is the range of the values?

First, decide on the stem and leaf.

In this case, the tens digit will be the stem and the units digit will be the leaf.

Key: 4 | 5 represents 45

4	5	6	7	8	9	
5	2	4	6	8	8	8
6	1	1	2	5		

a The modal value is the most common, which is 58.

b There are 15 values, so the median will be the value that is (15 + 1) ÷ 2, or the 8th value. Counting from either the top or the bottom, the median is 56.

c The range is the difference between the largest and the smallest value, which is 65 − 45 = 20

EXERCISE 4B

1 The heights of 15 tulips are measured.

43 cm, 39 cm, 41 cm, 29 cm, 36 cm,
34 cm, 43 cm, 48 cm, 38 cm, 35 cm,
41 cm, 38 cm, 43 cm, 28 cm, 48 cm

a Show the results in an ordered stem-and-leaf diagram, using this key.

Key: 4 | 3 represents 43 cm

b What is the modal height?

c What is the median height?

d What is the range of the heights?

2 A student records the number of text messages she receives each day for two weeks.

12, 18, 21, 9, 17, 23, 8, 2, 20, 13, 17, 22, 9, 9

a Show the results in an ordered stem-and-leaf diagram, using this key.

Key: 1 | 2 represents 12 messages

b What was the modal number of text messages received in a day?

c What was the median number of text messages received in a day?

3 Zachia wanted to know how many people attended a daily youth club each day for a month. She recorded the data.

13, 19, 20, 9, 18, 24, 7, 8, 19, 14, 18, 23, 9, 10, 15, 31, 28, 26, 12, 24

a Show these results in an ordered stem-and-leaf diagram.

b What is the median number of people at the youth club?

c What is the range of the numbers of people who attended the youth club?

D

D

PS 4 This stem-and-leaf diagram shows some heights of boys and girls in the same form.

6	15	3 5 5 7 7 9
2 5 5 6 8 9 9	16	1 1 5 6 6 7 8 9
3 4 5 5 7	17	4
2 3 3	18	

Explain what the diagram is telling you about the students in the form.

AU 5 The matches in a set of boxes were counted and the following numbers were recorded.

50, 52, 51, 53, 52, 51, 51, 53, 54, 55, 54, 52, 52, 51, 50, 53

Explain why a stem-and-leaf diagram is *not* a good way to represent this information.

4.3 Scatter diagrams

This section will show you how to:
- draw, interpret and use scatter diagrams

Key words
line of best fit
negative correlation
no correlation
positive correlation
scatter diagram
variable

A **scatter diagram** (also called a scattergraph or scattergram) is a method of comparing two **variables** by plotting on a graph their corresponding values (usually taken from a table). In other words, the variables are treated just like a set of (x, y) coordinates.

In this scatter diagram, the marks scored by students in an English test are plotted against the marks they scored in a mathematics test. This graph shows **positive correlation**. This means that the students who got high marks in the mathematics test also tended to get high marks in the English test.

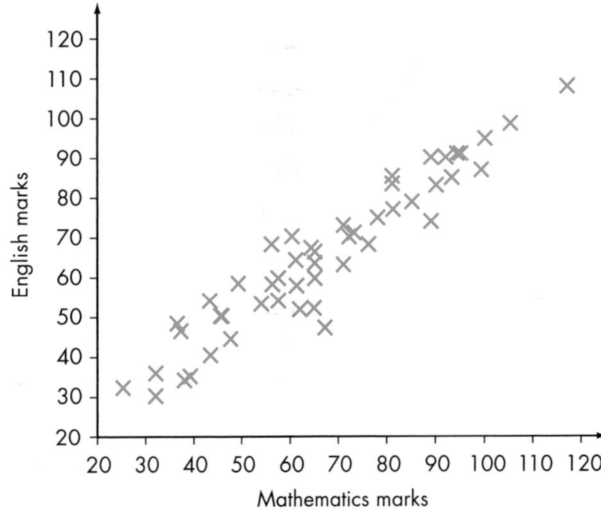

Correlation

This section will explain the different types of correlation.

Here are three statements that may or may not be true.

The taller people are, the wider their arm span is likely to be.
The older a car is, the lower its value will be.
The distance you live from your place of work will affect how much you earn.

These relationships could be tested by collecting data and plotting the data on a scatter diagram.

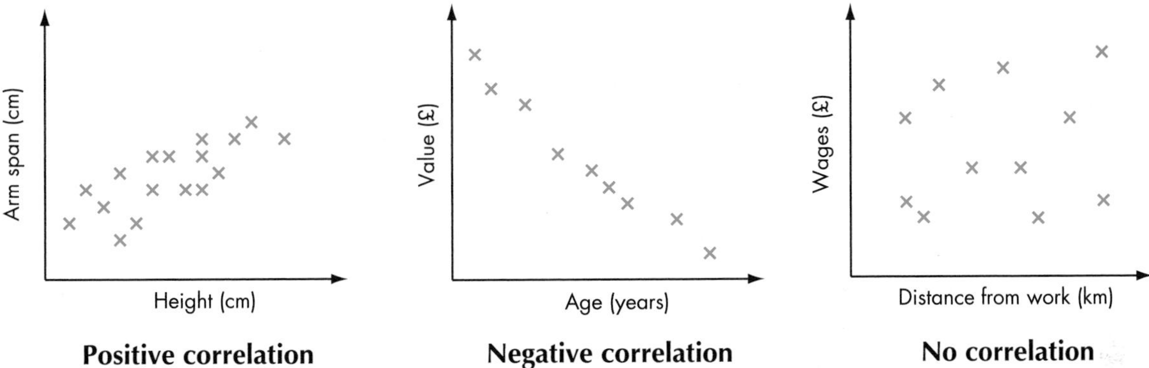

For example, the first statement may give a scatter diagram like the first one above. This diagram has positive correlation because as one quantity increases so does the other. From such a scatter diagram you could say that the taller someone is, the wider the arm span.

Testing the second statement may give a scatter diagram like the second one. This diagram has **negative correlation** because as one quantity increases, the other quantity decreases. From such a scatter diagram you could say that as a car gets older, its value decreases.

Testing the third statement may give a scatter diagram like the third one. This scatter diagram has **no correlation**. There is no relationship between the distance a person lives from work and how much that person earns.

EXAMPLE 3

The graphs show the relationship between the temperature and the amount of ice cream sold, and that between the age of people and the amount of ice cream they eat.

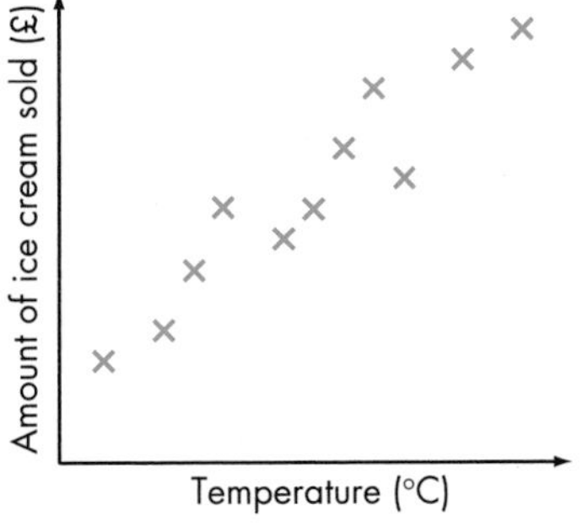

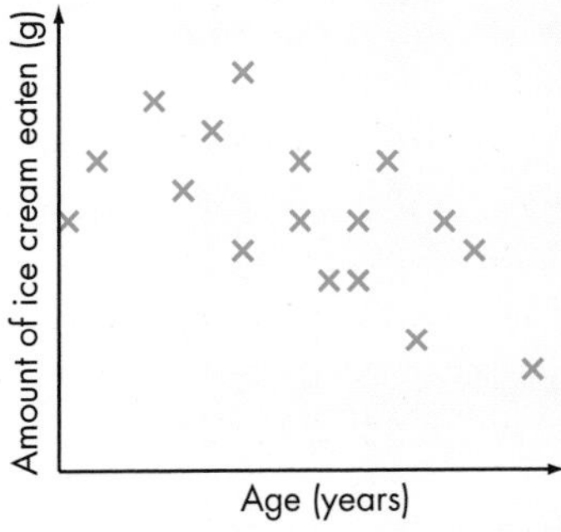

a Comment on the correlation of each graph. **b** What does each graph tell you?

The first graph has positive correlation and tells us that as the temperature increases, the amount of ice cream sold increases.

The second graph has negative correlation and tells us that as people get older, they eat less ice cream.

Line of best fit

This section will explain how to draw and use a **line of best fit**.

The line of best fit is a straight line that goes between all the points on a scatter diagram, passing as close as possible to all of them. You should try to have the same number of points on both sides of the line. Because you are drawing this line by eye, examiners make a generous allowance for the correct answer. The line of best fit for the scatter diagram on page 120 is shown below, left.

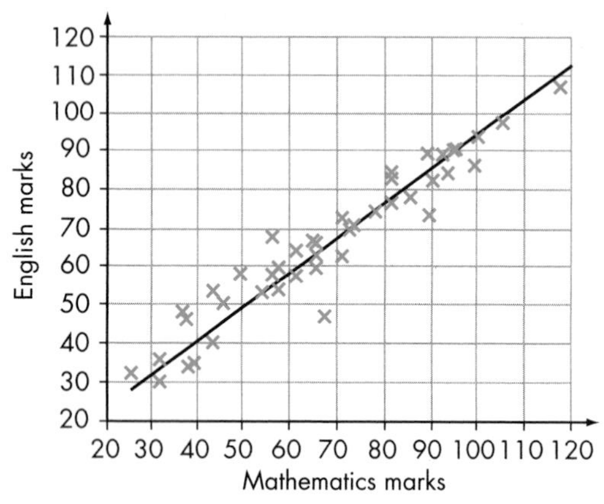

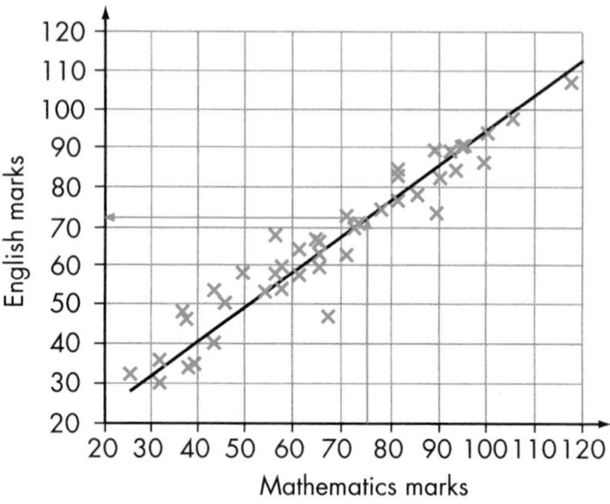

The line of best fit can be used to answer the following type of question: A girl took the mathematics test and scored 75 marks, but was ill for the English test. How many marks was she likely to have scored?

The answer is found by drawing a line up from 75 on the mathematics axis to the line of best fit and then drawing a line across to the English axis (above right). This gives 73, which is the mark she is likely to have scored in the English test.

EXERCISE 4C

D

1 Describe the correlation of each of these four graphs and write in words what each graph tells you.

a

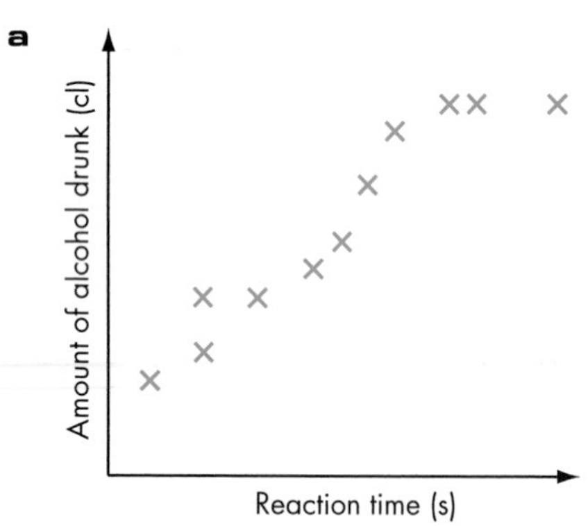

b

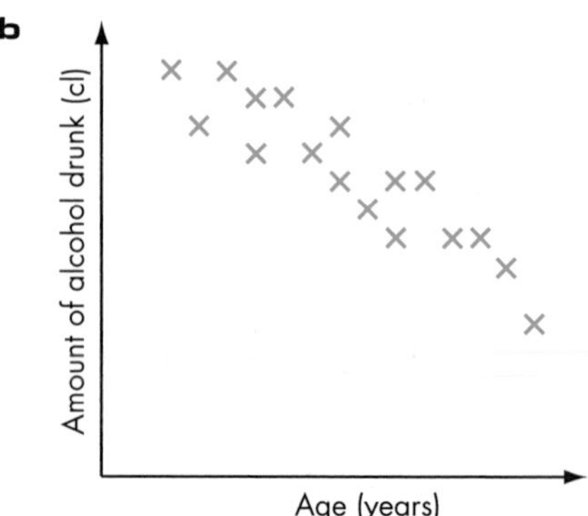

c

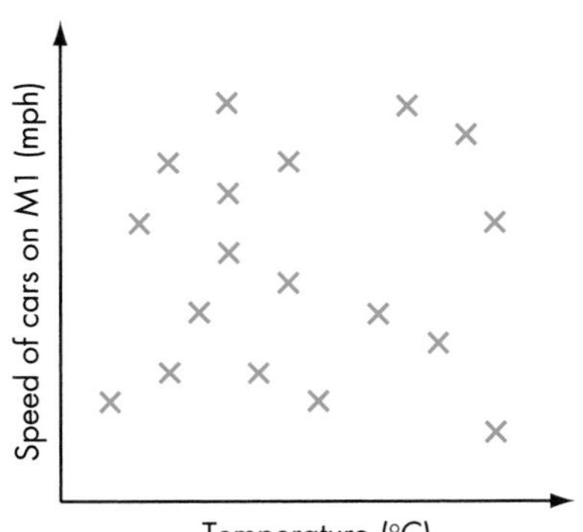

d

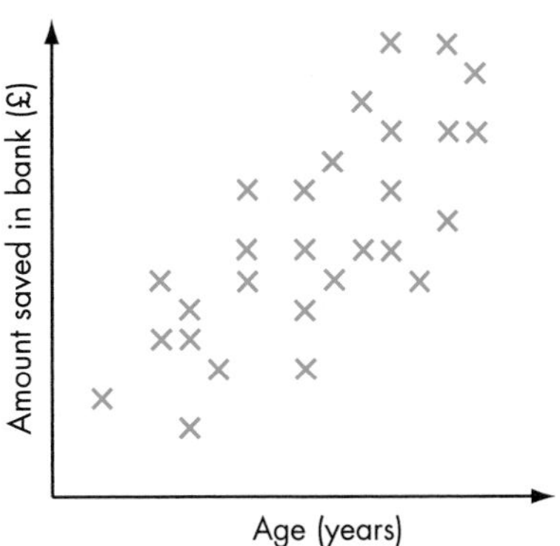

D

C

2 The table shows the results of a science experiment in which a ball is rolled along a desk top. The speed of the ball is measured at various points.

Distance from start (cm)	10	20	30	40	50	60	70	80
Speed (cm/s)	18	16	13	10	7	5	3	0

a Plot the data on a scatter diagram.

b Draw the line of best fit.

c If the ball's speed had been measured at 5 cm from the start, what is it likely to have been?

FM **d** Estimate how far from the start the ball was when its speed was 12 cm/s.

HINTS AND TIPS

Often in exams axes are given and most, if not all, of the points are plotted.

3 The table shows the marks for 10 students in their mathematics and geography examinations.

Student	Anna	Beryl	Cath	Dema	Ethel	Fatima	Greta	Hannah	Imogen	Joan
Maths	57	65	34	87	42	35	59	61	25	35
Geog	45	61	30	78	41	36	35	57	23	34

a Plot the data on a scatter diagram. Take the x-axis for the mathematics scores and mark it from 20 to 100. Take the y-axis for the geography scores and mark it from 20 to 100.

b Draw the line of best fit.

c One of the students was ill when she took the geography examination. Which student was it most likely to be?

FM **d** If another student, Kate, was absent for the geography examination but scored 75 in mathematics, what mark would you expect her to have got in geography?

e If another student, Lynne, was absent for the mathematics examination but scored 65 in geography, what mark would you expect her to have got in mathematics?

FM **4** The heights, in centimetres, of 20 mothers and their 15-year-old daughters were measured. These are the results.

Mother	153	162	147	183	174	169	152	164	186	178
Daughter	145	155	142	167	167	151	145	152	163	168

Mother	175	173	158	168	181	173	166	162	180	156
Daughter	172	167	160	154	170	164	156	150	160	152

a Plot these results on a scatter diagram. Take the x-axis for the mothers' heights from 140 to 200. Take the y-axis for the daughters' heights from 140 to 200.

b Is it true that the tall mothers have tall daughters?

FM **5** A teacher carried out a survey of his class. He asked students to say how many hours per week they spent playing sport and how many hours per week they spent watching TV. This table shows the results of the survey.

Student	1	2	3	4	5	6	7	8	9	10
Hours playing sport	12	3	5	15	11	0	9	7	6	12
Hours watching TV	18	26	24	16	19	27	12	13	17	14

Student	11	12	13	14	15	16	17	18	19	20
Hours playing sport	12	10	7	6	7	3	1	2	0	12
Hours watching TV	22	16	18	22	12	28	18	20	25	13

a Plot these results on a scatter diagram. Take the x-axis as the number of hours playing sport and the y-axis as the number of hours watching TV.

b If you knew that another student from the class watched 8 hours of TV a week, would you be able to predict how long she or he spent playing sport? Explain why.

FM **6** The table shows the time taken and distance travelled by a taxi driver for 10 journeys one day.

Distance (km)	1.6	8.3	5.2	6.6	4.8	7.2	3.9	5.8	8.8	5.4
Time (min)	3	17	11	13	9	15	8	11	16	10

a Draw a scatter diagram with time on the horizontal axis.

b Draw a line of best fit on your diagram.

c A taxi journey takes 5 minutes. How many kilometres would you expect the journey to have been?

d How long would you expect a journey of 4 km to take?

PS **7** Oliver records the time taken, in hours, and the average speed, in mph, for several different journeys.

Time (h)	0.5	0.8	1.1	1.3	1.6	1.75	2	2.4	2.6
Speed (mph)	42	38	27	30	22	23	21	9	8

Estimate the average speed for a journey of 90 minutes.

AU **8** Describe what you would expect the scatter graph to look like if someone said that it showed negative correlation.

4.4 Cumulative frequency diagrams

This section will show you how to:

- find a measure of dispersion (the interquartile range) and a measure of location (the median) using a graph

Key words

cumulative frequency
cumulative frequency diagram
dispersion
interquartile range
lower quartile
median
quartile
upper quartile

The **interquartile range** is a measure of the **dispersion** of a set of data. The advantage of the interquartile range is that it eliminates extreme values, and bases the measure of spread on the middle 50% of the data. This section will show how to find the interquartile range and the median of a set of data by drawing a **cumulative frequency diagram**.

Look back at the marks of the 50 students in the mathematics test (see page 120). These can be put into a grouped table, as shown below. Note that it includes a column for the **cumulative frequency**, which you can find by adding each frequency to the sum of all preceding frequencies.

Mark	Number of students	Cumulative frequency
21 to 30	1	1
31 to 40	6	7
41 to 50	6	13
51 to 60	8	21
61 to 70	8	29
71 to 80	6	35
81 to 90	7	42
91 to 100	6	48
101 to 110	1	49
111 to 120	1	50

This data can then be used to plot a graph of the top value of each group against its cumulative frequency. The points to be plotted are (30, 1), (40, 7), (50, 13), (60, 21), etc., which will give the graph shown below. Note that the cumulative frequency is *always* the vertical (y) axis.

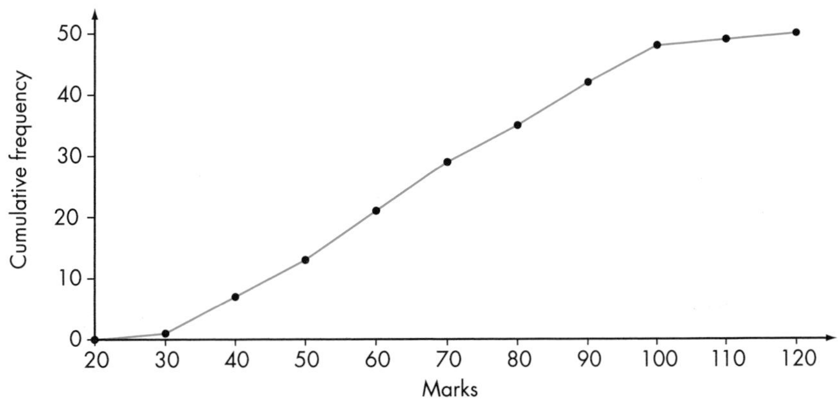

Also note that the scales on both axes are labelled at each graduation mark, in the usual way. **Do not** label the scales as shown here. It is **wrong**.

21–30 31–40 41–50

The plotted points can be joined in two different ways:

- by straight lines, to give a cumulative frequency polygon
- by a freehand curve, to give a cumulative frequency curve or ogive.

They are both called cumulative frequency diagrams.

In an examination you are most likely to be asked to draw a cumulative frequency diagram, and the type (polygon or curve) is up to you. Both will give similar results. The cumulative frequency diagram can be used in several ways, as you will now see.

The median

The **median** is the middle item of data once all the items have been put in order of size, from lowest to highest. So, if you have n items of data plotted as a cumulative frequency diagram, you can find the median from the middle value of the cumulative frequency, that is the $\frac{1}{2}n$th value.

But remember, if you want to find the median from a simple list of discrete data, you *must* use the $\frac{1}{2}(n + 1)$th value. The reason for the difference is that the cumulative frequency diagram treats the data as continuous, even when using data such as examination marks, which are discrete. The reason you can use the $\frac{1}{2}n$th value when working with cumulative frequency diagrams is that you are only looking for an estimate of the median.

There are 50 values in the table on page 125. The middle value will be the 25th value. Draw a horizontal line from the 25th value to meet the graph, then go down to the horizontal axis. This will give an estimate of the median. In this example, the median is about 65 marks.

The interquartile range

By dividing the cumulative frequency into four parts, you can obtain **quartiles** and the interquartile range.

The **lower quartile** is the item one-quarter of the way up the cumulative frequency axis and is given by the $\frac{1}{4}n$th value.

The **upper quartile** is the item three-quarters of the way up the cumulative frequency axis and is given by the $\frac{3}{4}n$th value.

The interquartile range is the difference between the lower and upper quartiles.

These are illustrated on the graph below.

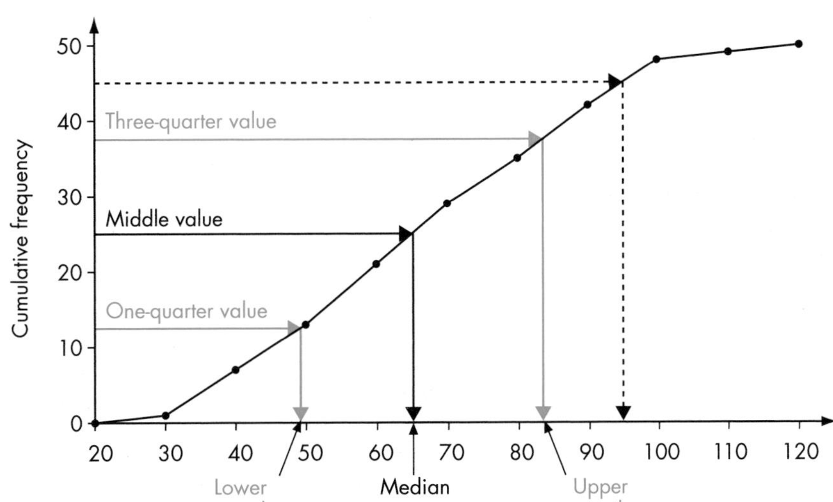

The quarter and three-quarter values out of 50 values are the 12.5th value and the 37.5th value. Draw lines across to the cumulative frequency curve from these values and down to the horizontal axis. These give the lower and upper quartiles. In this example, the lower quartile is 49 marks, the upper quartile is 83 marks and the interquartile range is 83 – 49 = 34 marks.

Note that problems like these are often followed up with an extra question such as: *The head of mathematics decides to give a special award to the top 10% of students. What would the cut-off mark be?*

The top 10% would be the top 5 students (10% of 50 is 5). Draw a line across from the 45th student to the graph and down to the horizontal axis. This gives a cut-off mark of 95.

EXAMPLE 4

This table shows the marks of 100 students in a mathematics test.

a Draw a cumulative frequency curve.

b Use your graph to find the median and the interquartile range.

c Students who score less than 44 have to have extra teaching. How many students will have to have extra teaching?

Mark	No. of students	Cumulative frequency
$21 \leqslant x \leqslant 30$	3	3
$31 \leqslant x \leqslant 40$	9	12
$41 \leqslant x \leqslant 50$	12	24
$51 \leqslant x \leqslant 60$	15	39
$61 \leqslant x \leqslant 70$	22	61
$71 \leqslant x \leqslant 80$	16	77
$81 \leqslant x \leqslant 90$	10	87
$91 \leqslant x \leqslant 100$	8	95
$101 \leqslant x \leqslant 110$	3	98
$111 \leqslant x \leqslant 120$	2	100

EXAMPLE 4 (continued)

The groups are given in a different way to those in the table on page 125. You will meet several ways of giving groups (for example, 21–30, $20 < x \leqslant 30$, $21 < x < 30$) but the important thing to remember is to plot the top point of each group against the corresponding cumulative frequency.

a and **b** Draw the graph and put on the lines for the median (50th value), lower and upper quartiles (25th and 75th values).

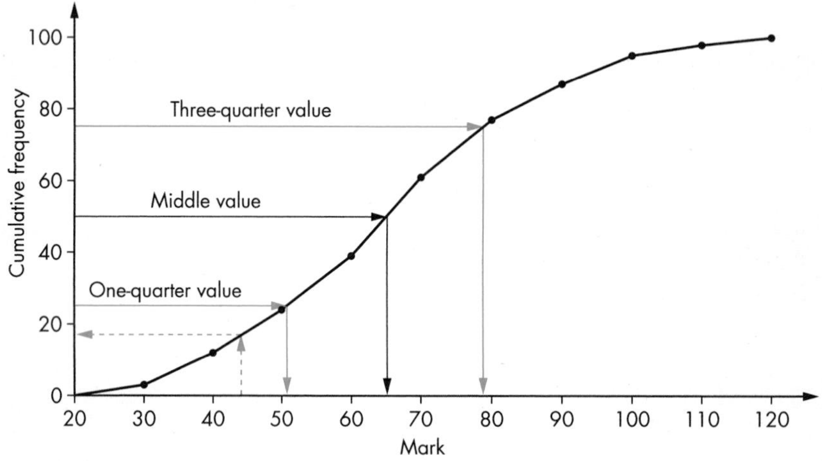

The required answers are read from the graph.

Median = 65 marks
Lower quartile = 51 marks
Upper quartile = 79 marks
Interquartile range = 79 – 51 = 28 marks

c At 44 on the mark axis, draw a perpendicular line to intersect the graph, and at the point of intersection draw a horizontal line across to the cumulative frequency axis, as shown. Number of students needing extra teaching is 18.

Note: An alternative way in which the table in Example 4 could have been set out is shown below. This arrangement has the advantage that the points to be plotted are taken straight from the last two columns. You have to decide which method you prefer. In examination papers, the columns of tables are sometimes given without headings, so you will need to be familiar with all the different ways in which the data can be set out.

Mark	No. of students	Less than	Cumulative frequency
$21 \leqslant x \leqslant 30$	3	30	3
$31 \leqslant x \leqslant 40$	9	40	12
$41 \leqslant x \leqslant 50$	12	50	24
$51 \leqslant x \leqslant 60$	15	60	39
$61 \leqslant x \leqslant 70$	22	70	61
$71 \leqslant x \leqslant 80$	16	80	77
$81 \leqslant x \leqslant 90$	10	90	87
$91 \leqslant x \leqslant 100$	8	100	95
$101 \leqslant x \leqslant 110$	3	110	98
$111 \leqslant x \leqslant 120$	2	120	100

EXERCISE 4D

FM 1 A class of 30 students was asked to estimate one minute. The teacher recorded the times the students actually said. The table on the right shows the results.

a Copy the table and complete a cumulative frequency column.

b Draw a cumulative frequency diagram.

c Use your diagram to estimate the median time and the interquartile range.

Time (seconds)	No. of students
$20 < x \leqslant 30$	1
$30 < x \leqslant 40$	3
$40 < x \leqslant 50$	6
$50 < x \leqslant 60$	12
$60 < x \leqslant 70$	3
$70 < x \leqslant 80$	3
$80 < x \leqslant 90$	2

FM 2 A group of 50 pensioners was given the same task as the children in question **1**. The results are shown in the table on the right.

a Copy the table and complete a cumulative frequency column.

b Draw a cumulative frequency diagram.

c Use your diagram to estimate the median time and the interquartile range.

d Which group, the students or the pensioners, would you say was better at estimating time? Give a reason for your answer.

Time (seconds)	No. of pensioners
$10 < x \leqslant 20$	1
$20 < x \leqslant 30$	2
$30 < x \leqslant 40$	2
$40 < x \leqslant 50$	9
$50 < x \leqslant 60$	17
$60 < x \leqslant 70$	13
$70 < x \leqslant 80$	3
$80 < x \leqslant 90$	2
$90 < x \leqslant 100$	1

FM 3 The sizes of 360 secondary schools in South Yorkshire are recorded in the table on the right.

a Copy the table and complete a cumulative frequency column.

b Draw a cumulative frequency diagram.

c Use your diagram to estimate the median size of the schools and the interquartile range.

d Schools with fewer than 350 students are threatened with closure. About how many schools are threatened with closure?

No. of students	No. of schools
100–199	12
200–299	18
300–399	33
400–499	50
500–599	63
600–699	74
700–799	64
800–899	35
900–999	11

B

4 The temperature at a seaside resort was recorded over a period of 50 days. The temperature was recorded to the nearest degree. The table on the right shows the results.

Temperature (°C)	No. of days
5–7	2
8–10	3
11–13	5
14–16	6
17–19	6
20–22	9
23–25	8
26–28	6
29–31	5

a Copy the table and complete a cumulative frequency column.

b Draw a cumulative frequency diagram. Note that as the temperature is to the nearest degree the top values of the groups are 7.5 °C, 10.5 °C, 13.5 °C, 16.5 °C, etc.

c Use your diagram to estimate the median temperature and the interquartile range.

FM 5 At the school charity fête, a game consists of throwing three darts and recording the total score. The results of the first 80 people to throw are recorded in the table on the right.

Total score	No. of players
$1 \leqslant x \leqslant 20$	9
$21 \leqslant x \leqslant 40$	13
$41 \leqslant x \leqslant 60$	23
$61 \leqslant x \leqslant 80$	15
$81 \leqslant x \leqslant 100$	11
$101 \leqslant x \leqslant 120$	7
$121 \leqslant x \leqslant 140$	2

a Draw a cumulative frequency diagram to show the data.

b Use your diagram to estimate the median score and the interquartile range.

c People who score over 90 get a prize. About what percentage of the people get a prize?

6 One hundred children in a primary school were asked to say how much pocket money they each got in a week. The results are in the table on the right.

Amount of pocket money (p)	No. of children
51–100	6
101–150	10
151–200	20
201–250	28
251–300	18
301–350	11
351–400	5
401–450	2

a Copy the table and complete a cumulative frequency column.

b Draw a cumulative frequency diagram.

c Use your diagram to estimate the median amount of pocket money and the interquartile range.

B

FM 7 James set his class an end of course test with two papers, A and B. He produced the cumulative frequency graphs below.

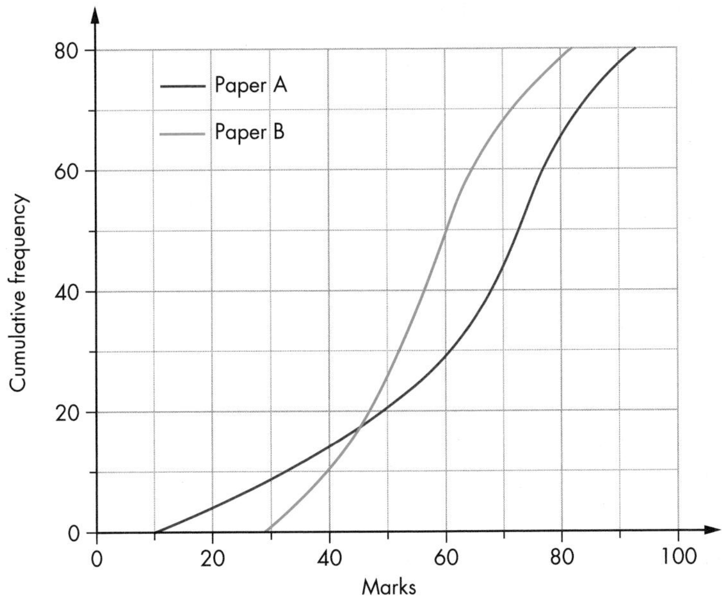

a What is the median score for each paper?

b What is the interquartile range for each paper?

c Which is the harder paper? Explain how you know.

James wanted 80% of the students to pass each paper and 20% of the students to get a top grade in each paper.

d What marks for each paper give:

i a pass **ii** the top grade?

FM PS 8 The lengths of time, in minutes, of 60 helpline telephone calls were recorded. A cumulative frequency diagram of this data is shown on the right.

Calculate the estimated mean length of telephone call.

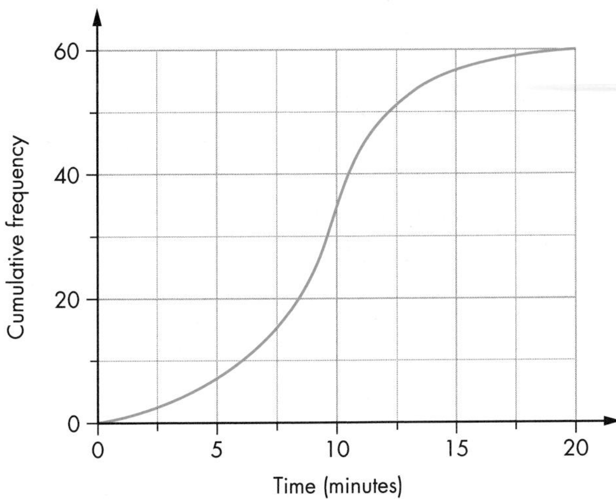

AU 9 Byron was given a cumulative frequency diagram showing the marks obtained by students in a mental maths test.

He was told the top 10% were given the top grade.

How would he find the marks needed to gain this top award?

4.5 Box plots

This section will show you how to:

- draw and read box plots

Key words
box-and-whisker plot
box plot
highest value
lower quartile
lowest value
median
upper quartile

Another way of displaying data for comparison is by means of a **box-and-whisker plot** (or just **box plot**). This requires five pieces of data. These are the **lowest value**, the **lower quartile** (Q_1), the **median** (Q_2), the **upper quartile** (Q_3) and the **highest value**. They are drawn in the following way.

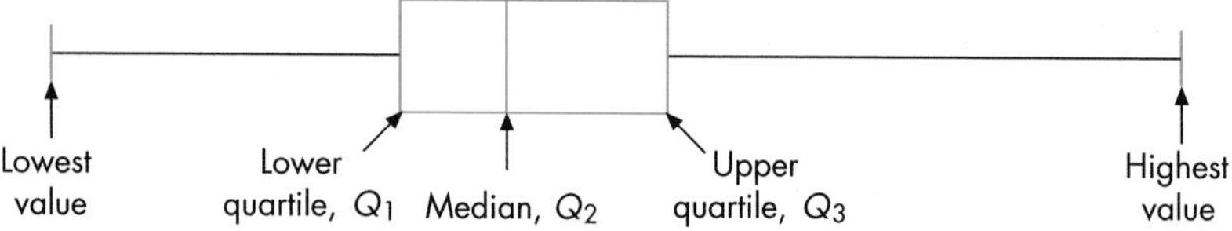

These data values are always placed against a scale so that they are accurately plotted.

The following diagrams show how the cumulative frequency curve, the frequency curve and the box plot are connected for three common types of distribution.

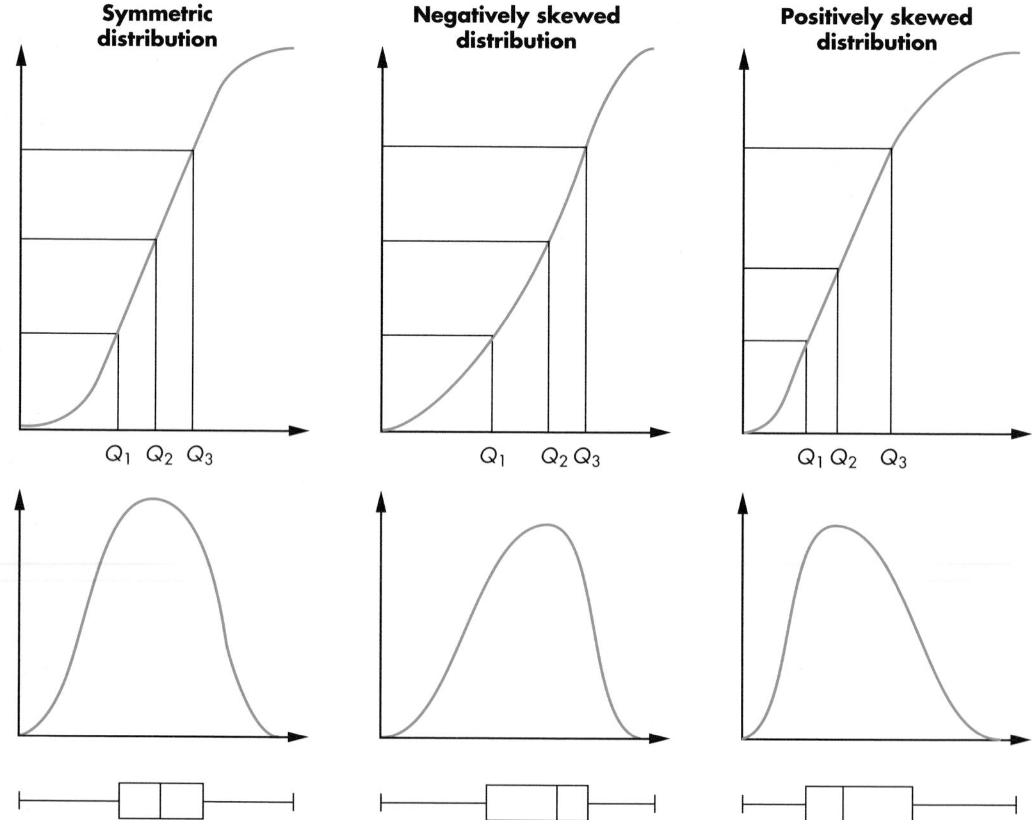

EXAMPLE 5

The box plot for the girls' marks in last year's examination is shown below.

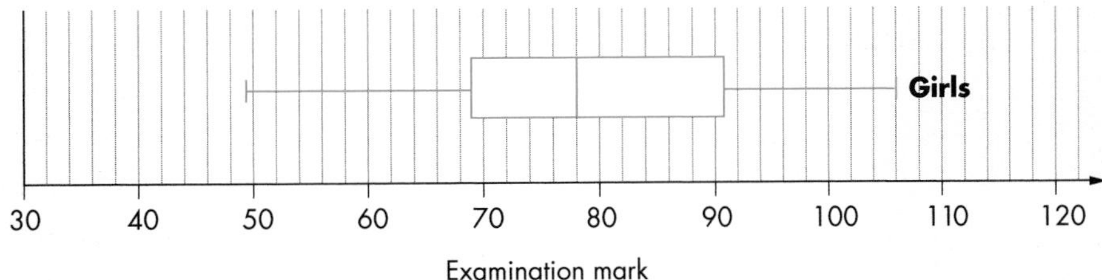

The boys' results for the same examination are: lowest mark 39, lower quartile 65, median 78, upper quartile 87, highest mark 112.

a On the same grid, draw the box plot for the boys' marks.

b Comment on the differences between the two distributions of marks.

a The data for boys and girls is plotted on the grid below.

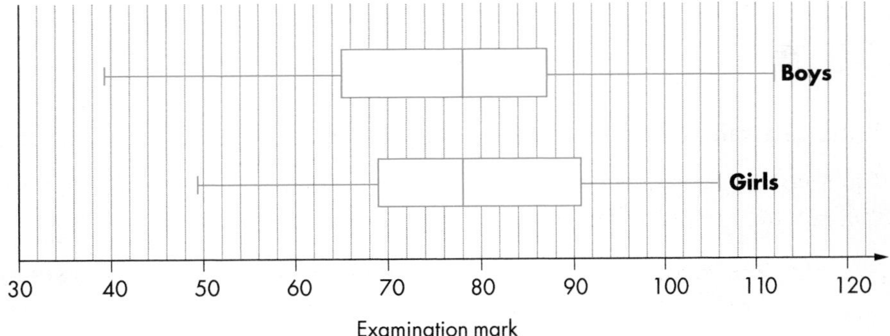

b The girls and boys have the same median mark but both the lower and upper quartiles for the girls are higher than those for the boys, and the girls' range is slightly smaller than the boys'.

This suggests that the girls did better than the boys overall, even though a boy got the highest mark.

EXERCISE 4E

B

FM 1 The box plot shows the times taken for a group of pensioners to do a set of 10 long-division calculations.

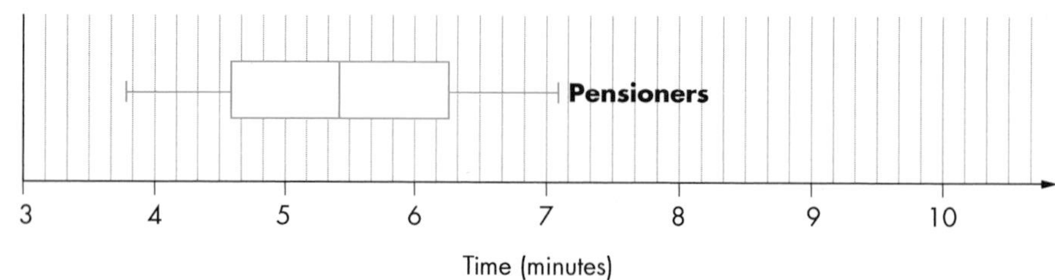

The same set of calculations was given to some students in Year 11. Their results are: shortest time 3 minutes 20 seconds, lower quartile 6 minutes 10 seconds, median 7 minutes, upper quartile 7 minutes 50 seconds and longest time 9 minutes 40 seconds.

a Copy the diagram and draw a box plot for the students' times.

b Comment on the differences between the two distributions.

FM 2 The box plot shows the sizes of secondary schools in Dorset.

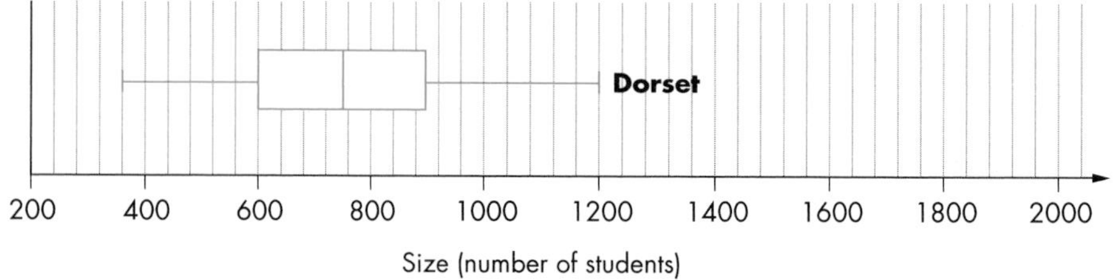

The data for schools in Rotherham is: smallest 280 students, lower quartile 1100 students, median 1400 students, upper quartile 1600 students, largest 1820 students.

a Copy the diagram and draw a box plot for the sizes of schools in Rotherham.

b Comment on the differences between the two distributions.

FM 3 The box plots for the noon temperature at two resorts, recorded over a year, are shown on the grid below.

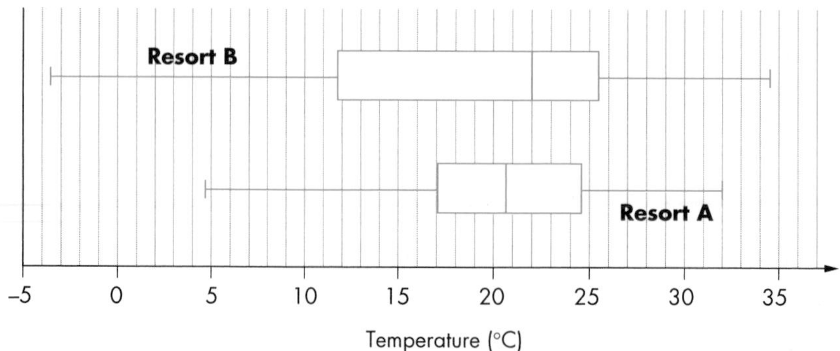

a Comment on the differences in the two distributions.

b Mary wants to go on holiday in July. Which resort would you recommend? Why?

FM **4** The following table shows some data on the annual salaries for 100 men and 100 women.

	Lowest salary	Lower quartile	Median salary	Upper quartile	Highest salary
Men	£6500	£16 000	£20 000	£22 000	£44 500
Women	£7000	£14 000	£16 000	£21 500	£33 500

a Draw box plots to compare both sets of data.

b Comment on the differences between the distributions.

FM **5** The table shows the monthly salaries of 100 families.

Monthly salary (£)	No. of families
1451–1500	8
1501–1550	14
1551–1600	25
1601–1650	35
1651–1700	14
1701–1750	4

a Draw a cumulative frequency diagram to show the data.

b Estimate the median monthly salary and the interquartile range.

c The lowest monthly salary was £1480 and the highest was £1740.

i Draw a box plot to show the distribution of salaries.

ii Is the distribution symmetric, negatively skewed or positively skewed?

FM **6** A health practice had two doctors, Dr Excel and Dr Collins.

The following box plots were created to illustrate the waiting times for their patients during October.

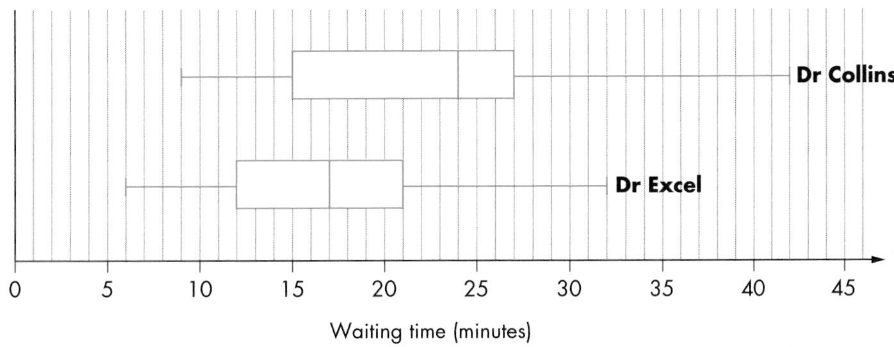

a For Dr Collins, what is:

i the median waiting time

ii the interquartile range for his waiting time

iii the longest time a patient had to wait in October?

b For Dr Excel, what is:

i the shortest waiting time for any patient in October

ii the median waiting time

iii the interquartile range for his waiting time?

c Anwar was deciding which doctor to try to see. Which one would you advise he sees? Why?

PS 7 The box plot for a school's end-of-year mathematics tests are shown below.

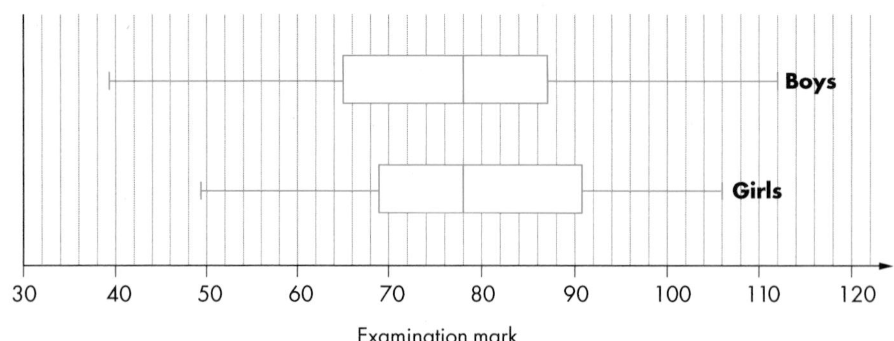

What is the difference between the means of the boys' and the girls' test results?

AU 8 Rodrigo was given a diagram showing box plots for the amount of daily sunshine in the resorts of Bude and Torquay for August but no scale was shown. He was told to write a report on the differences between the amounts of sunshine in both resorts.

Invent a report that could be possible for him to make from these box plots with no scales shown.

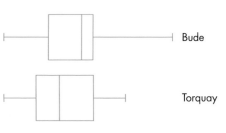

Bude

Torquay

9 Indicate whether the following sets of data are likely to be symmetric, negatively skewed or positively skewed.

- **a** Heights of adult males
- **b** Annual salaries of adult males
- **c** Shoe sizes of adult males
- **d** Weights of babies born in Britain
- **e** Speeds of cars on a motorway in the middle of the night
- **f** Speeds of cars on a motorway in the rush hour
- **g** Shopping bills in a supermarket the week before Christmas
- **h** Number of letters in the words in a teenage magazine
- **i** Time taken for students to get to school in the morning
- **j** Time taken for students to run 1 mile

AU 10 Below are four cumulative frequency diagrams and four box plots.

Match each cumulative frequency diagram with a box plot.

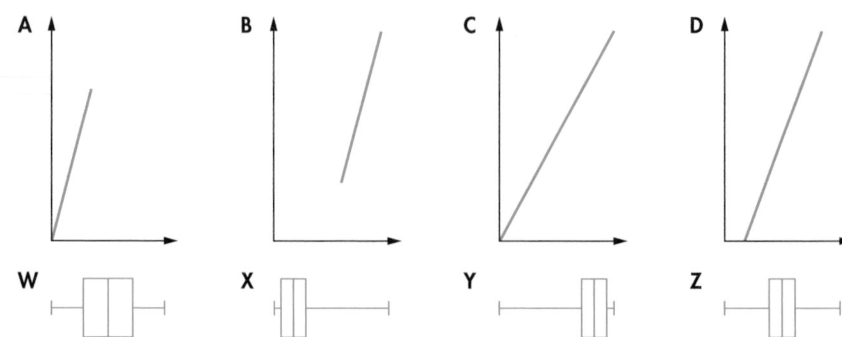

GRADE BOOSTER

- **D** You can draw an ordered stem-and-leaf diagram
- **D** You can recognise the different types of correlation
- **C** You can draw a line of best fit on a scatter diagram
- **C** You can interpret a scatter diagram
- **B** You can draw a cumulative frequency diagram
- **A** You can find medians and interquartile ranges from cumulative frequency diagrams
- **A** You can draw and interpret box plots

What you should know now

- How to read information from statistical diagrams, including stem-and-leaf diagrams
- How to plot scatter diagrams, recognise correlation, draw lines of best fit and use them to predict values
- How to construct a cumulative frequency diagram
- How to draw and interpret box plots

1 A team of 12 run a half-marathon.

Their times, to the nearest minute, are:

72	87	65	85	91	76
67	70	80	84	70	82

Copy and complete an ordered stem-and-leaf diagram to represent this data.

Remember to complete the key.

Key … | … represents … minutes

6	
7	
8	
9	

(3 marks)

AQA, May 2008, Paper 1 Higher, Question 9

2 The table shows the times taken for a certain train journey on 20 different occasions.

Time taken, t (min)	Frequency
$18 < t \leqslant 20$	4
$20 < t \leqslant 22$	6
$22 < t \leqslant 24$	5
$24 < t \leqslant 26$	3
$26 < t \leqslant 28$	2

Calculate an estimate of the mean journey time.

3 The scatter diagram shows the time that seven students spent practising for a typing test and the number of errors they made in the test.

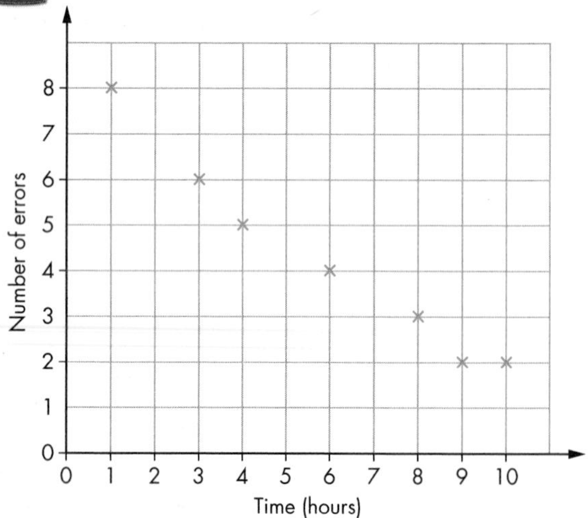

a Describe the relationship shown by the scatter graph. *(1 mark)*

b **i** Draw a line of best fit on the diagram. *(1 mark)*

ii Use your line of best fit to estimate the number of errors made if a student practised for two hours. *(1 mark)*

c Asif practised for two hours and only made one error. Give a possible reason why his number of errors was so low. *(1 mark)*

d Leanne says, "If I practise for 15 hours I will definitely not make any errors."

Is she correct?

Give a reason for your answer. *(1 mark)*

AQA, June 2008, Module 1 Higher, Question 1

4 The length and wingspan, in centimetres, of seven common garden birds is shown in the table.

Bird	Length (cm)	Wingspan (cm)
Starling	21	40
Blackbird	25	36
Blue tit	11	19
Greenfinch	15	26
Dove	32	51
Sparrow	15	23
Great tit	14	24

a Plot the data as a scatter graph on a grid as shown below.

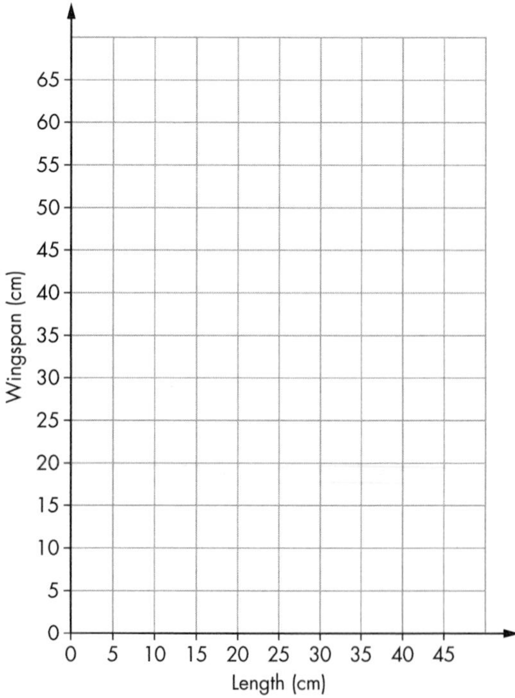

(2 marks)

B C D

b Describe the strength and type of correlation. *(1 mark)*

c Draw a line of best fit on your scatter graph. *(1 mark)*

d Use your line of best fit to estimate the wingspan of a thrush whose length is 20 cm. *(1 mark)*

e It is not sensible to use your line of best fit to estimate the wingspan of a pigeon whose length is 41 cm.

Explain why. *(1 mark)*

AQA, March 2008, Module 1 Higher, Question 1

5 The table shows the number of pages in some paperback books and their prices.

Pages	350	390	450	500	590	610	620	700	750	760
Cost (£)	6.00	5.50	6.80	7.40	6.50	8.20	7.50	8.25	8.80	7.80

a Draw a scatter diagram with prices on the horizontal axis.

b Draw a line of best fit on your diagram.

c A book has 600 pages. How much might you expect to have to pay for this book?

d How many pages would you expect in a book that cost £9?

6 The cumulative frequency diagram represents the heights of 40 sunflowers.

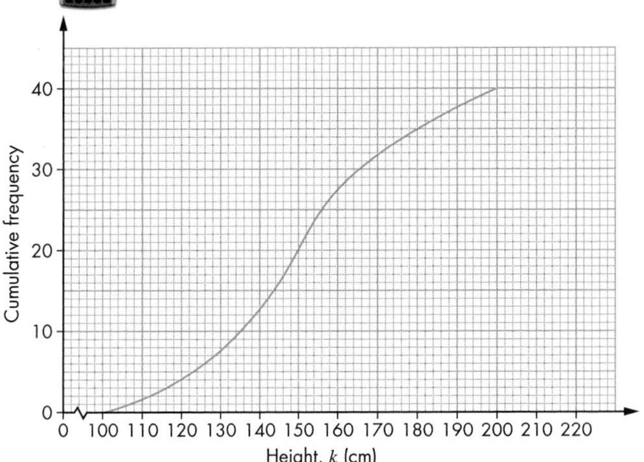

A second set of 40 sunflower plants was treated with fertiliser.

The box plot summarises the heights of the treated sunflowers.

Three sunflowers had the shortest height of 100 cm.

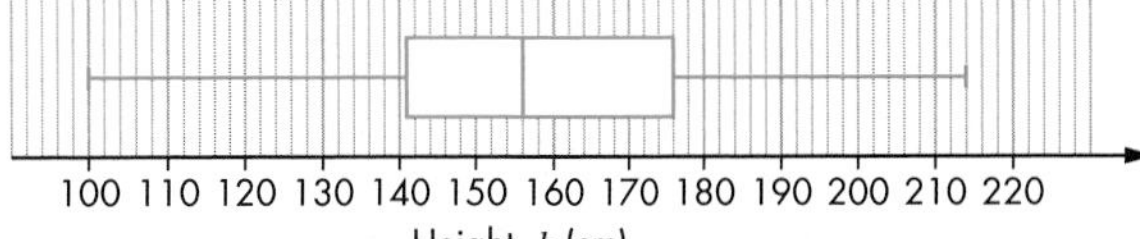

a Draw a cumulative frequency diagram for the treated sunflowers on a copy of the same grid as the first cumulative frequency diagram. *(4 marks)*

b Estimate the difference between the number of treated sunflowers and untreated sunflowers over height of 180 cm. *(2 marks)*

AQA, March 2009, Module 1 Higher, Question 3

7 The neck measurements of 200 women are represented by the cumulative frequency diagram.

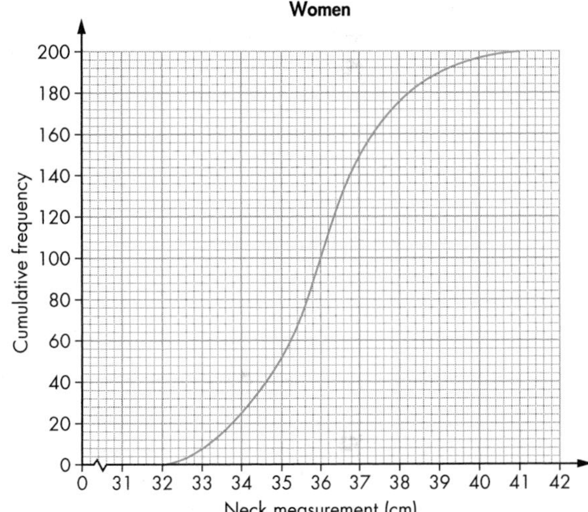

Use the cumulative frequency diagram to find:

a the median neck measurement *(1 mark)*

b the interquartile range of the neck measurements *(2 marks)*

c The neck measurements of 200 men are represented by the box plot.

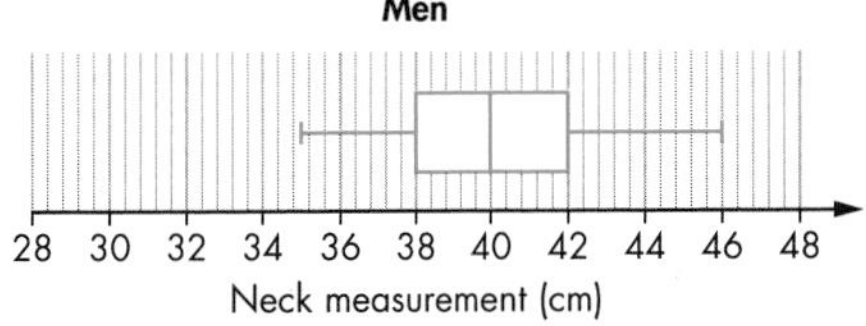

Write down two comparisons between the women's and the men's neck measurements. *(2 marks)*

AQA, March 2008, Module 1 Higher, Question 6

8 The box plot shows the marks of 40 students in a mathematics test.

Two students scored the lowest mark of 3.

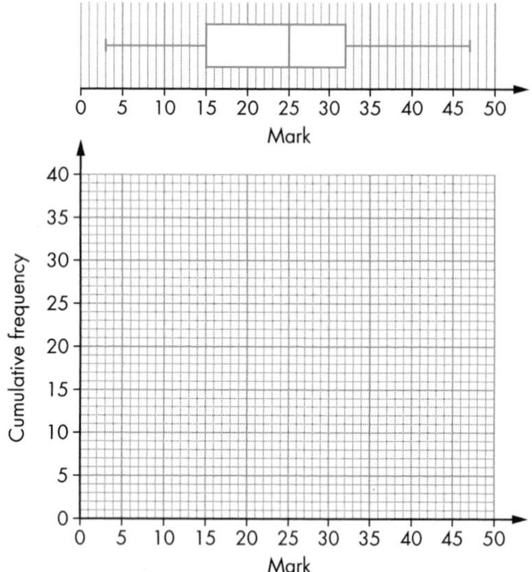

a Use the box plot or draw a cumulative frequency diagram for the marks of the 40 students. *(3 marks)*

b What is the probability that a student picked at random from the group scored more than 32 marks? *(1 mark)*

AQA, November 2008, Paper 2 Higher, Question 14

9 Kerry had looked at a cumulative frequency graph from a survey of 80 people.

She remembered that nobody had paid less than 50p for a firework and no one more than £6, the median price was £3, the lower quartile £2 and the upper quartile £4.

Estimate the mean cost of a firework in the survey.

10 Janine was given a cumulative frequency diagram showing the number of students gaining certain marks in a science test. She was told the top 15% were given the top grade.

How would you find the marks needed to gain this top award?

Worked Examination Questions

1 Derek makes men's and women's shirts. He needs to know the range of collar sizes so he measures 100 men's necks. The results are shown in the table.

Neck size, n (cm)	Frequency
$12 < n \leqslant 13$	5
$13 < n \leqslant 14$	16
$14 < n \leqslant 15$	28
$15 < n \leqslant 16$	37
$16 < n \leqslant 17$	10
$17 < n \leqslant 18$	4

a Draw a cumulative frequency diagram to show this information.

b Use the diagram to find:

i the median

ii the interquartile range.

c The box plot shows the neck sizes of 100 women.

11 12 13 14 15 16 17 Neck size, cm

Comment on the differences in the distribution of neck sizes for men and women.

1 a Cumulative frequencies: 5, 21, 49, 86, 96, 100

First work out the cumulative frequencies. The easiest way to do this is with another column on the table. This gets 1 mark for accuracy.

b

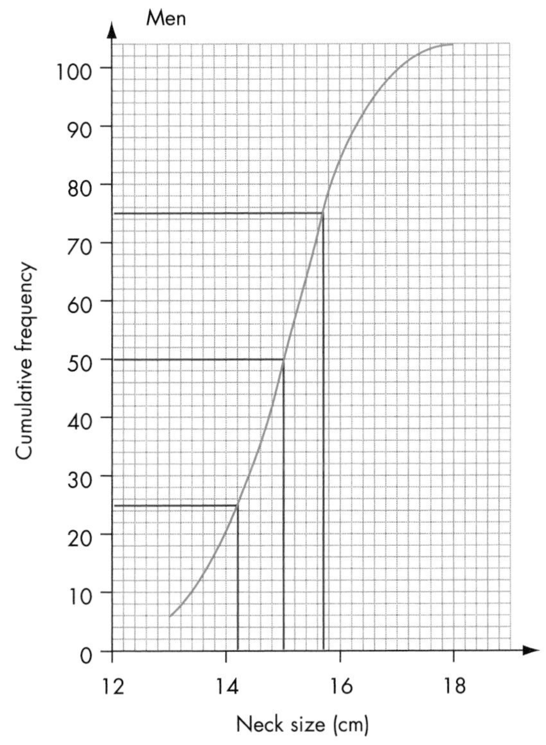

Plot the points (13, 5), (14, 21), etc. i.e the top value of each group against the cumulative frequency.
This gets 2 marks for accuracy (within 1 mm), losing 1 mark for each error to a minimum of 0.

Draw lines from 50 (median), 25 (lower quartile) and 75 (upper quartile) from the vertical axis across to the graph and down to the horizontal axis. Subtract lower quartile from upper quartile for the interquartile range.

This gets 1 mark for method of finding median and quartiles from the graph (this can be implied).

Median = 15 cm — This gets 1 mark for accuracy.

IQR = 15.7 – 14.2 = 1.5 cm — This gets 1 mark for method and 1 mark for accuracy.

c The men have a higher median (about 1.5 cm higher) and the women have a larger interquartile range (about 2.5 cm compared to 1.5 cm)

Comment on the differences between the medians and the interquartile ranges. Use numerical values to show you know how to read the box plot.
This gets up to 2 marks—1 mark for each difference.

Total: 9 marks

Worked Examination Questions

FM **2** Complaints had been received by the eye clinic in St John's hospital. The waiting times were very poor, so a survey was undertaken to compare St John's with another local hospital, St Luke's, over a one-week period in November. A report was produced that summarised the waiting times of each in cumulative frequency graphs as below.

a What is the median waiting time for each hospital?

b What is the interquartile range for each hospital?

c Compare the two hospitals.

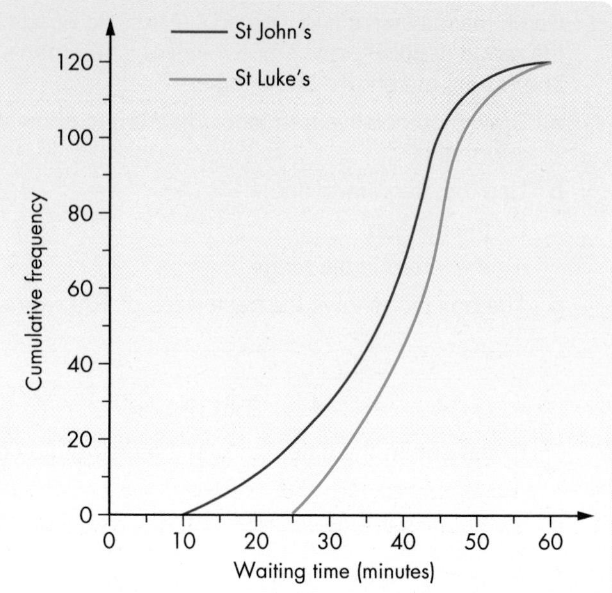

2

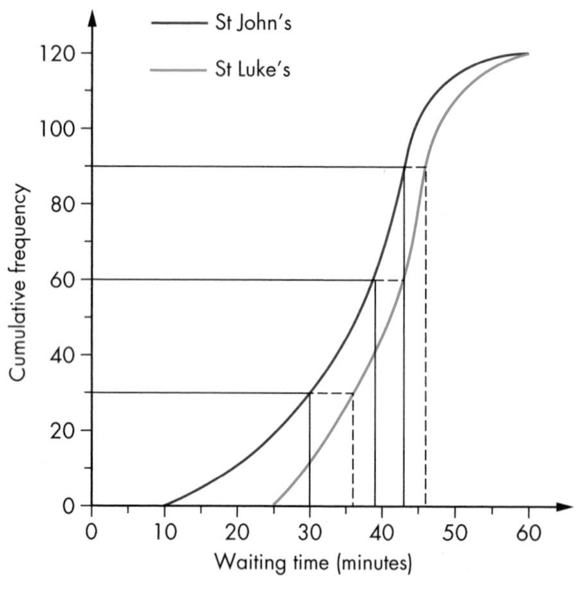

The examiners will be looking for evidence on the diagram that you are trying to find the median and the IQR. This gets 1 mark for method for identifying where the three quartiles are to be found.

This gets 1 mark for method for indicating where to read these quartiles.

a St John's: 39 minutes, St Luke's: 43 minutes

This gets 1 mark for accuracy for each correct answer.

b St John's: 43 – 30 = 13 minutes

St Luke's: 46 – 36 = 10 minutes

This gets 1 method mark for at least one attempt at subtracting the high and the low quartile.

This gets 1 accuracy mark for both answers correct.

c St John's has a higher interquartile range than St Luke's.

St Luke's has a longer median waiting time than St John's.

This gets 1 mark for each correct relevant statement (up to a maximum of 2 marks).

Total: 9 marks

Worked Examination Questions

PS **3**
- The older you are, the higher you score on the Speed test.
- The higher you score on the Speed test, the less TV you watch.
- The more TV you watch, the more hours you will sleep.

Suppose the above were all true. Sketch a scatter diagram to illustrate the relationship between age and hours slept.

3 Sketch a scatter diagram for each bullet.

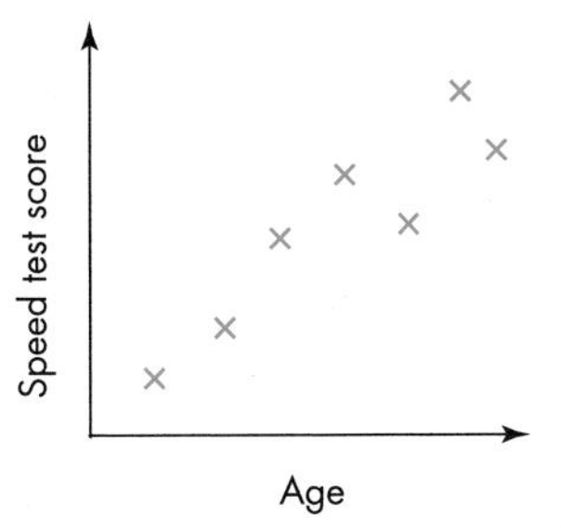

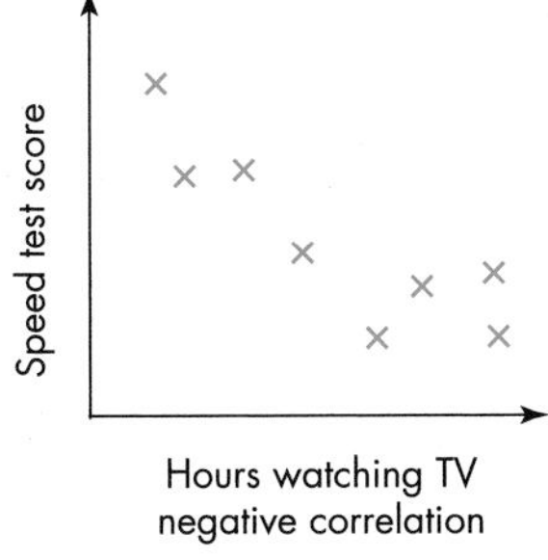

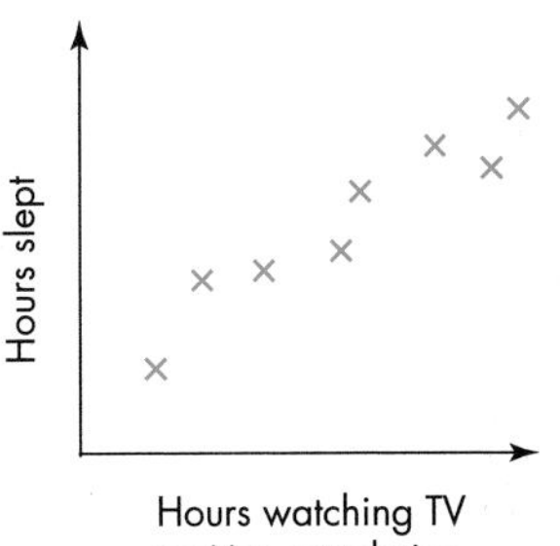

This gets 1 for showing some graphs similar to these.

Three diagrams will help to show the relationships.

Imagine the extremes of age, starting with the first diagram.

Older person scores high on Speed test.
High score on Speed test means the person watches TV for a short time.
Watching TV for a short time gives short sleep time.

This gets 2 for showing linkage for extremes like this.

Hence, 'High age relates to small hours sleep'.
Similarly, 'Low age relates to long sleep'.

This gets 1 mark for each extreme.

So the scatter diagram will show negative correlation and can be sketched as:

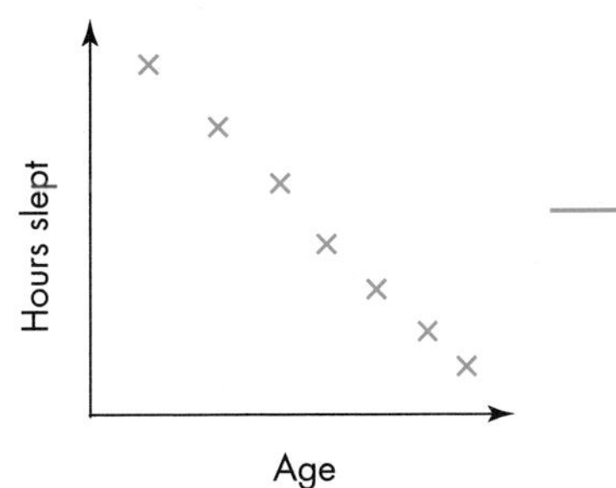

This gets 1 mark for stating negative correlation, or suitable words.

This gets 1 mark for sketch of negative correlation.

Total: 6 marks

AU **4** Gabriela was given a cumulative frequency diagram showing the number of students gaining marks in an English test. She was told that 85% of the students got passable scores. How would you find the pass mark?

4 Find 15% (100 – 85) of the total frequency on the cumulative frequency scale, read along to the graph and read down to the marks. The mark seen will be the pass mark.

This gets 1 mark for stating the need to find 15% of the frequency.

This gets 1 mark for for indicating how you would read the relevant mark for 15% of the frequency.

Total: 2 marks

4

Functional Maths
Reporting the weather

The weather often appears in the news headlines and a weather report is given regularly on the television. In this activity you are required to look at the data supplied in a weather report and interpret its meaning.

Your task

The type of information given on the map and in the table is found in most newspapers in the UK each day. The map gives a forecast of the weather for the day in several large towns, while the table summarises the weather on the previous day.

It is your task to use appropriate statistical diagrams and measures to summarise the data given in the map and table.

Then, you must write a report to describe fully the weather in the UK on Friday 21st April 2010. You should use your statistical analysis to support your descriptions.

Getting started

Look at the data provided in the table.

- Which cities had the most sun, which had the most rain and which were the warmest on this particular day?
- Is there any other information you can add?

Extension

Research weather in a different country. Draw together all your research, using diagrams, and compare your findings with the analysis that you have already done of the weather in the UK in April.

Friday 21st April 2010

	Sun (hrs)	Rain (mm)	Max (°C)	Min (°C)	Daytime weather
Aberdeen	5	3	10	5	rain
Barnstaple	5	0	12	8	sunny
Belfast	5	0	10	4	cloudy
Birmingham	5	0	11	5	sunny
Bournemouth	5	0	12	6	sunny
Bradford	5	1	10	5	rain
Brighton	5	0	11	5	mixed
Bristol	5	2	11	6	rain
Cardiff	5	2	11	6	rain
Carlisle	5	3	10	5	rain
Chester	5	3	10	4	rain
Eastbourne	5	0	9	5	windy
Edinburgh	5	0	9	5	cloudy
Falmouth	5	0	12	8	sunny
Glasgow	5	0	9	4	cloudy
Grimsby	5	1	10	4	mixed
Holyhead	5	0	8	3	windy
Ipswich	5	1	11	6	mixed
Isle of Man	5	0	9	3	windy
Isle of Wight	5	0	13	6	sunny
Leeds	5	0	11	6	cloudy
Lincoln	5	3	10	4	rain
Liverpool	5	1	12	6	mixed
London	5	2	13	6	rain
Manchester	5	0	13	7	sunny
Middlesbrough	5	1	11	6	rain
Newcastle	5	0	11	6	cloudy
Newquay	5	0	12	8	sunny
Nottingham	5	0	12	6	cloudy
Oxford	5	2	12	5	rain
Plymouth	6	0	12	9	sunny
Rhyl	5	1	9	4	mixed
Scunthorpe	5	1	10	4	mixed
Sheffield	5	0	12	7	sunny
Shrewsbury	5	0	9	4	windy
Southampton	5	0	12	6	sunny
Swindon	5	1	11	5	mixed
Weymouth	5	0	12	6	sunny
Windermere	5	2	10	4	mixed
York	5	0	11	5	cloudy

Why this chapter matters

Chance is a part of our everyday lives. Judgements are frequently made based on probability – take the weather forecast, for example. Every day we hear something like:

There is a forty per cent chance of rain today.

How do they know that?

- Records of data that predict possibility of rainfall go back as far as 1854, when meteorologists regarded the presence of nimbus clouds as an indication of a good chance of rain.
- A barometer was used to predict chances of rainfall. A sign of falling pressure on the barometer was taken as an indication of a good chance of rain.
- Finally, the direction of wind was used to determine the chances of rainfall. If the wind blew from a rainy part of the country, the chance of rain would be high.

nimbus cloud	barometer falling?	rain from rainy parts?	
no	no	no	very little chance of rain
		yes	rain unlikely
	yes	no	rain unlikely
		yes	rain likely
yes	no	no	rain unlikely
		yes	rain likely
	yes	no	rain unlikely
		yes	rain almost certain

The occurrence of all these three indicators would almost certainly mean that rain would come, as shown by a tree diagram of the time.

Probability originated from the study of games of chance, such as tossing a dice or spinning a roulette wheel. Mathematicians in the 16th and 17th centuries started to think about the mathematics of chance in games. Probability theory, as a branch of mathematics, came about in the 17th century when French gamblers asked mathematicians Blaise Pascal and Pierre de Fermat for help in their gambling.

Now, in the 21st century, probability is used to control the flow of traffic through road systems, the running of telephone exchanges, to look at patterns of the spread of infections and so on. These are just some of the everyday applications.

Chapter

5

Probability: Calculating probabilities

1 Experimental probability

2 Mutually exclusive and exhaustive events

3 Expectation

4 Two-way tables

5 Addition rule for events

6 Combined events

7 Tree diagrams

8 Independent events 1

9 Independent events 2

10 Conditional probability

This chapter will show you ...

D to C how to work out the probability of events, using either theoretical models or experimental models

D to A how to predict outcomes, using theoretical models, and compare experimental and theoretical data

C to A* how to calculate probabilities for combined events

Visual overview

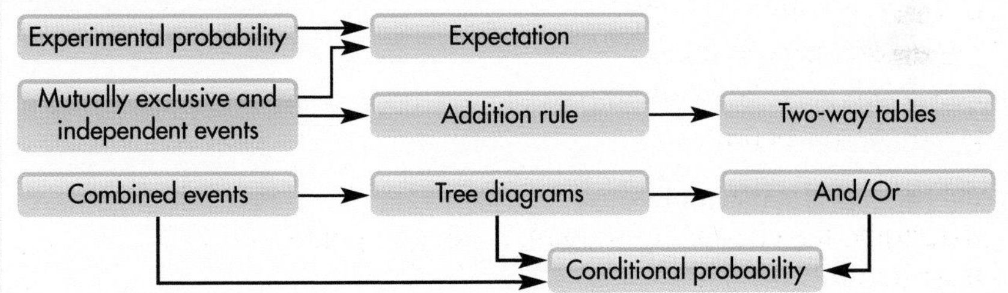

What you should already know

- That the probability scale goes from 0 to 1 **(KS3 level 4, GCSE grade F)**
- How to use the probability scale and to assess the likelihood of events, depending on their position on the scale **(KS3 level 4, GCSE grade F)**
- How to cancel, add and subtract fractions **(KS3 level 5, GCSE grade E)**

Quick check

Draw a probability scale and put an arrow to show the approximate probability of each of the following events happening.

a The next TV programme you watch will have been made in Britain.

b A person in your class will have been born in April.

c It will snow in July in Spain.

d In the next Olympic Games, a man will run the 100 m race in less than 20 seconds.

e During this week, you will drink some water or pop.

Terminology

The topic of probability has its own special terminology, which will be explained as it arises. For example, a **trial** is one go at performing something, such as throwing a dice or tossing a coin. So, if we throw a dice 10 times, we perform 10 trials.

Two other probability terms are **event** and **outcome**. An event is anything the probability of which we want to measure. An outcome is a result of the event.

Another probability term is **at random**. This means 'without looking' or 'not knowing what the outcome is in advance'.

Note: 'Dice' is used in this book in preference to 'die' for the singular form of the noun, as well as for the plural. This is in keeping with growing common usage, including in examination papers.

Probability facts

The probability of a *certain* outcome or event is 1 and the probability of an *impossible* outcome or event is 0.

Probability is *never greater than 1 or less than 0.*

Many probability examples involve coins, dice and packs of cards. Here is a reminder of their outcomes.

- Tossing a coin has two possible outcomes: head or tail.
- Throwing an ordinary six-sided dice has six possible outcomes: 1, 2, 3, 4, 5, 6.
- A pack of cards consists of 52 cards divided into four suits: Hearts (red), Spades (black), Diamonds (red) and Clubs (black). Each suit consists of 13 cards bearing the following values: 2, 3, 4, 5, 6, 7, 8, 9, 10, Jack, Queen, King and Ace. The Jack, Queen and King are called 'picture cards'. (The Ace is sometimes also called a picture card.) So the total number of outcomes is 52.

Probability is defined as:

$$\text{P(event)} = \frac{\text{number of ways the event can happen}}{\text{total number of all possible outcomes}}$$

This definition always leads to a fraction, which should be cancelled to its simplest form. Make sure that you know how to cancel fractions, with or without a calculator. It is acceptable to give a probability as a decimal or a percentage but a fraction is better.

This definition can be used to work out the probability of outcomes or events, as the following example shows.

EXAMPLE 1

A card is drawn from a normal pack of cards. What is the probability that it is one of the following?

a A red card **b** A Spade **c** A seven

d A picture card **e** A number less than 5 **f** A red King

a There are 26 red cards, so P(red card) = $\frac{26}{52} = \frac{1}{2}$

b There are 13 Spades, so P(Spade) = $\frac{13}{52} = \frac{1}{4}$

c There are four sevens, so P(seven) = $\frac{4}{52} = \frac{1}{13}$

d There are 12 picture cards, so P(picture card) = $\frac{12}{52} = \frac{3}{13}$

e If you count the value of an Ace as 1, there are 16 cards with a value less than 5. So, P(number less than 5) = $\frac{16}{52} = \frac{4}{13}$

f There are two red Kings, so P(red King) = $\frac{2}{52} = \frac{1}{26}$

5.1 Experimental probability

This section will show you how to:

- calculate experimental probabilities and relative frequencies
- estimate probabilities from experiments
- use different methods to estimate probabilities

Key words

experimental probability
relative frequency
trials

The value of number of heads ÷ number of tosses is called an **experimental probability**. As the number of **trials** or experiments increases, the value of the experimental probability gets closer to the true or theoretical probability.

Experimental probability is also known as the **relative frequency** of an event. The relative frequency of an event is an estimate for the theoretical probability. It is given by:

$$\text{relative frequency of an outcome or event} = \frac{\text{frequency of the outcome or event}}{\text{total number of trials}}$$

EXAMPLE 2

The frequency table shows the speeds of 160 vehicles that pass a radar speed check on a dual carriageway.

Speed (mph)	20–29	30–39	40–49	50–59	60–69	70+
Frequency	14	23	28	35	52	8

a What is the experimental probability that a vehicle is travelling faster than 70 mph?

b If 500 vehicles pass the speed check, estimate how many will be travelling faster than 70 mph.

a The experimental probability is the relative frequency, which is $\frac{8}{160} = \frac{1}{20}$

b The number of vehicles travelling faster than 70 mph will be $\frac{1}{20}$ of 500.

That is, $500 \div 20 = 25$ vehicles

Finding probabilities

There are three ways in which the probability of an event can be found.

- If you can work out the theoretical probability of an outcome or event — for example, drawing a King from a pack of cards — this is called using *equally likely outcomes*.
- Some events, such as people buying a certain brand of dog food, cannot be calculated using equally likely outcomes. To find the probability of such an event, you can perform an experiment or conduct a survey. This is called collecting *experimental data*. The more data you collect, the better the estimate is.
- The probability of some events, such as an earthquake occurring in Japan, cannot be found by either of the above methods. One of the things you can do is to look at data collected over a long period of time and make an estimate (sometimes called a *best guess*) at the chance of the event happening. This is called looking at *historical data*.

EXAMPLE 3

Which method (A, B or C) would you use to estimate the probabilities of the events **a** to **e**?

A: Use equally likely outcomes

B: Conduct a survey/collect data

C: Look at historical data

a Someone in your class will go abroad for a holiday this year.

b You will win the National Lottery.

c Your bus home will be late.

d It will snow on Christmas Day.

e You will pick a red seven from a pack of cards.

a You would have to ask all the members of your class what they intended to do for their holidays this year. You would therefore conduct a survey, method B.

b The odds on winning are about 14 million to 1. This is an equally likely outcome, method A.

c If you catch the bus every day, you can collect data over several weeks. This would be method C.

d If you check whether it snowed on Christmas Day for the last few years you would be able to make a good estimate of the probability. This would be method C.

e There are two red sevens out of 52 cards, so the probability of picking one can be calculated: P(red seven) $= \frac{2}{52} = \frac{1}{26}$

This is method A.

EXERCISE 5A

1 Naseer throws a fair, six-sided dice and records the number of sixes that he gets after various numbers of throws. The table shows his results.

No. of throws	10	50	100	200	500	1000	2000
No. of sixes	2	4	10	21	74	163	329

a Calculate the experimental probability of a six at each stage that Naseer recorded his results.

b How many ways can a normal dice land?

c How many of these ways give a six?

d What is the theoretical probability of throwing a six with a dice?

e If Naseer threw the dice a total of 6000 times, how many sixes would you expect him to get?

2 Marie made a five-sided spinner, like the one shown in the diagram. She used it to play a board game with her friend Sarah. The girls thought that the spinner wasn't very fair as it seemed to land on some numbers more than others. They spun the spinner 200 times and recorded the results. The results are shown in the table.

Side spinner lands on	1	2	3	4	5
No. of times	19	27	32	53	69

a Work out the experimental probability of each number.

b How many times would you expect each number to occur if the spinner is fair?

c Do you think that the spinner is fair? Give a reason for your answer.

C

3 Sarah thought she could make a much more accurate spinner. After she had made it, she tested it and recorded how many times she scored a 5. Her results are shown in the table.

No. of spins	10	50	100	500
No. of fives	3	12	32	107

a Sarah made a mistake in recording the number of fives. Which number in the second row above is wrong? Give a reason for your answer.

b These are the full results for 500 spins.

Side spinner lands on	1	2	3	4	5
No. of times	96	112	87	98	107

Do you think the spinner is fair? Give a reason for your answer.

4 A sampling bottle is a sealed bottle with a clear plastic tube at one end. into which one of the balls can be tipped. Kenny's sampling bottle contains 20 balls, which are either black or white. Kenny conducts an experiment to see how many black balls are in the bottle. He takes various numbers of samples and records how many of them showed a black ball. The results are shown in the table.

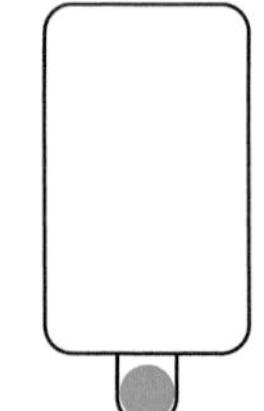

No. of samples	No. of black balls	Experimental probability
10	2	
100	25	
200	76	
500	210	
1000	385	
5000	1987	

a Copy the table and calculate the experimental probability of getting a black ball at each stage.

b Using this information, how many black balls do you think are in the bottle?

5 Another sampling bottle contains red, white and blue balls. It is known that there are 20 balls in the bottle altogether. Carrie performs an experiment to see how many of each colour are in the bottle. She starts off putting down a tally each time a colour shows in the clear plastic tube.

Red	White	Blue
𝍸 𝍸 𝍸 𝍸 II	𝍸 𝍸 𝍸 III	𝍸 𝍸 II

However, she forgets to count how many times she performs the experiment, so every now and again she counts up the tallies and records them in a table, like this.

Red	White	Blue	Total
22	18	12	52
48	31	16	95
65	37	24	126
107	61	32	200
152	93	62	307
206	128	84	418

The relative frequency of the red balls is calculated by dividing the frequency of red by the total number of trials, so at each stage these are:

0.423 0.505 0.516 0.535 0.495 0.493

These answers are rounded to 3 significant figures.

a Calculate the relative frequencies of the white balls at each stage, to 3 significant figures.

b Calculate the relative frequencies of the blue balls at each stage, to 3 significant figures.

c Round the final relative frequencies for Carrie's 418 trials, to 1 decimal place.

d What is the total of the answers in part **c**?

e How many balls of each colour do you think are in the bottle? Explain your answer.

6 Using card and a cocktail stick, make a six-sided spinner, as shown below.

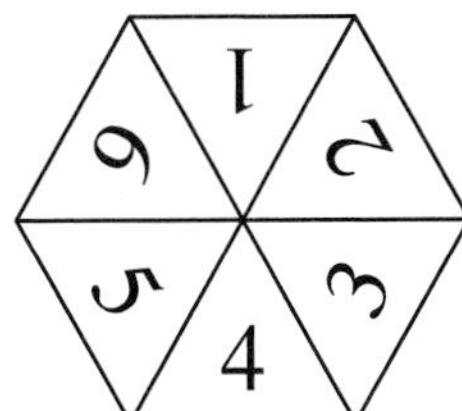

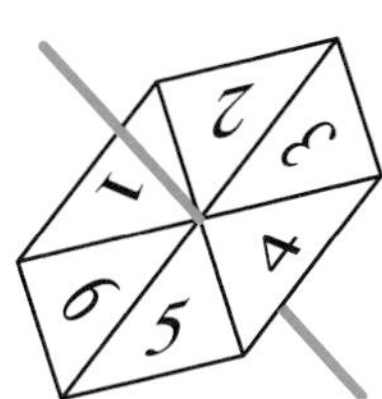

When you have made the spinner, spin it 120 times and record your results in a table like the one below.

Number	Tally	Total
1	~~IIII~~ II	
2	IIII	

a Which number occurred most frequently?

b How many times would you expect to get each number?

c Is your spinner fair?

d Explain your answer to part **c**.

7 Use a set of number cards from 1 to 10 (or make your own set) and work with a partner. Take turns to choose a card and keep a record each time of what card you get. Shuffle the cards each time and repeat the experiment 60 times. Put your results in a copy of this table.

Score	1	2	3	4	5	6	7	8	9	10
Total										

a How many times would you expect to get each number?

b Do you think you and your partner conducted this experiment fairly?

c Explain your answer to part **b**.

C

8 A four-sided dice has faces numbered 1, 2, 3 and 4. The score is the face on which it lands. Five students throw the dice to see if it is biased. They each throw it a different number of times. Their results are shown in the table.

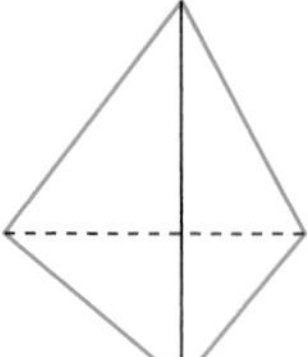

Student	Total no. of throws	Score			
		1	2	3	4
Alfred	20	7	6	3	4
Brian	50	19	16	8	7
Caryl	250	102	76	42	30
Deema	80	25	25	12	18
Emma	150	61	46	26	17

a Which student will have the most reliable set of results? Why?

b Add up all the score columns and work out the relative frequency of each score. Give your answers to 2 decimal places.

c Is the dice biased? Explain your answer.

9 Which of these methods would you use to estimate or state the probability of each of the events **a** to **h**?

Method A: Equally likely outcomes

Method B: Survey or experiment

Method C: Look at historical data

a How people will vote in the next election.

b A drawing pin dropped on a desk will land point up.

c A Premiership football team will win the FA Cup.

d You will win a school raffle.

e The next car to drive down the road will be red.

f You will throw a 'double six' with two dice.

g Someone in your class likes classical music.

h A person picked at random from your school will be a vegetarian.

10 If you were about to choose a card from a pack of yellow cards numbered from 1 to 10, what would be the chance of each of the events **a** to **i** occurring? Copy and complete each of these statements with a word or phrase chosen from 'impossible', 'not likely', '50–50 chance', 'quite likely' or 'certain'.

a The likelihood that the next card chosen will be a four is …

b The likelihood that the next card chosen will be pink is …

c The likelihood that the next card chosen will be a seven is …

d The likelihood that the next card chosen will be a number less than 11 is …

e The likelihood that the next card chosen will be a number bigger than 11 is …

f The likelihood that the next card chosen will be an even number is …

g The likelihood that the next card chosen will be a number more than five is …

h The likelihood that the next card chosen will be a multiple of 1 is …

i The likelihood that the next card chosen will be a prime number is …

AU 11 At a computer factory, tests were carried out to see how many faulty computer chips were produced in one week.

	Monday	Tuesday	Wednesday	Thursday	Friday
Sample	850	630	1055	896	450
No. faulty	10	7	12	11	4

On which day was it most likely that the highest number of faulty computer chips were produced?

PS 12 Andrew made an eight-sided spinner.

He tested it out to see if it was fair.

He spun the spinner and recorded the results.

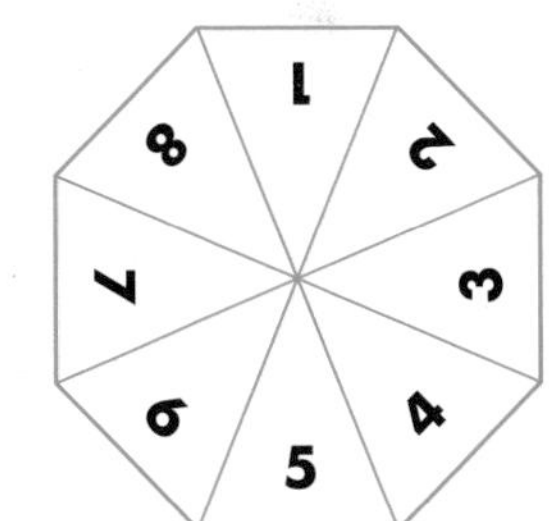

Unfortunately, his little sister spilt something over his results table, so he could not see the middle part.

No. spinner lands on	1	2	3			6	7	8
Frequency	18	19	22			19	20	22

Assuming the spinner was a fair one, complete the missing parts of the table for Andrew.

AU 13 Steve tossed a coin 1000 times to see how many heads he got.

He said, "If this is a fair coin, I should get 500 heads."

Explain why he is wrong.

AU 14 Roxy tests the eight-sided spinner shown by spinning it 100 times and recording the results.

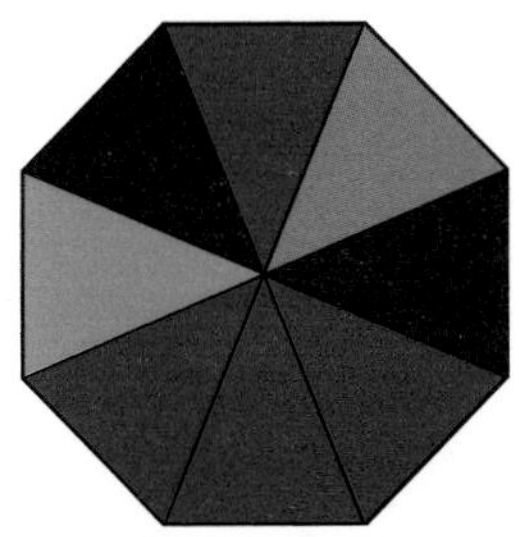

These are the results.

Colour	Red	Blue	Black	Green
Frequency	48	13	28	11

Roxy says the spinner is fair as the frequencies are around what is expected.

Sam says the spinner is unfair as there are far more reds than any other colour.

Who is correct? Back up your answer with some figures.

5.2 Mutually exclusive and exhaustive events

This section will show you how to:

- recognise mutually exclusive, complementary and exhaustive events

Key words
complementary
exhaustive events
mutually exclusive

If a bag contains three black, two yellow and five white balls and only one ball is allowed to be taken at random from the bag, then by the basic definition of probability:

$$\text{P(black ball)} = \frac{3}{10}$$

$$\text{P(yellow ball)} = \frac{2}{10} = \frac{1}{5}$$

$$\text{P(white ball)} = \frac{5}{10} = \frac{1}{2}$$

Also the probability of choosing a black ball or a yellow ball is $= \frac{5}{10} = \frac{1}{2}$

The events 'picking a yellow ball' and 'picking a black ball' can never happen at the same time when only one ball is taken out: that is, a ball can be either black or yellow. Such events are called **mutually exclusive**. Other examples of mutually exclusive events are tossing a head or a tail with a coin, drawing a King or an Ace from a pack of cards and throwing an even or an odd number with a dice.

An example of events that are not mutually exclusive would be drawing a red card and a King from a pack of cards. There are two red Kings, so these events could be true at the same time.

EXAMPLE 4

An ordinary dice is thrown.

a What is the probability of throwing:

i an even number **ii** an odd number?

b What is the total of the answers to part **a**?

c Is it possible to get a score on a dice that is both odd and even?

a **i** $\text{P(even)} = \frac{1}{2}$ **ii** $\text{P(odd)} = \frac{1}{2}$

b $\frac{1}{2} + \frac{1}{2} = 1$

c No

Events such as those in Example 4 are mutually exclusive because they can never happen at the same time. Because there are no other possibilities, they are also called **exhaustive events**. The probabilities of exhaustive events add up to 1.

EXAMPLE 5

A bag contains only black and white balls. The probability of picking at random a black ball from the bag is $\frac{7}{10}$.

a What is the probability of picking a white ball from the bag?

b Can you say how many black and white balls are in the bag?

a As 'picking a white ball' and 'picking a black ball' are mutually exclusive and exhaustive then:

$$P(\text{white}) = 1 - P(\text{black}) = 1 - \frac{7}{10} = \frac{3}{10}$$

b You cannot say precisely what the number of balls is although you can say that there could be seven black and three white, fourteen black and six white, or any combination of black and white balls in the ratio 7 : 3.

Complementary event

If there is an event A, the **complementary** event of A is:

Event A *not* happening

Any event is mutually exclusive and exhaustive to its complementary event. That is:

P(event A not happening) = 1 – P(event A happening)

which can be stated as:

P(event) + P(complementary event) = 1

For example, the probability of getting a King from a pack of cards is $\frac{4}{52} = \frac{1}{13}$, so the probability of *not* getting a King is:

$$1 - \frac{1}{13} = \frac{12}{13}$$

EXERCISE 5B

1 Say whether these pairs of events are mutually exclusive or not.

a Tossing a head with a coin/tossing a tail with a coin

b Throwing a number less than 3 with a dice/throwing a number greater than 3 with a dice

c Drawing a Spade from a pack of cards/drawing an Ace from a pack of cards

d Drawing a Spade from a pack of cards/drawing a red card from a pack of cards

e If two people are to be chosen from three girls and two boys: choosing two girls/choosing two boys

f Drawing a red card from a pack of cards/drawing a black card from a pack of cards

2 Which of the pairs of mutually exclusive events in question **1** are also exhaustive?

3 Each morning I run to work or get a lift. The probability that I run to work is $\frac{2}{5}$. What is the probability that I get a lift?

4 A letter is to be chosen at random from this set of letter-cards.

S T A T I S T I C S

a What is the probability that the letter is:

i an S **ii** a T **iii** a vowel?

b Which of these pairs of events are mutually exclusive?

i Picking an S/picking a T **ii** Picking an S/picking a vowel

iii Picking an S/picking another consonant **iv** Picking a vowel/picking a consonant

c Which pair of mutually exclusive events in part **b** is also exhaustive?

5 Two people are to be chosen for a job from this set of five people.

Jane Dave Anne Jack John

a List all of the possible pairs (there are 10 altogether).

b What is the probability that the pair of people chosen will:

i both be female **ii** both be male

iii both have the same initial **iv** have different initials?

c Which of these pairs of events are mutually exclusive?

i Picking two women/picking two men

ii Picking two people of the same sex/picking two people of opposite sex

iii Picking two people with the same initial/picking two men

iv Picking two people with the same initial/picking two women

d Which pair of mutually exclusive events in part **c** is also exhaustive?

6 A spinner consists of an outer ring of coloured sectors and an inner circle of numbered sectors, as shown.

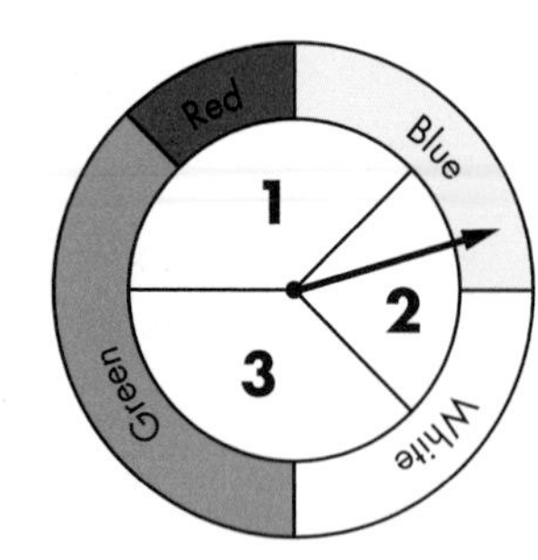

a The probability of getting 2 is $\frac{1}{4}$. The probabilities of getting 1 or 3 are equal. What is the probability of getting 3?

b The probability of getting blue is $\frac{1}{4}$. The probability of getting white is $\frac{1}{4}$. The probability of getting green is $\frac{3}{8}$. What is the probability of getting red?

C

c Which of these pairs of events are mutually exclusive?

i Getting 3/getting 2

ii Getting 3/getting green

iii Getting 3/getting blue

iv Getting blue/getting red

d Explain why it is not possible to get a colour that is mutually exclusive to the event 'getting an odd number'.

7 At the morning break, I have the choice of coffee, tea or hot chocolate. If the probability I choose coffee is $\frac{3}{5}$, the probability I choose tea is $\frac{1}{4}$, what is the probability I choose hot chocolate?

PS 8 Four friends, Kath, Ann, Sandra and Padmini, regularly ran races against each other in the park.

The chances of:

Kath winning the race is 0.7

Ann winning the race is $\frac{1}{6}$

Sandra winning the race is 12%.

What is the chance of Padmini winning the race?

B

9 Assemblies at school are always taken by the head, the deputy head or the senior teacher. If the head takes the assembly, the probability that she goes over time is $\frac{1}{2}$. If the deputy takes the assembly, the probability that he goes over time is $\frac{1}{4}$. Explain why it is not necessarily true to say that the probability that the senior teacher goes over time is $\frac{1}{4}$.

FM 10 A hotelier conducted a survey of guests staying at her hotel. The table shows some of the results of her survey.

Type of guest	Probability
Man	0.7
Woman	0.3
American man	0.2
American woman	0.05
Vegetarian	0.3
Married	0.6

a A guest was chosen at random. From the table, work out these probabilities.

i The guest was American.

ii The guest was single.

iii The guest was not a vegetarian.

b Explain why it is not possible to work out from the table the probability of a guest being a married vegetarian.

c From the table, give two examples of pairs of types of guest that would form a mutually exclusive pair.

d From the table, give one example of a pair of types of guest that would form an exhaustive pair.

B

FM **11** In a restaurant, the head waiter has worked out the probability of customers choosing certain dishes.

A starter	0.7
A pudding	0.4
Beef	0.3
Pork	0.2
Chicken	0.45
Vegetarian	0.08
Vegetables	0.8
Red wine	0.4
White wine	0.5

a What is the probability that the first person entering the restaurant:

i chooses a meat dish

ii chooses wine

iii does not have a starter?

b Explain why it is not possible to work out from the table the probability of someone having a starter or a pudding.

c Give an example of a choice from the table that would form a mutually exclusive pair.

AU **12** Ziq always walks, goes by bus or is given a lift by his dad to school.

If he walks, the probability that he is late for school is 0.3.

If he goes by bus, the probability that he is late for school is 0.1.

Explain why it is not necessarily true that if his dad gives him a lift, the chance of his being late for school is 0.6.

5.3 Expectation

This section will show you how to:

- predict the likely number of successful events, given the number of trials and the probability of any one event

Key words

expectation

When you know the probability of an event, you can predict how many times you would expect that event to happen in a certain number of trials. This is called **expectation**.

Note that this is what you *expect*. It is not what is going to happen. If what you expected always happened, life would be very dull and boring and the National Lottery would be a waste of time.

EXAMPLE 6

A bag contains 20 balls, nine of which are black, six white and five yellow. A ball is drawn at random from the bag, its colour is noted and then it is put back in the bag. This is repeated 500 times.

a How many times would you expect a black ball to be drawn?

b How many times would you expect a yellow ball to be drawn?

c How many times would you expect a black or a yellow ball to be drawn?

a P(black ball) = $\frac{9}{20}$

Expected number of black balls = $\frac{9}{20} \times 500 = 225$

b P(yellow ball) = $\frac{5}{20} = \frac{1}{4}$

Expected number of yellow balls = $\frac{1}{4} \times 500 = 125$

c Expected number of black or yellow balls = 225 + 125 = 350

EXAMPLE 7

Four in 10 cars sold in Britain are made by Japanese companies.

a What is the probability that the next car to drive down your road will be Japanese?

b If there are 2000 cars in a multistorey car park, how many of them would you expect to be Japanese?

a P(Japanese car) = $\frac{4}{10} = \frac{2}{5} = 0.4$

b Expected number of Japanese cars in 2000 cars = 0.4 × 2000 = 800 cars

EXERCISE 5C

1 I throw an ordinary dice 150 times. How many times can I expect to get a 6?

2 I toss a coin 2000 times. How many times can I expect to get a head?

3 I draw a card from a pack of cards and replace it. I do this 520 times. How many times would I expect to get:

a a black card **b** a King

c a Heart **d** the King of Hearts?

4 The ball in a roulette wheel can land in 37 spaces which are the numbers from 0 to 36 inclusive. I always bet on the same number, 13. If I play all evening and there are altogether 185 spins of the wheel in that time, how many times could I expect to win?

5 In a bag there are 30 balls, 15 of which are red, five yellow, five green and five blue. A ball is taken out at random and then replaced. This is repeated 300 times. How many times would I expect to get:

a a red ball **b** a yellow or blue ball

c a ball that is not blue **d** a pink ball?

6 The same experiment described in question **5** is carried out 1000 times. Approximately how many times would you expect to get: **a** a green ball **b** a ball that is not blue?

C

7 A sampling bottle contains red and white balls. It is known that the probability of getting a red ball is 0.3. 1500 samples are taken. How many of them would you expect to give a white ball?

8 Josie said, "When I throw a dice, I expect to get a score of 3.5."

"Impossible," said Paul, "you can't score 3.5 with a dice."

"Do this and I'll prove it," said Josie.

a Throw an ordinary dice 60 times. Copy and fill in the table for the expected number of times each score will occur.

Score						
Expected occurrences						

b Now work out the average score that is expected over 60 throws.

c There is an easy way to get an answer of 3.5 for the expected average score. Can you see what it is?

9 The probability of some cloud types being seen on any day is given below.

Cumulus	0.3
Stratocumulus	0.25
Stratus	0.15
Altocumulus	0.11
Cirrus	0.05
Cirrcocumulus	0.02
Nimbostratus	0.005
Cumulonimbus	0.004

a What is the probability of **not** seeing one of the above clouds in the sky?

b On how many days of the year would you expect to see altocumulus clouds in the sky?

B

PS 10 Every evening Tamara and Chris cut a pack of cards to see who washes up.

If they cut a King or a Jack, Chris washes up.

If they cut a Queen, Tamara washes up.

Otherwise they wash up together.

In a year of 365 days, how many days would you expect them to wash up together?

AU 11 A market gardener is supplied with tomato plant seedlings. She knows that the probability that any plant will develop a disease is 0.003.

How will she find out the number of tomato plants that are likely to develop a disease?

12 I have 20 tickets for a raffle and I know that the probability of my winning the prize is 0.05. How many tickets were sold altogether in the raffle?

5.4 Two-way tables

This section will show you how to:

- read two-way tables and use them to work out probabilities and interpret data

Key words

two-way table

A **two-way table** is a table that links together two variables. For example, this shows how many boys and girls are in a form and whether they are left-handed or right-handed.

	Boys	Girls
Left-handed	2	4
Right-handed	10	13

This table shows the colours and makes of cars in the school car park.

	Red	Blue	White
Ford	2	4	1
Vauxhall	0	1	2
Toyota	3	3	4
Peugeot	2	0	3

One variable is written in the rows of the table and the other variable is written in the columns of the table.

EXAMPLE 8

Using the first two-way table above, answer these questions.

a If a student is selected at random from the form, what is the probability that it will be a left-handed boy?

b It is known that a student selected at random is a girl. What is the probability that she is right-handed?

a $\frac{2}{29}$ **b** $\frac{13}{17}$

EXAMPLE 9

Using the second two-way table above, answer these questions.

a What percentage of the cars in the car park are red?

b What percentage of the white cars are Vauxhalls?

a 28%. Seven out of 25 is the same as 28 out of 100.

b 20%. Two out of 10 is 20%.

EXERCISE 5D

D

1 The two-way table shows the age and gender of a sample of 50 students in a school.

	Age (years)					
	11	**12**	**13**	**14**	**15**	**16**
No. of boys	4	3	6	2	5	4
No. of girls	2	5	3	6	4	6

a How many students are aged 13 years or less?

b What percentage of the students in the table are 16?

c A student from the table is selected at random. What is the probability that the student will be 14 years of age? Give your answer as a fraction in its simplest form.

d There are 1000 students in the school. Use the table to estimate how many boys there are in the school altogether.

2 The two-way table shows the numbers of adults and the numbers of cars in 50 houses in one street.

		No. of adults			
		1	**2**	**3**	**4**
No. of cars	**0**	2	1	0	0
	1	3	13	3	1
	2	0	10	6	4
	3	0	1	4	2

a How many houses have exactly two adults and two cars?

b How many houses altogether have three cars?

c What percentage of the houses have three cars?

d What percentage of the houses with just one car have three adults living in the house?

3 Jane has two four-sided spinners. One has the numbers 1 to 4 and the other has the numbers 5 to 8.

Both spinners are spun together.

This two-way table shows all the ways the two spinners can land.

Some of the total scores are filled in.

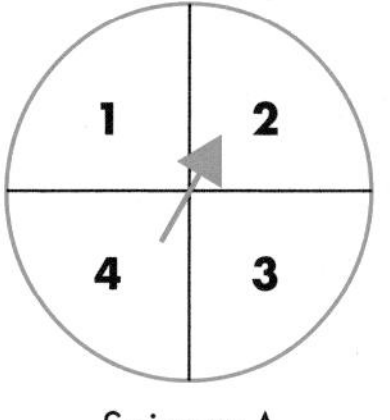

Spinner A

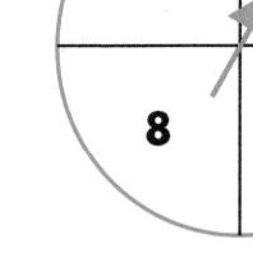

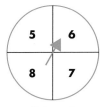

Spinner B

		Score on spinner A			
		1	**2**	**3**	**4**
Score on spinner B	**5**	6	7		
	6	7			
	7				
	8				

D

a Copy and complete the table to show all the possible total scores.

b How many of the total scores are 9?

c When the two spinners are spun together, what is the probability that the total score will be:

i 9 **ii** 8 **iii** a prime number?

4 The table shows information about the number of items in Flossy's music collection.

		Type of music		
		Pop	**Folk**	**Classical**
Format	**Tape**	16	5	2
	CD	51	9	13
	Mini disc	9	2	0

a How many pop tapes does Flossy have?

b How many items of folk music does Flossy have?

c How many CDs does Flossy have?

d If a CD is chosen at random from all the CDs, what is the probability that it will be a pop CD?

5 Zoe throws a fair coin and rolls a fair dice.

If the coin shows a head she records the score on the dice.
If the coin shows tails she doubles the number on the dice.

a Complete the two-way table to show Zoe's possible scores.

		No. on dice					
		1	**2**	**3**	**4**	**5**	**6**
Coin	**Head**	1	2				
	Tail	2	4				

b How many of the scores are square numbers?

c What is the probability of getting a score that is a square number?

C

AU **6** A gardener plants some sunflower seeds in a greenhouse and plants some in the garden. After they have fully grown, he measures the diameter of the sunflower heads. The table shows his results.

	Greenhouse	Garden
Mean diameter	16.8 cm	14.5 cm
Range of diameter	3.2 cm	1.8 cm

a The gardener, who wants to enter competitions, says, "The sunflowers from the greenhouse are better." Using the data in the table, give a reason to justify this statement.

b The gardener's wife, who does flower arranging, says, "The sunflowers from the garden are better." Using the data in the table, give a reason to justify this statement.

C

FM **7** The two-way table shows the wages for the men and women in a factory.

Wage, w (£) per week	Men	Women
£100 < w ⩽ £150	3	4
£150 < w ⩽ £200	7	5
£200 < w ⩽ £250	23	12
£250 < w ⩽ £300	48	27
£300 < w ⩽ £350	32	11
More than £350	7	1

a What percentage of the men earn between £250 and £300 per week?

b What percentage of the women earn between £250 and £300 per week?

c Is it possible to work out the mean wage of the men and women? Explain your answer.

AU **8** Reyki plants some tomato plants in her greenhouse, while her husband Daniel plants some in the garden.

After the summer they compared their tomatoes.

	Garden	Greenhouse
Mean diameter (cm)	1.8	4.2
Mean number of tomatoes per plant	24.2	13.3

Use the data in the table to explain who had the better crop of tomatoes.

PS **9** Two hexagonal spinners are spun.

Spinner A is numbered 3, 5, 7, 9, 11 and 13.

Spinner B is numbered 4, 5, 6, 7, 8 and 9.

What is the probability that when the two spinners are spun, the two numbers given will multiply to a total greater than 40?

10 Here are two fair spinners.

The spinners are spun.

The two numbers obtained are added together.

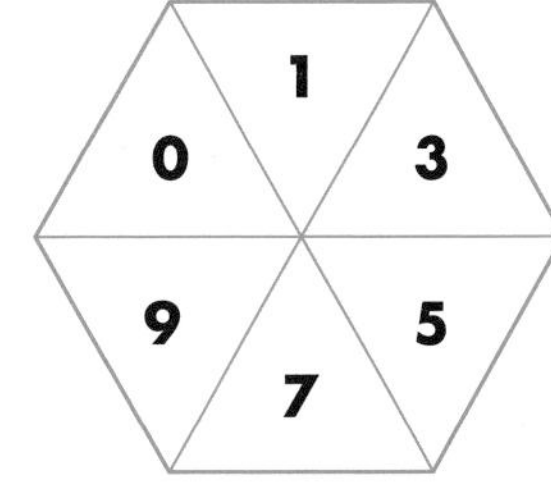

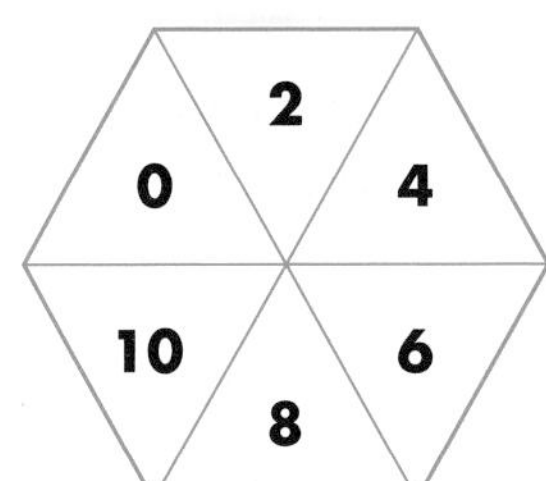

a Draw a two-way diagram showing all the possible scores.

b What is the most likely score?

c What is the probability of getting a total of 12?

d What is the probability of getting a total of 11 or more?

e What is the probability of getting a total that is an odd number?

5.5 Addition rule for events

This section will show you how to:
- work out the probability of two events such as P(A) or P(B)

Key words
either

You have used the addition rule already but it has not yet been formally defined.

When two events are mutually exclusive, you can work out the probability of **either** of them occurring by adding up the separate probabilities.

EXAMPLE 10

A bag contains twelve red balls, eight green balls, five blue balls and fifteen black balls. A ball is drawn at random. What is the probability of it being:

a red **b** black **c** red or black

d not green **e** neither green nor blue?

a $P(\text{red}) = \frac{12}{40} = \frac{3}{10}$ **b** $P(\text{black}) = \frac{15}{40} = \frac{3}{8}$

c $P(\text{red or black}) = P(\text{red}) + P(\text{black}) = \frac{3}{10} + \frac{3}{8} = \frac{27}{40}$

d $P(\text{not green}) = \frac{32}{40} = \frac{4}{5}$

e $P(\text{neither green nor blue}) = P(\text{red or black}) = \frac{27}{40}$

The last part of Example 10 is another illustration of how confusing probability can be. You might think:

$$P(\text{neither green nor blue}) = P(\text{not green}) + P(\text{not blue}) = \frac{32}{40} + \frac{35}{40} = \frac{67}{40}$$

This cannot be correct, as the answer is greater than 1. In fact, the events 'not green' and 'not blue' are not mutually exclusive, as there are lots of balls that satisfy both outcomes.

EXERCISE 5E

1 Iqbal throws an ordinary dice. What is the probability that he throws these scores?

a 2 **b** 5 **c** 2 or 5

2 Jennifer draws a card from a pack of cards. What is the probability that she draws these?

a A Heart **b** A Club **c** A Heart or a Club

3 Jasper draws a card from a pack of cards. What is the probability that he draws one of the following numbers?

a 2 **b** 6 **c** 2 or 6

D

D

4 A letter is chosen at random from the letters on these cards. What is the probability of choosing each of these?

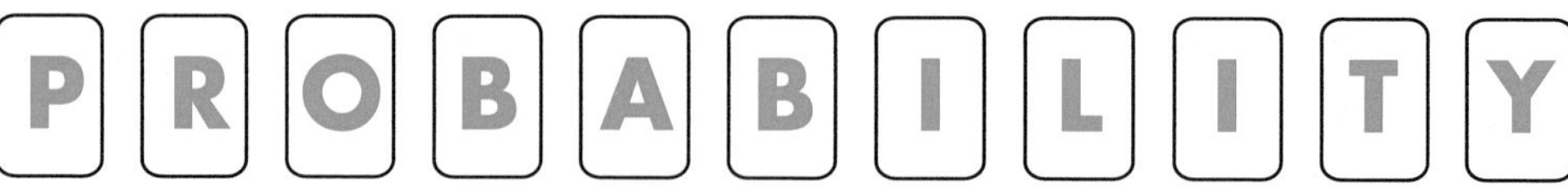

a A 'B' **b** A vowel **c** A 'B' or a vowel

5 A bag contains 10 white balls, 12 black balls and eight red balls. A ball is drawn at random from the bag. What is the probability of each of these outcomes?

a White **b** Black

c Black or white **d** Not red

e Not red or black

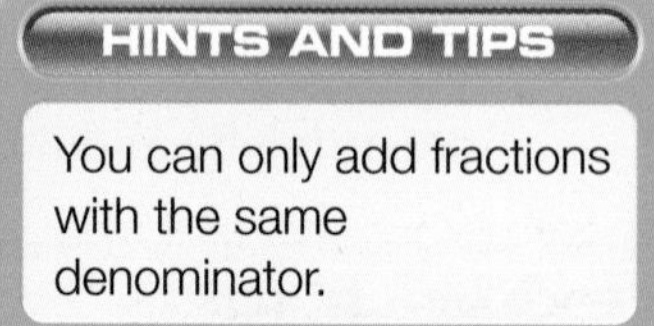

C

FM **6** At the School Fayre the tombola stall gives out a prize if you draw from the drum a numbered ticket that ends in 0 or 5. There are 300 tickets in the drum altogether and the probability of getting a winning ticket is 0.4.

a What is the probability of getting a losing ticket?

b How many winning tickets are there in the drum?

7 John needs his calculator for his mathematics lesson. It is always in his pocket, bag or locker.

The probability it is in his pocket is 0.35; the probability it is in his bag is 0.45. What is the probability that:

a he will have the calculator for the lesson

b it is in his locker?

8 A spinner has numbers and colours on it, as shown in the diagram. Their probabilities are given in the tables.

When the spinner is spun, what is the probability of each of the following?

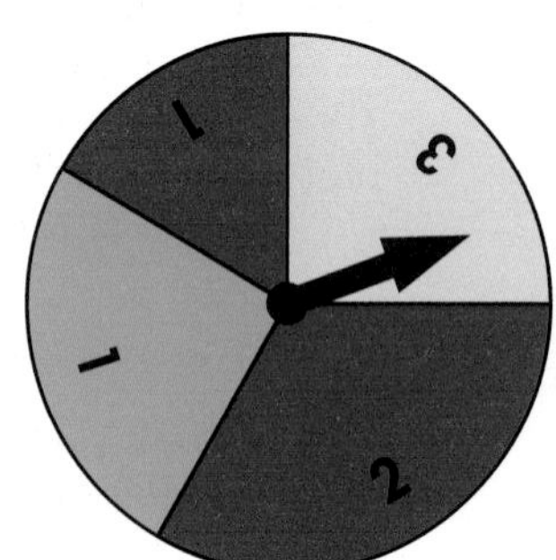

a Red or green

b 2 or 3

c 3 or green

d 2 or green

AU **e** **i** Explain why the answer to P(1 or red) is not 0.9.

ii What is the answer to P(1 or red)?

Red	0.5
Green	0.25
Blue	0.25

1	0.4
2	0.35
3	0.25

C

9 Debbie has 20 unlabelled CDs, 12 of which are rock, five are pop and three are classical. She picks a CD at random. What is the probability of these outcomes?

a Rock or pop

b Pop or classical

c Not pop

AU 10 The probability that it rains on Monday is 0.5. The probability that it rains on Tuesday is 0.5 and the probability that it rains on Wednesday is 0.5. Kelly argues that it is certain to rain on Monday, Tuesday or Wednesday because 0.5 + 0.5 + 0.5 = 1.5, which is bigger than 1 so that it is a certain event. Explain why she is wrong.

FM 11 Brian and Kathy put music onto their iPod so that at their wedding reception they had a variety of background music. They uploaded 100 different tracks onto the iPod.

40 love songs

35 musical show songs

15 classical music tracks

10 rock tracks

They set it to play the tracks continuously at random.

a What is the probability that:

i the first track played is a love song

ii the last track of the evening is either a musical show song or a classical track

iii the track when they start their meal is not a rock track?

b When they start cutting the cake they want a love song or a classical track playing. What is the probability that they will not get a track of their choice?

c The reception lasts for five and a half hours. What amount of time, in hours and minutes, would you expect the iPod to have been playing love song tracks?

PS 12 James, John and Joe play the *Count Dracula* game together every Saturday. John is always the favourite to win, with a probability of 0.75.

In the year 2009 there were 52 Saturdays and James won eight times.

What was the probability of Joe winning?

B

AU 13 A bag contains some red and some blue balls.

A ball is taken out at random and its colour noted. The ball is then replaced in the bag. Another ball is then taken out at random and its colour noted.

a Which of these **could not** be the probability of two red balls?

$\frac{9}{25}$ $\quad \frac{1}{9}$ $\quad \frac{13}{20}$

Give a reason for your choice.

b It is known that there are more blue balls than red balls in the bag.

Which of the probabilities in part **a** must be the probability of two red balls? Give a reason for your choice.

5.6 Combined events

This section will show you how to:
- work out the probability of two events occurring at the same time

Key words
probability space diagram
sample space diagram

There are many situations where two events occur together. Some examples are given below. Note that, in each case, all the possible outcomes of the events are shown in diagrams. These are called **probability space diagrams** or **sample space diagrams**.

Throwing two dice

Imagine that two fair dice, one red and one blue, are thrown. The red dice can land with any one of six scores: 1, 2, 3, 4, 5 or 6. The blue dice can also land with any one of six scores. This gives a total of 36 possible combinations. These are shown in the left-hand diagram, where each combination is given as (2, 3), etc. The first number is the score on the blue dice and the second number is the score on the red dice.

The combination (2, 3) gives a total score of 5. The total scores for all the combinations are shown in the right-hand diagram.

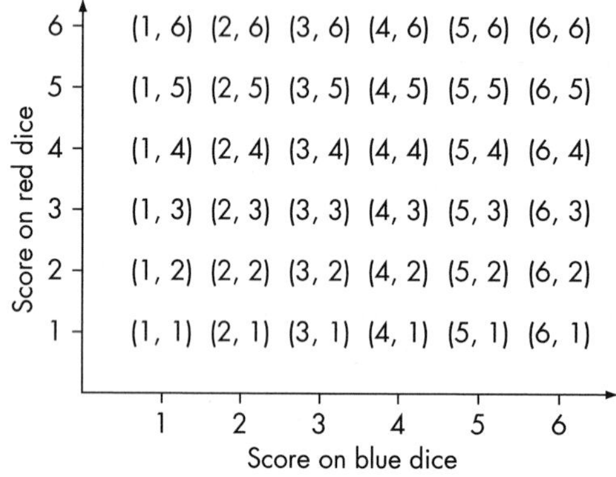

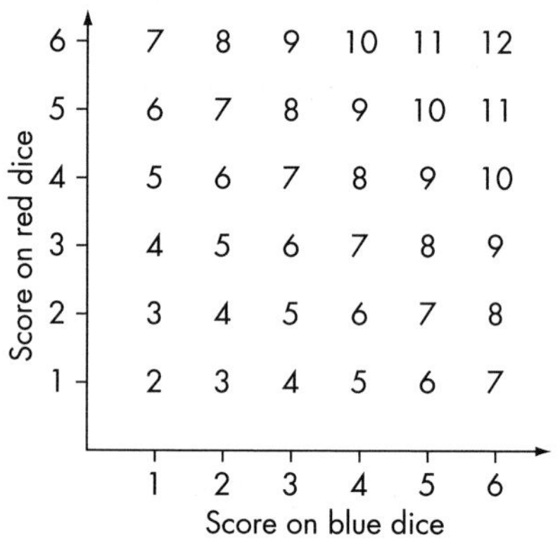

From the diagram on the right, you can see that there are two ways to get a score of 3. This gives a probability of:

$$P(3) = \frac{2}{36} = \frac{1}{18}$$

From the diagram on the left, you can see that there are six ways to get a 'double'. This gives a probability of:

$$P(\text{double}) = \frac{6}{36} = \frac{1}{36}$$

Throwing coins

Throwing one coin

There are two equally likely outcomes, head or tail.  

Throwing two coins together

There are four equally likely outcomes:   (H) (T)

(T) (H) (T) (T)

P(2 heads) $= \frac{1}{4}$

P(head and tail) = 2 ways out of 4 $= \frac{2}{4} = \frac{1}{2}$

Dice and coins

Throwing a dice and a coin

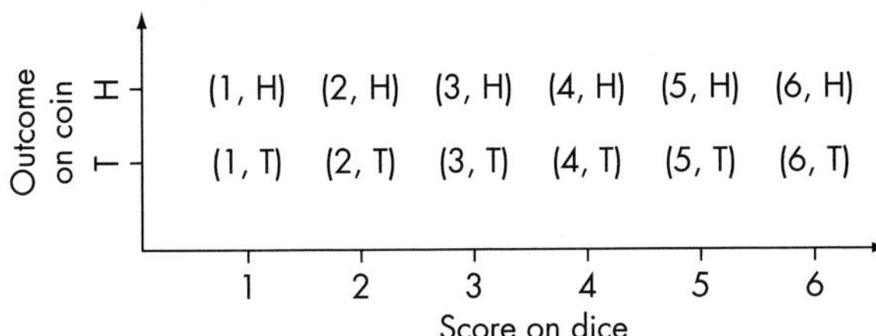

P (head and an even number) = 3 ways out of 12 $= \frac{3}{12} = \frac{1}{4}$

EXERCISE 5F

D

1 To answer these questions, use the right-hand diagram on page 170 for the total scores when two fair dice are thrown together.

a What is the most likely score?

b Which two scores are least likely?

c Write down the probabilities of all scores from two to 12.

d What is the probability of each of these scores?

i Bigger than 10 **ii** From 3 to 7 **iii** Even

iv A square number **v** A prime number **vi** A triangular number

2 Using the left-hand diagram on page 170 that shows, as coordinates, the outcomes when two fair dice are thrown together, what is the probability that:

a the score is an even 'double'

b at least one of the dice shows 2

c the score on one dice is twice the score on the other dice

d at least one of the dice shows a multiple of 3?

D

3 Using the left-hand diagram on page 170 that shows, as coordinates, the outcomes when two fair dice are thrown together, what is the probability that:

a both dice show a 6

b at least one of the dice shows a 6

c exactly one dice shows a 6?

4 This diagram shows the score for the event 'the difference between the scores when two fair dice are thrown'. Copy and complete the diagram.

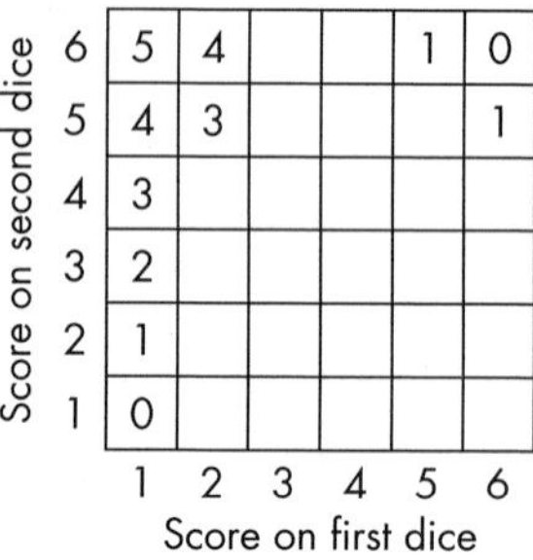

For the event described above, what is the probability of a difference of:

a 1 **b** 0 **c** 4

d 6 **e** an odd number?

5 When two fair coins are thrown together, what is the probability of each of these outcomes?

a two heads **b** A head and a tail

c At least one tail **d** No tails

Use the diagram of the outcomes when two coins are thrown together, on page 171.

C

6 Two fair five-sided spinners are spun together and the total score of the faces that they land on is worked out. Copy and complete this probability space diagram.

Score on second spinner					
5					10
4					
3	4				
2	3				
1	2				
	1	2	3	4	5

Score on first spinner

a What is the most likely score?

b When two five-sided spinners are spun together, what is the probability of:

i the total score being 5 **ii** the total score being an even number

iii the score being a 'double' **iv** the score being less than 7?

7 When three fair coins are tossed together, what is the probability of:

a three heads **b** two heads and one tail

c at least one tail **d** no tails?

8 When one coin is tossed, there are two outcomes. When two coins are tossed, there are four outcomes. When three coins are tossed, there are eight outcomes.

a How many outcomes will there be when four coins are tossed?

b How many outcomes will there be when five coins are tossed?

c How many outcomes will there be when 10 coins are tossed?

d How many outcomes will there be when n coins are tossed?

C

9 When a dice and a coin are thrown together, what is the probability of each of the following outcomes?

a You get a head on the coin and a 6 on the dice.

b You get a tail on the coin and an even number on the dice.

c You get a head on the coin and a square number on the dice.

Use the diagram on page 171 that shows the outcomes when a dice and a coin are thrown together.

FM **10** When Mel walked into her local shopping mall, she saw a competition taking place. Mel decided to have a go.

Roll 2 dice get a total of 11 and win a £10 note! Only £1 a go!

a Draw the sample space diagram for this event.

b What is the probability of winning a £10 note?

c How many goes should she have in order to expect to win at least once?

d If she had 40 goes, how many times could she expect to have won?

PS **11** I toss five coins. What is the probability that I will get more heads than tails?

AU **12** I roll a dice three times and add the three numbers obtained.

Explain the difficulty in drawing a sample space to show all the possible events.

5.7 Tree diagrams

This section will show you how to:

- use sample space diagrams and tree diagrams to work out the probability of combined events

Key words

combined events
probability space diagram
tree diagram

Imagine you have to draw two cards from this pack of six cards, but you must replace the first card before you select the second card.

One way you could show all the outcomes of this experiment is to construct a **probability space diagram**. For example, this could be an array set in a pair of axes, like those used for the two dice (see page 170), or a pictogram, like those used for the coins, or simply a list of all the outcomes.

By showing all the outcomes of the experiment as an array, you obtain the diagram below.

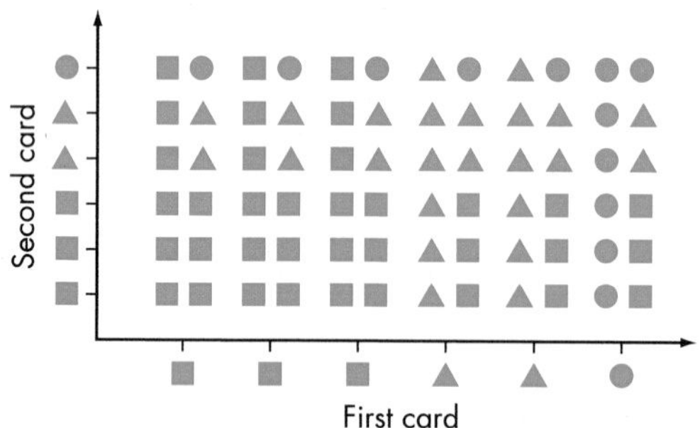

From the diagram, you can see immediately that the probability of picking, say, two squares, is 9 out of 36 pairs of cards. So:

$$P(2 \text{ squares}) = \frac{9}{36} = \frac{1}{4}$$

EXAMPLE 11

Using the probability space diagram above, what is the probability of getting each of these outcomes?

a A square and a triangle (in any order)

b Two circles

c Two shapes the same

a There are 12 combinations that give a square and a triangle together. There are six when a square is chosen first and six when a triangle is chosen first. So:

$$P(\text{square and triangle, in any order}) = \frac{12}{36}$$

b There is only one combination which gives two circles. So:

$$P(\text{two circles}) = \frac{1}{36}$$

c There are nine combinations of two squares together, four combinations of two triangles together and one combination of two circles together. These give a total of 14 combinations with two shapes the same. So:

$$P(\text{two shapes the same}) = \frac{14}{36}$$

An alternative method to tackling problems involving **combined events** is to use a **tree diagram**.

When you pick the first card, there are three possible outcomes: a square, a triangle or a circle. For a single event:

$$P(\text{square}) = \frac{3}{6} \qquad P(\text{triangle}) = \frac{2}{6} \qquad P(\text{circle}) = \frac{1}{6}$$

You can show this by depicting each event as a branch and writing its probability on the branch.

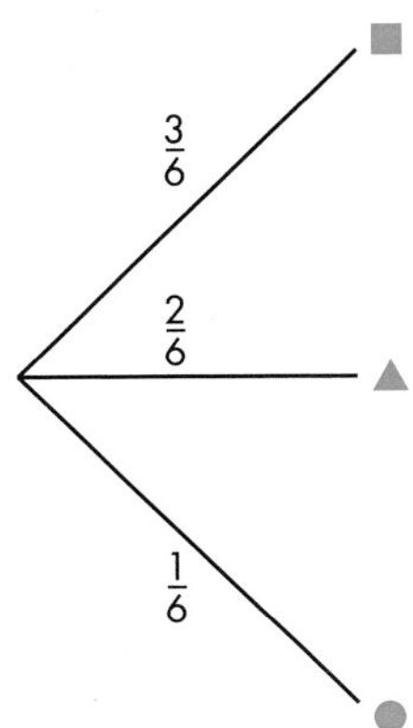

The diagram can then be extended to take into account a second choice. Because the first card has been replaced, you can still pick a square, a triangle or a circle. This is true no matter what is chosen the first time. You can demonstrate this by adding three more branches to the 'squares' branch in the diagram.

Here is the complete tree diagram.

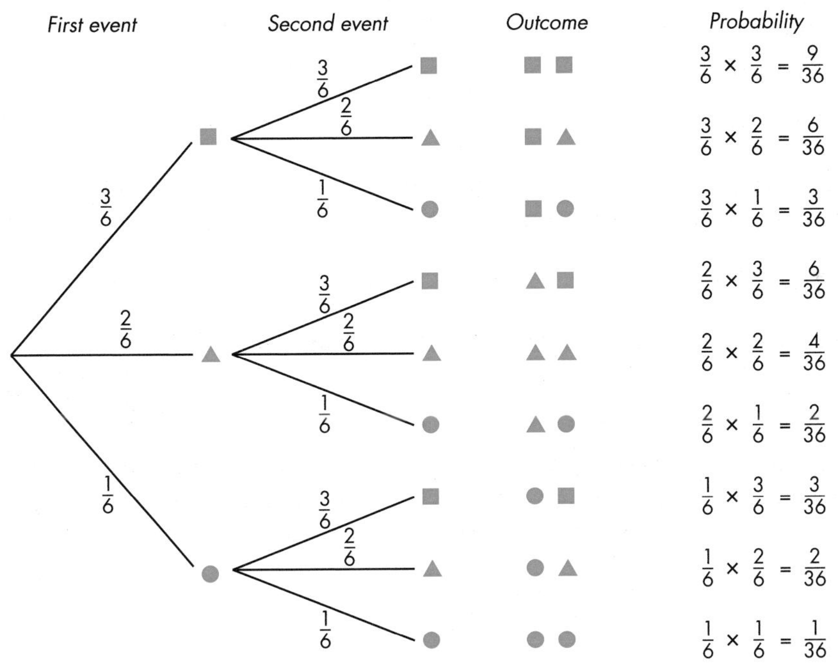

The probability of any outcome is calculated by multiplying all the probabilities on its branches. For instance:

$$\text{P(two squares)} = \frac{3}{6} \times \frac{3}{6} = \frac{9}{36}$$

$$\text{P(triangle followed by circle)} = \frac{2}{6} \times \frac{1}{6} = \frac{2}{36}$$

EXAMPLE 12

Using the tree diagram on the previous page, what is the probability of obtaining:

a two triangles

b a circle followed by a triangle

c a square and a triangle, in any order

d two circles

e two shapes the same?

a P(two triangles) = $\frac{4}{36}$

b P(circle followed by triangle) = $\frac{2}{36}$

c There are two places in the outcome column that have a square and a triangle. These are the second and fourth rows. The probability of each is $\frac{1}{6}$. Their combined probability is given by the addition rule.

P(square and triangle, in any order) = $\frac{6}{36} + \frac{6}{36} = \frac{12}{36}$

d P(two circles) = $\frac{1}{36}$

e There are three places in the outcome column that have two shapes the same. These are the first, fifth and last rows. The probabilities are respectively $\frac{1}{4}$, $\frac{1}{9}$ and $\frac{1}{36}$. Their combined probability is given by the addition rule.

P(two shapes the same) = $\frac{9}{36} + \frac{4}{36} + \frac{1}{36} = \frac{14}{36}$

Note that the answers to parts **c**, **d** and **e** are the same as the answers obtained in Example 11.

EXERCISE 5G

B

1 A coin is tossed twice. Copy and complete this tree diagram to show all the outcomes.

Use your tree diagram to work out the probability of each of these outcomes.

a Getting two heads

b Getting a head and a tail

c Getting at least one tail

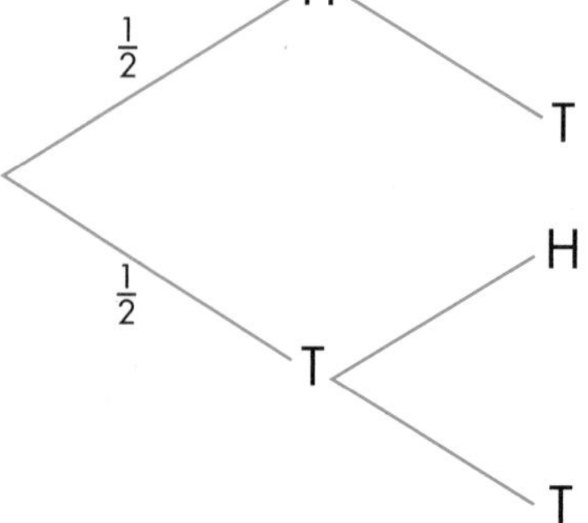

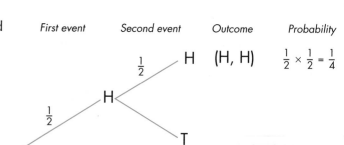

2 A card is drawn from a pack of cards. It is replaced, the pack is shuffled and another card is drawn.

a What is the probability that either card was an Ace?

b What is the probability that either card was not an Ace?

c Draw a tree diagram to show the outcomes of two cards being drawn as described. Use the tree diagram to work out the probability of each of these.

i Both cards will be Aces.

ii At least one of the cards will be an Ace.

FM 3 On my way to work, I drive through two sets of road works with traffic lights which only show green or red. I know that the probability of the first set being green is $\frac{1}{3}$ and the probability of the second set being green is $\frac{1}{2}$.

a What is the probability that the first set of lights will be red?

b What is the probability that the second set of lights will be red?

c Copy and complete the tree diagram below, showing the possible outcomes when passing through both sets of lights.

First event	*Second event*		*Outcome*	*Probability*
G ($\frac{1}{3}$)	G ($\frac{1}{2}$)		(G, G)	$\frac{1}{3} \times \frac{1}{2} = \frac{1}{6}$
	R			
R	G			
	R			

d Using the tree diagram, what is the probability of each of the following outcomes?

i I do not get held up at either set of lights.

ii I get held up at exactly one set of lights.

iii I get held up at least once.

e Over a school term I make 90 journeys to work. On how many days can I expect to get two green lights?

B

FM 4 Six out of every 10 cars in Britain are foreign made.

a What is the probability that any car will be British made?

b Two cars can be seen approaching in the distance. Draw a tree diagram to work out the probability of each of these outcomes.

i Both cars will be British made.

ii One car will be British and the other car will be foreign made.

5 Three coins are tossed. Copy and complete the tree diagram below and use it to answer the questions.

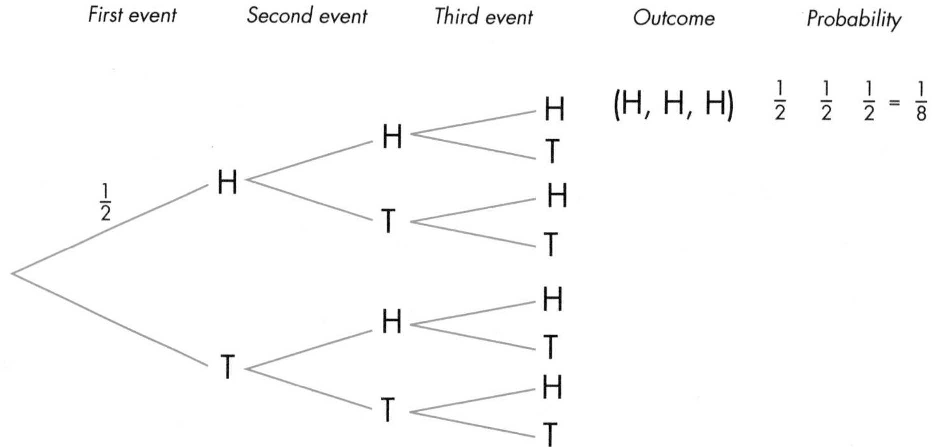

If a coin is tossed three times, what is the probability of each of these outcomes?

a Three heads

b Two heads and a tail

c At least one tail

FM 6 Thomas has to take a three-part language examination paper. The first part is speaking. He has a 0.4 chance of passing this part. The second is listening. He has a 0.5 chance of passing this part. The third part is writing. He has a 0.7 chance of passing this part. Draw a tree diagram covering three events, where the first event is passing or failing the speaking part of the examination, the second event is passing or failing the listening part and the third event is passing or failing the writing part.

a If he passes all three parts, his father will give him £20. What is the probability that he gets the money?

b If he passes two parts only, he can resit the other part. What is the chance he will have to resit?

c If he fails all three parts, he will be thrown off the course. What is the chance he is thrown off the course?

FM 7 In a group of 10 girls, six like the pop group Smudge and four like the pop group Mirage. Two girls are to be chosen for a pop quiz.

a What is the probability that the first girl chosen will be a Smudge fan?

b Draw a tree diagram to show the outcomes of choosing two girls and which pop groups they like. (Remember, once a girl has been chosen the first time she cannot be chosen again.)

c Use your tree diagram to work out the probability that:

i both girls chosen will like Smudge

ii both girls chosen will like the same group

iii both girls chosen will like different groups.

8 Look at all the tree diagrams that you have seen so far.

a What do the probabilities across any set of branches (outlined in the diagram below) always add up to?

b What do the final probabilities (outlined in the diagram below) always add up to?

c You should now be able to fill in all of the missing values in the diagram.

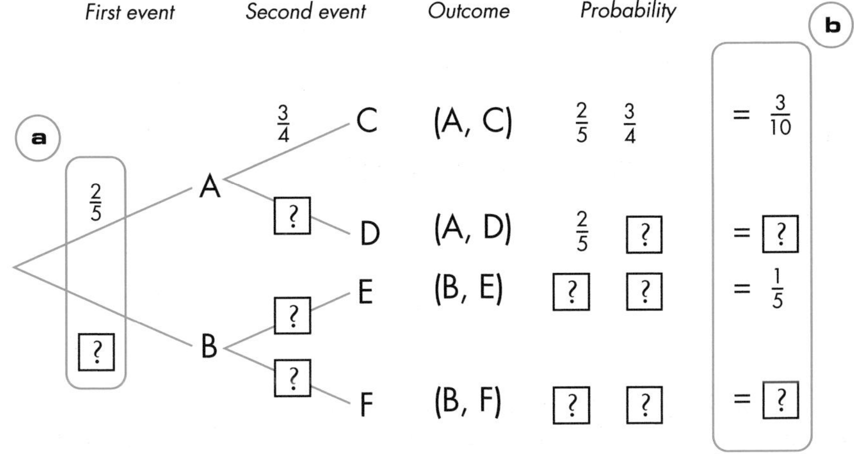

PS 9 When playing the game *Pontoon*, you are dealt two cards. If you get an Ace and a King, Queen or Jack you have been dealt a 'Royal Pontoon'.

What is the probability of being dealt a Royal Pontoon? Give your answer to 3 decimal places.

AU 10 I have a bag containing white, blue and green jelly babies. Explain how a tree diagram can help me find the probability of picking at random three sweets of different colours.

5.8 Independent events 1

This section will show you how to:
- use the connectors 'and' and 'or' to find the probability of combined events

Key words
and
independent events
or

If the outcome of event A does not effect the outcome of event B, then events A and B are called **independent events**. Most of the combined events you have looked at so far have been independent events.

It is possible to work out problems on combined events without using tree diagrams. The method explained in Example 13 is basically the same as that of a tree diagram but uses the words **and** and **or**.

EXAMPLE 13

The chance that Ashley hits a target with an arrow is $\frac{1}{4}$. He has two shots at the target. What is the probability of each of these outcomes?

a He hits the target both times.

b He hits the target once only.

c He hits the target at least once.

a P(hits both times) = P(first shot hits **and** second shot hits) $= \frac{1}{4} \times \frac{1}{4} = \frac{1}{16}$

b P(hits the target once only) = P(first hits **and** second misses **or** first misses **and** second hits) $= \left(\frac{1}{4} \times \frac{3}{4}\right) + \left(\frac{3}{4} \times \frac{1}{4}\right) = \frac{6}{16} = \frac{3}{8}$

c P(hits at least once) = P(both hit **or** one hits) $= \frac{1}{16} + \frac{3}{8} = \frac{7}{16}$

Note the connections between the word 'and' and the operation 'times', and the word 'or' and the operation 'add'.

EXERCISE 5H

B

1 Alf tosses a coin twice. The coin is biased so it has a probability of $\frac{2}{3}$ of landing on a head. What is the probability that he gets:

a two heads **b** a head and a tail (in any order)?

2 Bernice draws a card from a pack of cards, replaces it, shuffles the pack and then draws another card. What is the probability that the cards are:

a both Aces **b** an Ace and a King (in any order)?

B

3 A dice is thrown twice. What is the probability that both scores are:

a even **b** one even and one odd (in any order)?

4 I throw a dice three times. What is the probability of getting three sixes?

5 A bag contains 15 white beads and 10 black beads. I take out a bead at random, replace it and take out another bead. What is the probability that:

a both beads are black

b one bead is black and the other white (in any order)?

FM 6 The probability that I am late for work on Monday is 0.4. The probability that I am late on Tuesday is 0.2. What is the probability of each of the following outcomes?

a I am late for work on Monday and Tuesday.

b I am late for work on Monday and on time on Tuesday.

c I am on time on both Monday and Tuesday.

A

FM 7 Ronda has to take a three-part language examination paper. The first part is speaking. She has a 0.7 chance of passing this part. The second part is listening. She has a 0.6 chance of passing this part. The third part is writing. She has a 0.8 chance of passing this part.

a If she passes all three parts, her father will give her £20. What is the probability that she gets the money?

b If she passes two parts only, she can resit the other part. What is the chance she will have to resit?

c If she fails all three parts, she will be thrown off the course. What is the chance she is thrown off the course?

FM 8 Roy regularly goes to Bristol by train.
The probability of the train arriving in Bristol late is 0.05.
The probability of it raining in Bristol is 0.8.
What is the probability of:

a Roy getting to Bristol on time and it not raining

b Roy travelling to Bristol five days in a row and not being late at all

c Roy travelling to Bristol three days is a row and it raining every day?

PS 9 What is the probability of rolling the same number on a dice five times in a row?

AU 10 Explain why picking a red card from a pack of cards and picking a King from a pack of cards are not independent events.

AU 11 A fair dice rolls 8 sixes in a row. Which of the following is the probability of a six on the 9th throw?

0 $\quad \frac{1}{6} \quad$ 1

Explain your choice.

'At least' problems

In examination questions concerning combined events, it is common to ask for the probability of at least one of the events occurring. There are two ways to solve such problems.

- All possibilities can be written out, which takes a long time.
- Use P(at least one) = 1 – P(none)

The second option is much easier to work out and there is less chance of making a mistake.

EXAMPLE 14

A bag contains seven red and three black balls. A ball is taken out and replaced. This is repeated three times. What is the probability of getting:

a no red balls

b at least one red ball?

a P(no reds) = P(black, black, black) = $\frac{7}{10} \times \frac{7}{10} \times \frac{7}{10} = 0.343$

b P(at least one red) = 1 – P(no reds) = 1 – 0.343 = 0.657

Note that the answer to part **b** is 1 minus the answer to part **a**. Examination questions often build up answers in this manner.

EXERCISE 5I

1 A dice is thrown three times.

a What is the probability of not getting a 2?

b What is the probability of at least one 2?

2 Four coins are thrown. What is the probability of:

a four tails **b** at least one head?

FM **3** Adam, Bashir and Clem take a mathematics test. The probability that Adam passes is 0.6, the probability that Bashir passes is 0.9 and the probability that Clem passes is 0.7. What is the probability that:

a all three pass **b** Bashir and Adam pass but Clem does not

c all three fail **d** at least one passes?

4 A bag contains four red and six blue balls. A ball is taken out and replaced. Another ball is taken out. What is the probability that:

a both balls are red **b** both balls are blue **c** at least one is red?

5 **a** A dice is thrown three times. What is the probability of:

i three sixes **ii** no sixes **iii** at least one six?

b A dice is thrown four times. What is the probability of:

i four sixes **ii** no sixes **iii** at least one six?

c A dice is thrown five times. What is the probability of:

i five sixes **ii** no sixes **iii** at least one six?

d A dice is thrown n times. What is the probability of:

i n sixes **ii** no sixes **iii** at least one six?

FM 6 The probability that the school canteen serves chips on any day is $\frac{2}{3}$. In a week of five days, what is the probability that:

a chips are served every day

b chips are not served on any day

c chips are served on at least one day?

FM 7 The probability that Steve is late for work is $\frac{5}{6}$. The probability that Nigel is late for work is $\frac{9}{10}$. The probability that Gary is late for work is $\frac{1}{2}$. What is the probability that on a particular day:

a all three are late **b** none of them is late **c** at least one is late?

FM 8 A cricket test match is to be played in a coastal town of the West Indies. The test match lasts for five days.

In this town, at this time of year, the probability of rain on any day during the match is 0.35.

a What is the probability of no rain falling on any one day?

b What is the probability of no rain falling on two days in a row?

c On how many days during the cricket match could they expect rain?

d What is the probability of no rain falling during the cricket match?

e What is the probability of rain falling on at least one of the days of the cricket match?

PS 9 The probability of planting an orchid in Cardasica and it growing well is 0.6.

Kieron plants 10 orchids in Cardasica.

What is the probability that at least nine orchids will grow well?

AU 10 Jeff works for five days of the week in a call centre, cold calling people to sell them double glazing. Jeff's boss told him the probability of him making a sale each day. Explain how Jeff can work out the probability of making at least one sale in a week.

5.9 Independent events 2

This section will show you how to:

- use the connectors 'and' and 'or' in more advanced examples, to find the probability of combined events

Key words
and
independent events
or

More advanced use of 'and' and 'or'

You have already seen how certain probability problems related to **independent events** can be solved either by tree diagrams or by the use of the *and/or* method. Both methods are basically the same but the **and/or** method works better in the case of three events following one after another or in situations where the number of outcomes of one event is greater than two. This is simply because the tree diagram would get too large and involved.

EXAMPLE 15

Three cards are to be drawn from a pack of cards. Each card is to be replaced before the next one is drawn. What is the probability of drawing:

a three Kings

b exactly two Kings and one other card

c no Kings

d at least one King?

Let K be the event 'Drawing a King'. Let N be the event 'Not drawing a King'. Then:

a $P(KKK) = \frac{1}{13} \times \frac{1}{13} \times \frac{1}{13} = \frac{1}{2197}$

b P(exactly two Kings) = P(KKN) or P(KNK) or P(NKK)

$= (\frac{1}{13} \times \frac{1}{13} \times \frac{12}{13}) + (\frac{1}{13} \times \frac{12}{13} \times \frac{1}{13}) + (\frac{12}{13} \times \frac{1}{13} \times \frac{1}{13}) = \frac{36}{2197}$

c $P(\text{no Kings}) = P(NNN) = \frac{12}{13} \times \frac{12}{13} \times \frac{12}{13} = \frac{1728}{2197}$

d $P(\text{at least one King}) = 1 - P(\text{no Kings}) = 1 - \frac{1728}{2197} = \frac{469}{2197}$

Note that in part **b** the notation stands for the probability that the first card is a King, the second is a King and the third is not a King; or the first is a King, the second is not a King and the third is a King; or the first is not a King, the second is a King and the third is a King.

Note also that the probability of each component of part **b** is exactly the same. So you could have done the calculation as:

$3 \times \frac{1}{13} \times \frac{1}{13} \times \frac{12}{13} = \frac{36}{2197}$

Patterns of this kind often occur in probability.

EXERCISE 5J

1 A bag contains three black balls and seven red balls. A ball is taken out and replaced. This is repeated twice. What is the probability that:

a all three are black
b exactly two are black
c exactly one is black
d none is black?

2 A dice is thrown four times. What is the probability that:

a four sixes are thrown
b no sixes are thrown
c exactly one six is thrown?

FM **3** On my way to work I pass three sets of traffic lights. The probability that the first is green is $\frac{1}{2}$. The probability that the second is green is $\frac{1}{3}$. The probability that the third is green is $\frac{2}{3}$. What is the probability that:

a all three are green
b exactly two are green
c exactly one is green
d none are green
e at least one is green?

FM **4** Alf is late for school with a probability of 0.9. Bert is late with a probability of 0.7. Chas is late with a probability of 0.6. On any particular day what is the probability of:

a exactly one of them being late
b exactly two of them being late?

FM **5** Daisy takes four A-levels. The probability that she will pass English is 0.7. The probability that she will pass history is 0.6. The probability she will pass geography is 0.8. The probability that she will pass general studies is 0.9. What is the probability that:

a she passes all four subjects
b she passes exactly three subjects
c she passes at least three subjects?

FM **6** The driving test is in two parts, a written test and a practical test. It is known that 90% of people who take the written test pass and 60% of people who take the practical test pass. A person who passes the written test does not have to take it again. A person who fails the practical test does have to take it again.

a What is the probability that someone passes the written test?
b What is the probability that someone passes the practical test?
c What is the probability that someone passes both tests?
d What is the probability that someone passes the written test but takes two attempts to pass the practical test?

A

FM 7 Six out of 10 cars in Britain are made by foreign manufacturers. Three cars can be seen approaching in the distance.

a What is the probability that the first one is foreign?

b The first car is going so fast that its make could not be identified. What is the probability that the second car is foreign?

c What is the probability that exactly two of the three cars are foreign?

d Explain why, if the first car is foreign, the probability of the second car being foreign is still six out of 10.

8 Each day Mr Smith runs home from work. He has a choice of three routes: the road, the fields or the canal path. The road route is 4 miles, the fields route is 6 miles and the canal route is 5 miles. In a three-day period, what is the probability that Mr Smith runs a total distance of:

a exactly 17 miles **b** exactly 13 miles

c exactly 15 miles **d** over 17 miles?

9 A rock climber attempts a difficult route. There are three hard moves at points A, B and C in the climb. The climber has a probability of 0.6, 0.3 and 0.7 respectively of completing each of these moves. What is the probability that the climber:

a completes the climb **b** fails at move A

c fails at move B **d** fails at move C?

10 A car rally is being organised for the end of the year on 29 December, 30 December and 31 December.

If it snows on any of those days, the rally will finish and everyone must try to get home.

A long-range forecast gives the probability of snow on any one of these days as 0.25.

What is the probability that the rally will:

a last all three days **b** only last two days

c only last one day **d** not start?

PS 11 Evie's maths teacher told her that the probability of getting her mathematics homework correct is always the same and that, in any month of four homeworks, the chance of her getting at least one incorrect homework was 0.5904.

What is the probability of Evie getting her mathematics homework correct on any one night?

AU 12 James has been dealt two cards and knows that if he is now dealt a 10, Jack, Queen or a King he will win.

James thinks that the chance of his winning is now $\frac{16}{52}$.

Explain why he is wrong.

5.10 Conditional probability

This section will show you how to:

- work out the probability of combined events when the probabilities change after each event

Key words

conditional probability

The term **conditional probability** is used to describe the situation when the probability of an event is dependent on the outcome of another event. For instance, if a card is taken from a pack and not returned, then the probabilities for the next card drawn will be altered. The following example illustrates this situation.

EXAMPLE 16

A bag contains nine balls, of which five are white and four are black.

A ball is taken out and not replaced. Another is then taken out. If the first ball removed is black, what is the probability that:

a the second ball will be black

b both balls will be black?

When a black ball is removed, there are five white balls and three black balls left, reducing the total to eight.

Hence, when the second ball is taken out:

a P(second ball black) $= \frac{3}{8}$

b P(both balls black) $= \frac{4}{9} \times \frac{3}{8} = \frac{1}{6}$

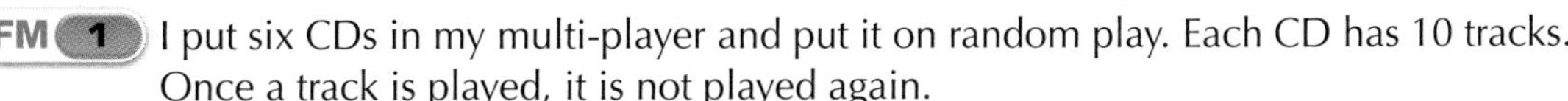

EXERCISE 5K

FM 1 I put six CDs in my multi-player and put it on random play. Each CD has 10 tracks. Once a track is played, it is not played again.

a What is the chance that track 5 on CD 6 is the first one played?

b What is the maximum number of tracks that could be played before a track from CD 6 is played?

A

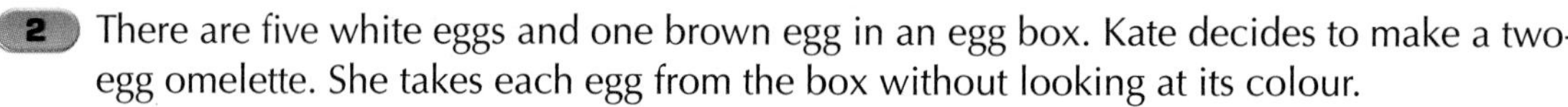

2 There are five white eggs and one brown egg in an egg box. Kate decides to make a two-egg omelette. She takes each egg from the box without looking at its colour.

a What is the probability that the first egg taken is brown?

b If the first egg taken is brown, what is the probability that the second egg taken will be brown?

c What is the probability that Kate gets an omelette made from:

i two white eggs

ii one white and one brown egg

iii two brown eggs?

3 A box contains 10 red and 15 yellow balls. One is taken out and not replaced. Another is taken out.

a If the first ball taken out is red, what is the probability that the second ball is:

i red **ii** yellow?

b If the first ball taken out is yellow, what is the probability that the second ball is:

i red **ii** yellow?

4 A fruit bowl contains six Granny Smith apples and eight Golden Delicious apples. Kevin takes two apples at random.

a If the first apple is a Granny Smith, what is the probability that the second is:

i a Granny Smith

ii a Golden Delicious?

b What is the probability that:

i both are Granny Smiths

ii both are Golden Delicious?

5 Ann has a bargain box of tins. They are unlabelled but she knows that six tins contain soup and four contain peaches.

a She opens two tins. What is the probability that:

i they are both soup

ii they are both peaches?

b What is the probability that she has to open two tins before she gets a tin of peaches?

c What is the probability that she has to open three tins before she gets a tin of peaches?

d What is the probability that she will get a tin of soup if she opens five tins?

FM AU **6** One in three cars on British roads is made in Britain. A car comes down the road. It is a British-made car. John says that the probability of the next car being British made is one in two because a British-made car has just gone past. Explain why he is wrong.

7 A bag contains three black balls and seven red balls. A ball is taken out and not replaced. This is repeated twice. What is the probability that:

a all three are black

b exactly two are black

c exactly one is black

d none is black?

8 On my way to work, I pass two sets of traffic lights. The probability that the first is green is $\frac{1}{3}$. If the first is green, the probability that the second is green is $\frac{1}{3}$. If the first is red, the probability that the second is green is $\frac{2}{3}$. What is the probability that:

a both are green

b none are green

c exactly one is green

d at least one is green?

9 A hand of five cards is dealt. What is the probability that:

a all five are Spades

b all five are the same suit

c they are four Aces and any other card

d they are four of a kind and any other card?

FM **10** An engineering test is in two parts, a written test and a practical test. It is known that 90% of those who take the written test pass. When a person passes the written test, the probability that he or she will also pass the practical test is 60%. When a person fails the written test, the probability that he or she will pass the practical test is 20%.

a What is the probability that someone passes both tests?

b What is the probability that someone passes one test?

c What is the probability that someone fails both tests?

d What is the combined probability of the answers to parts **a**, **b** and **c**?

A*

11 Each day Mr Smith runs home from work. He has a choice of three routes. The road, the fields or the canal path. On Monday, each route has an equal probability of being chosen. The route chosen on any day will not be picked the next day and so each of the other two routes has an equal probability of being chosen.

a Write down all the possible combinations so that Mr Smith runs home via the canal path on Wednesday (there are four of them).

b Calculate the probability that Mr Smith runs home via the canal path on Wednesday.

c Calculate the probability that Mr Smith runs home via the canal path on Tuesday.

d Using your results from parts **b** and **c**, write down the probability that Mr Smith runs home via the canal path on Thursday.

e Explain the answers to parts **b**, **c** and **d**.

FM 12 In the class box of calculators there are 10 calculators. Three of them are faulty.

What is the probability that:

a Dave takes the first and it is a good one

b Julie takes the second and it is a good one

c Andrew takes the third and it is faulty?

PS 13 What is the probability of being dealt four Aces in a row from a normal pack of cards?

AU 14 A bag contains some blue balls and some white balls, all the same size. Tony is asked to find the probability of taking out two balls of the same colour.

Explain to Tony how you would do this, explaining carefully the point where he is most likely to go wrong.

GRADE BOOSTER

- **D** You can calculate the probability of an outcome not happening if you know the probability it happening
- **D** You understand that the total probability of all possible outcomes in a particular situation is 1
- **D** You can predict the expected number of successes from a given number of trials if you know the probability of one success
- **C** You can calculate relative frequency from experimental evidence and compare this with the theoretical probability
- **B** You can draw a tree diagram to work out the probability of combined events
- **A** You can use *and/or* or a tree diagram to work out probabilities of specific outcomes of combined events
- **A*** You can work out the probabilities of combined events when the probability of each event changes depending on the outcome of the previous event

What you should know now

- How to calculate theoretical probabilities from different situations

EXAMINATION QUESTIONS

1 My wife asks me to tell her if the milk in the fridge has gone off or not. I say that it might have or it might not.

She says, "So the probability that it's off is 0.5 then."

How can I explain to her that this might not be so?

2 A five-sided spinner is labelled A, B, C, D and E.

The spinner is biased.

The table shows some of the probabilities of the spinner landing on each letter.

Letter	Probability
A	0.40
B	0.25
C	
D	
E	0.05

The probability that the spinner lands on C is equal to the probability that it lands on D.

a Calculate the probability that the spinner lands on D. *(3 marks)*

b Calculate the probability that the spinner lands on either A or B. *(2 marks)*

AQA, November 2008, Module 1 Higher, Question 7

3 I have ten coins. I spin them all at the same time and count the number of heads I have. If I do this one thousand times, how many times would I expect to have ten heads?

4 Bill and Ben have been practising equations when revising for their mathematics examination.

The probability that Bill gets an equation correct is 0.7.

The probability that Ben gets an equation correct is 0.4.

They both attempt another equation.

What is the probability that **exactly one** of them gets it correct?

You **must** show your working. *(4 marks)*

AQA, May 2008, Paper 1 Higher, Question 21

5 Josef and Myleen take part in different races at a school sports day.

The probability that Josef and Myleen both win their races is $\frac{5}{16}$.

The probability that Josef wins his race is $\frac{3}{8}$.

Work out the probability that Myleen wins her race. *(2 marks)*

AQA, June 2008, Module 1 Higher, Question 10

6 Sam has two bags of marbles.

Bag A contains 9 red marbles and 6 green marbles.

Bag B contains 3 red marbles and 7 green marbles.

Sam rolls a fair six-sided dice once.

If she rolls a six she takes a marble from bag A.

If she does not roll a six she takes a marble from bag B.

Calculate the probability that Sam chooses a red marble. *(3 marks)*

AQA, June 2008, Module 1 Higher, Question 5

7 Alan buys a box of tulip bulbs with the promise that one-quarter are red, one-quarter are yellow, one-quarter are purple and one-quarter are white.

What is the probability that:

a the first one he takes out is a purple tulip

b the first two he takes out are the same colour

c the first three he takes out are different colours?

8 There are 600 marbles in a bag.

The colours of the marbles are yellow, red, blue, black or white.

A marble is picked at random.

The probability that the marble is yellow is 0.2.

a Work out the number of yellow marbles in the bag. *(2 marks)*

b The probability that the marble is white is 0.1.

There are 57 black marbles in the bag.

There are twice as many blue marbles as red marbles.

Work out the number of red marbles in the bag. *(4 marks)*

AQA, March 2009, Module 1 Higher, Question 2

9 The types of people watching a film at a cinema are shown in the table.

	Male	Female
Adult	21	14
Child	10	5

Two of these people are chosen at random to receive free cinema tickets.

Calculate the probability that the two people are adults of the same gender. *(4 marks)*

AQA, March 2008, Module 1 Higher, Question 4

10 Leonardo is revising for his Higher tier GCSE Mathematics examination.

He came across this question.

> Two events A and B are independent.
>
> The probability of B is double the probability of A.
>
> The probability of both A and B occurring is $\frac{9}{32}$.
>
> Find the probability that event A occurs.

Complete Leonardo's solution.

> Let the probability of event A occurring = p
>
> Therefore, the probability of event B occurring = $2p$

(3 marks)

AQA, November 2007, Paper 1 Higher, Question 18

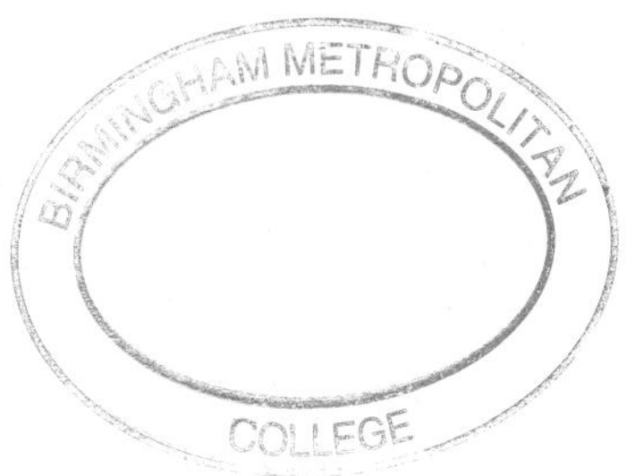

Worked Examination Questions

1 Harry is a pensioner. The probability that Harry goes into town on a Tuesday is $\frac{2}{5}$. The probability that Harry goes into town on a Tuesday and visits the library is $\frac{3}{20}$.

a One Tuesday Harry is in town. Calculate the probability that he visits the library.

b Calculate the probability that Harry goes into town on a Tuesday and does not visit the library.

1

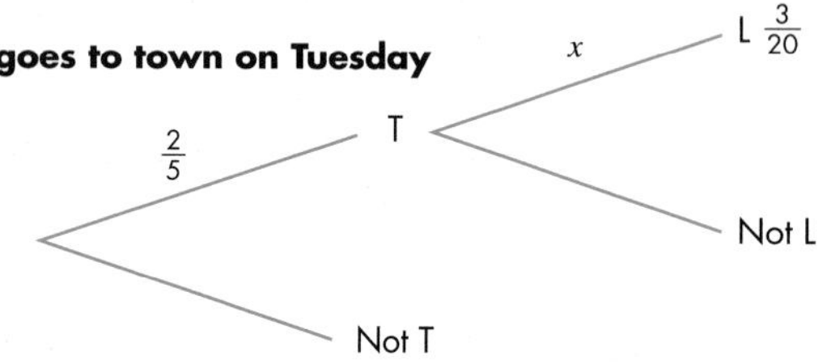

Draw the part of the tree diagrams that you know about or equivalent method. This gets 1 mark for method.

a P(Harry goes to town on Tuesday) × $x = \frac{3}{20}$

$\frac{2}{5} \times x = \frac{3}{20}$

Set up an equation. This gets 1 mark for method.

P(Harry visits the library when in town on Tuesday) $= \frac{3}{20} \div \frac{2}{5}$

$= \frac{3}{20} \times \frac{5}{2} = \frac{3}{8}$

Substitute in the probabilities and solve the equation. Remember to turn the fraction upside down and multiply by it when you divide.

This gets 1 method mark for the multiplication statement.

This gets 1 accuracy mark for correct answer.

b P(Harry does not visit the library) $= 1 - \frac{3}{8} = \frac{5}{8}$

P(Harry goes into town and does not visit the library) $= \frac{2}{5} \times \frac{5}{8} = \frac{1}{4}$

First work out the probability of the complementary event then use the 'and' rule for combined events.

This gets 1 method mark for finding complementary event.

This gets 1 method mark for using the 'and' rule.

This gets 1 mark for accuracy.

Total: 7 marks

FM **2** In a raffle 400 tickets have been sold. There is only one prize.

Mr Raza buys five tickets for himself and sells another 40.

Mrs Raza buys 10 tickets for herself and sells another 50.

Mrs Hewes buys eight tickets for herself and sells just 12 others.

a What is the probability of:

i Mr Raza winning the raffle

ii Mr Raza selling the winning ticket

iii Mr Raza either winning the raffle or selling the winning ticket?

b What is the probability of either Mr or Mrs Raza selling the winning ticket?

c What is the probability of Mrs Hewes not winning the lottery?

Worked Examination Questions

2 a i $\frac{5}{400}$ — This gets 1 mark.

ii $\frac{40}{400}$ — This gets 1 mark.

iii $\frac{(5+40)}{400} = \frac{45}{400}$ — This gets 1 mark for method of adding the probabilities and 1 mark for accuracy.

b $\frac{(40+50)}{400} = \frac{90}{400}$ — This gets 1 mark for method and 1 mark for accuracy.

c $1 - \frac{8}{400} = \frac{392}{400}$ — This gets 1 mark for method of subtracting from 1 and 1 mark for accuracy.

Total: 8 marks

PS 3 Nic is rehearsing for a driving test. This test is made up of two parts, a practical and a theory. She is told that the probability of passing exactly one of these two tests is 0.44 and the probability of passing the practical is 0.8.

What is the probability of passing the theory test?

3 Create a tree diagram of what is known.

This gets 1 method mark for creating a suitable diagram that shows all the relevant probabilities.

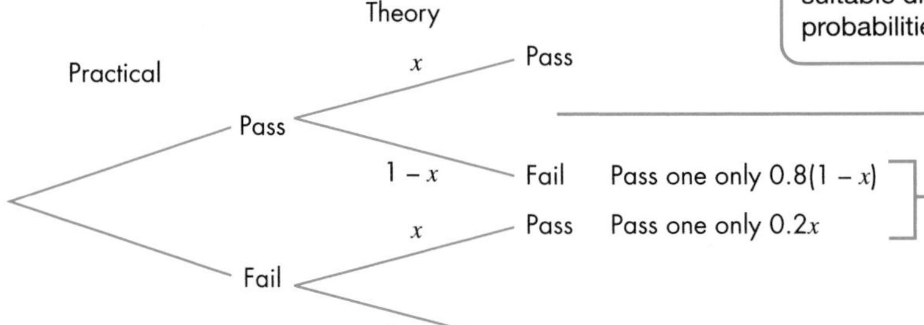

This gets 1 method mark for assigning P(pass theory) as x and P(fail theory) as $1 - x$.

This gets 1 accuracy mark for stating both these algebraic expressions.

$P(\text{pass one only}) = 0.8(1 - x) + 0.2x = 0.44$ — This gets 1 method mark for setting up this equation.

$0.8 - 0.8x + 0.2x = 0.44$

$0.8 - 0.6x = 0.44$ — This gets 1 method mark for simplifying to a correct expression similar to this one.

$x = \frac{0.8 - 0.44}{0.6} = 0.6$ — This gets 1 accuracy mark for getting to 0.6.

Total: 6 marks

AU 4 Harry is given a bag of coloured balls. He takes ten balls out as a sample of what might be in there and finds they are only blue and white balls.

He says, "There are no red balls in the bag."

Is he correct? Give a reason to support your answer.

4 No, he is incorrect as there might be at least one red ball in the bag but not chosen in the sample. — You need the statement 'No' and a reason similar to this one for 1 mark.

Total: 1 mark

5 Functional Maths
Fairground games

Joe had a stall at the local fair and wanted to make a reasonable profit from the game below.

In this game, the player rolls two balls down the sloping board and wins a prize if they land in slots that total more than seven.

Joe wants to know how much he should charge for each go and what the price should be. He would also like to know how much profit he is likely to make.

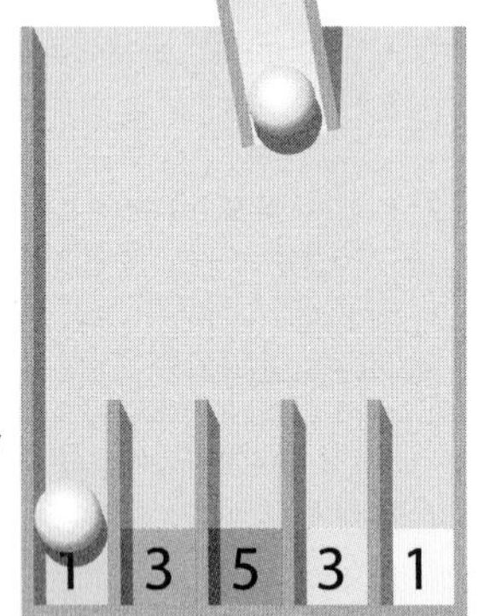

Getting started

Practise calculating probabilities using the spinner and questions below.

- What is the probability of spinning the spinner and getting:
  - a one
  - a five
  - a two
  - a number other than five?

  Give your answer as a fraction and as a decimal.
- If you spun the spinner 20 times, how many times would you expect to get:
  - a five
  - not five
  - an odd number?
- If you spun the spinner 100 times, how many times would you expect to get:
  - a two
  - not a two
  - a prime number?

Now, think about which probabilities you must calculate, in order to help Joe, and to design your own profitable game.

Your task

For this task you can work individually or in pairs.

1 Write a report for Joe which includes:

- a diagram to show the probability of each outcome
- the probability of at least three different outcomes
- the probability of winning
- at least three different ways of setting up the game, showing the cost of one go, the value of the prize and the expected profit for varying numbers of people playing the game.

Based on this information, advise Joe on how he should set up the game. Justify your decision.

2 Design your own fairground game. Describe the rules for winning, show the probability of winning using a tree diagram, and give costings and the projected profit.

Explain why you think your game should be used at the next local fair.

Why this chapter matters

How accurate are we?

In real life it is not always sensible to use exact values. Sometimes it would be impossible to have exact measurements. People often round values without realising it. Rounding is done so that values are sensible.

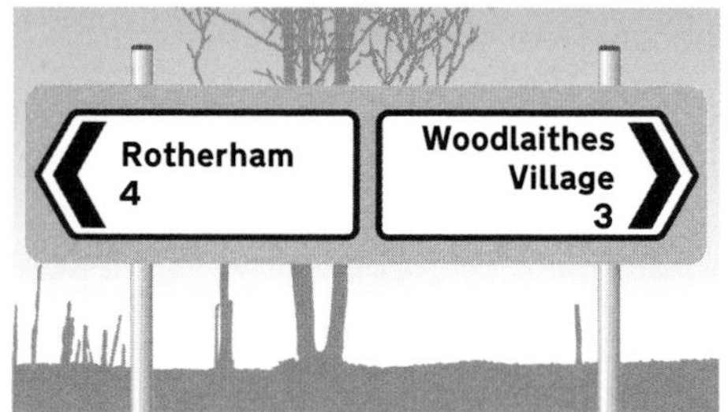

Is it exactly 3 miles to Woodlaithes Village and exactly 4 miles to Rotherham?

Does this box contain exactly 750 g of flakes when full?

Was his time exactly 13.4 seconds?

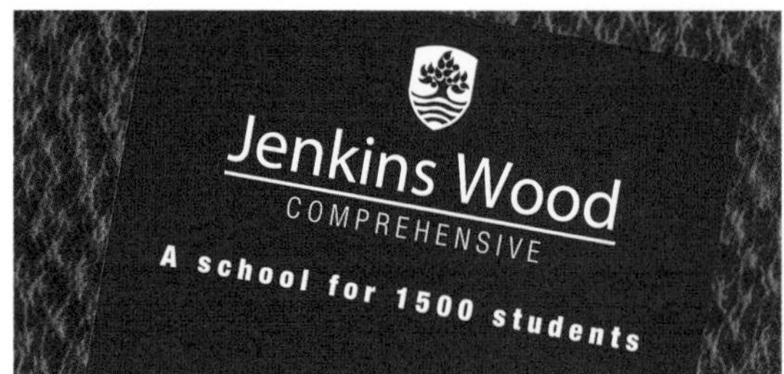

Does the school have exactly 1500 students?

Imagine if people tried to use exact values all the time. Would life seem strange?

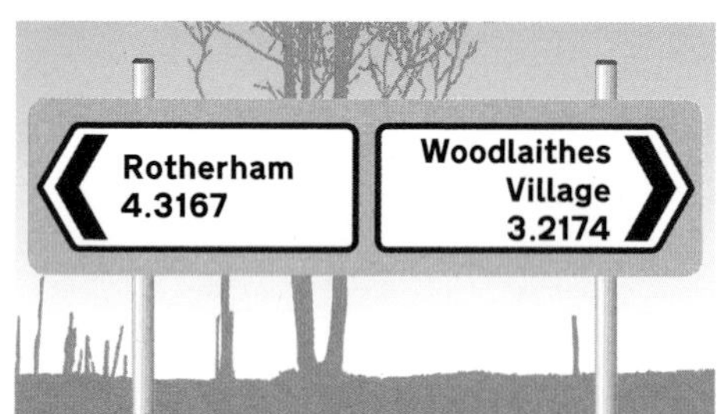

Chapter 6

Number: Number and limits of accuracy

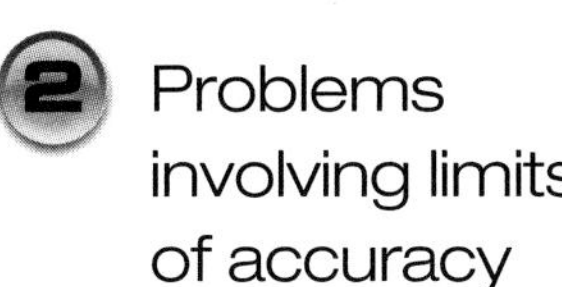

This chapter will show you …

C how to find the limits of numbers rounded to certain accuracies

B how to use limits of accuracy in calculations

Visual overview

Limits of accuracy → Calculating with limits of accuracy

What you should already know

- How to round numbers to the nearest 10, 100 or 1000 **(KS3 level 4, GCSE grade G)**
- How to round numbers to a given number of decimal places **(KS3 level 5, GCSE grade F)**
- How to round numbers to a given number of significant figures **(KS3 level 6–7, GCSE grade E)**

Quick check

1 Round 6374 to:
 a the nearest 10
 b the nearest 100
 c the nearest 1000.

2 Round 2.389 to:
 a one decimal place
 b two decimal places.

3 Round 47.28 to:
 a one significant figure
 b three significant figures.

6.1 Limits of accuracy

This section will show you how to:
- find the limits of accuracy of numbers that have been rounded to different degrees of accuracy

Key words
continuous data
discrete data
limits of accuracy
lower bound
upper bound

Any recorded measurements have usually been rounded.

The true value will be somewhere between the **lower bound** and the **upper bound**.

The lower and upper bounds are sometimes known as the **limits of accuracy**.

Discrete data

Discrete data can only take certain values within a given range; amounts of money and numbers of people are examples of discrete data.

EXAMPLE 1

A coach is carrying 50 people, to the nearest 10.

What are the minimum and maximum numbers of people on the coach?

45 is the lowest whole number that rounds to 50 to the nearest 10.
54 is the highest whole number that rounds to 50 to the nearest 10.

So minimum = 45 and maximum = 54

The limits are 45 $\leqslant$ number of people $\leqslant$ 54

Remember that you can only have a whole number of people.

Continuous data

Continuous data can take any value, within a given range; length and mass are examples of continuous data.

Upper and lower bounds

A journey of 26 miles measured to the nearest mile could actually be as long as 26.4999999… miles or as short as 25.5 miles. It could not be 26.5 miles, as this would round up to 27 miles. However, 26.499 999 9… is virtually the same as 26.5.

You overcome this difficulty by saying that 26.5 is the upper bound of the measured value and 25.5 is its lower bound. You can therefore write:

25.5 miles $\leqslant$ actual distance $<$ 26.5 miles

which states that the actual distance is *greater than or equal to* 25.5 miles but *less than* 26.5 miles.

When stating the upper bound, follow the accepted practice, as demonstrated here, which eliminates the difficulties of using recurring decimals.

A mathematical peculiarity

Let:	$x = 0.999\ 999\ldots$ (1)
Multiply by 10:	$10x = 9.999\ 999\ldots$ (2)
Subtract (1) from (2):	$9x = 9$
Divide by 9:	$x = 1$
So, we have:	$0.\dot{9} = 1$

Hence, it is valid to give the upper bound without using recurring decimals.

EXAMPLE 2

A stick of wood measures 32 cm, to the nearest centimetre.

What are the lower and upper limits of the actual length of the stick?

The lower limit is 31.5 cm as this is the lowest value that rounds to 32 cm to the nearest centimetre.

The upper limit is 32.499 999 999... cm as this is the highest value that rounds to 32 cm to the nearest centimetre as 32.5 cm would round to 33 cm.

However, you say that 32.5 cm is the upper bound. So you write:

31.5 cm ≤ length of stick < 32.5 cm

Note the use of the strict inequality (<) for the upper bound.

EXAMPLE 3

A time of 53.7 seconds is accurate to 1 decimal place.

What are the limits of accuracy?

The smallest possible value is 53.65 seconds.

The largest possible value is 53.749 999 999... but 53.75 seconds is the upper bound.

So the limits of accuracy are 53.65 seconds ≤ time < 53.75 seconds.

EXAMPLE 4

A skip has a mass of 220 kg measured to 3 significant figures. What are the limits of accuracy of the mass of the skip?

The smallest possible value is 219.5 kg.

The largest possible value is 220.499 999 99... kg but 220.5 kg is the upper bound.

So the limits of accuracy are 219.5 kg ≤ mass of skip < 220.5 kg.

EXERCISE 6A

C

1 Write down the limits of accuracy of the following.

- **a** 7 cm measured to the nearest centimetre
- **b** 120 g measured to the nearest 10 g
- **c** 3400 km measured to the nearest 100 km
- **d** 50 mph measured to the nearest miles per hour
- **e** £6 given to the nearest pound
- **f** 16.8 cm to the nearest tenth of a centimetre
- **g** 16 kg to the nearest kilogram
- **h** A football crowd of 14 500 given to the nearest 100
- **i** 55 miles given to the nearest mile
- **j** 55 miles given to the nearest 5 miles

B

2 Write down the limits of accuracy for each of the following values, which are rounded to the given degree of accuracy.

- **a** 6 cm (1 significant figure)
- **b** 17 kg (2 significant figures)
- **c** 32 min (2 significant figures)
- **d** 238 km (3 significant figures)
- **e** 7.3 m (1 decimal place)
- **f** 25.8 kg (1 decimal place)
- **g** 3.4 h (1 decimal place)
- **h** 87 g (2 significant figures)
- **i** 4.23 mm (2 decimal places)
- **j** 2.19 kg (2 decimal places)
- **k** 12.67 min (2 decimal places)
- **l** 25 m (2 significant figures)
- **m** 40 cm (1 significant figure)
- **n** 600 g (2 significant figures)
- **o** 30 min (1 significant figure)
- **p** 1000 m (2 significant figures)
- **q** 4.0 m (1 decimal place)
- **r** 7.04 kg (2 decimal places)
- **s** 12.0 s (1 decimal place)
- **t** 7.00 m (2 decimal places)

3 Write down the lower and upper bounds of each of these values, rounded to the accuracy stated.

- **a** 8 m (1 significant figure)
- **b** 26 kg (2 significant figures)
- **c** 25 min (2 significant figures)
- **d** 85 g (2 significant figures)
- **e** 2.40 m (2 decimal places)
- **f** 0.2 kg (1 decimal place)
- **g** 0.06 s (2 decimal places)
- **h** 300 g (1 significant figure)
- **i** 0.7 m (1 decimal place)
- **j** 366 d (3 significant figures)
- **k** 170 weeks (2 significant figures)
- **l** 210 g (2 significant figures)

B

PS **4** A bus has 53 seats of which 37 are occupied.

The driver estimates that at the next bus stop 20 people, to the nearest 10, will get on and no one will get off.

If he is correct, is it possible they will all get a seat?

FM **5** A chain is 30 m long, to the nearest metre.

A chain is needed to fasten a boat to a harbour wall, a distance that is also 30 m, to the nearest metre.

Which statement is definitely true? Explain your decision.

A: The chain will be long enough.

B: The chain will not be long enough.

C: It is impossible to tell whether or not the chain is long enough.

AU **6** A bag contains 2.5 kg of soil, to the nearest 100 g.

What is the least amount of soil in the bag?

Give your answer in kilograms and grams.

7 Billy has 40 identical marbles. Each marble has a mass of 65 g (to the nearest gram).

a What is the greatest possible mass of one marble?

b What is the least possible mass of one marble?

c What is the greatest possible mass of all the marbles?

d What is the least possible mass of all the marbles?

6.2 Problems involving limits of accuracy

This section will show you how to:

- combine limits of two or more variables together to solve problems

Key words
limits of accuracy
maximum
minimum

When rounded values are used for a calculation, the **minimum** and **maximum** possible exact values of the calculation can vary by large amounts.

There are four operations that can be performed on **limits of accuracy** — addition, subtraction, multiplication and division.

Addition and subtraction

Suppose you have two bags, each with the mass given to the nearest kilogram.

The limits for bag A are 4.5 kg $\leqslant$ mass $<$ 5.5 kg

The limits for bag B are 8.5 kg $\leqslant$ mass $<$ 9.5 kg

The minimum total mass of the two bags is 4.5 kg + 8.5 kg = 13 kg

The maximum total mass of the two bags is 5.5 kg + 9.5 kg = 15 kg

The minimum difference between the masses of the two bags is 8.5 kg – 5.5 kg = 3 kg

The maximum difference between the masses of the two bags is 9.5 kg – 4.5 kg = 5 kg

The table shows the combinations to give the minimum and maximum values for addition and subtraction of two numbers, a and b.

a and b lie within limits $a_{min} \leqslant a < a_{max}$ and $b_{min} \leqslant b < b_{max}$

Operation	Minimum	Maximum
Addition ($a + b$)	$a_{min} + b_{min}$	$a_{max} + b_{max}$
Subtraction ($a - b$)	$a_{min} - b_{max}$	$a_{max} - b_{min}$

Multiplication and division

Suppose a car is travelling at an average speed of 30 mph, to the nearest 5 mph, for 2 hours, to the nearest 30 minutes.

The limits for the average speed are:

27.5 mph $\leqslant$ average speed $<$ 32.5 mph

The limits for the time are:

1 hour 45 minutes (1.75 hours) $\leqslant$ time $<$ 2 hours 15 minutes (2.25 hours)

The minimum distance travelled = 27.5 × 1.75 = 48.125 miles

The maximum distance travelled = 32.5 × 2.25 = 73.125 miles

Suppose a lorry is travelling for 100 miles, to the nearest 10 miles, and takes 2 hours, to the nearest 30 minutes.

The limits for the distance are:

95 miles $\leqslant$ distance $<$ 105 miles

The limits for the time are the same as for the car.

The minimum average speed is $\frac{95}{2.25} = 42$ mph

The maximum average speed is $\frac{105}{1.75} = 60$ mph

The table shows the combinations to give the minimum and maximum values for multiplication and division of two numbers a and b.

a and b lie within limits $a_{min} \leqslant a < a_{max}$ and $b_{min} \leqslant b < b_{max}$

Operation	Minimum	Maximum
Multiplication ($a \times b$)	$a_{min} \times b_{min}$	$a_{max} \times b_{max}$
Division ($a \div b$)	$a_{min} \div b_{max}$	$a_{max} \div b_{min}$

When solving problems involving limits, write down all the limits for each value, then decide which combination to use to obtain the required solution.

When rounding answers, be careful to ensure your answers are within the acceptable range of the limits.

EXAMPLE 5

A rectangle has sides given as 6 cm by 15 cm, to the nearest centimetre.

Calculate the limits of accuracy of the area of the rectangle.

Write down the limits: 5.5 cm $\leqslant$ width $<$ 6.5 cm, 14.5 cm $\leqslant$ length $<$ 15.5 cm

For maximum area, multiply maximum width by maximum length, and for minimum area, multiply minimum width by minimum length.

The upper bound of the width is 6.5 cm and of the length is 15.5 cm. So the upper bound of the area of the rectangle is:

6.5 cm × 15.5 cm = 100.75 cm^2

The lower bound of the width is 5.5 cm and of the length is 14.5 cm. So the lower bound of the area of the rectangle is:

5.5 cm × 14.5 cm = 79.75 cm^2

Therefore, the limits of accuracy for the area of the rectangle are:

79.75 cm^2 $\leqslant$ area $<$ 100.75 cm^2

EXAMPLE 6

The distance from Barnsley to Sheffield is 15 miles, to the nearest mile. The time Jeff took to drive between Barnsley and Sheffield was 40 minutes, to the nearest 10 minutes.

Calculate the upper limit of Jeff's average speed.

Write down the limits: 14.5 miles $\leqslant$ distance $<$ 15.5 miles, 35 mins $\leqslant$ time $<$ 45 mins

speed = distance ÷ time

To get the maximum speed you need the maximum distance ÷ minimum time.

15.5 miles ÷ 35 mins = 0.443 (3 significant figures) miles per minute

0.443 mph × 60 = 26.6 mph

The upper limit of Jeff's average speed = 26.6 mph

EXERCISE 6B

B

1 Boxes have a mass of 7 kg, to the nearest kilogram.

What are the minimum and maximum masses of 10 of these boxes?

FM 2 A machine cuts lengths of rope from a 50-m roll.
The lengths are 2.5 m long, to 1 decimal place.

What are the minimum and maximum numbers of pieces of rope that can be cut?

A

FM 3 Books each have a mass of 1200 g, to the nearest 100 g.

a What is the greatest possible mass of 10 books?
Give your answer in kilograms.

b A trolley can safely hold up to 25 kg of books.
How many books can safely be put on the trolley?

PS 4 Jack says, "I am five years old." Jill says, "I am eight years old."

What is the greatest difference between their ages?

Show how you worked out your answer.

5 For each of these rectangles, find the limits of accuracy of the area. The measurements are shown to the level of accuracy indicated in brackets.

a 5 cm × 9 cm (nearest cm) **b** 4.5 cm × 8.4 cm (1 decimal place)

c 7.8 cm × 18 cm (2 significant figures)

6 A rectangular garden has sides of 6 m and 4 m, measured to the nearest metre.

a Write down the limits of accuracy for each length.

b What is the maximum area of the garden?

c What is the minimum perimeter of the garden?

7 A cinema screen is measured as 6 m by 15 m, to the nearest metre. Calculate the limits of accuracy for the area of the screen.

8 The measurements, to the nearest centimetre, of a box are given as 10 cm × 7 cm × 4 cm. Calculate the limits of accuracy for the volume of the box.

FM 9 Mr Sparks is an electrician. He has a 50-m roll of cable, correct to the nearest metre.
He uses 10 m on each job, to the nearest metre.

If he does four jobs, what is the maximum amount of cable he will have left?

AU 10 Jon and Matt are exactly 7 miles apart. They are walking towards each other.
Jon is walking at 4 mph and Matt is walking at 2 mph.
Both speeds are given to the nearest mile per hour.

Without doing any time calculations, decide whether it is possible for them to meet in 1 hour. Justify your answer.

11 The area of a rectangular field is given as 350 m^2, to the nearest 10 m^2. One length is given as 16 m, to the nearest metre. Find the limits of accuracy for the other length of the field.

12 In triangle ABC, AB = 9 cm, BC = 7 cm, and ∠ABC = 37°. All the measurements are given to the nearest unit. Calculate the limits of accuracy for the area of the triangle.

13 The price of pure gold is £18.25 per gram. The density of gold is 19.3 g/cm^3. (Assume these figures are exact.) A solid gold bar in the shape of a cuboid has sides 4.6 cm, 2.2 cm and 6.6 cm. These measurements are made to the nearest 0.1 cm.

a **i** What are the limits of accuracy for the volume of this gold bar?

ii What are the upper and lower limits of the cost of this bar?

The gold bar was weighed and given a mass of 1296 g, to the nearest gram.

b What are the upper and lower limits for the cost of the bar now?

c Explain why the price ranges are so different.

FM **14** A stopwatch records the time for the winner of a 100-metre race as 14.7 seconds, measured to the nearest one-tenth of a second.

a What are the greatest and least possible times for the winner?

b The length of the 100-metre track is correct to the nearest 1 m. What are the greatest and least possible lengths of the track?

c What is the fastest possible average speed of the winner, with a time of 14.7 seconds in the 100-metre race?

15 A cube has a side measured as 8 cm, to the nearest millimetre. What is the greatest percentage error of the following?

a The calculated area of one face **b** The calculated volume of the cube

16 A cube has a volume of 40 cm^3, to the nearest cm^3. Find the range of possible values of the side length of the cube.

17 A cube has a volume of 200 cm^3, to the nearest 10 cm^3. Find the limits of accuracy of the side length of the cube.

18 A model car travels 40 m, measured to one significant figure, at a speed of 2 m/s, measured to one significant figure. Between what limits does the time taken lie?

PS **19** Here is a formula for calculating the tension, T newtons, in some coloured springs.

$$T = \frac{20x}{l}$$

x is the length that the spring is extended. l is the unstretched length of the spring.

If x and l are accurate to one decimal place, decide which colour of spring, if any, has the greater tension.

Red spring: $x = 3.4$ cm and $l = 5.3$ cm
Green spring: $x = 1.5$ cm and $l = 2.4$ cm
Blue spring: $x = 0.5$ cm and $l = 0.9$ cm

GRADE BOOSTER

B You can find measures of accuracy for numbers given to whole-number accuracies

A You can find measures of accuracy for numbers given to decimal-place or significant-figure accuracies

A* You can calculate the limits of compound measures

What you should know now

- How to find the limits of numbers given to various accuracies
- How to find the limits of compound measures by combining the appropriate limits of the variables involved

1 A school has 1850 pupils to the nearest 10.

a What is the least number of pupils at the school?

b What is the greatest number of pupils at the school?

2 The longest river in Britain is the River Severn. It is 220 miles long to the nearest 10 miles. What is the least length it could be?

3 A notice board is a rectangle with a length of 80 cm and a width of 40 cm. Both measurements are correct to the nearest centimetre.

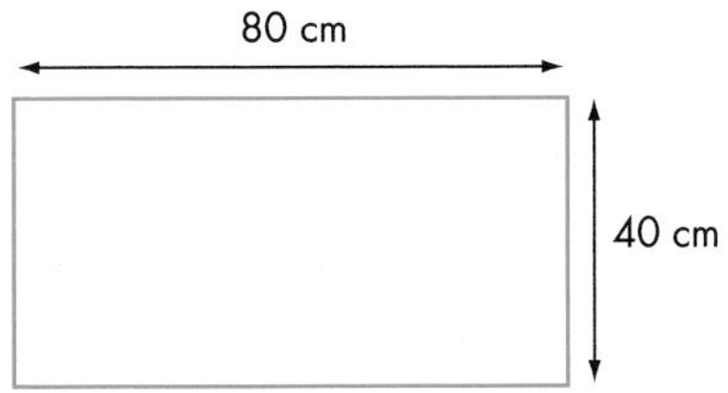

a What is the least possible length of the notice board?

b What is the greatest possible width of the notice board?

c What is the greatest possible area of the notice board?

4 The base of a triangle is 10 cm measured to the nearest centimetre. The area of the triangle is 100 cm^2 measured to the nearest square centimetre. Calculate the least and greatest values of the height of the triangle.

5 Tim fits television aerials in houses.

He buys 100 metres of television cable.

Each house needs 10 metres of television cable.

The length of cable which Tim buys is correct to the nearest metre.

The length of cable needed for each house is correct to the nearest half metre.

After working on nine houses, what is the minimum length of cable which Tim could have left?

You **must** show your working. *(5 marks)*

AQA, November 2005, Module 3, Question 13

6 John is telling a friend that he had a lorry load of top soil delivered for his garden.

He says that he had about 4 cubic metres delivered and that, with VAT, he paid about £80.

The volume is given to the nearest cubic metre.

The cost is given to the nearest £5.

Find the maximum price that John could have paid for one cubic metre of top soil. *(5 marks)*

AQA, February 2005, Module 3, Question 9

7 A formula used in kinematics is $s = \dfrac{v^2 - u^2}{2a}$.

Calculate the greatest possible value of s if $v = 6.2$, $u = 3.6$ and $a = 9.8$, all values accurate to 2 significant figures.

8 A circle has an area of 100 cm^2, measured to the nearest square centimetre. What is the lower bound of the radius? *(3 marks)*

AQA, June 2005, Paper 2 Higher, Question 20

9 $x = 1.8$ measured to 1 decimal place,

$y = 4.0$ measured to 2 significant figures,

$z = 2.56$ measured to 3 significant figures.

Calculate the upper limit of $\dfrac{x^2 + y}{z}$.

10 A girl runs 60 metres in a time of 8.0 seconds. The distance is measured to the nearest metre and the time is measured to 2 significant figures. What is the least possible speed?

11 **a** Calculate the length of the diagonal x in this cube of side 3 m.

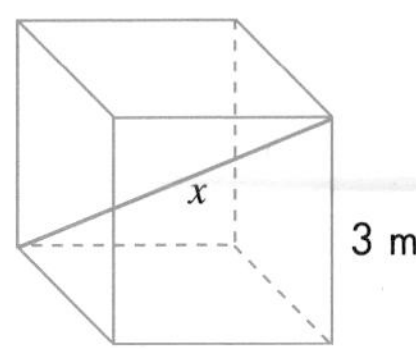

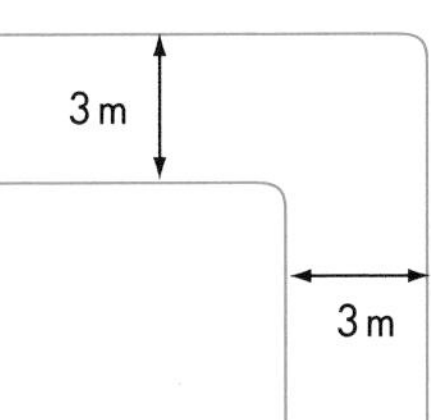

b A man is carrying a pole of length 5 m down a long corridor. The pole is measured to the nearest centimetre. At the end of the corridor is a right-angled corner. The corridor is 3 m wide and 3 m high, both measurements correct to the nearest 10 cm. Will the pole be certain to get round the corner?

12 In the calculation $\frac{380}{72-44}$

All the numbers have been rounded to two significant figures.

Work out the minimum possible value of the calculation. *(3 marks)*

AQA, June 2009, Module 3 Higher, Question 9

13 The attendance at a rugby match is 72 000.

This number is correct to the nearest 1000.

The number of females attending the match is 16 000.

This number is correct to the nearest 500.

Work out the maximum number of males that could be attending the match.

You must show your working. *(4 marks)*

AQA, March 2008, Module 3 Higher, Question 10

14 In the expression $\frac{PQ}{R}$

P = 50 to one significant figure

Q = 1000 to two significant figures

R = 0.4477 to four significant figures

Find the minimum value of $\frac{PQ}{R}$. *(4 marks)*

AQA, June 2008, Module 3 Higher, Question 10

15 Marvin is travelling by air.

Marvin has some scales that weigh items up to 3 kg.

The scales are accurate to the nearest 50 g.

Marvin weighs his case and luggage in four separate lots.

The values shown on his scales are

2 kg 400 g, 2 kg 800 g, 2 kg 750 g and 1 kg 850 g.

At the airport his case and luggage are weighed as one item.

The scales at the airport are accurate to the nearest 100 g.

The allowance is 10 kg.

Can Marvin be sure his case and luggage does not exceed the allowance?

You **must** show your working. *(4 marks)*

AQA, November 2007, Paper 2 Higher, Question 21

Worked Examination Questions

1 The magnification of a lens is given by the formula

$$m = \frac{v}{u}$$

In an experiment, u is measured as 8.5 cm and v is measured as 14.0 cm, both correct to the nearest 0.1 cm. Find the least possible value of m. You must show full details of your calculation.

1 $8.45 \leq u < 8.55$

$13.95 \leq v < 14.05$

Write down the limits of both variables. This gets 1 mark each.

Least m = least u ÷ greatest v = 8.45 ÷ 14.05

As the calculation is a division the least value will be given by least u ÷ greatest v. This gets 1 mark for method.

= 0.6014234875

This gets 1 mark for accuracy.

= 0.601 or 0.6

It is good practice to round to a suitable degree of accuracy.

Total: 4 marks

2 A long rod with a square cross-section is made with a side of 5 cm. A circular hole is drilled with a radius of 3.6 cm. All measurements are to the nearest $\frac{1}{10}$ cm. Will the rod fit into the circle?

This is a using and applying maths question. You need to have a strategy to solve it.

Step 1: Find the largest possible diagonal of the square using Pythagoras' theorem.

Step 2: Work out the smallest possible diameter of the circle.

Step 3: Compare the values to see if the diagonal is smaller than the diameter.

2 Limits of side of square

$4.95 < \text{side} < 5.05$

Limits of radius

$3.55 < \text{radius} < 3.65$

Always start by writing down the limits of the variables in the question.

These get 1 mark each.

Largest diagonal = $\sqrt{(5.05^2 + 5.05^2)}$

Evidence of using Pythagoras' theorem gives 1 method mark.

= 7.14177849

= 7.142 (4 significant figures)

Work out the square root but do not round to less than 4 sf.
This gets 1 mark for method and 1 mark for accuracy.

Smallest diameter = 2 × 3.55 = 7.1

Work out the smallest diameter.
This gets 1 mark for method.

As 7.142 > 7.1, the rod may not fit in the circle.

Obtaining 7.1 and giving the correct conclusion gets 1 mark for accuracy.

Total: 7 marks

6 Functional Maths
Buying a house

Estate agents regularly measure the dimensions of rooms. For this they use an electronic signal reader, which makes measurements to a stated accuracy.

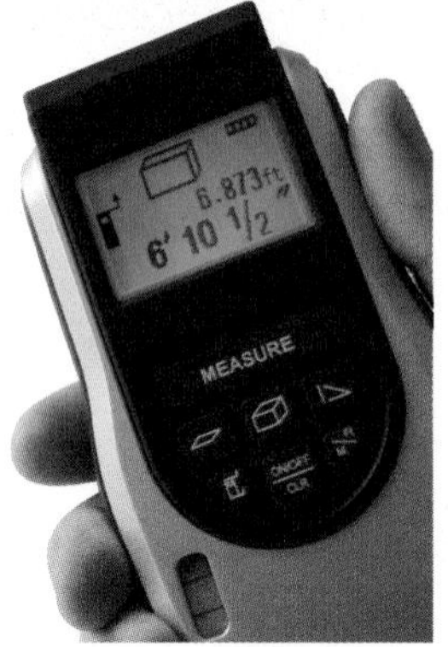

Getting started

Below are three measurements, given in metres.

- 4 m
- 109 m
- 80 m

If each of these measurements is an approximation and only expressed to the nearest metre, what is the smallest number each measurement could be? If each measurement was actually measured to the nearest centimetre, to be more accurate, what is the largest number each measurement could be?

Discuss the difference between these two answers.

Your task

An estate agent has measured the rooms in a house. The figures are shown in the plan opposite.

The measurements are given correct to 10 cm.

You are interested in buying the house but want to know its measurements more accurately as this could affect the price that you offer for it.

- Work out the maximum and minimum area of the floor space in the house, writing down and explaining your calculations so that you can inform your family later.
- Based on your calculations, work out the amount of flooring that will be needed for each room. You must also work out the maximum and minimum cost (inclusive of VAT) of your flooring options for each room so that you can factor the additional cost into your final price for the house.

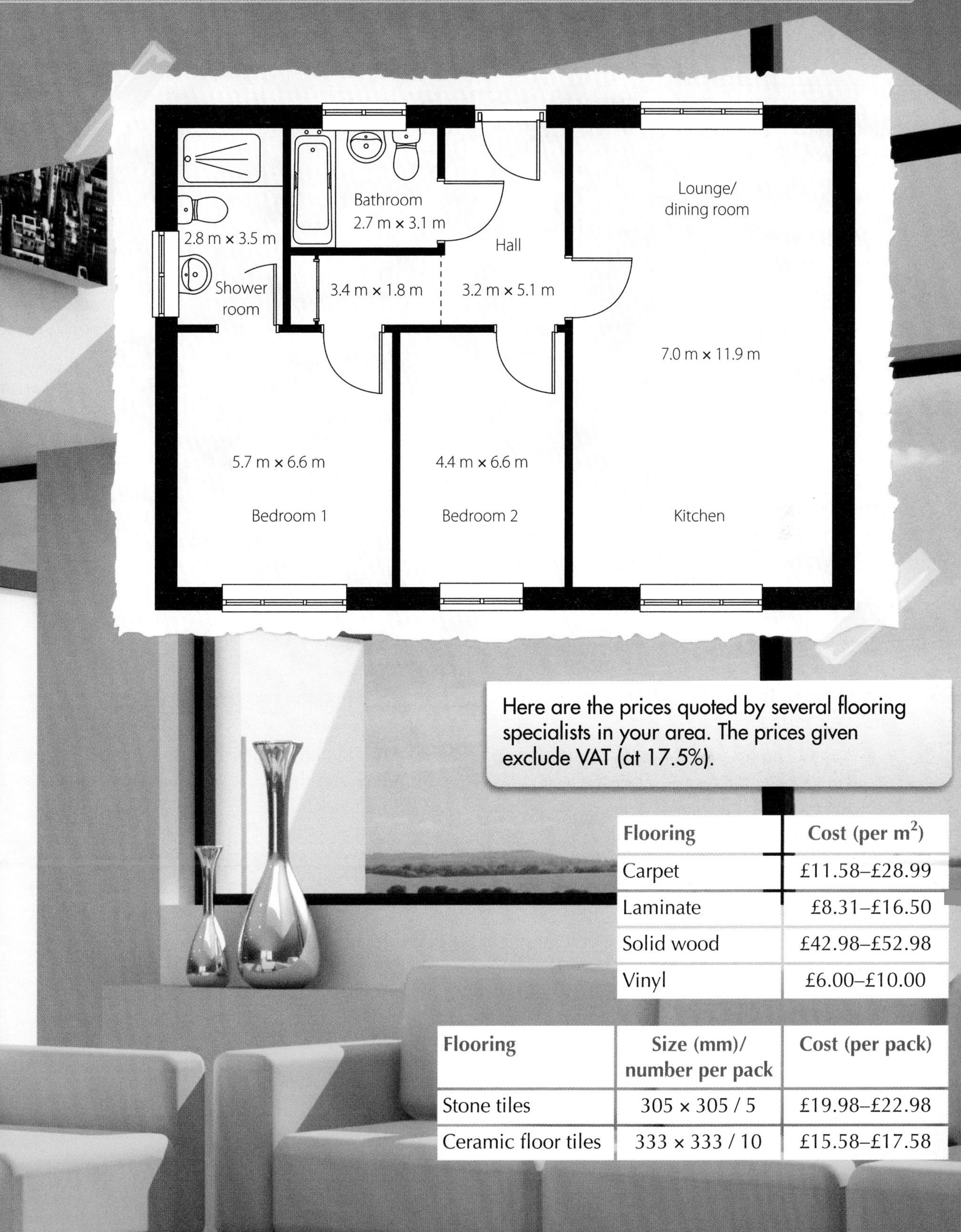

Here are the prices quoted by several flooring specialists in your area. The prices given exclude VAT (at 17.5%).

Flooring	Cost (per m^2)
Carpet	£11.58–£28.99
Laminate	£8.31–£16.50
Solid wood	£42.98–£52.98
Vinyl	£6.00–£10.00

Flooring	Size (mm)/ number per pack	Cost (per pack)
Stone tiles	305 × 305 / 5	£19.98–£22.98
Ceramic floor tiles	333 × 333 / 10	£15.58–£17.58

Why this chapter matters

How good is your mental arithmetic? In everyday life you will often need to use mental arithmetic to carry out calculations.

Improving your mental arithmetic skills will make mathematics easier and more enjoyable.

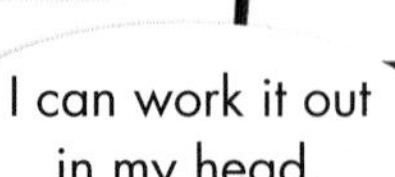
I can work it out in my head.

Work out 43×11
I will use my calculator.

Mental arithmetic

- In 1980 Shakuntala Devi claimed to multiply two 13-digit numbers in 28 seconds.
- In 1999 Alberto Coto of Spain set the record for adding up 100 single-digit numbers in 19.23 seconds.
- In 2009 an 11-year-old Australian correctly answered 129 106 arithmetic questions within 48 hours to win the World Maths Day Challenge; 1.9 million students from over 225 countries entered and altogether answered 452 682 682 mental arithmetic questions correctly.

Quick ways of doing mental arithmetic

1 Multiplying a two-digit number by 11

Work out 43 × 11.

Write 4 … 3
Now add the two digits.
4 + 3 = 7
Put the 7 in the middle, between the 4 and the 3.
Answer: 473

Work out 59 × 11.

Write 5 … 9
Now add the two digits.
5 + 9 = 14
Put the units digit (4) in the middle, between the 5 and the 9, and carry the tens digit (1) to the first number.
$\underset{1}{5}\ 4\ 9 = 649$
Answer: 649

2 Doubling and halving

To multiply large numbers, when at least one is even, try doubling one number and halving the other.

Work out 24 × 16.

This is the same as 48 × 8
This is the same as 96 × 4
This is the same as 192 × 2
This is the same as 384 × 1
Answer: 384

2 Square a number that ends in 5

Work out 45.

Take the number of 10s. (4)
Add 1. (5)
Multiply these two numbers. 4 × 5 = 20
Put 25 on the end.
Answer: 2025

Work out 75.

Take the number of 10s. (7)
Add 1. (8)
Multiply these numbers. 7 × 8 = 56
Put 25 on the end.
Answer: 5625

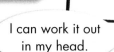

Chapter 7 Number: More number

1. Multiples, factors, prime numbers, powers and roots
2. Prime factors, LCM and HCF
3. Negative numbers

This chapter will show you ...

- **D** how to calculate with integers and decimals
- **D** how to round numbers to a given number of significant figures
- **C** how to find prime factors, least common multiples (LCM) and highest common factors (HCF)

Visual overview

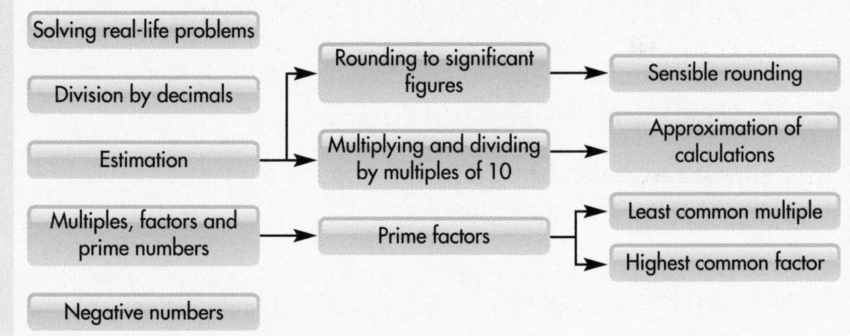

What you should already know

- How to add, subtract, multiply and divide with integers **(KS3 level 4, GCSE grade G)**
- What multiples, factors, square numbers and prime numbers are **(KS3 level 4, GCSE grade G/E)**
- The BIDMAS/BODMAS rule and how to substitute values into simple algebraic expressions **(KS3 level 5, GCSE grade F)**

Quick check

1 Work out the following.

a 9×233 **b** $792 \div 22$ **c** $2^2 \times 3^2$

2 Write down the following.

a A multiple of 7

b A prime number between 10 and 20

c A square number under 80

d The factors of 9

3 Work out the following.

a 8^2 **b** 12^2 **c** $2^2 + 3^2$

7.1 Multiples, factors, prime numbers, powers and roots

This section will show you how to:

- find multiples and factors
- identify prime numbers
- identify square numbers and triangular numbers
- find square roots
- identify cubes and cube roots

Key words

cube roots
cubes
factor
multiple
prime number
square roots
squares
triangle number
triangular number

Multiples. Any number in the multiplication table. For example, the multiples of 7 are 7, 14, 21, 28, 35, … .

Factors. Any whole number that divides exactly into another number. For example, factors of 24 are 1, 2, 3, 4, 6, 8, 12, 24.

Prime numbers. Any number that only has two factors, 1 and itself. For example, 11, 17, 37 are prime numbers.

Squares. A number that comes from multiplying a number by itself. For example, 1, 4, 9, 16, 25, 36 … are square numbers.

Triangular or triangle numbers. Numbers that can make triangular patterns. For example, 1, 3, 6, 10, 15, 21, 28 … are triangular numbers.

Square roots. The square root of a given number is a number which, when multiplied by itself, produces the given number. For example, the square root of 9 is 3, since $3 \times 3 = 9$.

A square root is represented by the symbol $\sqrt{\ }$. For example, $\sqrt{16} = 4$.

Because $-4 \times -4 = 16$, there are always two square roots of every positive number.

So $\sqrt{16} = +4$ or -4. This can be written as $\sqrt{16} = \pm 4$, which is read as plus or minus four.

Cubes. The cube of a number is a number multiplied by itself and then by itself again. For example, the cube of 4 is $4 \times 4 \times 4 = 64$.

Cube roots. The cube root of a number is the number that when multiplied by itself twice gives the cube. For example, the cube root of 27 is 3 because $3 \times 3 \times 3 = 27$ and the cube root of -8 is -2 because $-2 \times -2 \times -2 = -8$.

EXERCISE 7A

1 From this box choose the number that fits each of these descriptions. (One number per description.)

12			21
	8		15
13		17	
9			18
	10		6
14		16	

a A multiple of 3 and a multiple of 4

b A square number and an odd number

c A factor of 24 and a factor of 18

d A prime number and a factor of 39

e An odd factor of 30 and a multiple of 3

f A number with four factors and a multiple of 2 and 7

g A number with five factors exactly

h A triangular number and a factor of 20

i An even number and a factor of 36 and a multiple of 9

j A prime number that is one more than a square number

k If you write the factors of this number out in order they make a number pattern in which each number is twice the one before

l An odd triangular number that is a multiple of 7

FM **2** If hot-dog sausages are sold in packs of 10 and hot-dog buns are sold in packs of eight, how many of each do you have to buy to have complete hot dogs with no wasted sausages or buns?

3 Rover barks every 8 seconds and Spot barks every 12 seconds. If they both bark together, how many seconds will it be before they both bark together again?

4 A bell chimes every 6 seconds. Another bell chimes every 5 seconds. If they both chime together, how many seconds will it be before they both chime together again?

PS **5** Fred runs round a running track in 4 minutes. Debbie runs round in 3 minutes. If they both start together on the line at the end of the finishing straight, when will they both be on the same line together again? How many laps will Debbie have run? How many laps will Fred have run?

6 Copy these sums and write out the *next four* lines.

$$1 = 1$$
$$1 + 3 = 4$$
$$1 + 3 + 5 = 9$$
$$1 + 3 + 5 + 7 = 16$$

7 Write down the negative square root of each of these.

a 4 **b** 25 **c** 49 **d** 1 **e** 81

f 121 **g** 144 **h** 400 **i** 900 **j** 169

D

8 Write down the cube root of each of these.

a 1 **b** 27 **c** 64 **d** 8 **e** 1000

f –8 **g** –1 **h** 8000 **i** 64 000 **j** –64

9 The triangular numbers are 1, 3, 6, 10, 15, 21 …

a Continue the sequence until you get the first triangular number that is greater than 100.

b Add consecutive pairs of triangular numbers, starting with 1 + 3 = 4, 3 + 6 = 9. What do you notice?

AU 10 Here are four numbers.

8 28 49 64

Copy and complete the table by putting each of the numbers in the correct box.

	Square number	Factor of 56
Cube number		
Multiple of 7		

PS 11 The following numbers are described as triangular numbers.

1, 3, 6, 10, 15

a Investigate why they are called triangular numbers.

b Write down the next five triangular numbers.

12 John is writing out his 4 times table. Mary is writing out her 6 times table. They notice that some answers are the same.

In which other times tables do these common answers also appear?

C

PS 13 **a** $36^3 = 46656$. Work out 1^3, 4^3, 9^3, 16^3, 25^3.

b $\sqrt{46656} = 216$. Use a calculator to find the square roots of the numbers you worked out in part **a**.

c 216 = 36 × 6. Can you find a similar connection between the answer to part **b** and the numbers cubed in part **a**?

d What type of numbers are 1, 4, 9, 16, 25, 36?

B

14 Write down the values of these numbers.

a $\sqrt{0.04}$ **b** $\sqrt{0.25}$ **c** $\sqrt{0.36}$ **d** $\sqrt{0.81}$

e $\sqrt{1.44}$ **f** $\sqrt{0.64}$ **g** $\sqrt{1.21}$ **h** $\sqrt{2.25}$

15 Estimate the answers to these.

a $\dfrac{13.7 + 21.9}{\sqrt{0.239}}$ **b** $\dfrac{29.6 \times 11.9}{\sqrt{0.038}}$ **c** $\dfrac{87.5 - 32.6}{\sqrt{0.8} - \sqrt{0.38}}$

7.2 Prime factors, LCM and HCF

This section will show you how to:
- identify prime factors
- identify the least common multiple (LCM) of two numbers
- identify the highest common factor (HCF) of two numbers

Key words
highest common factor (HCF)
index notation
least common multiple (LCM)
prime factor
prime factor tree
product
product of prime factors

Start with a number, such as 110, and find two numbers that, when multiplied together, give that number, for example, 2 × 55. Are they both prime? No, 55 isn't. So take 55 and repeat the operation, to get 5 × 11. Are these both prime? Yes. So:

$110 = 2 \times 5 \times 11$

The **prime factors** of 110 are 2, 5 and 11.

This method is not very logical and you need to know your multiplication tables well to use it. There are, however, two methods that you can use to make sure you do not miss any of the prime factors. The next two examples show you how to use the first of these methods.

EXAMPLE 1

Find the prime factors of 24.

Divide 24 by any prime number that goes into it. (2 is an obvious choice.)

Divide the answer (12) by a prime number. Repeat this process until you have a prime number as the answer.

2	24
2	12
2	6
	3

So the prime factors of 24 are 2 and 3.

$24 = 2 \times 2 \times 2 \times 3$

A quicker and neater way to write this answer is to use **index notation**, expressing the answer using powers. (Powers are dealt with on pages 268–276.)

In index notation, the prime factors of 24 are $2^3 \times 3$.

EXAMPLE 2

Find the prime factors of 96.

2	96
2	48
2	24
2	12
2	6
	3

So, the prime factors of 96 are 2 and 3.

$96 = 2 \times 2 \times 2 \times 2 \times 2 \times 3 = 2^5 \times 3$

When 24 is expressed as $2 \times 2 \times 2 \times 3$ it has been written as a **product of its prime factors**.

Another name for the product $2 \times 2 \times 2 \times 3$ or $2^3 \times 3$ is the *prime factorisation* of 24.

The prime factorisation of 96 is $2 \times 2 \times 2 \times 2 \times 2 \times 3$ or $2^5 \times 3$, which is also the produce of its prime factors.

The second method uses **prime factor trees**. You start by dividing the number into a pair of factors. Then you divide this, and carry on dividing until you get to prime numbers.

EXAMPLE 3

Find the prime factors of 76.

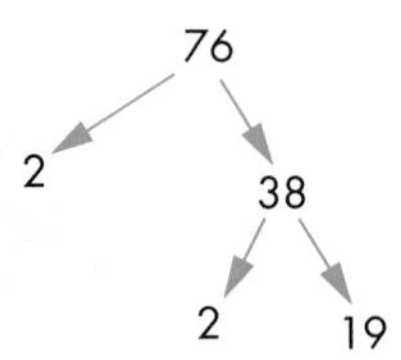

Stop dividing the factors here because 2, 2 and 19 are all prime numbers.

So, the prime factors of 76 are 2 and 19.

$76 = 2 \times 2 \times 19 = 2^2 \times 19$

EXAMPLE 4

Find the prime factors of 420.

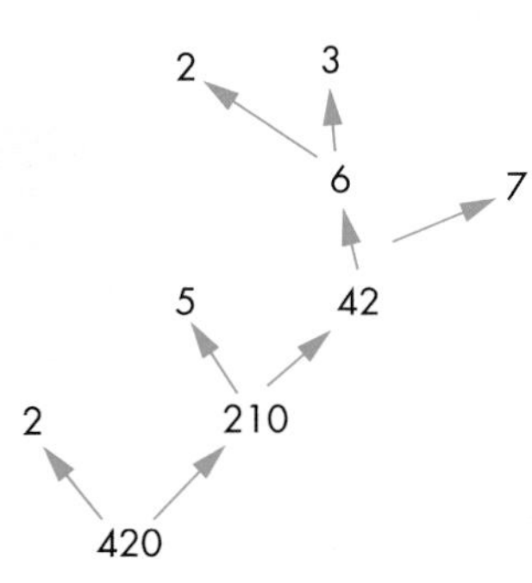

The process can be done upside down to make an upright tree.

So, the prime factors of 420 are 2, 3, 5 and 7.

$420 = 2 \times 5 \times 2 \times 3 \times 7$

$= 2^2 \times 3 \times 5 \times 7$

EXERCISE 7B

1 Copy and complete these prime factor trees.

a

2

2

84

84 = 2 2 … …

b

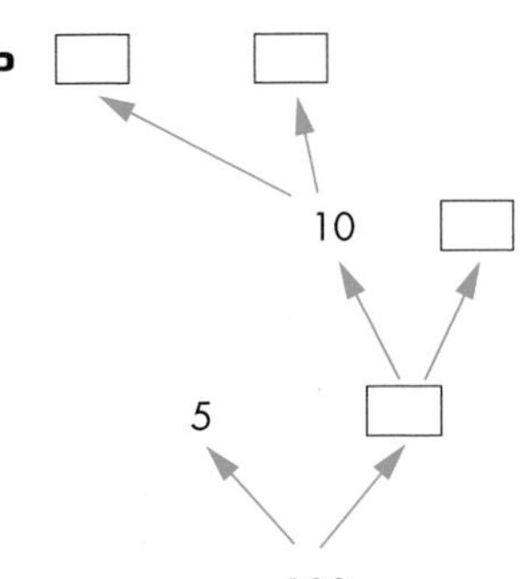

100 = 5 2 … …

c

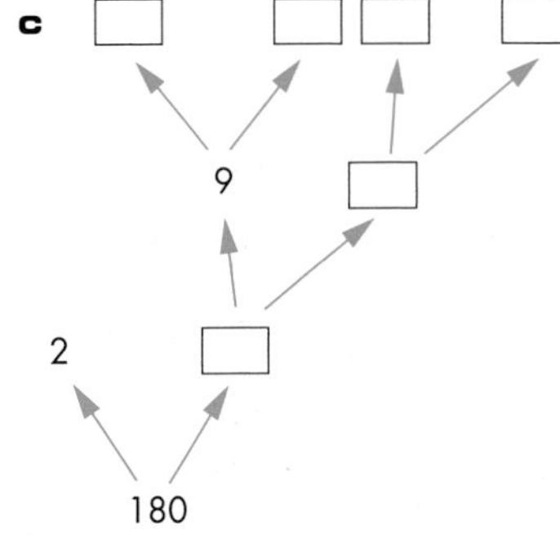

180 = 2 … … … …

d

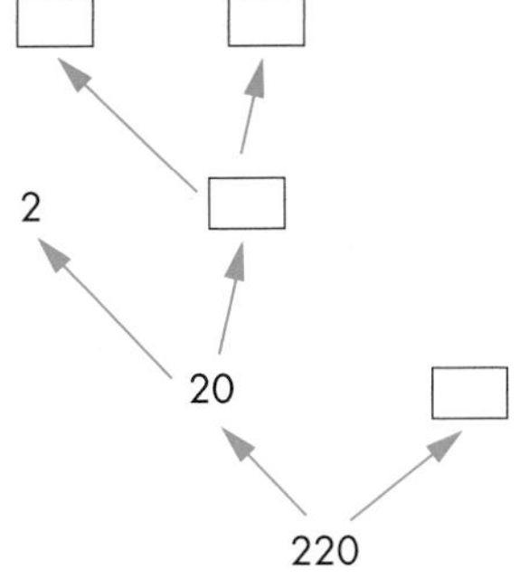

220 = 2 ... ...

e

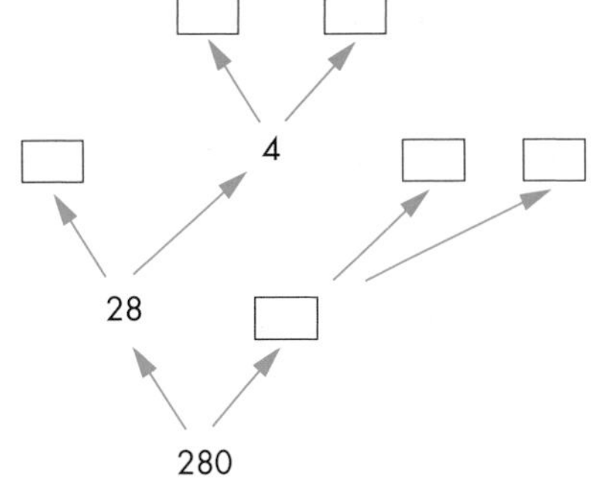

280 = ...

f

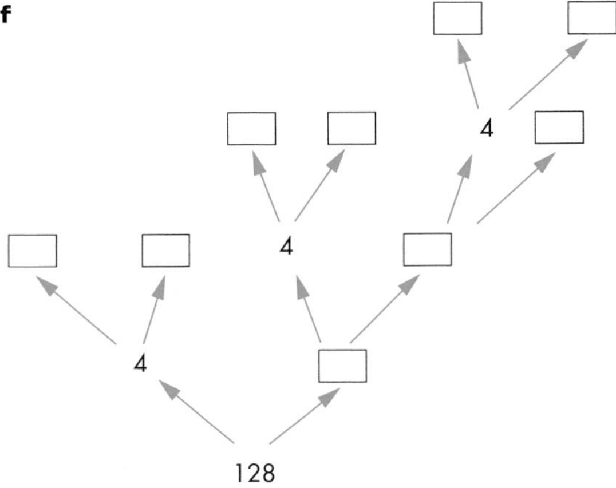

128 = ...

g

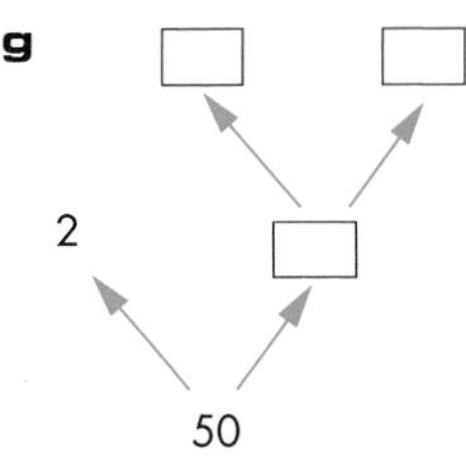

50 = ...

2 Use index notation, for example:

$100 = 2 \times 2 \times 5 \times 5 = 2^2 \times 5^2$

and $540 = 2 \times 2 \times 3 \times 3 \times 3 \times 5 = 2^2 \times 3^3 \times 5$

to rewrite your answers to question **1**, parts **a** to **g**.

3 Write the numbers from 1 to 50 as products of their prime factors. Use index notation. For example:

$1 = 1$ $2 = 2$ $3 = 3$

$4 = 2^2$ $5 = 5$ $6 = 2 \times 3$ ...

4 **a** What is special about the numbers 2, 4, 8, 16, 32, ...?

b What are the next two terms in this series?

c What are the next three terms in the series 3, 9, 27, ...?

d Continue the series 4, 16, 64, ..., for three more terms.

e Rewrite all the series in parts **a**, **b**, **c** and **d** in index notation. For example, the first series is:

$2^1, 2^2, 2^3, 2^4, 2^5, 2^6, 2^7, \ldots$

C

AU 5 **a** Express 60 as a product of prime factors.

b Write your answer to part **a** in index form.

c Use your answer to part **b** to write 120, 240 and 480 each as a product of prime factors in index form.

PS 6 $1001 = 7 \times 11 \times 13$

$1001^2 = 1002001$

$1001^3 = 1003003001$

a Write 1002001 as a product of prime factors in index form.

b Write 1003003001 as a product of prime factors in index form.

c Write 1001^{10} as a product of prime factors in index form.

7 Harriet wants to share £40 between three of her grandchildren. Explain why it is not possible for them to get equal shares.

Least common multiple

The **least common multiple** or *lowest common multiple* (LCM) of two numbers is the smallest number that appears in the multiplication tables of both numbers.

For example, the LCM of 3 and 5 is 15, the LCM of 2 and 7 is 14 and the LCM of 6 and 9 is 18.

There are two ways of working out the LCM.

EXAMPLE 5

Find the LCM of 18 and 24.

Write out the 18 times table: 18, 36, 54, (72), 90, 108, … .

Write out the 24 times table: 24, 48, (72), 96, 120, …

You can see that 72 is the smallest (least) number in both (common) tables (multiples).

EXAMPLE 6

Find the LCM of 42 and 63.

Write 42 in prime factor form. $42 = 2 \times 3 \times 7$

Write 63 in prime factor form. $63 = 3^2 \times 7$

Write down the smallest number in prime factor form that includes all the prime factors of 42 and of 63.

You need $2 \times 3^2 \times 7$ (this includes $2 \times 3 \times 7$ and $3^2 \times 7$).

Then work it out.

$2 \times 3^2 \times 7 = 2 \times 9 \times 7 = 18 \times 7 = 126$

The LCM of 42 and 63 is 126.

Highest common factor

The **highest common factor** (HCF) of two numbers is the biggest number that divides exactly into both of them.

For example, the HCF of 24 and 18 is 6, the HCF of 45 and 36 is 9 and the HCF of 15 and 22 is 1.

There are two ways of working out the HCF.

EXAMPLE 7

Find the HCF of 28 and 16.

Write out the factors of 28. 1, 2, (4), 7, 14, 28

Write out the factors of 16. 1, 2, (4), 8, 16

You can see that 4 is the biggest (highest) number in both (common) lists (factors).

EXAMPLE 8

Find the HCF of 48 and 120.

Write 48 in prime factor form. $48 = 2^4 \times 3$

Write 120 in prime factor form. $120 = 2^3 \times 3 \times 5$

Write down the biggest number in prime factor form that is in the prime factors of 48 and 120.

You need $2^3 \times 3$ (this is in both $2^4 \times 3$ and $2^3 \times 3 \times 5$).

Then work it out. $2^3 \times 3 = 8 \times 3 = 24$

The HCF of 48 and 120 is 24.

EXERCISE 7C

C

1 Find the LCM of each pair of numbers.

a 4 and 5 **b** 7 and 8

c 2 and 3 **d** 4 and 7

e 2 and 5 **f** 3 and 5

g 3 and 8 **h** 5 and 6

2 What connection is there between the LCMs and the pairs of numbers in question **1**?

3 Find the LCM of each pair of numbers.

a 4 and 8 **b** 6 and 9

c 4 and 6 **d** 10 and 15

PS 4 Does the connection you found in question **2** still work for the numbers in question **3**? If not, explain why not?

C

5 Find the LCM of each pair of numbers.

a 24 and 56 **b** 21 and 35

c 12 and 28 **d** 28 and 42

e 12 and 32 **f** 18 and 27

g 15 and 25 **h** 16 and 36

FM 6 Cheese slices are sold in packs of eight.

Bread rolls are sold in packs of six.

What is the least number of each pack that needs to be bought to have the same number of cheese slices and bread rolls?

7 Find the HCF of each pair of numbers.

a 24 and 56 **b** 21 and 35

c 12 and 28 **d** 28 and 42

e 12 and 32 **f** 18 and 27

g 15 and 25 **h** 16 and 36

i 42 and 27 **j** 48 and 64

k 25 and 35 **l** 36 and 54

PS 8 In prime factor form $1250 = 2 \times 5^4$ and $525 = 3 \times 5^2 \times 7$.

a Which of these are common multiples of 1250 and 525?

i $2 \times 3 \times 5^3 \times 7$

ii $2^3 \times 3 \times 5^4 \times 7^2$

iii $2 \times 3 \times 5^4 \times 7$

iv $2 \times 3 \times 5 \times 7$

b Which of these are common factors of 1250 and 525?

i 2×3

ii 2×5

iii 5^2

iv $2 \times 3 \times 5 \times 7$

AU PS 9 The HCF of two numbers is 6.

The LCM of the same two numbers is 72.

What are the numbers?

7.3 Negative numbers

This section will show you how to:

- multiply and divide positive and negative numbers

Key words
negative
order
positive

Multiplying and dividing with negative numbers

The rules for multiplying and dividing with **negative** numbers are very easy.

- When the signs of the numbers are the same, the answer is **positive**.
- When the signs of the numbers are different, the answer is negative.

Here are some examples.

$2 \times 4 = 8$ $\quad 12 \div -3 = -4$

$-2 \times -3 = 6$ $\quad -12 \div -3 = 4$

Negative numbers on a calculator

You can enter a negative number into your calculator and check the result.

Enter –5 by pressing the keys **5** and . (You may need to press **(–)** or **–** followed by **5**, depending on the type of calculator that you have.) You will see the calculator shows –5.

Now try these two calculations.

–8 – 7 → **8** **(–)** **–** **7** **=** –15

6 – –3 → **6** **–** **(–)** **3** **=** 9

EXERCISE 7D

1 Write down the answers to the following.

a -3×5 **b** -2×7

c -4×6 **d** -2×-3

e -7×-2 **f** $-12 \div -6$

g $-16 \div 8$ **h** $24 \div -3$

i $16 \div -4$ **j** $-6 \div -2$

k 4×-6 **l** 5×-2

m 6×-3 **n** -2×-8

o -9×-4

D

D

2 Write down the answers to the following.

a $-3 + -6$ **b** -2×-8 **c** $2 + -5$

d 8×-4 **e** $-36 \div -2$ **f** -3×-6

g $-3 - -9$ **h** $48 \div -12$ **i** -5×-4

j $7 - -9$ **k** $-40 \div -5$ **l** $-40 + -8$

m $4 - -9$ **n** $5 - 18$ **o** $72 \div -9$

3 What number do you multiply –3 by to get the following?

a 6 **b** –90 **c** –45

d 81 **e** 21

4 Evaluate the following.

a $-6 + (4 - 7)$ **b** $-3 - (-9 - -3)$ **c** $8 + (2 - 9)$

5 Evaluate the following.

a $4 \times (-8 \div -2)$ **b** $-8 - (3 \times -2)$ **c** $-1 \times (8 - -4)$

PS 6 Write down six different multiplications that give the answer –12.

PS 7 Write down six different division sums that give the answer –4.

AU 8 **a** Work out: 12×-2

b The average temperature drops by two degrees celsius every day for 12 days. By how much has the temperature dropped altogether?

c The temperature drops by six degrees celsius for the next three days. Write down the calculation to work out the total change in temperature over these three days.

PS 9 Put these calculations in order from lowest result to highest.

-15×4 $-72 \div 4$ $-56 \div -8$ 13×-6

Hierarchy of operations

Reminder: The **order** in which you *must* do mathematical operations should follow the BIDMAS or BODMAS rule.

B	Brackets	B	Brackets
I	Indices (Powers)	O	Order (Powers)
D	Division	D	Division
M	Multiplication	M	Multiplication
A	Addition	A	Addition
S	Subtraction	S	Subtraction

Errors are often made because of negative signs or doing calculations in the wrong order. For example:

$2 + 3 \times 4$ is equal to $2 + 12 = 14$ and **not** 5×4.

-6^2 is **not** the same as $(-6)^2$.

$-6^2 = -(6 \times 6) = -36$ but $(-6)^2 = -6 \times -6 = 36$

EXAMPLE 9

Work out each of the following.

a $(8 - 3^2) \times 9 \div (-1 + 4)$ **b** $5 \times [6^2 + (5 - 8)^2]$

a The brackets are calculated first.

$(8 - 3^2) \times 9 \div (-1 + 4) = (8 - 9) \times 9 \div 3 = -1 \times 9 \div 3 = -9 \div 3 = -3$

b This has nested brackets. The inside (round) bracket is calculated first:

$5 \times [6^2 + (5 - 8)^2] = 5 \times [6^2 + (-3)^2] = 5 \times [36 + 9] = 5 \times 45 = 225$

EXERCISE 7E

D

1 Work out each of these. Remember to work out the brackets first.

a $-2 \times (-3 + 5) =$ **b** $6 \div (-2 + 1) =$ **c** $(5 - 7) \times -2 =$

d $-5 \times (-7 - 2) =$ **e** $-3 \times (-4 \div 2) =$ **f** $-3 \times (-4 + 2) =$

2 Work out each of these.

a $-6 \times -6 + 2 =$ **b** $-6 \times (-6 + 2) =$ **c** $-6 \div 6 - 2 =$

d $12 \div (-4 + 2) =$ **e** $12 \div -4 + 2 =$ **f** $2 \times (-3 + 4) =$

g $-(5)^2 =$ **h** $(-5)^2 =$ **i** $(-1 + 3)^2 - 4 =$

j $-(1 + 3)^2 - 4 =$ **k** $-1 + 3^2 - 4 =$ **l** $-1 + (3 - 4)^2 =$

PS 3 Copy each of these and then put in brackets where necessary to make each one true.

a $3 \times -4 + 1 = -11$ **b** $-6 \div -2 + 1 = 6$ **c** $-6 \div -2 + 1 = 4$

d $4 + -4 \div 4 = 3$ **e** $4 + -4 \div 4 = 0$ **f** $16 - -4 \div 2 = 10$

4 $a = -2$, $b = 3$, $c = -5$.

Work out the values of the following.

a $(a + c)^2$ **b** $-(a + b)^2$ **c** $(a + b)c$ **d** $a^2 + b^2 - c^2$

5 Work out each of the following.

a $(6^2 - 4^2) \times 2$ **b** $9 \div (1 - 4)^2$

c $2 \times [8^2 - (2 - 7)^2]$ **d** $[(3 + 2)^2 - (5 - 6)^2] \div 6$

D

AU **6** Use each of the numbers 2, 3 and 4 and each of the symbols –, × and ÷ to make a calculation with an answer –6.

7 Use any four different numbers to make a calculation with answer –8.

C

PS **8** Use the numbers 5, 6, 7, 8 and 9 in order, from smallest to largest, together with one of each of the symbols + , –, × ÷ and two pairs of brackets to make a calculation with an answer of $\frac{25}{8}$.

For example, making a calculation with an answer of $\frac{43}{9}$:

$(5 + 6) - (7 \times 8) \div 9 = \frac{43}{9}$

GRADE BOOSTER

- **D** You can recognise and work out multiples, factors and primes
- **D** You can multiply and divide with negative numbers
- **C** You can write a number as the product of its prime factors
- **C** You can work out the LCM and HCF of pairs of numbers
- **B** You can work out the square roots of some decimal numbers
- **B** You can estimate answers involving the square roots of decimals

What you should know now

- How to write a number in prime factor form and find LCMs and HCFs
- How to find the square roots of some decimal numbers

EXAMINATION QUESTIONS

1 **a** Write 42 as the product of its prime factors.

b Find the least common multiple of 28 and 42.

2 As the product of prime factors $60 = 2^2 \times 3 \times 5$

a What number is represented by $2 \times 3^2 \times 5$?

b Find the least common multiple (LCM) of 60 and 48.

c Find the highest common factor (HCF) of 60 and 78.

3 Write 40 as the product of prime factors.

Give your answer in index form. *(3 marks)*

AQA, June 2009, Module 3 Higher, Question 4

4 The Least Common Multiple (LCM) of two numbers is 36.

Find one possible pair for the two numbers. *(1 mark)*

AQA, November 2007, Module 3 Higher, Question 5

5 Mary set up her Christmas tree with two sets of twinkling lights.

Set A would twinkle every 3 seconds.

Set B would twinkle every 4 seconds.

How many times in a minute will both sets be twinkling at the same time?

6 Emily, Jack and Mia are tapping on the desk in time to Tom clapping his hands to a regular beat.

Emily taps on every fifth clap.

Jack taps on every sixth clap.

Mia taps on every eighth clap.

They all start together on the first clap.

How many claps will it be before Emily, Jack and Mia all tap at the same time again?

7 **a** You are given that $8x^3 = 1000$. Find the value of x.

b Write 150 as the product of its prime factors.

8 **a** p and q are prime numbers such that $pq^3 = 250$

Find the values of p and q.

b Find the highest common factor of 250 and 80.

9 **a** a and b are prime numbers such that $(ab)^3 = 1000$. What are the values of a and b?

b p and q are integers such that $(pq)^3 = 216$. Explain why it is not possible to find values of p and q.

Worked Examination Questions

1 Estimate the result of the calculation

$$\frac{195.71 - 53.62}{\sqrt{0.0375}}$$

Show the estimates you make.

1 $\frac{200 - 50}{\sqrt{0.04}}$ — First round each number to 1 significant figure. Rounding the two numbers in the numerator to 1sf gets 1 mark for method.

$\frac{150}{0.2}$ — Working out the numerator and taking out the square root in the denominator gets 1 mark.

$\frac{150}{0.2} = \frac{1500}{2} = 750$ — Change the problem so it becomes division by an integer 750 gets 1 mark for accuracy.

Total: 3 marks

FM **2** I earn £30 000 in 12 months.

Half of this is spent on tax.

How much do I have left each month?

2 30 000 ÷ 2 or £15 000 — Work out how much I spend on tax or how much I have left. This is the same calculation as it is half of £30 000 and gets 1 mark for method. Note: the answer of £15 000 does not need to be worked out at this stage.

30 000 ÷ 2 ÷ 12 — The next step is to calculate one-twelfth of £30 000 ÷ 2. This gets 1 mark for method.

= £1250 — This gets 1 mark for accuracy.

Total: 3 marks

PS **3** Two numbers have been rounded.
The first number is 360 to two significant figures.
The second number is 500 to one significant figure.

What is the smallest sum of the two original numbers?

3 The smallest that the first number could be is 355.
The smallest that the second number could be is 450. — Realising that each number needs to be the smallest possible gets 1 mark for method. Either value 355 or 450 gets 1 mark for accuracy.

Smallest sum = 355 + 450 = 805 — Correctly adding the two smallest numbers gets 1 mark for accuracy.

Total: 3 marks

Functional Maths
Creating your own allotment

Today, many people living in towns and cities do not have their own gardens. Allotments give these people the opportunity to enjoy gardening regardless of not having their own garden. Allotments are also increasingly popular as a way of producing home-grown cheap fruit and vegetables. You have just started renting an allotment so that can grow your own fruit and vegetables. The allotment is divided into rows for planting. The whole plot is 3 m wide and each row is 5 m long.

Your task

1 Design the plant layout for the allotment using the information that you will gather from the table.
Consider as many different arrangements as possible.
You must explain your choices, stating the assumptions that you have made.

2 You have a shed at your allotment, one wall of which you can use for storage. The wall is 3 m long and 3 m high.
You store most of your gardening tools and equipment in these boxes in your shed.

Type of box	Length (cm)	Width (cm)	Height (cm)	Number of boxes
Flower seeds	10 cm	10 cm	10 cm	10
Vegetable seeds	15 cm	15 cm	10 cm	10
Wire, string, nails	20 cm	15 cm	15 cm	5
Gloves	30 cm	20 cm	15 cm	2
Hand tools (trowels, etc.)	50 cm	40 cm	30 cm	2
Tool attachments	80 cm	70 cm	50 cm	1

You are putting up shelves in your shed. Show how many shelves you would put up and how you would arrange the boxes to fit as many into your shed as possible.

You should consider these points when you design your shelf layout:

- space between shelves
- height from the floor
- where you will place each box
- the convenience of removing items from the boxes
- place the largest box away from the door as it sticks out the most.

Facts

This table shows how much distance is needed between plants and between rows for the key vegetables in your allotment.

Vegetable	Distance between plants (cm)	Distance between rows (cm)
Potatoes	30 cm	50 cm
Carrots	10 cm	20 cm
Broad beans	10 cm	30 cm
Onions	10 cm	20 cm
Cucumber	30 cm	60 cm
Lettuce	20 cm	30 cm

Handy hints

You may find these rules helpful when planning your allotment:

- use one type of vegetable for each complete row
- do not have more than two rows of the same vegetable
- if different plants are next to each other, make sure that the largest necessary distance between rows is left between them
- make sure that vegetables are not planted too near to the edge of the allotment
- use graph paper to represent the allotment
- use a code to represent each plant.

Why this chapter matters

If you were asked to circle one of these to describe mathematics, which would it be?

Art Science Sport Language

In fact, you could circle them all.

Mathematics is important in **art**. The *Mona Lisa*, probably the most famous painting in the world, uses the proportions of the 'Golden Ratio' (approximately 1.618). This 'Golden Ratio' as shown by the red rectangles marked on this copy of the painting, is supposed to be particularly attractive to the human eye.

Obviously, you cannot do much **science** without using mathematics. In 1962, a *Mariner* space probe went off course and had to be destroyed because someone had used a wrong symbol in a mathematical formula that was part of its programming.

Is mathematics used in **sport**? There are national and international competitions each year that use mathematics. For example, there is a world Sudoku championship each year, and university students compete in the Mathematics Olympiad each year.

But perhaps the most important description in the list above is maths as a **language**.

Mathematics is the only universal language. If you write the equation $3x = 9$, it will be understood by people in all countries.

Algebra is the way that the language of mathematics is expressed.

Algebra comes from the Arabic *al-jabr* which means something similar to 'completion'. It was used in a book written in 820AD by a Persian mathematician called al-Khwarizmi.

The use of symbols developed until the middle of the 17th century, when René Descartes introduced what is regarded as the basis of the algebra we use today.

Chapter 8

Algebra: Expressions and equations

This chapter will show you ...

- **D** how to manipulate basic algebraic expressions by multiplying terms together, expanding brackets and collecting like terms
- **C** how to factorise linear expressions
- **B** how to solve linear equations
- **B** how to solve simultaneous equations
- **A** how to rearrange formulae

Visual overview

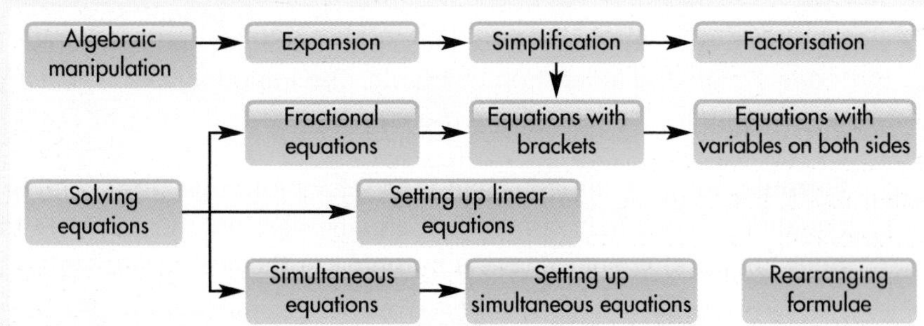

What you should already know

- The basic language of algebra **(KS3 level 5, GCSE grade E)**
- How to collect together like terms **(KS3 level 5, GCSE grade E)**
- How to multiply together terms such as $2m \times 3m$ **(KS3 level 5, GCSE grade E)**

Quick check

1 Expand the following.

a $2(x + 6)$ **b** $4(x - 3)$ **c** $6(2x - 1)$

2 Simplify the following.

a $4y + 2y - y$ **b** $3x + 2 + x - 5$ **c** $2(x + 1) - 3(x + 2)$

3 Simplify the following.

a $3 \times 2x$ **b** $4y \times 2y$ **c** $c^2 \times 2c$

4 Solve the following equations

a $2x + 4 = 6$ **b** $3x - 5 = 4$ **c** $\frac{x}{3} + 2 = 5$

d $\frac{x}{2} = 4$ **e** $\frac{x}{3} = 8$ **f** $\frac{2x}{5} = 6$

8.1 Basic algebra

This section will show you how to:

- recognise expressions, equations, formulae and identities
- substitute into, manipulate and simplify algebraic expressions

Key words

brackets, coefficient, equation, expand, expression, formula, identity, like terms, simplification, substitute, term, variable

Here are some algebraic words that you need to know.

Variable. Letters that are used to represent numbers are called variables. These letters can take on any value, so they are said to *vary*.

Expression. An expression is any combination of letters and numbers.

For example, $2x + 4y$ and $\frac{p-6}{5}$ are expressions.

Equation. You will study these later in this chapter and in Chapter 10. An equation contains an 'equals' sign and at least one variable. The important fact is that a value can be found for the variable. This is called *solving the equation*.

Formula. You may already have seen lots of formulae (the plural of formula). These are like equations in that they contain an 'equals' sign, but there is more than one variable and they are rules for working out things such as area or the cost of taxi fares.

For example, $V = x^3$, $A = \frac{1}{2}bh$ and $C = 3 + 4m$ are formulae.

Identity. These look like formulae, but the important fact about an identity is that it is true for all values, whether numerical or algebraic.

For example, $5n \equiv 2n + 3n$ and $(x + 1)^2 \equiv x^2 + 2x + 1$ are identities. Note that the special sign $\equiv$ is used in an identity.

Term. Terms are the separate parts of expressions, equations, formulae and identities.

For example, in $3x + 2y - 7$, there are three terms: $3x$, $+2y$ and -7.

EXAMPLE 1

Say if each of the following is an expression (E), equation (Q), formula (F) or identity (I).

A: $x - 5 = 7$ B: $P = 4x$ C: $2x - 3y$ D: $3n - n = 2n$

A is an equation (Q) as it can be solved to give $x = 12$.

B is a formula (F). This is the formula for the perimeter of a square with a side of x.

C is an expression (E) with two terms.

D is an identity (I) as it is true for all values of n.

Substitution

EXAMPLE 2

Find the value of $3x^2 - 5$ when **a** $x = 3$ **b** $x = -4$

Whenever you **substitute** a number for a variable in an expression always put the value in **brackets** before working it out. This will avoid errors in calculation, especially with negative numbers.

a When $x = 3$ $3(3)^2 - 5 = 3 \times 9 - 5 = 27 - 5 = 22$

b When $x = -4$ $3(-4)^2 - 5 = 3 \times 16 - 5 = 48 - 5 = 43$

EXAMPLE 3

Find the value of $L = a^2 - 8b^2$ when $a = -6$ and $b = \frac{1}{2}$.

Substitute for the letters.

$L = (-6)^2 - 8(\frac{1}{2})^2$

$L = 36 - 8 \times \frac{1}{4} = 36 - 2 = 34$

Note: If you do not use brackets and write -6^2, this could be wrongly evaluated as -36.

EXERCISE 8A

1 Find the value of $4b + 3$ when: **a** $b = 2.5$ **b** $b = -1.5$ **c** $b = \frac{1}{2}$

2 Evaluate $\frac{x}{3}$ when: **a** $x = 6$ **b** $x = 24$ **c** $x = -30$

3 Find the value of $\frac{12}{y}$ when: **a** $y = 2$ **b** $y = 4$ **c** $y = -6$

4 Evaluate $3w - 4$ when: **a** $w = -1$ **b** $w = -2$ **c** $w = 3.5$

5 Find the value of $\frac{24}{y}$ when: **a** $x = -5$ **b** $x = \frac{1}{2}$ **c** $x = \frac{3}{4}$

6 Where $P = \frac{5w - 4y}{w + y}$, find P when:

a $w = 3$ and $y = 2$ **b** $w = 6$ and $y = 4$ **c** $w = 2$ and $y = 3$

7 Where $A = b^2 + c^2$, find A when:

a $b = 2$ and $c = 3$ **b** $b = 5$ and $c = 7$ **c** $b = -1$ and $c = -4$

8 Where $A = \frac{180(n - 2)}{n + 5}$, find A when:

a $n = 7$ **b** $n = 3$ **c** $n = -1$

D

D

9 Where $Z = \dfrac{y^2 + 4}{4 + y}$, find Z when:

a $y = 4$ **b** $y = -6$ **c** $y = -1.5$

FM 10 A taxi company uses the following rule to calculate their fares.

Fare = £2.50 plus 50p per kilometre.

a How much is the fare for a journey of 3 km?

b Farook pays £9.00 for a taxi ride. How far was the journey?

c Maisy knows that her house is 5 miles from town. She has £5.50 left in her purse after a night out. Has she got enough for a taxi ride home?

FM 11 A holiday cottage costs £150 per day to rent.
A group of friends decide to rent the cottage for seven days.

a Which of the following formulae would represent the cost per day if there are n people in the group and they share the cost equally?

$\dfrac{150}{n}$ $\dfrac{150}{7n}$ $\dfrac{1050}{n}$ $\dfrac{150n}{7}$

b Eventually 10 people go on the holiday.
When they get the bill, they find that there is a discount for a seven-day rental. After the discount, they each find it costs them £12.50 less than they expected.

How much does a seven-day rental cost?

HINTS AND TIPS

To check your choice in part **a**, make up some numbers and try them in the formulae. For example, take $n = 5$.

AU 12 Kaz knows that x, y and z have the values 2, 8 and 11, but she does not know which variable has which value.

a What is the maximum value that the expression $2x + 6y - 3z$ could have?

b What is the minimum value that the expression $5x - 2y + 3z$ could have?

HINTS AND TIPS

You can just try all combinations but, if you think for a moment, the $6y$ term obviously has to be the biggest, and this will give you a clue to the other terms.

FM 13 The formula for the electricity bill each quarter in a household is £7.50 + £0.07 per unit.
A family uses 6720 units in a quarter.

a How much is their total bill?

b The family pay a direct debit of £120 per month towards their electricity costs.
By how much will they be in credit or debit after the quarter?

AU 14 x and y are different positive whole numbers.
Choose values for x and y so that the expression

$5x + 3y$

a evaluates to an odd number

b evaluates to a prime number.

You will need to remember the prime numbers, 2, 3, 5, 7, 11, 13, 17, 19, …

PS 15 The formula for the area, A, of a rectangle with length l and width w is $A = lw$.

The formula for the area, T, of a triangle with base b and height h is $T = \frac{1}{2}bh$.

Find values of l, w, b and h so that $A = T$.

AU 16 **a** p is an odd number and q is an even number.

Say if the following expressions are odd or even.

i $p + q$ **ii** $p^2 + q$ **iii** $2p + q$ **iv** $p^2 + q^2$

b x, y and z are all odd numbers.

Write an expression using x, y and z so that the value of the expression is always even.

There are many answers for part (b) and part (a).

PS 17 A formula for the cost of delivery, in pounds, of orders from a do-it-yourself warehouse is:

$$D = 2M - \frac{C}{5}$$

where D is the cost of the delivery, M is the distance in miles from the store and C is the cost of the goods to be delivered.

a How much is the delivery cost when $M = 30$ and $C = 200$?

b Bob buys goods worth £300 and lives 10 miles from the store.

i The formula gives that the cost of delivery is a negative value. What is this value?

ii Explain why Bob will not get a rebate from the store.

c Martha buys goods worth £400. She calculates that her cost of delivery will be zero.

What is the greatest distance Martha could live from the store?

18 Say if each of the following is an expression (E), equation (Q), formula (F) or identity (I).

A: $2x - 5$

B: $s = \sqrt{A}$

C: $2(x + 3) = 2x + 6$

D: $2x - 3 = 1$

AU 19 Marvin hires a car for the day for £40. He wants to know how much it costs him for each mile he drives.

Petrol is 98p per litre and the car does 10 miles per litre.

Marvin works out the following formula for the cost per mile, C in pounds, for M miles driven:

$$C = 0.098 + \frac{40}{M}$$

a Explain each term of the formula.

b How much will it cost per mile if Marvin drives 200 miles that day?

HINTS AND TIPS

Use the information in the question in your explanation.

Expansion

In mathematics, to '**expand**' usually means 'multiply out'. For example, expressions such as $3(y + 2)$ and $4y^2(2y + 3)$ can be expanded by multiplying them out.

Remember that there is an invisible multiplication sign between the outside number and the opening bracket. So $3(y + 2)$ is really $3 \times (y + 2)$ and $4y^2(2y + 3)$ is really $4y^2 \times (2y + 3)$.

You expand by multiplying *everything inside* the brackets by what is outside the brackets.

So in the case of the two examples above,

$$3(y + 2) = 3 \times (y + 2) = 3 \times y + 3 \times 2 = 3y + 6$$

$$4y^2(2y + 3) = 4y^2 \times (2y + 3) = 4y^2 \times 2y + 4y^2 \times 3 = 8y^3 + 12y^2$$

Look at these next examples of expansion, which show clearly how the term outside the brackets has been multiplied with the terms inside them.

$2(m + 3) = 2m + 6$ | $y(y^2 - 4x) = y^3 - 4xy$

$3(2t + 5) = 6t + 15$ | $3x^2(4x + 5) = 12x^3 + 15x^2$

$m(p + 7) = mp + 7m$ | $-3(2 + 3x) = -6 - 9x$

$x(x - 6) = x^2 - 6x$ | $-2x(3 - 4x) = -6x + 8x^2$

$4t(t^3 + 2) = 4t^4 + 8t$ | $3t(2 + 5t - p) = 6t + 15t^2 - 3pt$

Note: The signs change when a negative quantity is outside the brackets. For example,

$a(b + c) = ab + ac$ | $a(b - c) = ab - ac$

$-a(b + c) = -ab - ac$ | $-a(b - c) = -ab + ac$

$-(a - b) = -a + b$ | $-(a + b - c) = -a - b + c$

Note: A minus sign on its own in front of the brackets is actually –1, so:

$$-(x + 2y - 3) = -1 \times (x + 2y - 3) = -1 \times x + -1 \times 2y + -1 \times -3 = -x - 2y + 3$$

The effect of a minus sign outside the brackets is to change the sign of everything inside the brackets.

EXERCISE 8B

D

1 Expand these expressions.

a $2(3 + m)$ **b** $5(2 + l)$ **c** $3(4 - y)$ **d** $4(5 + 2k)$

e $3(2 - 4f)$ **f** $2(5 - 3w)$ **g** $5(2k + 3m)$ **h** $4(3d - 2n)$

i $t(t + 3)$ **j** $k(k - 3)$ **k** $4t(t - 1)$ **l** $2k(4 - k)$

m $4g(2g + 5)$ **n** $5h(3h - 2)$ **o** $y(y^2 + 5)$ **p** $h(h^3 + 7)$

q $k(k^2 - 5)$ **r** $3t(t^2 + 4)$ **s** $3d(5d^2 - d^3)$ **t** $3w(2w^2 + t)$

u $5a(3a^2 - 2b)$ **v** $3p(4p^3 - 5m)$ **w** $4h^2(3h + 2g)$ **x** $2m^2(4m + m^2)$

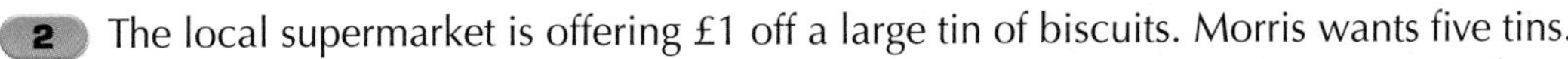

2 The local supermarket is offering £1 off a large tin of biscuits. Morris wants five tins.

a If the price of one tin is £t, which of the expressions below represents how much it will cost Morris to buy five tins?

$5(t - 1)$ $\quad$ $5t - 1$ $\quad$ $t - 5$ $\quad$ $5t - 5$

b Morris has £20 to spend. Will he have enough money for five tins? Show working to justify your answer.

AU 3 Dylan wrote the following.

$3(5x - 4) = 8x - 4$

Dylan has made two mistakes.

Explain the mistakes that Dylan has made.

HINTS AND TIPS

It is not enough to give the right answer. You must try to explain why Dylan wrote 8 for 3 × 5 instead of 15.

PS 4 The expansion $2(x + 3) = 2x + 6$ can be shown by this diagram.

	x	3
2	$2x$	6

a What expansion is shown in this diagram?

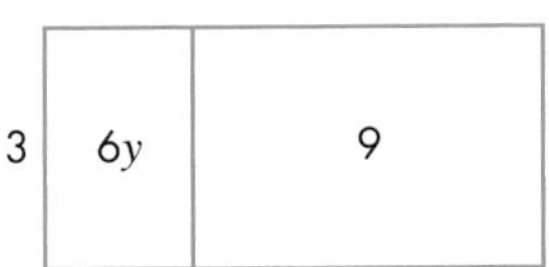

b Write down an expansion that is shown on this diagram.

$12z$	8

Simplification

Simplification is the process whereby an expression is written down as simply as possible, with any **like terms** being combined. Like terms are terms that have the same letter(s) raised to the same power and can differ only in their numerical **coefficients** (numbers in front). For example,

m, $3m$, $4m$, $-m$ and $76m$ are all like terms in m

t^2, $4t^2$, $7t^2$, $-t^2$, $-3t^2$ and $98t^2$ are all like terms in t^2

pt, $5tp$, $-2pt$, $7pt$, $-3tp$ and $103pt$ are all like terms in pt

Note: All the terms in tp are also like terms to all the terms in pt.

When simplifying an expression, you can only add or subtract like terms. For example,

$4m + 3m = 7m$	$3y + 4y + 3 = 7y + 3$	$4h - h = 3h$
$2t^2 + 5t^2 = 7t^2$	$2m + 6 + 3m = 5m + 6$	$7t + 8 - 2t = 5t + 8$
$3ab + 2ba = 5ab$	$5k - 2k = 3k$	$10g - 4 - 3g = 7g - 4$

Expand and simplify

When two brackets are expanded there are often like terms that can be collected together. Algebraic expressions should always be simplified as much as possible.

EXAMPLE 4

$$3(4 + m) + 2(5 + 2m) = 12 + 3m + 10 + 4m = 22 + 7m$$

EXAMPLE 5

$$3t(5t + 4) - 2t(3t - 5) = 15t^2 + 12t - 6t^2 + 10t = 9t^2 + 22t$$

EXERCISE 8C

D

1 Simplify these expressions.

a $4t + 3t$ **b** $3d + 2d + 4d$ **c** $5e - 2e$ **d** $3t - t$

e $2t^2 + 3t^2$ **f** $6y^2 - 2y^2$ **g** $3ab + 2ab$ **h** $7a^2d - 4a^2d$

AU 2 Find the missing terms to make these equations true.

a $4x + 5y + \ldots - \ldots = 6x + 3y$

b $3a - 6b - \ldots + \ldots = 2a + b$

PS 3 ABCDEF is an 'L' shape.
$AB = DE = x$
$AF = 3x - 1$ and $EF = 2x + 1$

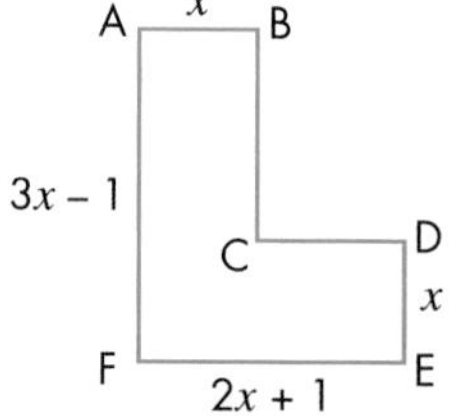

a Explain why the length $BC = 2x - 1$

b Find the perimeter of the shape in terms of x.

c If $x = 2.5$ cm what is the perimeter of the shape?

HINTS AND TIPS

Make sure your explanation uses expressions. Do not try to explain in words alone.

C

4 Expand and simplify.

a $3(4 + t) + 2(5 + t)$ **b** $5(3 + 2k) + 3(2 + 3k)$

c $4(3 + 2f) + 2(5 - 3f)$ **d** $5(1 + 3g) + 3(3 - 4g)$

5 Expand and simplify.

a $4(3 + 2h) - 2(5 + 3h)$ **b** $5(3g + 4) - 3(2g + 5)$

c $5(5k + 2) - 2(4k - 3)$ **d** $4(4e + 3) - 2(5e - 4)$

HINTS AND TIPS

Be careful with minus signs. For example, $-2(5e - 4) = -10e + 8$

C

6 Expand and simplify.

a $m(4 + p) + p(3 + m)$ **b** $k(3 + 2h) + h(4 + 3k)$

c $4r(3 + 4p) + 3p(8 - r)$ **d** $5k(3m + 4) - 2m(3 - 2k)$

7 Expand and simplify.

a $t(3t + 4) + 3t(3 + 2t)$ **b** $2y(3 + 4y) + y(5y - 1)$

c $4e(3e - 5) - 2e(e - 7)$ **d** $3k(2k + p) - 2k(3p - 4k)$

8 Expand and simplify.

a $4a(2b + 3c) + 3b(3a + 2c)$ **b** $3y(4w + 2t) + 2w(3y - 4t)$

c $5m(2n - 3p) - 2n(3p - 2m)$ **d** $2r(3r + r^2) - 3r^2(4 - 2r)$

FM 9 A two-carriage train has f first-class seats and $2s$ standard-class seats.

A three-carriage train has $2f$ first-class seats and $3s$ standard-class seats.

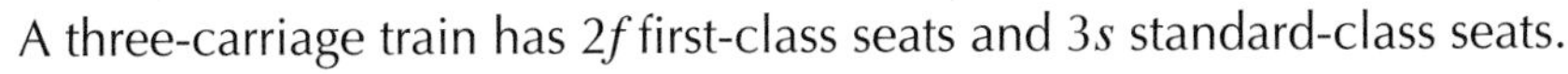

On a weekday, 5 two-carriage trains and 2 three-carriage trains travel from Hull to Liverpool.

a Write down an expression for the total number of first-class and standard-class seats available during the day.

b On average in any day, half of the first-class seats are used at a cost of £60.
On average in any day, three-quarters of the standard-class seats are used at a cost of £40.

How much money does the rail company earn in an average day on this route?
Give your answer in terms of f and s.

c $f = 15$ and $s = 80$. It costs the rail company £30 000 per day to operate this route.
How much profit do they make on an average day?

AU 10 Fill in whole-number values so that the following expansion is true.

$3(\ldots x + \ldots y) + 2(\ldots x + \ldots y) = 11x + 17$

HINTS AND TIPS

There is more than one answer. You don't have to give them all.

PS 11 A rectangle with sides 5 and $3x + 2$ has a smaller rectangle with sides 3 and $2x - 1$ cut from it.

Work out the remaining area.

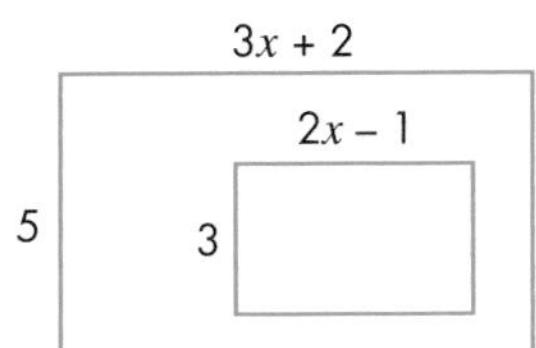

HINTS AND TIPS

Write out the expression for the difference between the two triangles and then work it out.

8.2 Factorisation

This section will show you how to:
- factorise an algebraic expression

Key words
common factor
factorisation

Factorisation is the opposite of expansion. It puts an expression back into the brackets it may have come from.

In factorisation, you have to look for the **common factors** in *every* term of the expression.

EXAMPLE 6

Factorise each expression.

a $6t + 9m$ **b** $6my + 4py$ **c** $5k^2 - 25k$ **d** $10a^2b - 15ab^2$

a First look at the numerical coefficients 6 and 9.

These have a common factor of 3.

Then look at the letters, t and m.

These do not have any common factors as they do not appear in both terms.

The expression can be thought of as $3 \times 2t + 3 \times 3m$, which gives the factorisation:

$$6t + 9m = 3(2t + 3m)$$

Note: You can always check a factorisation by expanding the answer.

b First look at the numbers.

These have a common factor of 2. m and p do not occur in both terms but y does, and is a common factor, so the factorisation is:

$$6my + 4py = 2y(3m + 2p)$$

c 5 is a common factor of 5 and 25 and k is a common factor of k^2 and k.

$$5k^2 - 25k = 5k(k - 5)$$

d 5 is a common factor of 10 and 15, a is a common factor of a^2 and a, b is a common factor of b and b^2.

$$10a^2b - 15ab^2 = 5ab(2a - 3b)$$

Note: If you multiply out each answer, you will get the expressions you started with.

EXERCISE 8D

D

1 Factorise the following expressions.

a $6m + 12t$ **b** $9t + 3p$ **c** $8m + 12k$

d $4r + 8t$ **e** $mn + 3m$ **f** $5g^2 + 3g$

g $4w - 6t$ **h** $3y^2 + 2y$ **i** $4t^2 - 3t$

j $3m^2 - 3mp$ **k** $6p^2 + 9pt$ **l** $8pt + 6mp$

m $8ab - 4bc$ **n** $5b^2c - 10bc$ **o** $8abc + 6bed$

p $4a^2 + 6a + 8$ **q** $6ab + 9bc + 3bd$ **r** $5t^2 + 4t + at$

s $6mt^2 - 3mt + 9m^2t$ **t** $8ab^2 + 2ab - 4a^2b$ **u** $10pt^2 + 15pt + 5p^2t$

C

FM 2 Three friends have a meal together. They each have a main meal costing £6.75 and a dessert costing £3.25.

Chris says that the bill will be $3 \times 6.75 + 3 \times 3.25$.

Mary says that she has an easier way to work out the bill as $3 \times (6.75 + 3.25)$.

a Explain why Chris' and Mary's methods both give the correct answer.

b Explain why Mary's method is better. **c** What is the total bill?

3 Factorise the following expressions where possible. List those that do not factorise.

a $7m - 6t$ **b** $5m + 2mp$ **c** $t^2 - 7t$

d $8pt + 5ab$ **e** $4m^2 - 6mp$ **f** $a^2 + b$

g $4a^2 - 5ab$ **h** $3ab + 4cd$ **i** $5ab - 3b^2c$

AU 4 Three students are asked to factorise the expression $12m - 8$. These are their answers.

Aidan	Bernice	Craig
$2(6m - 4)$	$4(3m - 2)$	$4m(3 - \frac{2}{m})$

All the answers are accurately factorised, but only one is the normally accepted answer.

a Which student gave the correct answer?

b Explain why the other two students' answers are not acceptable as correct answers.

AU 5 Explain why $5m + 6p$ cannot be factorised.

B

PS 6 Alvin has correctly factorised the top and bottom of an algebraic fraction and cancelled out the terms to give a final answer of $2x$. Unfortunately some of his work has had coffee spilt on it. What was the original fraction?

$$\frac{4x\ldots}{2\ldots} = \frac{4\ldots}{2(x-3)} = 2x$$

8.3 Solving linear equations

This section will show you how to:

- solve equations in which the variable (the letter) appears as part of the numerator of a fraction
- solve equations where you have to expand brackets first
- solve equations where the variable appears on both sides of the equals sign
- set up equations from given information and then solve them

Key words
brackets
do the same to both sides
equation
rearrange
solution
solve

Fractional equations

To **solve equations** with fractions you will need to multiply both sides of the equation by the denominator at some stage. It is important to do the inverse operations in the right order.

In examples 7 and 9, you must eliminate the constant term first before multiplying by the denominator of the fraction. In Example 8, all of the left-hand side is part of the fraction, so multiply both sides by the denominator first. It is essential to check your answer in the original equation.

Work through the following examples noting how to **rearrange** the equations.

EXAMPLE 7

Solve this equation. $\frac{x}{3} + 1 = 5$

First subtract 1 from both sides: $\frac{x}{3} = 4$

Now multiply both sides by 3: $x = 12$

Check: $\frac{12}{3} + 1 = 4 + 1 = 5$

EXAMPLE 8

Solve this equation. $\frac{x - 2}{5} = 3$

First multiply both sides by 5: $x - 2 = 15$

Now add 2 to both sides: $x = 17$

Check: $\frac{17 - 2}{5} = \frac{15}{5} = 3$

EXAMPLE 9

Solve this equation. $\frac{3x}{4} - 3 = 1$

First add 3 to both sides: $\frac{3x}{4} = 4$

Now multiply both sides by 4: $3x = 16$

Now divide both sides by 3: $x = \frac{15}{5} = 5\frac{1}{3}$

Check: $\frac{3 \times 5\frac{1}{3}}{4} - 3 = \frac{16}{4} - 3 = 4 - 3 = 1$

EXERCISE 8E

1 Solve these equations.

a $\frac{f}{5} + 2 = 8$ **b** $\frac{w}{3} - 5 = 2$ **c** $\frac{x}{8} + 3 = 12$

d $\frac{5t}{4} + 3 = 18$ **e** $\frac{3y}{2} - 1 = 8$ **f** $\frac{2x}{3} + 5 = 12$

g $\frac{t}{5} + 3 = 1$ **h** $\frac{x + 3}{2} = 5$ **i** $\frac{t - 5}{2} = 3$

j $\frac{3x + 10}{2} = 8$ **k** $\frac{2x + 1}{3} = 5$ **l** $\frac{5y - 2}{4} = 3$

m $\frac{6y + 3}{9} = 1$ **n** $\frac{2x - 3}{5} = 4$ **o** $\frac{5t + 3}{4} = 1$

AU 2 The solution to the equation $\frac{2x - 3}{5} = 3$ is $x = 9$.

Make up *two* more *different* equations of the form $\frac{ax \pm b}{5} = d$,

for which the answer is also 3, where a, b, c and d are positive whole numbers.

AU 3 A teacher asked her class to solve the equation $\frac{2x + 4}{5} = 6$.

Amanda wrote:

$2x + 4 = 6 \times 5$

$2x + 4 - 4 = 30 - 4$

$2x = 26$

$2x \div 2 = 26 \div 2$

$x = 13$

Betsy wrote:

$\frac{2x}{5} = 6 + 4$

$2x = 6 + 4 + 5$

$2x = 15$

$2x - 2 = 15 - 2$

$x = 13$

When the teacher read out the correct answer of 13, both students ticked their work as correct.

a Which student used the correct method?

b Explain the mistakes the other student made.

D

C

Brackets

When we have an equation that contains **brackets**, we first must multiply out the brackets and then solve the resulting equation.

EXAMPLE 10

Solve $5(x + 3) = 25$

First multiply out the brackets to get:

$5x + 15 = 25$

Rearrange: $5x = 25 - 15 = 10$

Divide by 5: $\frac{5x}{5} = \frac{10}{5}$

$x = 2$

EXAMPLE 11

Solve $3(2x - 7) = 15$

Multiply out the brackets to get:

$6x - 21 = 15$

Add 21 to both sides: $6x = 36$

Divide both sides by 6: $x = 6$

EXERCISE 8F 

D

1 Solve each of the following equations. Some of the answers may be decimals or negative numbers. Remember to check that each answer works for its original equation. Use your calculator if necessary.

a $2(x + 5) = 16$
b $5(x - 3) = 20$
c $3(t + 1) = 18$
d $4(2x + 5) = 44$
e $2(3y - 5) = 14$
f $5(4x + 3) = 135$
g $4(3t - 2) = 88$
h $6(2t + 5) = 42$
i $2(3x + 1) = 11$
j $4(5y - 2) = 42$
k $6(3k + 5) = 39$
l $5(2x + 3) = 27$
m $9(3x - 5) = 9$
n $2(x + 5) = 6$
o $5(x - 4) = -25$
p $3(t + 7) = 15$
q $2(3x + 11) = 10$
r $4(5t + 8) = 12$

HINTS AND TIPS

Once the brackets have been expanded the equations become straightforward. Remember to multiply *everything* inside the brackets with what is outside.

D

AU 2 Fill in values for a, b and c so that the answer to this equation is $x = 4$.

$$a(bx + 3) = c$$

PS 3 My son is x years old. In five years' time, I will be twice his age and both our ages will be multiples of 10. The sum of our ages will be between 50 and 100. How old am I now?

HINTS AND TIPS

Set up an equation and put it equal to 60, 70, 80, etc. Solve the equation and see if the answer fits the conditions.

Equations with the variable on both sides

When a letter (or variable) appears on both sides of an equation, it is best to use the '**do the same to both sides**' method of **solution**, and collect all the terms containing the letter on the left-hand side of the equation. But when there are more of the letters on the right-hand side, it is easier to turn the equation round. When an equation contains brackets, they must be multiplied out first.

EXAMPLE 12

Solve this equation. $5x + 4 = 3x + 10$

There are more xs on the left-hand side, so leave the equation as it is.

Subtract $3x$ from both sides: $2x + 4 = 10$

Subtract 4 from both sides: $2x = 6$

Divide both sides by 2: $x = 3$

EXAMPLE 13

Solve this equation. $2x + 3 = 6x - 5$

There are more xs on the right-hand side, so turn the equation round.

$6x - 5 = 2x + 3$

Subtract $2x$ from both sides: $4x - 5 = 3$

Add 5 to both sides: $4x = 8$

Divide both sides by 4: $x = 2$

EXAMPLE 14

Solve this equation. $3(2x + 5) + x = 2(2 - x) + 2$

Multiply out both brackets: $6x + 15 + x = 4 - 2x + 2$

Simplify both sides: $7x + 15 = 6 - 2x$

There are more xs on the left-hand side, so leave the equation as it is.

Add $2x$ to both sides: $9x + 15 = 6$

Subtract 15 from both sides: $9x = -9$

Divide both sides by 9: $x = -1$

EXERCISE 8G

D

1 Solve each of the following equations.

a $2x + 3 = x + 5$ **b** $5y + 4 = 3y + 6$

c $4a - 3 = 3a + 4$ **d** $5t + 3 = 2t + 15$

e $7p - 5 = 3p + 3$ **f** $6k + 5 = 2k + 1$

g $4m + 1 = m + 10$ **h** $8s - 1 = 6s - 5$

HINTS AND TIPS

Remember: 'Change sides, change signs'. Show all your working. Rearrange *before* you simplify. If you try to do these at the same time you could get it wrong.

PS 2 Terry says:

I am thinking of a number. I multiply it by 3 and subtract 2.

June says:

I am thinking of a number. I multiply it by 2 and add 5.

Terry and June find that they both thought of the same number and both got the same final answer.

What number did they think of?

HINTS AND TIPS

Set up equations; put them equal and solve.

C

3 Solve each of the following equations.

a $2(d + 3) = d + 12$ **b** $5(x - 2) = 3(x + 4)$

c $3(2y + 3) = 5(2y + 1)$ **d** $3(h - 6) = 2(5 - 2h)$

e $4(3b - 1) + 6 = 5(2b + 4)$ **f** $2(5c + 2) - 2c = 3(2c + 3) + 7$

AU 4 Explain why the equation $3(2x + 1) = 2(3x + 5)$ cannot be solved.

HINTS AND TIPS

Expand the brackets and collect terms on one side as usual. What happens?

PS 5 Wilson has eight coins of the same value and seven pennies.

Chloe has 11 coins of the same value as those that Wilson has and she also has five pennies.

Wilson says, "If you give me one of your coins and four pennies, we will have the same amount of money."

What is the value of the coins that Wilson and Chloe have?

HINTS AND TIPS

Call the coin x and set up the equations, e.g. Wilson has $8x + 7$, and then take one x and 4 from Chloe and add one x and 4 to Wilson. Then put the equations equal and solve.

AU 6 Explain why these are an infinite number of solutions to the equation:

$$2(6x + 9) = 3(4x + 6)$$

8.4 Simultaneous equations

This section will show you how to:

- solve simultaneous linear equations in two variables

Key words
balance the coefficients
check
coefficient
eliminate
simultaneous equations
substitute
variable

A pair of **simultaneous equations** is exactly that — two equations (usually linear) for which you want the same solution, and which you therefore *solve together*. For example,

$x + y = 10$ has many solutions:

$x = 2, y = 8 \qquad x = 4, y = 6 \qquad x = 5, y = 5 \ldots$

and $2x + y = 14$ has many solutions:

$x = 2, y = 10 \qquad x = 3, y = 8 \qquad x = 4, y = 6 \ldots$

But only *one* solution, $x = 4$ and $y = 6$, satisfies both equations at the same time.

Elimination method

Here, you solve simultaneous equations by the *elimination method*. There are six steps in this method. **Step 1** is to **balance the coefficients** of one of the **variables**. **Step 2** is to **eliminate** this variable by adding or subtracting the equations. **Step 3** is to solve the resulting linear equation in the other variable. **Step 4** is to **substitute** the value found back into one of the previous equations. **Step 5** is to solve the resulting equation. **Step 6** is to **check** that the two values found satisfy the original equations.

EXAMPLE 15

Solve the equations: $6x + y = 15$ and $4x + y = 11$

Label the equations so that the method can be clearly explained.

$6x + y = 15 \qquad (1)$

$4x + y = 11 \qquad (2)$

Step 1: Since the y-term in both equations has the same **coefficient** there is no need to balance them.

Step 2: Subtract one equation from the other. (Equation (1) minus equation (2) will give positive values.)

$(1) - (2) \qquad 2x = 4$

Step 3: Solve this equation: $\qquad x = 2$

EXAMPLE 15 (continued)

Step 4: Substitute $x = 2$ into one of the original equations. (Usually the one with smallest numbers involved.)

So substitute into: $4x + y = 11$

which gives: $8 + y = 11$

Step 5: Solve this equation: $y = 3$

Step 6: Test the solution in the original equations. So substitute $x = 2$ and $y = 3$ into $6x + y$, which gives $12 + 3 = 15$ and into $4x + y$, which gives $8 + 3 = 11$. These are correct, so you can confidently say the solution is $x = 2$ and $y = 3$.

EXAMPLE 16

Solve these equations.

$$5x + y = 22 \qquad (1)$$
$$2x - y = 6 \qquad (2)$$

Step 1: Both equations have the same y-coefficient but with *different* signs so there is no need to balance them.

Step 2: As the signs are different, *add* the two equations, to eliminate the y-terms.

(1) + (2) $7x = 28$

Step 3: Solve this equation: $x = 4$

Step 4: Substitute $x = 4$ into one of the original equations, $5x + y = 22$,

which gives: $20 + y = 22$

Step 5: Solve this equation: $y = 2$

Step 6: Test the solution by putting $x = 4$ and $y = 2$ into the original equations, $2x - y$, which gives $8 - 2 = 6$ and $5x + y$ which gives $20 + 2 = 22$. These are correct, so the solution is $x = 4$ and $y = 2$.

Substitution method

This is an alternative method (which is covered again in Chapter 13). Which method you use depends very much on the coefficients of the variables and the way that the equations are written in the first place. There are five steps in the substitute method.

Step 1 is to rearrange one of the equations into the form $y = \dots$ or $x = \dots$.

Step 2 is to substitute the right-hand side of this equation into the other equation in place of the variable on the left-hand side.

Step 3 is to expand and solve this equation.

Step 4 is to substitute the value into the $y = \dots$ or $x = \dots$ equation.

Step 5 is to check that the values work in both original equations.

EXAMPLE 17

Solve the simultaneous equations: $y = 2x + 3$, $3x + 4y = 1$

Because the first equation is in the form $y = \dots$ it suggests that the substitution method should be used.

Again label the equations to help with explaining the method.

$y = 2x + 3$ (1)

$3x + 4y = 1$ (2)

Step 1: As equation (1) is in the form $y = \dots$ there is no need to rearrange an equation.

Step 2: Substitute the right-hand side of equation (1) into equation (2) for the variable y.

$$3x + 4(2x + 3) = 1$$

Step 3: Expand and solve the equation. $3x + 8x + 12 = 1$, $11x = -11$, $x = -1$

Step 4: Substitute $x = -1$ into $y = 2x + 3$: $y = -2 + 3 = 1$

Step 5: Test the values in $y = 2x + 3$ which gives $1 = -2 + 3$ and $3x + 4y = 1$, which gives $-3 + 4 = 1$. These are correct so the solution is $x = -1$ and $y = 1$.

EXERCISE 8H

1 Solve these simultaneous equations.

In question **1** parts **a** to **i** the coefficients of one of the variables are the same so there is no need to balance them. Subtract the equations when the identical terms have the same sign. Add the equations when the identical terms have opposite signs. In parts **j** to **l** use the substitution method.

a $4x + y = 17$
$2x + y = 9$

b $5x + 2y = 13$
$x + 2y = 9$

c $2x + y = 7$
$5x - y = 14$

d $3x + 2y = 11$
$2x - 2y = 14$

e $3x - 4y = 17$
$x - 4y = 3$

f $3x + 2y = 16$
$x - 2y = 4$

g $x + 3y = 9$
$x + y = 6$

h $2x + 5y = 16$
$2x + 3y = 8$

i $3x - y = 9$
$5x + y = 11$

j $2x + 5y = 37$
$y = 11 - 2x$

k $4x - 3y = 7$
$x = 13 - 3y$

l $4x - y = 17$
$x = 2 + y$

B

B

PS 2 In this sequence, the next term is found by multiplying the previous term by a and then adding b. a and b are positive whole numbers.

3 14 47 … …

a Explain why $3a + b = 14$

b Set up another equation in a and b.

c Solve the equations to solve for a and b.

d Work out the next two terms in the sequence.

Balancing coefficients in one equation only

You were able to solve all the pairs of equations in Exercise 5H, question **1** simply by adding or subtracting the equations in each pair, or just by substituting without rearranging. This does not always happen. The next examples show what to do when there are no identical terms to begin with, or when you need to rearrange.

EXAMPLE 18

Solve these equations. $3x + 2y = 18$ (1)

$2x - y = 5$ (2)

Step 1: Multiply equation (2) by 2. There are other ways to balance the coefficients but this is the easiest and leads to less work later. With practice, you will get used to which will be the best way to balance the coefficients.

$2 \times (2)$ $4x - 2y = 10$ (3)

Label this equation as number (3).

Be careful to multiply every term and not just the y-term, it sometimes helps to write:

$2 \times (2x - y = 5) \Rightarrow 4x - 2y = 10$ (3)

Step 2: As the signs of the y-terms are opposite, add the equations.

(1) + (3) $7x = 28$

Be careful to add the correct equations. This is why labelling them is useful.

Step 3: Solve this equation: $x = 4$

Step 4: Substitute $x = 4$ into any equation, say $2x - y = 5 \Rightarrow 8 - y = 5$

Step 5: Solve this equation: $y = 3$

Step 6: Check: (1), $3 \times 4 + 2 \times 3 = 18$ and (2), $2 \times 4 - 3 = 5$, which are correct so the solution is $x = 4$ and $y = 3$.

EXAMPLE 19

Solve the simultaneous equations: $3x + y = 5$ (1)

$5x - 2y = 10$ (2)

Step 1: Multiply the first equation by 2: $6x + 2y = 10$ (3)

Step 2: Add (1) + (3): $11x = 22$

Step 3: Solve: $x = 2$

Step 4: Substitute back: $3 \times 2 + y = 5$

Step 5: Solve: $y = -1$

Step 6: Check: (1) $3 \times 2 - 1 = 5$ and (2) $5 \times 2 - 2x -1 = 10 + 2 = 12$, which are correct.

EXERCISE 8I

1 Solve parts **a** to **c** by the substitution method and the rest by first changing one of the equations in each pair to obtain identical terms, and then adding or subtracting the equations to eliminate those terms.

a $5x + 2y = 4$
$4x - y = 11$

b $4x + 3y = 37$
$2x + y = 17$

c $x + 3y = 7$
$2x - y = 7$

d $2x + 3y = 19$
$6x + 2y = 22$

e $5x - 2y = 26$
$3x - y = 15$

f $10x - y = 3$
$3x + 2y = 17$

g $3x + 5y = 15$
$x + 3y = 7$

h $3x + 4y = 7$
$4x + 2y = 1$

i $5x - 2y = 24$
$3x + y = 21$

k $5x - 2y = 4$
$3x - 6y = 6$

l $2x + 3y = 13$
$4x + 7y = 31$

m $3x - 2y = 3$
$5x + 6y = 12$

AU **2** **a** Mary is solving the simultaneous equations $4x - 2y = 8$ and $2x - y = 4$.

She finds a solution of $x = 5$, $y = 6$ which works for both equations.

Explain why this is not a unique solution.

b Max is solving the simultaneous equations $6x + 2y = 9$ and $3x + y = 7$.

Why is it impossible to find a solution that works for both equations?

B

Balancing coefficients in both equations

There are also cases where *both* equations have to be changed to obtain identical terms. The next example shows you how this is done.

Note: The substitution method is not suitable for these types of equations as you end up with fractional terms.

EXAMPLE 20

Solve these equations. $4x + 3y = 27$ (1)

$5x - 2y = 5$ (2)

Both equations have to be changed to obtain identical terms in either x or y. However, you can see that if you make the y-coefficients the same, you will add the equations. This is always safer than subtraction, so this is obviously the better choice. We do this by multiplying the first equation by 2 (the y-coefficient of the other equation) and the second equation by 3 (the y-coefficient of the other equation).

Step 1: (1) × 2 or 2 × ($4x + 3y = 27$) ⇒ $8x + 6y = 54$ (3)

(2) × 3 or 3 × ($5x - 2y = 5$) ⇒ $15x - 6y = 15$ (4)

Label the new equations (3) and (4).

Step 2: Eliminate one of the variables: (3) + (4) $23x = 69$

Step 3: Solve the equation: $x = 3$

Step 4: Substitute into equation (1): $12 + 3y = 27$

Step 5: Solve the equation: $y = 5$

Step 6: Check: (1), $4 \times 3 + 3 \times 5 = 12 + 15 = 27$, and (2), $5 \times 3 - 2 \times 5 = 15 - 10 = 5$, which are correct so the solution is $x = 3$ and $y = 5$.

EXERCISE 8J

B

1 Solve the following simultaneous equations.

a $2x + 5y = 15$
$3x - 2y = 13$

b $2x + 3y = 30$
$5x + 7y = 71$

c $2x - 3y = 15$
$5x + 7y = 52$

d $3x - 2y = 15$
$2x - 3y = 5$

e $5x - 3y = 14$
$4x - 5y = 6$

f $3x + 2y = 28$
$2x + 7y = 47$

g $2x + y = 4$
$x - y = 5$

h $5x + 2y = 11$
$3x + 4y = 8$

i $x - 2y = 4$
$3x - y = -3$

j $3x + 2y = 2$
$2x + 6y = 13$

k $6x + 2y = 14$
$3x - 5y = 10$

l $2x + 4y = 15$
$x + 5y = 21$

m $3x - y = 5$
$x + 3y = -20$

n $3x - 4y = 4.5$
$2x + 2y = 10$

o $x - 5y = 15$
$3x - 7y = 17$

PS 2 Here are four equations.

A: $5x + 2y = 1$

B: $4x + y = 9$

C: $3x - y = 5$

D: $3x + 2y = 3$

Here are four sets of (x, y) values.

$(1, -2)$, $(-1, 3)$, $(2, 1)$, $(3, -3)$

Match each pair of (x, y) values to a pair of equations.

HINTS AND TIPS

You could solve each possible set of pairs but there are six to work out. Alternatively you can substitute values into the equations to see which work.

B

AU 3 Find the area of the triangle enclosed by these three equations.

$y - x = 2$ $\quad x + y = 6$ $\quad 3x + y = 6$

AU 4 Find the area of the triangle enclosed by these three equations.

$x - 2y = 6$ $\quad x + 2y = 6$ $\quad x + y = 3$

HINTS AND TIPS

Find the point of intersection of each pair of equations, plot the points on a grid and use any method to work out the area of the resulting triangle.

A

8.5 Rearranging formulae

This section will show you how to:

- rearrange formulae, using the same methods as for solving equations

Key words

expression
rearrange
subject
transpose
variable

The **subject** of a formula is the **variable** (letter) in the formula which stands on its own, usually on the left-hand side of the equals sign. For example, x is the subject of each of the following equations.

$x = 5t + 4$ $\quad x = 4(2y - 7)$ $\quad x = \frac{1}{t}$

To change the existing subject to a different variable, you have to **rearrange** (**transpose**) the formula to get that variable on the left-hand side. You do this by using the same rules as for solving equations. Move the terms concerned from one side of the equals sign to the other. The main difference is that when you solve an equation each step gives a numerical value. When you rearrange a formula each step gives an algebraic **expression**.

EXAMPLE 21

Make m the subject of this formula. $T = m - 3$

Move the 3 so that the m is on its own. $T + 3 = m$

Reverse the formula. $m = T + 3$

EXAMPLE 22

From the formula $P = 4t$, express t in terms of P.

(This is another common way of asking you to make t the subject.)

Divide both sides by 4: $\frac{P}{4} = \frac{4t}{4}$

Reverse the formula: $t = \frac{P}{4}$

EXAMPLE 23

From the formula $C = 2m^2 + 3$, make m the subject.

Move the 3 so that the $2m^2$ is on its own $C - 3 = 2m^2$

Divide both sides by 2: $\frac{C-3}{2} = \frac{2m^2}{2}$

Reverse the formula: $m^2 = \frac{C-3}{2}$

Take the square root on both sides: $m = \sqrt{\frac{C-3}{2}}$

EXERCISE 8K

C

HINTS AND TIPS

Remember about inverse operations, and the rule 'change sides, change signs'.

1. $T = 3k$ Make k the subject.
2. $X = y - 1$ Express y in terms of X.
3. $Q = \frac{p}{3}$ Express p in terms of Q.
4. $A = 4r + 9$ Make r the subject.
5. $W = 3n - 1$ Make n the subject.
6. $p = m + t$ **a** Make m the subject. **b** Make t the subject.
7. $g = \frac{m}{v}$ Make m the subject.
8. $t = m^2$ Make m the subject.
9. $C = 2\pi r$ Make r the subject.
10. $A = bh$ Make b the subject.

11 $P = 2l + 2w$ Make l the subject.

12 $m = p^2 + 2$ Make p the subject.

FM 13 The formula for converting degrees Fahrenheit to degrees Celsius is $C = \frac{5}{9}(F - 32)$.

a Show that when $F = -40$, C is also equal to -40.

b Find the value of C when $F = 68$.

c Use this flow diagram to establish the formula for converting degrees Celsius to degrees Fahrenheit.

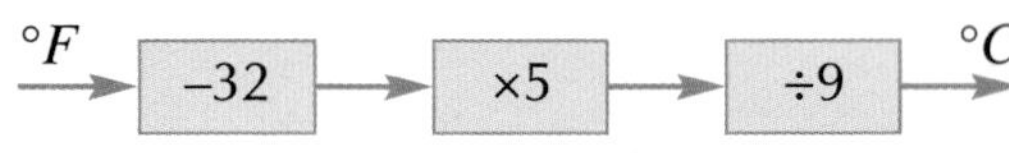

FM 14 Kieran notices that the price of five cream buns is 75p more than the price of nine mince pies.
Let the price of a cream bun be x pence and the price of a mince pie be y pence.

a Express the cost of one mince pie, y, in terms of the price of a cream bun, x.

b If the price of a cream bun is 60p, how much is a mince pie?

> **HINTS AND TIPS**
> Set up a formula, using the first sentence of information, then rearrange it.

PS 15 Distance, speed and time are connected by the formula:

distance = speed × time.

A delivery driver drove 126 km in 1 hour and 45 minutes. On the return journey, he was held up at some road works so his average speed decreased by 9 km per hour.

How long was he held up at the road works?

> **HINTS AND TIPS**
> Work out the average speed for the first journey, then work out the average speed for the return journey.

16 $v = u + at$ **a** Make a the subject. **b** Make t the subject.

17 $A = \frac{1}{4}\pi d^2$ Make d the subject.

18 $W = 3n + t$ **a** Make n the subject. **b** Express t in terms of n and W.

19 $x = 5y - w$ **a** Make y the subject. **b** Express w in terms of x and y.

20 $k = 2p^2$ Make p the subject.

21 $v = u^2 - t$ **a** Make t the subject. **b** Make u the subject.

22 $k = m + n^2$ **a** Make m the subject. **b** Make n the subject.

23 $T = 5r^2$ Make r the subject.

24 $K = 5n^2 + w$ **a** Make w the subject. **b** Make n the subject.

GRADE BOOSTER

- **D** You can expand linear brackets
- **D** You can substitute numbers into expressions
- **D** You can factorise simple linear expresions
- **D** You can solve simple linear equations which include the variable inside brackets
- **D** You can solve linear equations where the variable occurs in the numerator of a fraction
- **D** You can solve linear equations where the variable appears on both sides of the equals sign.
- **C** You can expand and simplify expressions
- **C** You can rearrange simple formulae
- **C** You can solve linear fractional equations
- **C** You can solve linear equations where brackets have to be expanded
- **B** You can solve two simultaneous linear equations
- **B** You can rearrange more complicated formulae
- **A** You can set up and solve two simultaneous equations from a practical problem

---

What you should know now

- How to manipulate and simplify algebraic expressions, including those with linear brackets
- How to factorise linear expressions
- How to solve all types of linear equations
- How to set up and/or solve a pair of linear simultaneous equations

1 Solve the equation $\frac{1}{2}x - 5 = \frac{1}{4}x + 3$ *(3 marks)*

AQA, June 2005, Paper 1 Intermediate, Question 20 (a)

2 **a** **i** Expand and simplify $(y + 5)(y - 1)$ *(2 marks)*

ii When y is an odd number, explain why $(y + 5)(y - 1)$ is an even number. *(1 mark)*

b Factorise $2xy - 6y^2$ *(2 marks)*

AQA, November 2006, Paper 1 Higher, Questions 8(c) and (d),

3 Expand and simplify $(x - 3)(x + 4)$ *(2 marks)*

AQA, June 2008, Paper 2 Higher, Question 11

4 **a** Draw arrows to join each item on the left with its correct description on the right.

One of them has been done for you.

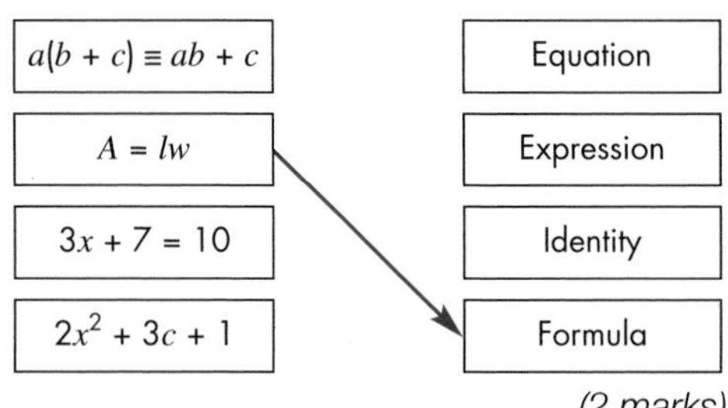

(2 marks)

b A two-stage operation is shown:

Fill values in the boxes so that when the input is an odd number, the output is also an odd number. *(2 marks)*

AQA, November 2008, Paper 2 Higher, Question 9

5 Solve the equations.

a $\frac{17 - x}{3} = 4.5$

b $2(y - 3) = 5 - 3y$

c $3(2z - 1) + 4(z + 3) = 5(2z - 1) + 4(3z - 1)$

6 **a** Simplify:

i $y^7 \times y^2$ *(1 mark)*

ii $y^7 \div y^2$ *(1 mark)*

iii $(y^7)^2$ *(1 mark)*

b **i** If $y = -1$, which answer in part **a** is positive? *(1 mark)*

ii If $y = 0.5$, which answer in part **a** has the greatest value? *(1 mark)*

AQA, November 2005, Paper 1 Higher, Question 8

7 **a** Solve the equation:

$4(x + 3) = 9(x - 2)$ *(3 marks)*

b Solve these simultaneous equations.

$5x + 3y = 6$

$3x - 7y = 19$

You must show your working.

Do not use trial and improvement. *(4 marks)*

AQA, June 2006, Paper 2 Higher, Question 10

8 **a** Factorise:

$5x^2 + 20x$ *(1 mark)*

b Factorise:

$x^2 - 49$ *(1 mark)*

c Factorise fully:

$(3x + 4)^2 - (2x + 1)^2$ *(3 marks)*

AQA, June 2006, Paper 2 Higher, Question 15

9 **a** Solve $\frac{x}{4} + 1 = 6$ *(2 marks)*

b Solve $\frac{4}{y + 1} = 3$ *(2 marks)*

c Factorise fully $6ab^2 - 2ab$ *(2 marks)*

d Factorise $3x^2 + 5x - 12$ *(2 marks)*

AQA, June 2007, Paper 1 Higher, Question 14

10 Solve the simultaneous equations:

$5x + 6y = 28$

$x + 3y = 2$

You must show your working.

Do not use trial and improvement. *(3 marks)*

AQA, June 2007, Paper 1 Higher, Question 12

11 **a** Show clearly that $(p + q)^2 \equiv p^2 + 2pq + q^2$

b Hence, or otherwise, write the expression below in the form $ax^2 + bx + c$.

$(2x + 3)^2 + 2(2x + 3)(x - 1) + (x - 1)^2$ *(3 marks)*

AQA, November 2006, Paper 2 Higher, Question 12

Worked Examination Questions

1 $4x + 3y = 6$

$3x - 2y = 13$

Solve these simultaneous equations algebraically. Show your method clearly.

1 $4x + 3y = 23$ (1)

$3x - 2y = 13$ (2)

Label the equations and decide on the best way to get the coefficients of one variable the same.

(1) × 2 $8x + 6y = 46$ (3)

(2) × 3 $9x - 6y = 39$ (4)

(3) + (4) $17x = 85$

Making the y coefficients the same will be the most efficient way as the resulting equations will be added.

This gets 1 mark for method.

$x = 5$

Substitute into (1) $20 + 3y = 23$

$y = 1$

Solve the resulting equation. Substitute into one of the original equations. Work out the other value.

$4 \times 5 + 3 \times 1 = 23$ ✓

$3 \times 5 - 2 \times 1 = 13$ ✓

Check that these values work in the original equations.

Total: 6 marks

2 Temperatures can be measured in degrees Celsius (°C), degrees Fahrenheit (°F) or kelvin (K). The relationships between the scales of temperature are given by

$$C = \frac{5(F - 32)}{9}$$

$$K = C + 273$$

Express F

i in terms of C

ii in terms of K

2 i $9C = 5(F - 32)$ ✓

$9C = 5F - 160$

$5F = 9C + 160$

$$F = \frac{9C + 160}{5}$$

This gets 1 mark for multiplying both sides of the equation by 9; 1 mark for expanding the bracket and adding 160 to both sides; 1 mark for changing the equation round and dividing by 5.

ii $C = K - 273$

$$F = \frac{9(K - 273) + 160}{5}$$

$$F = \frac{9K - 2457 + 160}{5}$$

$$F = \frac{9K - 2297}{5}$$

Make C the subject of the second equation. Substitute for C in the answer to part **i**. Expand the bracket and tidy up the top line of the fraction. You get 1 mark each for the above steps for method and accuracy and 1 independent mark.

Total: 6 marks

Worked Examination Questions

3 Nicky did a 22 km hill race. She ran x km to the top of the hill at an average speed of 8 km/h. She then ran y kilometres down the hill at an average speed of y km/h. She finished the race in 2 hours and 10 minutes.

Find out how long it took Nicky to get to the top of the hill.

3 $x + y = 22$ — Set up two simultaneous equations using the information given. This scores 1 mark for method.

$\frac{x}{8} + \frac{y}{15} = 2\frac{1}{6}$

$15x + 8y = 260$ — Multiply the second equation by 120 (LCM of 15, 8 and 6). This scores 1 mark for accuracy.

$8x + 8y = 176$ — Balance the coefficients and subtract to eliminate y. This scores 1 mark for method.

$7x = 84$

$x = 12$

Time = 12 ÷ 8 = 1 hour 30 minutes — Solve for x (A1) and work out the time using distance ÷ speed. This scores 1 mark for accuracy.

Total: 5 marks

8

Functional Maths
Walking using Naismith's rule

Many people go walking each weekend. It is good exercise and can be a very enjoyable pastime.

When walkers set out they often try to estimate the length of time the walk will take. There are many factors that could influence this, but one rule that can help in estimating how long the walk will take is Naismith's rule.

Naismith's rule

Naismith's rule is a rule of thumb that you can use when planning a walk by calculating how long it will take. The rule was devised by William Naismith, a Scottish mountaineer, in 1892.

The basic rule is:

Allow 1 hour for every 3 miles (5 km) forward, plus $\frac{1}{2}$ hour for every 1000 feet (300 m) ascent (height).

Getting started

Before you begin your main task, you may find it useful to fill in the following table to practise using Naismith's rule.

Can you use algebra to display the rule?

Day	Distance (km)	Height (m)	Time (m)
1	16	250	
2	18	0	
3	11	340	
4	13	100	
5	14	120	

Now, in small groups think about:

- What kind of things influence the speed at which you walk?
- Do different types of routes make people walk at different rates?
- If there is a large group of people will they all walk at the same rate?

Use all the ideas you have just discussed as you move on to your main task.

Your task

You are going to compare data to see if Naismith's rule is still a useful way to work out how much time to allow for different walks.

The table on the right shows the actual times taken by a school group as they did five different walks in five days. Use this information to work out the following

1 If the group had started at the same times and had the same breaks how long would the group have taken each day, according to Naismith's rule?

2 Do you think Naismith's rule is still valid today? Explain your reasons.

3 If your friend was going to climb Ben Nevis, setting out at 11.30 am, would you advise them to do the walk? You will need to research the distance and climb details of the pathway up Ben Nevis, in order to advise them fully.

Day	Distance (km)	Height (m)	Time (minutes)	Time (hours/minutes)	Start	Breaks	Finish
1	16	250	265	4h 15m	10.00	2h	4:15 pm
2	18	0	270	4h 30m	10.00	1h 30m	4:00 pm
3	11	340	199	3h 19m	09.30	2h 30m	3:19 pm
4	13	100	205	3h 15m	10.30	2h 30m	4:15 pm
5	14	120	222	3h 42m	10.30	2h 30m	4:42 pm

Extension

Produce a report that compares and contrasts the walking times for some of Britain's most famous walks, such as Ben Nevis, Snowdon, Helvellyn and the Pennine Way. Your report should contain realistic guidance on how best to approach these long walks, including:

- suggested day-by-day plans supported by mathematical evidence
- starting times
- places to rest
- how the walks will vary for walkers of different fitness levels
- how weather conditions could affect the walk and precautions that should be taken.

Using this information, evaluate how similar the walks are, and which walk would be the toughest for an average walker to complete.

Why this chapter matters

Very large and very small numbers can often be difficult to read. Scientists use standard form as a shorthand way of representing numbers.

The planets

Mercury is the closest planet to the Sun (and is very hot). It orbits 60 million km (6×10^7 km) away from the Sun.

Venus rotates the opposite way to the other planets and has a diameter of 12 100 km (12.1×10^4 km).

Earth takes 365 days to orbit the Sun and 24 hours to complete a rotation.

Mars has the largest volcano in the solar system. It is almost 600 km across and rises 24 km above the surface. This is five times bigger than the biggest volcano on Earth.

Jupiter is made of gas. It has no solid land so visiting it is not recommended! It has a huge storm which rages across its surface. This is about 8 km high, 40 000 km long and 14 000 km wide. It looks like a red spot and is called 'the Great Red Spot'.

Saturn is the largest planet in the solar system. It is about 120 000 km across (1.2×10^5 km) and 1400 million km from the Sun (1.4×10^9 km).

Uranus takes 84 days to orbit the Sun.

Neptune is similar to Jupiter in that it is a gas planet and has violent storms. Winds can blow at up to 2000 km per hour, so a cloud can circle Neptune in about 16 hours.

Pluto is the furthest planet from the Sun. Some astronomers dispute whether it can be classed as a planet. The average surface temperature on Pluto is about –230 °C.

The mass of an electron is about 0.000 000 000 000 000 000 000 000 000 000 91 kg.
This is written 9.1×10^{-31} kg.

The mass of the Earth is about 5 970 000 000 000 000 000 000 000 kg.
This is written 5.97×10^{24} kg.

Chapter

Number: Powers, standard form and surds

This chapter will show you ...

- **D** how to calculate using powers (indices)
- **C** how to work out a reciprocal
- **B** how to write numbers in standard form and how to calculate with standard form
- **A** how to convert fractions to terminating decimals and recurring decimals, and vice versa
- **A to A*** how to calculate with surds

Visual overview

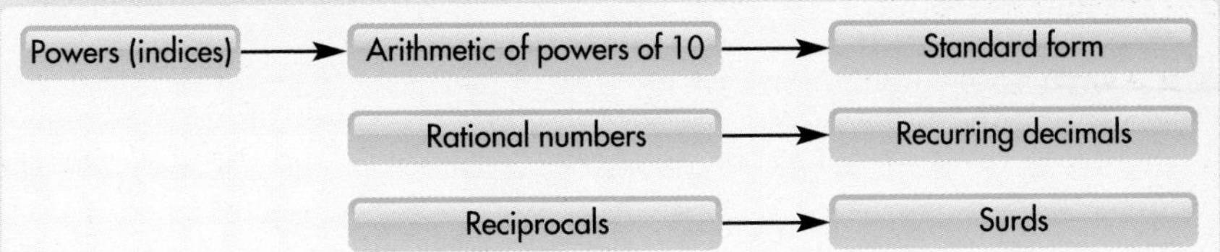

What you should already know

- How to convert a fraction to a decimal **(KS3 level 4, GCSE grade E)**
- How to convert a decimal to a fraction **(KS3 level 4, GCSE grade E)**
- How to find the lowest common denominator of two fractions **(KS3 level 5, GCSE grade D)**
- The meaning of square root and cube root **(KS3 level 5, GCSE grade E)**

Quick check

1 Convert the following fractions to decimals.

a $\frac{6}{10}$ **b** $\frac{11}{25}$ **c** $\frac{3}{8}$

2 Convert the following decimals to fractions.

a 0.17 **b** 0.64 **c** 0.858

3 Work these out. **a** $\frac{2}{3}+\frac{1}{5}$ **b** $\frac{5}{8}-\frac{2}{5}$

4 Write down the values. **a** $\sqrt{25}$ **b** $\sqrt[3]{64}$

9.1 Powers (indices)

This section will show you how to:
- use powers (also known as indices)

Key words
cube
index
indices
power
reciprocal
square

Powers are a convenient way of writing repetitive multiplications. (Powers are also called **indices**, singular **index**.)

The power tells you the number of times a number is multiplied by itself. For example:

$4^6 = 4 \times 4 \times 4 \times 4 \times 4 \times 4$ six lots of 4 multiplied together
$6^4 = 6 \times 6 \times 6 \times 6$ four lots of 6 multiplied together
$7^3 = 7 \times 7 \times 7$
$12^2 = 12 \times 12$

You are expected to know **square** numbers (power 2) up to $15^2 = 225$

You should also know the **cubes** of numbers (power 3):

$1^3 = 1$, $2^3 = 8$, $3^3 = 27$, $4^3 = 64$, $5^3 = 125$ and $10^3 = 1000$

EXAMPLE 1

a What is the value of:

i 7 squared **ii** 5 cubed?

b Write each of these numbers out in full.

i 4^6 **ii** 6^4 **iii** 7^3 **iv** 12^2

c Write the following multiplications using powers.

i $3 \times 3 \times 3 \times 3 \times 3 \times 3 \times 3 \times 3$

ii $13 \times 13 \times 13 \times 13 \times 13$

iii $7 \times 7 \times 7 \times 7$

iv $5 \times 5 \times 5 \times 5 \times 5 \times 5 \times 5$

a The value of 7 squared is $7^2 = 7 \times 7 = 49$

The value of 5 cubed is $5^3 = 5 \times 5 \times 5 = 125$

b **i** $4^6 = 4 \times 4 \times 4 \times 4 \times 4 \times 4$ **ii** $6^4 = 6 \times 6 \times 6 \times 6$

iii $7^3 = 7 \times 7 \times 7$ **iv** $12^2 = 12 \times 12$

c **i** $3 \times 3 \times 3 \times 3 \times 3 \times 3 \times 3 \times 3 = 3^8$

ii $13 \times 13 \times 13 \times 13 \times 13 = 13^5$

iii $7 \times 7 \times 7 \times 7 = 7^4$

iv $5 \times 5 \times 5 \times 5 \times 5 \times 5 \times 5 = 5^7$

Working out powers on your calculator

The power button on your calculator will probably look like this $x^{\blacksquare}$.

To work out 5^7 on your calculator use the power key.

5^7 = **5** **$x^{\blacksquare}$** **7** = 78 125

Two special powers

Power 1

Any number to the power 1 is the same as the number itself. This is always true so normally you do not write the power 1.

For example: $5^1 = 5$ $32^1 = 32$ $(-8)^1 = -8$

Power zero

Any number to the power 0 is equal to 1.

For example: $5^0 = 1$ $32^0 = 1$ $(-8)^0 = 1$

You can check these results on your calculator.

EXERCISE 9A

1 Write these expressions using index notation. Do not work them out yet.

a $2 \times 2 \times 2 \times 2$ **b** $3 \times 3 \times 3 \times 3 \times 3$

c 7×7 **d** $5 \times 5 \times 5$

e $10 \times 10 \times 10 \times 10 \times 10 \times 10 \times 10$ **f** $6 \times 6 \times 6 \times 6$

g 4 **h** $1 \times 1 \times 1 \times 1 \times 1 \times 1 \times 1$

i $0.5 \times 0.5 \times 0.5 \times 0.5$ **j** $100 \times 100 \times 100$

2 Write these power terms out in full. Do not work them out yet.

a 3^4 **b** 9^3 **c** 6^2 **d** 10^5 **e** 2^{10}

f 8^1 **g** 0.1^3 **h** 2.5^2 **i** 0.7^3 **j** 1000^2

3 Using the power key on your calculator (or another method), work out the values of the power terms in question **1**.

4 Using the power key on your calculator (or another method), work out the values of the power terms in question **2**.

FM **5** A storage container is in the shape of a cube. The length of the container is 5 m.

To work out the volume of a cube, use the formula:

volume = (length of edge)^3

Work out the total storage space in the container.

D

D

C

AU **6** Write each number as a power of a different number.

The first one has been done for you.

a $32 = 2^5$ **b** 100 **c** 8 **d** 25

7 Without using a calculator, work out the values of these power terms.

a 2^0 **b** 4^1 **c** 5^0 **d** 1^9 **e** 1^{235}

8 The answers to question **7**, parts **d** and **e**, should tell you something special about powers of 1. What is it?

PS **9** Write the answer to question **1**, part **j** as a power of 10.

PS **10** Write the answer to question **2**, part **j** as a power of 10.

11 Using your calculator, or otherwise, work out the values of these power terms.

a $(-1)^0$ **b** $(-1)^1$ **c** $(-1)^2$ **d** $(-1)^4$ **e** $(-1)^5$

PS **12** Using your answers to question **11**, write down the answers to these power terms.

a $(-1)^8$ **b** $(-1)^{11}$ **c** $(-1)^{99}$ **d** $(-1)^{80}$ **e** $(-1)^{126}$

PS **13** The number 16 777 216 is a power of 2.

It is also a power of 4, a power of 8 and a power of 16.

Write the number using each of the powers.

Negative powers (or negative indices)

A negative index is a convenient way of writing the **reciprocal** of a number or term. (That is, one divided by that number or term.) For example,

$$x^{-a} = \frac{1}{x^a}$$

Here are some other examples.

$$5^{-2} = \frac{1}{5^2} \qquad 3^{-1} = \frac{1}{3} \qquad 5x^{-2} = \frac{5}{x^2}$$

EXAMPLE 2

Rewrite the following in the form 2^n.

a 8 **b** $\frac{1}{4}$ **c** -32 **d** $-\frac{1}{64}$

a $8 = 2 \times 2 \times 2 = 2^3$ **b** $\frac{1}{4} = \frac{1}{2^2} = 2^{-2}$

c $-32 = -2^5$ **d** $-\frac{1}{64} = -\frac{1}{2^6} = -2^{-6}$

EXERCISE 9B

HINTS AND TIPS

If you move a power from top to bottom, or vice versa, the sign changes. Negative power means the reciprocal: it does not mean the answer is negative.

B

1 Write down each of these in fraction form.

a 5^{-3} **b** 6^{-1} **c** 10^{-5} **d** 3^{-2} **e** 8^{-2}

f 9^{-1} **g** w^{-2} **h** t^{-1} **i** x^{-m} **j** $4m^{-3}$

2 Write down each of these in negative index form.

a $\frac{1}{3^2}$ **b** $\frac{1}{5}$ **c** $\frac{1}{10^3}$ **d** $\frac{1}{m}$ **e** $\frac{1}{t^n}$

A

3 Change each of the following expressions into an index form of the type shown.

a All of the form 2^n

i 16 **ii** $\frac{1}{2}$ **iii** $\frac{1}{16}$ **iv** –8

b All of the form 10^n

i 1000 **ii** $\frac{1}{10}$ **iii** $\frac{1}{100}$ **iv** 1 million

c All of the form 5^n

i 125 **ii** $\frac{1}{5}$ **iii** $\frac{1}{25}$ **iv** $\frac{1}{625}$

d All of the form 3^n

i 9 **ii** $\frac{1}{27}$ **iii** $\frac{1}{81}$ **iv** –243

4 Rewrite each of the following expressions in fraction form.

a $5x^{-3}$ **b** $6t^{-1}$ **c** $7m^{-2}$ **d** $4q^{-4}$ **e** $10y^{-5}$

f $\frac{1}{2}x^{-3}$ **g** $\frac{1}{2}m^{-1}$ **h** $\frac{3}{4}t^{-4}$ **i** $\frac{4}{5}y^{-3}$ **j** $\frac{7}{8}x^{-5}$

5 Write each fraction in index form.

a $\frac{7}{x^3}$ **b** $\frac{10}{p}$ **c** $\frac{5}{t^2}$ **d** $\frac{8}{m^5}$ **e** $\frac{3}{y}$

6 Find the value of each of the following.

a $x = 5$

i x^2 **ii** x^{-3} **iii** $4x^{-1}$

b $t = 4$

i t^3 **ii** t^{-2} **iii** $5t^{-4}$

c $m = 2$

i m^3 **ii** m^{-5} **iii** $9m^{-1}$

d $w = 10$

i w^6 **ii** w^{-3} **iii** $25w^{-2}$

A

PS 7 Two different numbers can be written in the form 2^n.

The sum of the numbers is 40.

What is the difference of the numbers?

AU 8 x and y are integers.

$x^2 - y^3 = 0$

Work out possible values of x and y.

AU 9 You are given that $8^7 = 2\,097\,152$

Write down the value of 8^{-7}.

PS 10 Put these in order from smallest to largest:

$x^5 \quad x^{-5} \quad x^0$

a when x is greater than 1

b when x is between 0 and 1

c when $x = -10$

Rules for multiplying and dividing numbers in index form

When you *multiply* powers of the same number or variable, you *add* the indices. For example,

$3^4 \times 3^5 = 3^{(4+5)} = 3^9$

$2^3 \times 2^4 \times 2^5 = 2^{12}$

$10^4 \times 10^{-2} = 10^2$

$10^{-3} \times 10^{-1} = 10^{-4}$

$a^x \times a^y = a^{(x+y)}$

When you *divide* powers of the same number or variable, you *subtract* the indices. For example,

$a^4 \div a^3 = a^{(4-3)} = a^1 = a$

$b^4 \div b^7 = b^{-3}$

$10^4 \div 10^{-2} = 10^6$

$10^{-2} \div 10^{-4} = 10^2$

$a^x \div a^y = a^{(x-y)}$

When you *raise* a power to a further power, you *multiply* the indices. For example,

$(a^2)^3 = a^{2 \times 3} = a^6$

$(a^{-2})^4 = a^{-8}$

$(a^2)^6 = a^{12}$

$(a^x)^y = a^{xy}$

Here are some examples of different kinds of expressions using powers.

$2a^2 \times 3a^4 = (2 \times 3) \times (a^2 \times a^4) = 6 \times a^6 = 6a^6$

$4a^2b^3 \times 2ab^2 = (4 \times 2) \times (a^2 \times a) \times (b^3 \times b^2) = 8a^3b^5$

$12a^5 \div 3a^2 = (12 \div 3) \times (a^5 \div a^2) = 4a^3$

$(2a^2)^3 = (2)^3 \times (a^2)^3 = 8 \times a^6 = 8a^6$

EXERCISE 9C

C

1 Write these as single powers of 5.

a $5^2 \times 5^2$ **b** 5×5^2 **c** $5^{-2} \times 5^4$ **d** $5^6 \times 5^{-3}$ **e** $5^{-2} \times 5^{-3}$

2 Write these as single powers of 6.

a $6^5 \div 6^2$ **b** $6^4 \div 6^4$ **c** $6^4 \div 6^{-2}$ **d** $6^{-3} \div 6^4$ **e** $6^{-3} \div 6^{-5}$

3 Simplify these and write them as single powers of a.

a $a^2 \times a$ **b** $a^3 \times a^2$ **c** $a^4 \times a^3$

d $a^6 \div a^2$ **e** $a^3 \div a$ **f** $a^5 \div a^4$

AU 4 **a** $a^x \times a^y = a^{10}$

Write down a possible pair of values of x and y.

b $a^x \div a^y = a^{10}$

Write down a possible pair of values of x and y.

B

5 Write these as single powers of 4.

a $(4^2)^3$ **b** $(4^3)^5$ **c** $(4^1)^6$

d $(4^3)^{-2}$ **e** $(4^{-2})^{-3}$ **f** $(4^7)^0$

6 Simplify these expressions.

a $2a^2 \times 3a^3$ **b** $3a^4 \times 3a^{-2}$ **c** $(2a^2)^3$

d $-2a^2 \times 3a^2$ **e** $-4a^3 \times -2a^5$ **f** $-2a^4 \times 5a^{-7}$

7 Simplify these expressions.

a $6a^3 \div 2a^2$ **b** $12a^5 \div 3a^2$

c $15a^5 \div 5a$ **d** $18a^{-2} \div 3a^{-1}$

e $24a^5 \div 6a^{-2}$ **f** $30a \div 6a^5$

HINTS AND TIPS

Deal with numbers and indices separately and do not confuse the rules. For example: $12a^5 \div 4a^2 = (12 \div 4) \times (a^5 \div a^2)$

8 Simplify these expressions.

a $2a^2b^3 \times 4a^3b$ **b** $5a^2b^4 \times 2ab^{-3}$ **c** $6a^2b^3 \times 5a^{-4}b^{-5}$

d $12a^2b^4 \div 6ab$ **e** $24a^{-3}b^4 \div 3a^2b^{-3}$

B

9 Simplify these expressions.

a $\dfrac{6a^4b^3}{2ab}$ **b** $\dfrac{2a^2bc^2 \times 6abc^3}{4ab^2c}$ **c** $\dfrac{3abc \times 4a^3b^2c \times 6c^2}{9a^2bc}$

FM 10 Write down **two** possible:

a multiplication questions with an answer of $12x^2y^5$

b division questions with an answer of $12x^2y^5$.

A

PS 11 a, b and c are three different positive integers.

What is the smallest possible value of a^2b^3c?

FM PS 12 Use the general rule for dividing powers of the same number, $\dfrac{a^x}{a^y} = a^{x-y}$, to prove that any number raised to the power zero is 1.

Indices of the form $\frac{1}{n}$

Consider the problem $7^x \times 7^x = 7$. This can be written as:

$$7^{(x+x)} = 7$$

$$7^{2x} = 7^1 \Rightarrow 2x = 1 \Rightarrow x = \tfrac{1}{2}$$

If you now substitute $x = \frac{1}{2}$ back into the original equation, you see that:

$$7^{\frac{1}{2}} \times 7^{\frac{1}{2}} = 7$$

This makes $7^{\frac{1}{2}}$ the same as $\sqrt{7}$.

You can similarly show that $7^{\frac{1}{3}}$ is the same as $\sqrt[3]{7}$. And that, generally,

$$x^{\frac{1}{n}} = \sqrt[n]{x} \text{ (}n\text{th root of } x\text{)}$$

So in summary:

Power $\frac{1}{2}$ is the same as positive square root.

Power $\frac{1}{3}$ is the same as cube root.

Power $\frac{1}{n}$ is the same as nth root.

For example,

$49^{\frac{1}{2}} = \sqrt{49} = 7$ $8^{\frac{1}{3}} = \sqrt[3]{8} = 2$ $10\,000^{\frac{1}{4}} = \sqrt[4]{10\,000} = 10$ $36^{-\frac{1}{2}} = \dfrac{1}{\sqrt{36}} = \dfrac{1}{6}$

EXERCISE 9D

A

1 Evaluate the following.

a $25^{\frac{1}{2}}$ **b** $100^{\frac{1}{2}}$ **c** $64^{\frac{1}{2}}$ **d** $81^{\frac{1}{2}}$ **e** $625^{\frac{1}{2}}$

f $27^{\frac{1}{3}}$ **g** $64^{\frac{1}{3}}$ **h** $1000^{\frac{1}{3}}$ **i** $125^{\frac{1}{3}}$ **j** $512^{\frac{1}{3}}$

k $144^{\frac{1}{2}}$ **l** $400^{\frac{1}{2}}$ **m** $625^{\frac{1}{4}}$ **n** $81^{\frac{1}{4}}$ **o** $100\,000^{\frac{1}{5}}$

p $729^{\frac{1}{6}}$ **q** $32^{\frac{1}{5}}$ **r** $1024^{\frac{1}{10}}$ **s** $1296^{\frac{1}{4}}$ **t** $216^{\frac{1}{3}}$

A*

u $16^{-\frac{1}{2}}$ **v** $8^{-\frac{1}{3}}$ **w** $81^{-\frac{1}{4}}$ **x** $3125^{-\frac{1}{5}}$ **y** $1\,000\,000^{-\frac{1}{6}}$

2 Evaluate the following.

a $\left(\frac{25}{36}\right)^{\frac{1}{2}}$ **b** $\left(\frac{100}{36}\right)^{\frac{1}{2}}$ **c** $\left(\frac{64}{81}\right)^{\frac{1}{2}}$ **d** $\left(\frac{81}{25}\right)^{\frac{1}{2}}$ **e** $\left(\frac{25}{64}\right)^{\frac{1}{2}}$

f $\left(\frac{27}{125}\right)^{\frac{1}{3}}$ **g** $\left(\frac{8}{512}\right)^{\frac{1}{3}}$ **h** $\left(\frac{1000}{64}\right)^{\frac{1}{3}}$ **i** $\left(\frac{64}{125}\right)^{\frac{1}{3}}$ **j** $\left(\frac{512}{343}\right)^{\frac{1}{3}}$

3 Use the general rule for raising a power to another power to prove that $x^{\frac{1}{n}}$ is equivalent to $\sqrt[n]{x}$.

PS 4 Which of these is the odd one out?

$16^{-\frac{1}{4}}$ $64^{-\frac{1}{2}}$ $8^{-\frac{1}{3}}$

Show how you decided.

AU 5 Imagine that you are the teacher.

Write down how you would teach the class that $27^{-\frac{1}{3}}$ is equal to $\frac{1}{3}$.

PS 6 $x^{-\frac{2}{3}} = y^{\frac{1}{3}}$

Find values for x and y that make this equation work.

Indices of the form $\frac{a}{b}$

Here are two examples of this form.

$t^{\frac{2}{3}} = t^{\frac{1}{3}} \times t^{\frac{1}{3}} = (\sqrt[3]{t})^2$ $81^{\frac{3}{4}} = (\sqrt[4]{81})^3 = 3^3 = 27$

EXAMPLE 3

Evaluate the following. **a** $16^{-\frac{1}{4}}$ **b** $32^{-\frac{4}{5}}$

When dealing with the negative index remember that it means reciprocal.

Do problems like these one step at a time.

Step 1: Rewrite the calculation as a fraction by dealing with the negative power.

Step 2: Take the root of the base number given by the denominator of the fraction.

Step 3: Raise the result to the power given by the numerator of the fraction.

Step 4: Write out the answer as a fraction.

a **Step 1:** $16^{-\frac{1}{4}} = \left(\frac{1}{16}\right)^{\frac{1}{4}}$ **Step 2:** $16^{\frac{1}{4}} = \sqrt[4]{16} = 2$ **Step 3:** $2^1 = 2$ **Step 4:** $16^{-\frac{1}{4}} = \frac{1}{2}$

b **Step 1:** $32^{-\frac{4}{5}} = \left(\frac{1}{32}\right)^{\frac{4}{5}}$ **Step 2:** $32^{\frac{1}{5}} = \sqrt[5]{32} = 2$ **Step 3:** $2^4 = 16$ **Step 4:** $32^{-\frac{4}{5}} = \frac{1}{16}$

EXERCISE 9E

1 Evaluate the following.

a $32^{\frac{4}{5}}$ **b** $125^{\frac{2}{3}}$ **c** $1296^{\frac{3}{4}}$ **d** $243^{\frac{4}{5}}$

2 Rewrite the following in index form.

a $\sqrt[3]{t^2}$ **b** $\sqrt[4]{m^3}$ **c** $\sqrt[5]{k^2}$ **d** $\sqrt{x^3}$

3 Evaluate the following.

a $8^{\frac{2}{3}}$ **b** $27^{\frac{2}{3}}$ **c** $16^{\frac{3}{2}}$ **d** $625^{\frac{5}{4}}$

4 Evaluate the following.

a $25^{-\frac{1}{2}}$ **b** $36^{-\frac{1}{2}}$ **c** $16^{-\frac{1}{4}}$ **d** $81^{-\frac{1}{4}}$

e $16^{-\frac{1}{2}}$ **f** $8^{-\frac{1}{3}}$ **g** $32^{-\frac{1}{5}}$ **h** $27^{-\frac{1}{3}}$

5 Evaluate the following.

a $25^{-\frac{3}{2}}$ **b** $36^{-\frac{3}{2}}$ **c** $16^{-\frac{3}{4}}$ **d** $81^{-\frac{3}{4}}$

e $64^{-\frac{4}{3}}$ **f** $8^{-\frac{2}{3}}$ **g** $32^{-\frac{2}{5}}$ **h** $27^{-\frac{2}{3}}$

6 Evaluate the following.

a $100^{-\frac{5}{2}}$ **b** $144^{-\frac{1}{2}}$ **c** $125^{-\frac{2}{3}}$ **d** $9^{-\frac{3}{2}}$

e $4^{-\frac{5}{2}}$ **f** $64^{-\frac{5}{6}}$ **g** $27^{-\frac{4}{3}}$ **h** $169^{-\frac{1}{2}}$

PS 7 Which of these is the odd one out?

$16^{-\frac{3}{4}}$ $64^{-\frac{1}{2}}$ $8^{-\frac{2}{3}}$

Show how you decided.

AU 8 Imagine that you are the teacher.

Write down how you would teach the class that $27^{-\frac{2}{3}}$ is equal to $\frac{1}{9}$.

9.2 Standard form

This section will show you how to:
- change a number into standard form
- calculate using numbers in standard form

Key words
powers
standard form
standard index form

Arithmetic of powers of 10

Multiplying

You have already done some arithmetic with multiples of 10 in Chapter 1. You will now look at **powers** of 10.

How many zeros does a million have? What is a million as a power of 10? This table shows some of the pattern of the powers of 10.

Number	0.001	0.01	0.1	1	10	100	1000	10 000	100 000
Powers	10^{-3}	10^{-2}	10^{-1}	100	10^1	10^2	10^3	10^4	10^5

What pattern is there in the top row? What pattern is there to the powers in the bottom row?

To multiply by any power of 10, you simply move the digits according to these two rules.

- When the index is *positive*, move the digits to the *left* by the same number of places as the value of the index.
- When the index is *negative*, move the digits to the *right* by the same number of places as the value of the index.

EXAMPLE 4

Write these as ordinary numbers.

a 12.356×10^2 **b** 3.45×10^1

c 753.4×10^{-2} **d** 6789×10^{-1}

a $12.356 \times 10^2 = 1235.6$ **b** $3.45 \times 10^1 = 34.5$

c $753.4 \times 10^{-2} = 7.534$ **d** $6789 \times 10^{-1} = 678.9$

In certain cases, you have to insert the 'hidden' zeros.

EXAMPLE 5

Write these as ordinary numbers.

a 75×10^4 **b** 2.04×10^5

c 6.78×10^{-3} **d** 0.897×10^{-4}

a $75 \times 10^4 = 750\,000$ **b** $2.04 \times 10^5 = 204\,000$

c $6.78 \times 10^{-3} = 0.00678$ **d** $0.897 \times 10^{-4} = 0.000\,0897$

Dividing

To divide by any power of 10, you simply move the digits according to these two rules.

- When the index is *positive*, move the digits to the *right* by the same number of places as the value of the index.
- When the index is *negative*, move the digits to the *left* by the same number of places as the value of the index.

EXAMPLE 6

Write these as ordinary numbers.

a $712.35 \div 10^2$ **b** $38.45 \div 10^1$

c $3.463 \div 10^{-2}$ **d** $6.789 \div 10^{-1}$

a $712.35 \div 10^2 = 7.1235$ **b** $38.45 \div 10^1 = 3.845$

c $3.463 \div 10^{-2} = 346.3$ **d** $6.789 \div 10^{-1} = 67.89$

In certain cases, you have to insert the 'hidden' zeros.

EXAMPLE 7

Write these as ordinary numbers.

a $75 \div 10^4$ **b** $2.04 \div 10^5$

c $6.78 \div 10^{-3}$ **d** $0.08 \div 10^{-4}$

a $75 \div 10^4 = 0.0075$ **b** $2.04 \div 10^5 = 0.000\,0204$

c $6.78 \div 10^{-3} = 6780$ **d** $0.08 \div 10^{-4} = 800$

When doing the next exercise, remember:

$10\,000 = 10 \times 10 \times 10 \times 10 = 10^4$ $\quad 1 = 10^0$

$1000 = 10 \times 10 \times 10 = 10^3$ $\quad 0.1 = 1 \div 10 = 10^{-1}$

$100 = 10 \times 10 = 10^2$ $\quad 0.01 = 1 \div 100 = 10^{-2}$

$10 = 10 = 10^1$ $\quad 0.001 = 1 \div 1000 = 10^{-3}$

EXERCISE 9F

D

1 Write down the value of each of the following.

a 3.1×10 **b** 3.1×100 **c** 3.1×1000 **d** $3.1 \times 10\,000$

2 Write down the value of each of the following.

a 6.5×10 **b** 6.5×10^2 **c** 6.5×10^3 **d** 6.5×10^4

3 Write down the value of each of the following.

a $3.1 \div 10$ **b** $3.1 \div 100$ **c** $3.1 \div 1000$ **d** $3.1 \div 10\,000$

4 Write down the value of each of the following.

a $6.5 \div 10$ **b** $6.5 \div 10^2$ **c** $6.5 \div 10^3$ **d** $6.5 \div 10^4$

5 Evaluate the following.

a 2.5×100 **b** 3.45×10 **c** 4.67×1000 **d** 34.6×10

e 20.789×10 **f** 56.78×1000 **g** 2.46×10^2 **h** 0.076×10

i 0.999×10^6 **j** 234.56×10^2 **k** 98.7654×10^3 **l** 43.23×10^6

m $0.003\,4578 \times 10^5$ **n** 0.0006×10^7 **o** $0.005\,67 \times 10^4$ **p** 56.0045×10^4

6 Evaluate the following.

a $2.5 \div 100$ b $3.45 \div 10$ c $4.67 \div 1000$ d $34.6 \div 10$

e $20.789 \div 100$ f $56.78 \div 1000$ g $2.46 \div 10^2$ h $0.076 \div 10$

i $0.999 \div 10^6$ j $234.56 \div 10^2$ k $98.7654 \div 10^3$ l $43.23 \div 10^6$

m $0.003\,4578 \div 10^5$ n $0.0006 \div 10^7$ o $0.005\,67 \div 10^4$ p $56.0045 \div 10^4$

7 Without using a calculator, work out the following.

a 2.3×10^2 b 5.789×10^5 c 4.79×10^3 d 5.7×10^7

e 2.16×10^2 f 1.05×10^4 g 3.2×10^{-4} h 9.87×10^3

8 Which of these statements is true about the numbers in question **7**?

a The first part is always a number between 1 and 10.

b There is always a multiplication sign in the middle of the expression.

c There is always a power of 10 at the end.

d Calculator displays sometimes show numbers in this form.

AU PS **9** The mass of Mars is 6.4×10^{23} kg.

The mass of Venus is 4.9×10^{24} kg.

Without working out the answers, explain how you can tell which planet is the heavier.

PS **10** A number is between one million and 10 million. It is written in the form 4.7×10^n.

What is the value of n?

D C B

Standard form

Standard form is also known as **standard index form**.

Standard form is a way of writing very large and very small numbers using powers of 10. In this form, a number is given a value between 1 and 10 multiplied by a power of 10. That is,

$a \times 10^n$ where $1 \leqslant a < 10$, and n is a whole number.

Follow through these examples to see how numbers are written in standard form.

$52 = 5.2 \times 10 = \mathbf{5.2 \times 10^1}$

$73 = 7.3 \times 10 = \mathbf{7.3 \times 10^1}$

$625 = 6.25 \times 100 = \mathbf{6.25 \times 10^2}$ The numbers in bold are in standard form.

$389 = 3.89 \times 100 = \mathbf{3.89 \times 10^2}$

$3147 = 3.147 \times 1000 = \mathbf{3.147 \times 10^3}$

When writing a number in this way, you must always follow two rules.

- The first part must be a number between 1 and 10 (1 is allowed but 10 isn't).
- The second part must be a whole-number (negative or positive) power of 10. Note that you would *not normally* write the power 1.

Standard form on a calculator

A number such as 123 000 000 000 is obviously difficult to key into a calculator. Instead, you enter it in standard form (assuming you are using a scientific calculator):

$123\,000\,000\,000 = 1.23 \times 10^{11}$

The key strokes to enter this into your calculator will be:

1 • 2 3 ×10ˣ 1 1

Your calculator display will display the number either as an ordinary number, if there is enough space, or in standard form.

Standard form of numbers less than 1

These numbers are written in standard form. Make sure that you understand how they are formed.

a $0.4 = 4 \times 10^{-1}$ **b** $0.05 = 5 \times 10^{-2}$ **c** $0.007 = 7 \times 10^{-3}$

d $0.123 = 1.23 \times 10^{-1}$ **e** $0.007\,65 = 7.65 \times 10^{-3}$ **f** $0.9804 = 9.804 \times 10^{-1}$

g $0.0098 = 9.8 \times 10^{-3}$ **h** $0.000\,0078 = 7.8 \times 10^{-6}$

On a calculator you would enter 1.23×10^{-6}, for example, as:

1 • 2 3 ×10ˣ (–) 6

Try entering some of the numbers **a** to **h** (above) into your calculator for practice.

EXERCISE 9G

D

1 Write down the value of each of the following.

a 3.1×0.1 **b** 3.1×0.01 **c** 3.1×0.001 **d** 3.1×0.0001

2 Write down the value of each of the following.

a 6.5×10^{-1} **b** 6.5×10^{-2} **c** 6.5×10^{-3} **d** 6.5×10^{-4}

PS **3** **a** What is the largest number you can enter into your calculator?

b What is the smallest number you can enter into your calculator?

4 Work out the value of each of the following.

a $3.1 \div 0.1$ **b** $3.1 \div 0.01$ **c** $3.1 \div 0.001$ **d** $3.1 \div 0.0001$

5 Work out the value of each of the following.

a $6.5 \div 10^{-1}$ **b** $6.5 \div 10^{-2}$ **c** $6.5 \div 10^{-3}$ **d** $6.5 \div 10^{-4}$

C

6 Write these numbers out in full.

a 2.5×10^{2} **b** 3.45×10 **c** 4.67×10^{-3} **d** 3.46×10

e 2.0789×10^{-2} **f** 5.678×10^{3} **g** 2.46×10^{2} **h** 7.6×10^{3}

i 8.97×10^{5} **j** 8.65×10^{-3} **k** 6×10^{7} **l** 5.67×10^{-4}

C

7 Write these numbers in standard form.

a 250 **b** 0.345 **c** 46 700

d 3 400 000 000 **e** 20 780 000 000 **f** 0.000 567 8

g 2460 **h** 0.076 **i** 0.000 76

j 0.999 **k** 234.56 **l** 98.7654

m 0.0006 **n** 0.005 67 **o** 56.0045

In questions **8** to **10**, write the numbers given in each question in standard form.

8 One year, 27 797 runners completed the New York marathon.

9 The largest number of dominoes ever toppled by one person is 281 581, although 30 people set up and toppled 1 382 101.

10 The asteroid *Phaethon* comes within 12 980 000 miles of the Sun, whilst the asteroid *Pholus*, at its furthest point, is a distance of 2997 million miles from the Earth. The closest an asteroid ever came to Earth was 93 000 miles from the planet.

B

AU 11 How many times bigger is 3.2×10^6 than 3.2×10^4?

PS FM 12 The speed of sound (Mach 1) is 1236 kilometres per hour or about 1 mile in 5 seconds.

A plane travelling at Mach 2 would be travelling at twice the speed of sound.

How many miles would a plane travelling at Mach 3 cover in 1 minute?

Calculating with standard form

Calculations involving very large or very small numbers can be done more easily using standard form.

In these examples, you will see how to work out the area of a pixel on a computer screen, and how long it takes light to reach the Earth from a distant star.

EXAMPLE 8

A pixel on a computer screen is 2×10^{-2} cm long by 7×10^{-3} cm wide.

What is the area of the pixel?

The area is given by length times width.

$$\text{Area} = 2 \times 10^{-2}\text{ cm} \times 7 \times 10^{-3}\text{ cm}$$
$$= (2 \times 7) \times (10^{-2} \times 10^{-3})\text{ cm}^2 = 14 \times 10^{-5}\text{ cm}^2$$

Note that you multiply the numbers and add the powers of 10. (You should not need to use a calculator to do this calculation.) The answer is not in standard form as the first part is not between 1 and 10, so you have to change it to standard form.

$$14 = 1.4 \times 10^1$$

So area = $14 \times 10^{-5}\text{ cm}^2 = 1.4 \times 10^1 \times 10^{-5}\text{ cm}^2 = 1.4 \times 10^{-4}\text{ cm}^2$

EXAMPLE 9

The star *Betelgeuse* is 1.8×10^{15} miles from Earth. Light travels at 1.86×10^5 miles per second.

a How many seconds does it take light to travel from *Betelgeuse* to Earth? Give your answer in standard form.

b How many years does it take light to travel from *Betelgeuse* to Earth?

a Time = distance ÷ speed = 1.8×10^{15} miles ÷ 1.86×10^5 miles per second

$= (1.8 \div 1.86) \times (10^{15} \div 10^5)$ seconds

$= 0.967\,741\,935 \times 10^{10}$ seconds

Note that you divide the numbers and subtract the powers of 10. To change the answer to standard form, first round it, which gives:

$0.97 \times 10^{10} = 9.7 \times 10^9$ seconds

b To convert from seconds to years, you have to divide first by 3600 to get to hours, then by 24 to get to days, and finally by 365 to get to years.

$9.7 \times 10^9 \div (3600 \times 24 \times 365) = 307.6$ years

EXERCISE 9H

B

1 These numbers are not in standard form. Write them in standard form.

a 56.7×10^2 **b** 0.06×10^4 **c** 34.6×10^{-2}

d 0.07×10^{-2} **e** 56×10 **f** $2 \times 3 \times 10^5$

g $2 \times 10^2 \times 35$ **h** 160×10^{-2} **i** 23 million

j 0.0003×10^{-2} **k** 25.6×10^5 **l** $16 \times 10^2 \times 3 \times 10^{-1}$

m $2 \times 10^4 \times 56 \times 10^{-4}$ **n** $(18 \times 10^2) \div (3 \times 10^3)$ **o** $(56 \times 10^3) \div (2 \times 10^{-2})$

2 Work out the following. Give your answers in standard form.

a $2 \times 10^4 \times 5.4 \times 10^3$ **b** $1.6 \times 10^2 \times 3 \times 10^4$ **c** $2 \times 10^4 \times 6 \times 10^4$

d $2 \times 10^{-4} \times 5.4 \times 10^3$ **e** $1.6 \times 10^{-2} \times 4 \times 10^4$ **f** $2 \times 10^4 \times 6 \times 10^{-4}$

g $7.2 \times 10^{-3} \times 4 \times 10^2$ **h** $(5 \times 10^3)^2$ **i** $(2 \times 10^{-2})^3$

3 Work out the following. Give your answers in standard form, rounding to an appropriate degree of accuracy where necessary.

a $2.1 \times 10^4 \times 5.4 \times 10^3$ **b** $1.6 \times 10^3 \times 3.8 \times 10^3$ **c** $2.4 \times 10^4 \times 6.6 \times 10^4$

d $7.3 \times 10^{-6} \times 5.4 \times 10^3$ **e** $(3.1 \times 10^4)^2$ **f** $(6.8 \times 10^{-4})^2$

g $5.7 \times 10 \times 3.7 \times 10$ **h** $1.9 \times 10^{-2} \times 1.9 \times 10^9$ **i** $5.9 \times 10^3 \times 2.5 \times 10^{-2}$

j $5.2 \times 10^3 \times 2.2 \times 10^2 \times 3.1 \times 10^3$ **k** $1.8 \times 10^2 \times 3.6 \times 10^3 \times 2.4 \times 10^{-2}$

B

4 Work out the following. Give your answers in standard form.

a $(5.4 \times 10^4) \div (2 \times 10^3)$ **b** $(4.8 \times 10^2) \div (3 \times 10^4)$ **c** $(1.2 \times 10^4) \div (6 \times 10^4)$

d $(2 \times 10^{-4}) \div (5 \times 10^3)$ **e** $(1.8 \times 10^4) \div (9 \times 10^{-2})$ **f** $\sqrt{(36 \times 10^{-4})}$

g $(5.4 \times 10^{-3}) \div (2.7 \times 10^2)$ **h** $(1.8 \times 10^6) \div (3.6 \times 10^3)$ **i** $(5.6 \times 10^3) \div (2.8 \times 10^2)$

5 Work out the following. Give your answers in standard form, rounding to an appropriate degree of accuracy where necessary.

a $(2.7 \times 10^4) \div (5 \times 10^2)$ **b** $(2.3 \times 10^4) \div (8 \times 10^6)$ **c** $(3.2 \times 10^{-1}) \div (2.8 \times 10^{-1})$

d $(2.6 \times 10^{-6}) \div (4.1 \times 10^3)$ **e** $\sqrt{(8 \times 10^4)}$ **f** $\sqrt{(30 \times 10^{-4})}$

g $5.3 \times 10^3 \times 2.3 \times 10^2 \div (2.5 \times 10^3)$ **h** $1.8 \times 10^2 \times 3.1 \times 10^3 \div (6.5 \times 10^{-2})$

6 A typical adult has about 20 000 000 000 000 red corpuscles. Each red corpuscle has a mass of about 0.000 000 000 1 g. Write both of these numbers in standard form and work out the total mass of red corpuscles in a typical adult.

PS 7 A man puts one grain of rice on the first square of a chess board, two on the second square, four on the third, eight on the fourth and so on.

a How many grains of rice will he put on the 64th square of the board?

b How many grains of rice will there be altogether?

Give your answers in standard form.

HINTS AND TIPS

Compare powers of 2 with the running totals. By the fourth square you have 15 grains altogether, and $2^4 = 16$.

8 The surface area of the Earth is approximately 2×10^8 square miles. The area of the Earth's surface that is covered by water is approximately 1.4×10^8 square miles.

a Calculate the area of the Earth's surface *not* covered by water. Give your answer in standard form.

b What percentage of the Earth's surface is not covered by water?

9 The Moon is a sphere with a radius of 1.080×10^3 miles. The formula for working out the surface area of a sphere is:

surface area = $4\pi r^2$

Calculate the surface area of the Moon.

10 Evaluate $\frac{E}{M}$ when $E = 1.5 \times 10^3$ and $M = 3 \times 10^{-2}$, giving your answer in standard form.

11 Work out the value of $\frac{3.2 \times 10^7}{1.4 \times 10^2}$ giving your answer in standard form, correct to 2 significant figures.

12 In 2009, British Airways carried 33 million passengers. Of these, 70% passed through Heathrow Airport. On average, each passenger carried 19.7 kg of luggage. Calculate the total mass of the luggage carried by these passengers.

B

FM 13 In 2009 the world population was approximately 6.77×10^9. In 2010 the world population is approximately 6.85×10^9.

By how much did the population rise? Give your answer as an ordinary number.

A

PS 14 Here are four numbers written in standard form.

1.6×10^4 4.8×10^6 3.2×10^2 6.4×10^3

a Work out the smallest answer when two of these numbers are multiplied together.

b Work out the largest answer when two of these numbers are added together.

Give your answers in standard form.

FM 15 Many people withdraw money from their banks by using hole-in-the-wall machines. Each day there are eight million withdrawals from 32 000 machines. What is the average number of withdrawals per machine?

PS 16 The mass of Saturn is 5.686×10^{26} tonnes. The mass of the Earth is 6.04×10^{21} tonnes. How many times heavier is Saturn than the Earth? Give your answer in standard form to a suitable degree of accuracy.

AU 17 A number, when written in standard form, is greater than 100 million and less than 1000 million.

Write down a possible value of the number, in standard form.

9.3 Rational numbers and reciprocals

This section will show you how to:

- recognise rational numbers, reciprocals, terminating decimals and recurring decimals
- convert terminal decimals to fractions
- convert fractions to recurring decimals
- find reciprocals of numbers or fractions

Key words
rational number
reciprocal
recurring decimal
terminating decimal

Rational numbers

A **rational number** is a number that can be written as a fraction, for example, $\frac{1}{4}$ or $\frac{10}{3}$.

When a fraction is converted to a decimal it will either be:

- a **terminating decimal** or
- a **recurring decimal**.

A terminating decimal has a finite number of digits. For example, $\frac{1}{4} = 0.25$, $\frac{1}{8} = 0.125$.

A recurring decimal has a digit, or block of digits, that repeat. For example, $\frac{1}{3} = 0.3333 \ldots$, $\frac{2}{11} = 0.181818 \ldots$

Recurring digits can be shown by putting a dot over the first and last digit of the group that repeats.

0.3333 … becomes $0.\dot{3}$

0.181818 … becomes $0.\dot{1}\dot{8}$

0.123123123 … becomes $0.\dot{1}2\dot{3}$

0.58333 … becomes $0.58\dot{3}$

0.6181818 … becomes $0.6\dot{1}\dot{8}$

0.4123123123 … become $0.4\dot{1}2\dot{3}$

Converting fractions into recurring decimals

A fraction that does not convert to a terminating decimal will give a recurring decimal. You may already know that $\frac{1}{3} = 0.333\ldots = 0.\dot{3}$

This means that the 3s go on forever and the decimal never ends.

To convert the fraction, you can usually use a calculator to divide the numerator by the denominator. Note that calculators round the last digit so it may not always be a true recurring decimal in the display. Use a calculator to check the following recurring decimals.

$$\frac{2}{11} = 0.181\,818\ldots = 0.\dot{1}\dot{8}$$

$$\frac{4}{15} = 0.2666\ldots = 0.2\dot{6}$$

$$\frac{8}{13} = 0.615\,384\,615\,384\,6\ldots = 0.\dot{6}15\,38\dot{4}$$

Converting terminal decimals into fractions

To convert a terminating decimal to a fraction, take the decimal number as the numerator. Then the denominator is 10, 100, 1000 …, depending on the number of decimal places. Because a terminating decimal has a specific number of decimal places, you can use place value to work out exactly where the numerator and the denominator end. For example:

- $0.7 = \frac{7}{10}$
- $0.23 = \frac{23}{100}$
- $0.045 = \frac{45}{1000} = \frac{9}{200}$
- $2.34 = \frac{234}{100} = \frac{117}{50} = 2\frac{17}{50}$
- $0.625 = \frac{625}{1000} = \frac{5}{8}$

Converting recurring decimals into fractions

To convert a recurring decimal to a fraction you have to use the algebraic method shown in the examples below.

EXAMPLE 10

Convert $0.\dot{7}$ to a fraction.

Let x be the fraction. Then:

	$x = 0.777\,777\,777\ldots$	(1)
Multiply (1) by 10	$10x = 7.777\,777\,777\ldots$	(2)
Subtract (2) – (1)	$9x = 7$	
	$\Rightarrow x = \frac{7}{9}$	

EXAMPLE 11

Convert $0.\dot{5}6\dot{4}$ to a fraction.

Let x be the fraction. Then:

	$x = 0.564\,564\,564\ldots$	(1)
Multiply (1) by 1000	$1000x = 564.564\,564\,564\ldots$	(2)
Subtract (2) – (1)	$999x = 564$	
	$\Rightarrow x = \frac{564}{999} = \frac{188}{333}$	

As a general rule, multiply by 10 if one digit recurs, multiply by 100 if two digits recur, multiply by 1000 if three digits recur, and so on.

Finding reciprocals of numbers or fractions

The **reciprocal** of any number is 1 divided by the number.

For example, the reciprocal of 2 is $1 \div 2 = \frac{1}{2} = 0.5$

The reciprocal of 0.25 is $1 \div 0.25 = 4$

You can find the reciprocal of a fraction by inverting it.

For example, the reciprocal of $\frac{2}{3}$ is $\frac{3}{2}$.

The reciprocal of $\frac{7}{4}$ is $\frac{4}{7}$.

EXERCISE 9I

1 Work out each of these fractions as a decimal. Give them as terminating decimals or recurring decimals as appropriate.

a $\frac{1}{2}$ **b** $\frac{1}{3}$ **c** $\frac{1}{4}$ **d** $\frac{1}{5}$ **e** $\frac{1}{6}$ **f** $\frac{1}{7}$ **g** $\frac{1}{8}$ **h** $\frac{1}{9}$ **i** $\frac{1}{10}$ **j** $\frac{1}{13}$

PS 2 There are several patterns to be found in recurring decimals. For example,

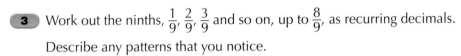

$\frac{1}{7} = 0.142\,857\,142\,857\,142\,857\,142\,857\ldots$

$\frac{2}{7} = 0.285\,714\,285\,714\,285\,714\,285\,714\ldots$

$\frac{3}{7} = 0.428\,571\,428\,571\,428\,571\,428\,571\ldots$

and so on.

a Write down the decimals for $\frac{4}{7}, \frac{5}{7}, \frac{6}{7}$ to 24 decimal places.

b What do you notice?

3 Work out the ninths, $\frac{1}{9}, \frac{2}{9}, \frac{3}{9}$ and so on, up to $\frac{8}{9}$, as recurring decimals.

Describe any patterns that you notice.

4 Work out the elevenths, $\frac{1}{11}, \frac{2}{11}, \frac{3}{11}$ and so on, up to $\frac{10}{11}$, as recurring decimals.

Describe any patterns that you notice.

5 Write each of these fractions as a decimal. Use your results to write the list in order of size, smallest first.

$\frac{4}{9}$ $\frac{5}{11}$ $\frac{3}{7}$ $\frac{9}{22}$ $\frac{16}{37}$ $\frac{6}{13}$

6 Write each of the following as a fraction with a denominator of 120. Use your results to put them in order of size, smallest first.

$\frac{19}{60}$ $\frac{7}{24}$ $\frac{3}{10}$ $\frac{2}{5}$ $\frac{5}{12}$

7 Convert each of these terminating decimals to a fraction.

a 0.125 **b** 0.34 **c** 0.725 **d** 0.3125

e 0.89 **f** 0.05 **g** 2.35 **h** 0.218 75

8 Use a calculator to work out the reciprocal of each of the following.

a 12 **b** 16 **c** 20 **d** 25 **e** 50

9 Write down the reciprocal of each of the following fractions.

a $\frac{3}{4}$ **b** $\frac{5}{6}$ **c** $\frac{2}{5}$ **d** $\frac{7}{10}$ **e** $\frac{11}{20}$ **f** $\frac{4}{15}$

10 **a** Write the fractions and their reciprocals from question **9** as decimals. Write them as terminating decimals or recurring decimals as appropriate.

b Is it always true that a terminating decimal has a reciprocal that is a recurring decimal?

AU 11 Explain why zero has no reciprocal.

AU 12 **a** Work out the reciprocal of the reciprocal of 10.

b Work out the reciprocal of the reciprocal of 2.

c What do you notice?

C

AU 13 x and y are two positive numbers.

If x is less than y, which statement is true?

The reciprocal of x is less than the reciprocal of y.

The reciprocal of x is greater than the reciprocal of y.

It is impossible to tell.

Give an example to support your answer.

AU 14 Explain why a number multiplied by its reciprocal is equal to 1. Use examples to show that this is true for negative numbers.

A

15 $x = 0.242\,424\ \ldots$

a What is $100x$?

b By subtracting the original value from your answer to part **a**, work out the value of $99x$.

c What is x as a fraction?

16 Convert each of these recurring decimals to a fraction.

a $0.\dot{8}$ **b** $0.\dot{3}\dot{4}$ **c** $0.\dot{4}\dot{5}$

d $0.\dot{5}6\dot{7}$ **e** $0.\dot{4}$ **f** $0.0\dot{4}$

g $0.1\dot{4}$ **h** $0.0\dot{4}\dot{5}$ **i** $2.\dot{7}$

j $7.\dot{6}\dot{3}$ **k** $3.\dot{3}$ **l** $2.\dot{0}\dot{6}$

A*

PS 17 **a** $\frac{1}{7}$ is a recurring decimal. $(\frac{1}{7})^2 = \frac{1}{49}$ is also a recurring decimal.

Is it true that when you square any fraction that is a recurring decimal, you get another fraction that is also a recurring decimal? Try this with at least four numerical examples before you make a decision.

b $\frac{1}{4}$ is a terminating decimal. $(\frac{1}{4})^2 = \frac{1}{16}$ is also a terminating decimal.

Is it true that when you square any fraction that is a terminating decimal, you get another fraction that is also a terminating decimal? Try this with at least four numerical examples before you make a decision.

c What type of fraction do you get when you multiply a fraction that gives a recurring decimal by another fraction that gives a terminating decimal? Try this with at least four numerical examples before you make a decision.

PS 18 **a** Convert the recurring decimal $0.\dot{9}$ to a fraction.

b Prove that $0.4\dot{9}$ is equal to 0.5

9.4 Surds

This section will show you how to:
- simplify surds
- calculate and manipulate surds, including rationalising a denominator

Key words
exact values
rationalise
surds

It is useful to be able to work with **surds**, which are roots of rational numbers written as, for example,

$\sqrt{2}$ $\sqrt{5}$ $\sqrt{15}$ $\sqrt{9}$ $\sqrt{3}$ $\sqrt{10}$

These are also referred to as **exact values**.

Here are four general rules for simplifying surds.

You can check that these rules work by taking numerical examples.

$\sqrt{a} \times \sqrt{b} = \sqrt{ab}$ $\quad C\sqrt{a} \times D\sqrt{b} = CD\sqrt{ab}$

$\sqrt{a} \div \sqrt{b} = \sqrt{\frac{a}{b}}$ $\quad C\sqrt{a} \div D\sqrt{b} = \frac{C}{D}\sqrt{\frac{a}{b}}$

For example,

$\sqrt{2} \times \sqrt{2} = \sqrt{4} = 2$ $\quad \sqrt{2} \times \sqrt{10} = \sqrt{20} = \sqrt{(4 \times 5)} = \sqrt{4} \times \sqrt{5} = 2\sqrt{5}$

$\sqrt{2} \times \sqrt{3} = \sqrt{6}$ $\quad \sqrt{6} \times \sqrt{15} = \sqrt{90} = \sqrt{9} \times \sqrt{10} = 3\sqrt{10}$

$\sqrt{2} \times \sqrt{8} = \sqrt{16} = 4$ $\quad 3\sqrt{5} \times 4\sqrt{3} = 12\sqrt{15}$

EXERCISE 9J

1 Simplify each of the following. Leave your answers in surd form if necessary.

a $\sqrt{2} \times \sqrt{3}$ **b** $\sqrt{5} \times \sqrt{3}$ **c** $\sqrt{2} \times \sqrt{2}$ **d** $\sqrt{2} \times \sqrt{8}$
e $\sqrt{5} \times \sqrt{8}$ **f** $\sqrt{3} \times \sqrt{3}$ **g** $\sqrt{6} \times \sqrt{2}$ **h** $\sqrt{7} \times \sqrt{3}$
i $\sqrt{2} \times \sqrt{7}$ **j** $\sqrt{2} \times \sqrt{18}$ **k** $\sqrt{6} \times \sqrt{6}$ **l** $\sqrt{5} \times \sqrt{6}$

2 Simplify each of the following. Leave your answers in surd form if necessary.

a $\sqrt{12} \div \sqrt{3}$ **b** $\sqrt{15} \div \sqrt{3}$ **c** $\sqrt{12} \div \sqrt{2}$ **d** $\sqrt{24} \div \sqrt{8}$
e $\sqrt{40} \div \sqrt{8}$ **f** $\sqrt{3} \div \sqrt{3}$ **g** $\sqrt{6} \div \sqrt{2}$ **h** $\sqrt{21} \div \sqrt{3}$
i $\sqrt{28} \div \sqrt{7}$ **j** $\sqrt{48} \div \sqrt{8}$ **k** $\sqrt{6} \div \sqrt{6}$ **l** $\sqrt{54} \div \sqrt{6}$

3 Simplify each of the following. Leave your answers in surd form if necessary.

a $\sqrt{2} \times \sqrt{3} \times \sqrt{2}$ **b** $\sqrt{5} \times \sqrt{3} \times \sqrt{15}$ **c** $\sqrt{2} \times \sqrt{2} \times \sqrt{8}$ **d** $\sqrt{2} \times \sqrt{8} \times \sqrt{3}$
e $\sqrt{5} \times \sqrt{8} \times \sqrt{8}$ **f** $\sqrt{3} \times \sqrt{3} \times \sqrt{3}$ **g** $\sqrt{6} \times \sqrt{2} \times \sqrt{48}$ **h** $\sqrt{7} \times \sqrt{3} \times \sqrt{3}$
i $\sqrt{2} \times \sqrt{7} \times \sqrt{2}$ **j** $\sqrt{2} \times \sqrt{18} \times \sqrt{5}$ **k** $\sqrt{6} \times \sqrt{6} \times \sqrt{3}$ **l** $\sqrt{5} \times \sqrt{6} \times \sqrt{30}$

A

A

4 Simplify each of the following. Leave your answers in surd form.

a $\sqrt{2} \times \sqrt{3} \div \sqrt{2}$ **b** $\sqrt{5} \times \sqrt{3} \div \sqrt{15}$ **c** $\sqrt{32} \times \sqrt{2} \div \sqrt{8}$ **d** $\sqrt{2} \times \sqrt{8} \div \sqrt{8}$

e $\sqrt{5} \times \sqrt{8} \div \sqrt{8}$ **f** $\sqrt{3} \times \sqrt{3} \div \sqrt{3}$ **g** $\sqrt{8} \times \sqrt{12} \div \sqrt{48}$ **h** $\sqrt{7} \times \sqrt{3} \div \sqrt{3}$

i $\sqrt{2} \times \sqrt{7} \div \sqrt{2}$ **j** $\sqrt{2} \times \sqrt{18} \div \sqrt{3}$ **k** $\sqrt{6} \times \sqrt{6} \div \sqrt{3}$ **l** $\sqrt{5} \times \sqrt{6} \div \sqrt{30}$

5 Simplify each of these expressions.

a $\sqrt{a} \times \sqrt{a}$ **b** $\sqrt{a} \div \sqrt{a}$ **c** $\sqrt{a} \times \sqrt{a} \div \sqrt{a}$

6 Simplify each of the following surds into the form $a\sqrt{b}$.

a $\sqrt{18}$ **b** $\sqrt{24}$ **c** $\sqrt{12}$ **d** $\sqrt{50}$ **e** $\sqrt{8}$ **f** $\sqrt{27}$

g $\sqrt{48}$ **h** $\sqrt{75}$ **i** $\sqrt{45}$ **j** $\sqrt{63}$ **k** $\sqrt{32}$ **l** $\sqrt{200}$

m $\sqrt{1000}$ **n** $\sqrt{250}$ **o** $\sqrt{98}$ **p** $\sqrt{243}$

7 Simplify each of these.

a $2\sqrt{18} \times 3\sqrt{2}$ **b** $4\sqrt{24} \times 2\sqrt{5}$ **c** $3\sqrt{12} \times 3\sqrt{3}$ **d** $2\sqrt{8} \times 2\sqrt{8}$

e $2\sqrt{27} \times 4\sqrt{8}$ **f** $2\sqrt{48} \times 3\sqrt{8}$ **g** $2\sqrt{45} \times 3\sqrt{3}$ **h** $2\sqrt{63} \times 2\sqrt{7}$

i $2\sqrt{32} \times 4\sqrt{2}$ **j** $\sqrt{1000} \times \sqrt{10}$ **k** $\sqrt{250} \times \sqrt{10}$ **l** $2\sqrt{98} \times 2\sqrt{2}$

8 Simplify each of these.

a $4\sqrt{2} \times 5\sqrt{3}$ **b** $2\sqrt{5} \times 3\sqrt{3}$ **c** $4\sqrt{2} \times 3\sqrt{2}$ **d** $2\sqrt{2} \times 2\sqrt{8}$

e $2\sqrt{5} \times 3\sqrt{8}$ **f** $3\sqrt{3} \times 2\sqrt{3}$ **g** $2\sqrt{6} \times 5\sqrt{2}$ **h** $5\sqrt{7} \times 2\sqrt{3}$

i $2\sqrt{2} \times 3\sqrt{7}$ **j** $2\sqrt{2} \times 3\sqrt{18}$ **k** $2\sqrt{6} \times 2\sqrt{6}$ **l** $4\sqrt{5} \times 3\sqrt{6}$

9 Simplify each of these.

a $6\sqrt{12} \div 2\sqrt{3}$ **b** $3\sqrt{15} \div \sqrt{3}$ **c** $6\sqrt{12} \div \sqrt{2}$ **d** $4\sqrt{24} \div 2\sqrt{8}$

e $12\sqrt{40} \div 3\sqrt{8}$ **f** $5\sqrt{3} \div \sqrt{3}$ **g** $14\sqrt{6} \div 2\sqrt{2}$ **h** $4\sqrt{21} \div 2\sqrt{3}$

i $9\sqrt{28} \div 3\sqrt{7}$ **j** $12\sqrt{56} \div 6\sqrt{8}$ **k** $25\sqrt{6} \div 5\sqrt{6}$ **l** $32\sqrt{54} \div 4\sqrt{6}$

10 Simplify each of these.

a $4\sqrt{2} \times \sqrt{3} \div 2\sqrt{2}$ **b** $4\sqrt{5} \times \sqrt{3} \div \sqrt{15}$ **c** $2\sqrt{32} \times 3\sqrt{2} \div 2\sqrt{8}$

d $6\sqrt{2} \times 2\sqrt{8} \div 3\sqrt{8}$ **e** $3\sqrt{5} \times 4\sqrt{8} \div 2\sqrt{8}$ **f** $12\sqrt{3} \times 4\sqrt{3} \div 2\sqrt{3}$

g $3\sqrt{8} \times 3\sqrt{12} \div 3\sqrt{48}$ **h** $4\sqrt{7} \times 2\sqrt{3} \div 8\sqrt{3}$ **i** $15\sqrt{2} \times 2\sqrt{7} \div 3\sqrt{2}$

j $8\sqrt{2} \times 2\sqrt{18} \div 4\sqrt{3}$ **k** $5\sqrt{6} \times 5\sqrt{6} \div 5\sqrt{3}$ **l** $2\sqrt{5} \times 3\sqrt{6} \div \sqrt{30}$

11 Simplify each of these expressions.

a $a\sqrt{b} \times c\sqrt{b}$ **b** $a\sqrt{b} \div c\sqrt{b}$ **c** $a\sqrt{b} \times c\sqrt{b} \div a\sqrt{b}$

PS 12 Find the value of a that makes each of these surds true.

a $\sqrt{5} \times \sqrt{a} = 10$ **b** $\sqrt{6} \times \sqrt{a} = 12$ **c** $\sqrt{10} \times 2\sqrt{a} = 20$

d $2\sqrt{6} \times 3\sqrt{a} = 72$ **e** $2\sqrt{a} \times \sqrt{a} = 6$ **f** $3\sqrt{a} \times 3\sqrt{a} = 54$

A*

13 Simplify the following.

a $\left(\frac{\sqrt{3}}{2}\right)^2$ **b** $\left(\frac{5}{\sqrt{3}}\right)^2$ **c** $\left(\frac{\sqrt{5}}{4}\right)^2$ **d** $\left(\frac{6}{\sqrt{3}}\right)^2$ **e** $\left(\frac{\sqrt{8}}{2}\right)^2$

AU 14 Decide whether each statement is true or false.

Show your working.

a $\sqrt{(a+b)} = \sqrt{a} + \sqrt{b}$ **b** $\sqrt{(a-b)} = \sqrt{a} - \sqrt{b}$

PS 15 Write down a product of two different surds which has an integer answer.

Calculating with surds

The following two examples show how surds can be used in solving problems.

EXAMPLE 12

In the right-angled triangle ABC, the side BC is $\sqrt{6}$ cm and the side AC is $\sqrt{18}$ cm.

Calculate the length of AB.
Leave your answer in surd form.

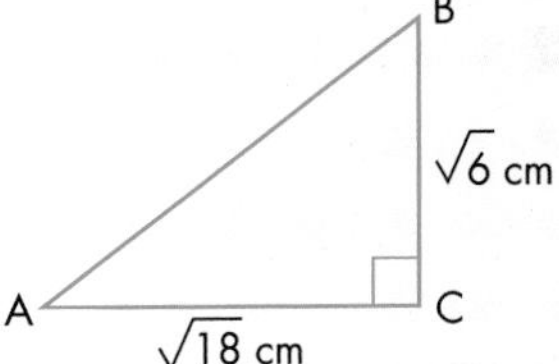

Note: A rule connecting the three sides of a right-angled triangle is

$$a^2 + b^2 = c^2$$

or $a^2 = c^2 - b^2$

This is known as Pythagoras' theorem, which you will meet in Unit 3.

Using Pythagoras' theorem:

$$AC^2 + BC^2 = AB^2$$

$$(\sqrt{18})^2 + (\sqrt{6})^2 = 18 + 6 = 24$$

$$\Rightarrow AB = \sqrt{24} \text{ cm}$$

$$= 2\sqrt{6} \text{ cm}$$

EXAMPLE 13

Calculate the area of a square with a side of $2 + \sqrt{3}$ cm.

Give your answer in the form $a + b\sqrt{3}$.

$$\text{Area} = (2 + \sqrt{3})^2 \text{ cm}^2$$

$$= (2 + \sqrt{3})(2 + \sqrt{3}) \text{ cm}^2$$

$$= 4 + 2\sqrt{3} + 2\sqrt{3} + 3 \text{ cm}^2$$

$$= 7 + 4\sqrt{3} \text{ cm}^2$$

Rationalising a denominator

When surds are written as fractions in answers they are usually given with a rational denominator.

Multiplying the numerator and denominator by an appropriate square root will make the denominator into a whole number.

EXAMPLE 14

Rationalise the denominator of: **a** $\frac{1}{\sqrt{3}}$ and **b** $\frac{2\sqrt{3}}{\sqrt{8}}$

a Multiply the numerator and denominator by $\sqrt{3}$.

$$\frac{1 \times \sqrt{3}}{\sqrt{3} \times \sqrt{3}} = \frac{\sqrt{3}}{3}$$

b Multiply the numerator and denominator by $\sqrt{8}$.

$$\frac{2\sqrt{3} \times \sqrt{8}}{\sqrt{8} \times \sqrt{8}} = \frac{2\sqrt{24}}{8} = \frac{4\sqrt{6}}{8} = \frac{\sqrt{6}}{2}$$

or

$$\sqrt{8} = 2\sqrt{2}$$

So $\frac{2\sqrt{3}}{\sqrt{8}} = \frac{2\sqrt{3}}{2\sqrt{2}} = \frac{\sqrt{3}}{\sqrt{2}}$

Multiplying the numerator and denominator by $\sqrt{2}$:

$$\frac{\sqrt{3} \times \sqrt{2}}{\sqrt{2} \times \sqrt{2}} = \frac{\sqrt{6}}{2}$$

EXERCISE 9K

A*

1 Show that:

a $(2 + \sqrt{3})(1 + \sqrt{3}) = 5 + 3\sqrt{3}$

b $(1 + \sqrt{2})(2 + \sqrt{3}) = 2 + 2\sqrt{2} + \sqrt{3} + \sqrt{6}$

c $(4 - \sqrt{3})(4 + \sqrt{3}) = 13$

2 Expand and simplify where possible.

a $\sqrt{3}(2 - \sqrt{3})$ **b** $\sqrt{2}(3 - 4\sqrt{2})$ **c** $\sqrt{5}(2\sqrt{5} + 4)$

d $3\sqrt{7}(4 - 2\sqrt{7})$ **e** $3\sqrt{2}(5 - 2\sqrt{8})$ **f** $\sqrt{3}(\sqrt{27} - 1)$

3 Expand and simplify where possible.

a $(1 + \sqrt{3})(3 - \sqrt{3})$ **b** $(2 + \sqrt{5})(3 - \sqrt{5})$ **c** $(1 - \sqrt{2})(3 + 2\sqrt{2})$

d $(3 - 2\sqrt{7})(4 + 3\sqrt{7})$ **e** $(2 - 3\sqrt{5})(2 + 3\sqrt{5})$ **f** $(\sqrt{3} + \sqrt{2})(\sqrt{3} + \sqrt{8})$

g $(2 + \sqrt{5})^2$ **h** $(1 - \sqrt{2})^2$ **i** $(3 + \sqrt{2})^2$

4 Work out the missing lengths in each of these triangles, giving the answer in as simple a form as possible. (Refer to Pythagoras' theorem in Example 12.)

a

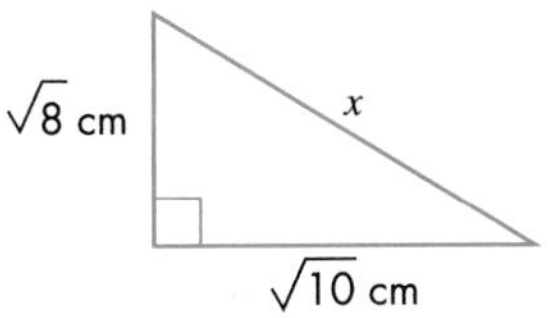

b

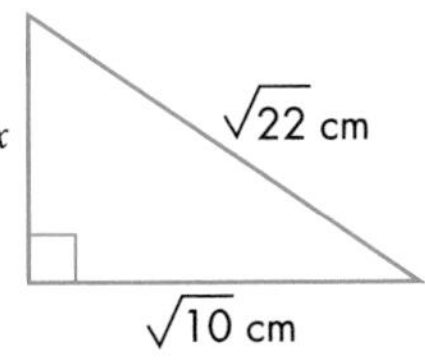

c

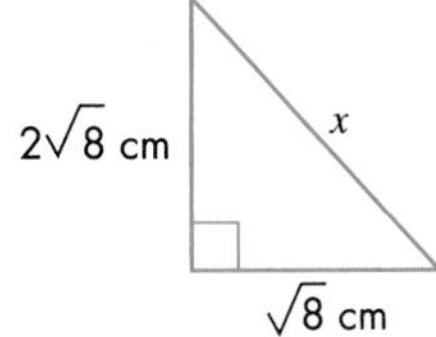

5 Calculate the area of each of these rectangles, simplifying your answers where possible. (The area of a rectangle with length l and width w is $A = l \times w$.)

a

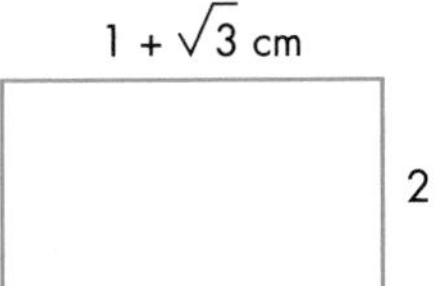

b

2 + √10 cm

√5 cm

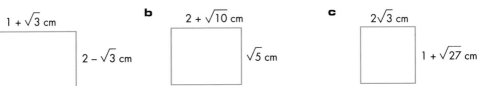

c

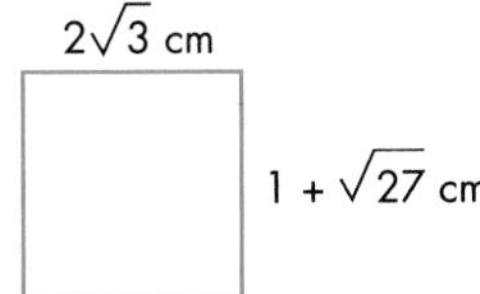

6 Rationalise the denominators of these expressions.

a $\frac{1}{\sqrt{3}}$ **b** $\frac{1}{\sqrt{2}}$ **c** $\frac{1}{\sqrt{5}}$ **d** $\frac{1}{2\sqrt{3}}$ **e** $\frac{3}{\sqrt{3}}$ **f** $\frac{5}{\sqrt{2}}$

g $\frac{3\sqrt{2}}{\sqrt{8}}$ **h** $\frac{5\sqrt{3}}{\sqrt{6}}$ **i** $\frac{\sqrt{7}}{\sqrt{3}}$ **j** $\frac{1+\sqrt{2}}{\sqrt{2}}$ **k** $\frac{2-\sqrt{3}}{\sqrt{3}}$ **l** $\frac{5+2\sqrt{3}}{\sqrt{3}}$

7 **a** Expand and simplify the following.

i $(2 + \sqrt{3})(2 - \sqrt{3})$ **ii** $(1 - \sqrt{5})(1 + \sqrt{5})$ **iii** $(\sqrt{3} - 1)(\sqrt{3} + 1)$

iv $(3\sqrt{2} + 1)(3\sqrt{2} - 1)$ **v** $(2 - 4\sqrt{3})(2 + 4\sqrt{3})$

b What happens in the answers to part **a**? Why?

AU PS **8** **a** Write down two surds that, when multiplied, give a rational number.

b Write down two surds that, when multiplied, do not give a rational number.

AU PS **9** **a** Write down two surds that, when divided, give a rational number.

b Write down two surds that, when divided, do not give a rational number.

FM **10** An engineer uses a formula to work out the number of metres of cable he needs to complete a job. His calculator displays the answer as $10\sqrt{70}$. The button for converting this to a decimal is not working.

He has 80 metres of cable. Without using a calculator, decide whether he has enough cable. Show clearly how you decide.

11 Write $(3 + \sqrt{2})^2 - (1 - \sqrt{8})^2$ in the form $a + b\sqrt{c}$ where a, b and c are integers.

12 $x^2 - y^2 \equiv (x + y)(x - y)$ is an identity which means it is true for any values of x and y whether they are numeric or algebraic.

Show that it is true for $x = 1 + \sqrt{2}$ and $y = 1 - \sqrt{8}$

GRADE BOOSTER

- **D** You can write and calculate with numbers written in index form
- **C** You can multiply and divide numbers written in index form
- **B** You can write numbers in standard form and use these in various problems
- **A** You know how to use the rules of indices for negative and fractional values
- **A** You can convert recurring decimals to fractions
- **A** You can simplify surds
- **A*** You can manipulate expressions containing surds and rationalise denominators
- **A*** You can solve problems using surds

What you should know now

- How to write numbers in standard form
- How to solve problems using numbers in standard form
- How to manipulate indices, both integer (positive and negative) and fractional
- How to compare fractions by converting them to decimals
- How to convert decimals into fractions
- What surds are and how to manipulate them

1 **a** Write down the value of 13^2. *(1 mark)*

b Explain how you know that 14^2 is not equal to 192. *(1 mark)*

AQA, June 2008, Module 5, Paper 1 Higher, Question 6

2 **a** Simplify $8^4 \times 8^5$ *(1 mark)*

Leave your answer as a power of 8.

b Simplify $w^6 \div w^2$ *(1 mark)*

c Chris simplifies $3x \times 4x^5$

His answer is $7x^5$

Explain the mistakes he has made. *(2 marks)*

d Simplify fully $15y^6z^3 \div 5y^2z$ *(2 marks)*

AQA, November 2008, Module 5, Paper 1 Higher, Question 8

3 

Astronomers measure distances in the solar system in astronomical units (AU). One AU is 150 000 000 kilometres. The distance from the Sun to Pluto is 39.5 AU. How many kilometres is the Sun from Pluto? Give your answer in standard form to a sensible degree of accuracy. *(3 marks)*

AQA, June 2005, Paper 2 Higher, Question 9

4 Simplify **a** $\dfrac{6a^2b \times 4ab^3}{8a^2b^2}$ **b** $(3x^3y^2)^4$

5 Express the recurring decimal 0.5333333… as a fraction. Give your answer in its simplest form.

6 The mass of one atom of hydrogen is 1.67×10^{-24} grams.

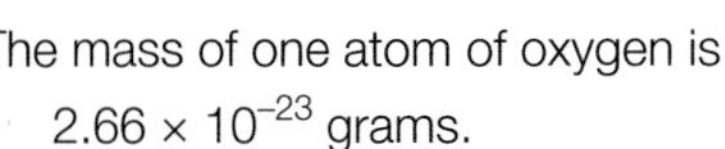

The mass of one atom of oxygen is 2.66×10^{-23} grams.

a One molecule of water has two atoms of hydrogen and one atom of oxygen.

The total mass of one molecule of water is given by

$$2 \times 1.67 \times 10^{-24} + 2.66 \times 10^{-23}$$

Work out the total mass.

Give your answer in standard form. *(2 marks)*

b Calculate the number of molecules in one gram of water.

Give your answer in standard form. *(2 marks)*

AQA, November 2007, Paper 2 Higher, Question 14

7 Express the recurring decimal $0.0\dot{7}\dot{2}$ as a fraction.

Give your answer in its simplest form.

You **must** show your working. *(3 marks)*

AQA, June 2008, Paper 2 Higher, Question 19

8 The area of this rectangle is 40 cm^2.

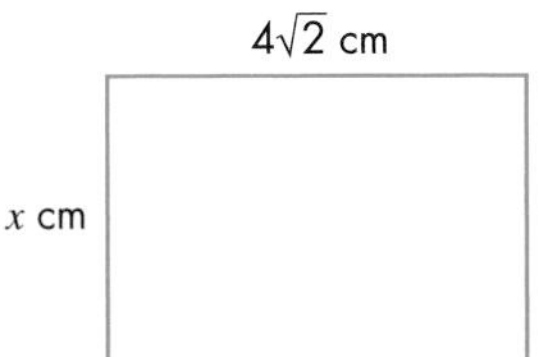

Find the value of x. Give your answer in the form $a\sqrt{b}$ where a and b are integers.

9 **a** Prove that $0.\dot{7}\dot{2} = \dfrac{8}{11}$

b Hence, or otherwise, express $0.3\dot{7}\dot{2}$ as a fraction.

10 **a** **i** Show that $\sqrt{20} = 2\sqrt{5}$ *(1 mark)*

ii Expand and simplify $(\sqrt{2} + \sqrt{10})^2$ *(2 marks)*

b Is this triangle right-angled? *(3 marks)*

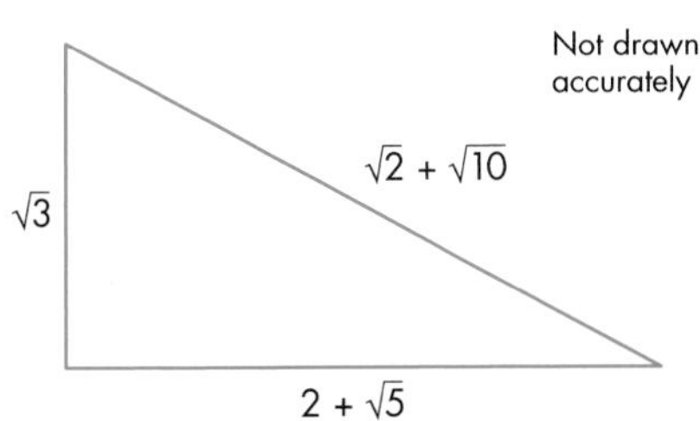

You **must** show your working.

AQA, June 2005, Paper 1 Higher, Question 16

PS 11 Two rectangles, A and B, are equal in area.

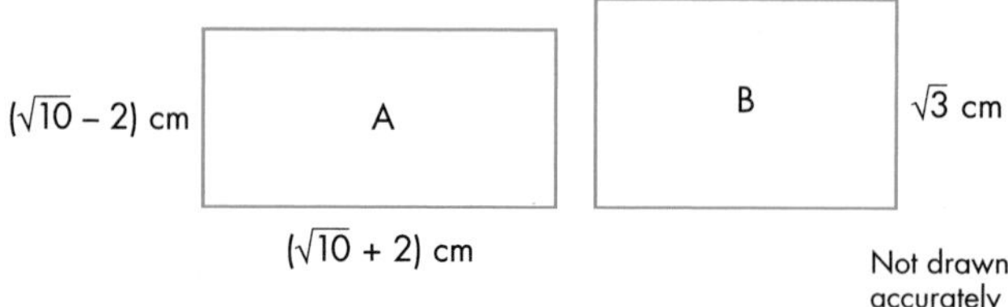

Calculate the length of rectangle B.

Give your answer in the form $p\sqrt{3}$. *(4 marks)*

AQA, November 2005, Paper 1 Higher, Question 19

12 **a** **i** Show that $\sqrt{32} = 4\sqrt{2}$

ii Expand and simplify $(\sqrt{2} + \sqrt{12})^2$

b Show clearly that this triangle is right angled.

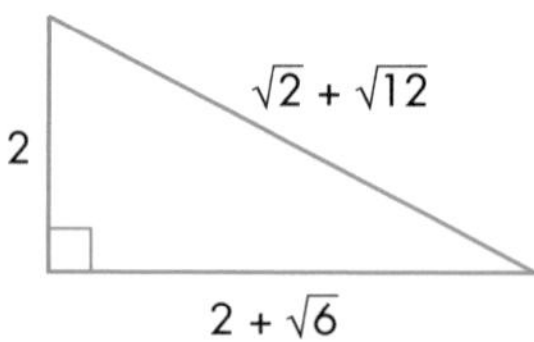

Worked Examination Questions

1 a Expand and simplify as far as possible $(\sqrt{2} + 3)(\sqrt{2} - 1)$.

b Show clearly that $\frac{3}{\sqrt{6}} + \frac{\sqrt{6}}{6} = \frac{5\sqrt{6}}{6}$

1 a $\sqrt{2} \times \sqrt{2} + \sqrt{2} \times -1 + 3 \times \sqrt{2} + 3 \times -1$

Expand the brackets to get four terms.
This scores 1 mark for method.

$2 - \sqrt{2} + 3\sqrt{2} - 3 = -1 + 2\sqrt{2}$

Simplify the terms and collect together like terms.
This scores 1 mark for accuracy of the four terms and 1 mark for accuracy of final answer.

b $\frac{3}{\sqrt{6}} \times \frac{\sqrt{6}}{\sqrt{6}} = \frac{3\sqrt{6}}{6}$

Rationalise the denominator of the first fraction by multiplying the numerator and denominator by $\sqrt{6}$.
This scores 1 mark for method.

$\frac{3\sqrt{6}}{6} + \frac{2\sqrt{6}}{6}$

Obtain a common denominator.
This scores 1 mark for method.

$= \frac{5\sqrt{6}}{6}$

Put these together to give the final answer.
This scores 1 mark for accuracy.

Total: 6 marks

PS AU **2 a** Complete the table of values.

7^3	7^2	7^1	7^0	7^{-1}	7^{-2}	7^{-3}
343		7		$\frac{1}{7}$	$\frac{1}{49}$	

b Use your answers to part **a** to work the value of $7 \div 7^{-2}$

2 a $7^2 = 49$

This fact should be known.
This scores 1 mark.

$7^0 = 1$

Any number to the power 0 is equal to 1.
This scores 1 mark.

$7^{-3} = \frac{1}{343}$

Look for the pattern.
This scores 1 mark.

b $7^{1 - -2} = 7^3 = 343$

Use the rules of indices to obtain 7^3 and 343.
This scores 1 mark.
There is only one mark since the value of 7^3 is given.

Total: 4 marks

9 Functional Maths
Oil crisis

Throughout the world, people are concerned about our energy supplies. At present, we rely greatly on fossil fuels such as oil for our energy. This is a cause for concern for two main reasons: burning fossil fuels causes damage to the environment and supplies of fossil fuels are now running out. Understanding the figures related to energy use throughout the world is vital in finding a solution to the energy crisis.

Getting started

Use your knowledge of science and current affairs to bring together what you know about energy resources. The questions below may help you.

- Which sources of energy do we use in the UK?
- Where does energy come from?
- Which forms of energy are considered to be 'green'?

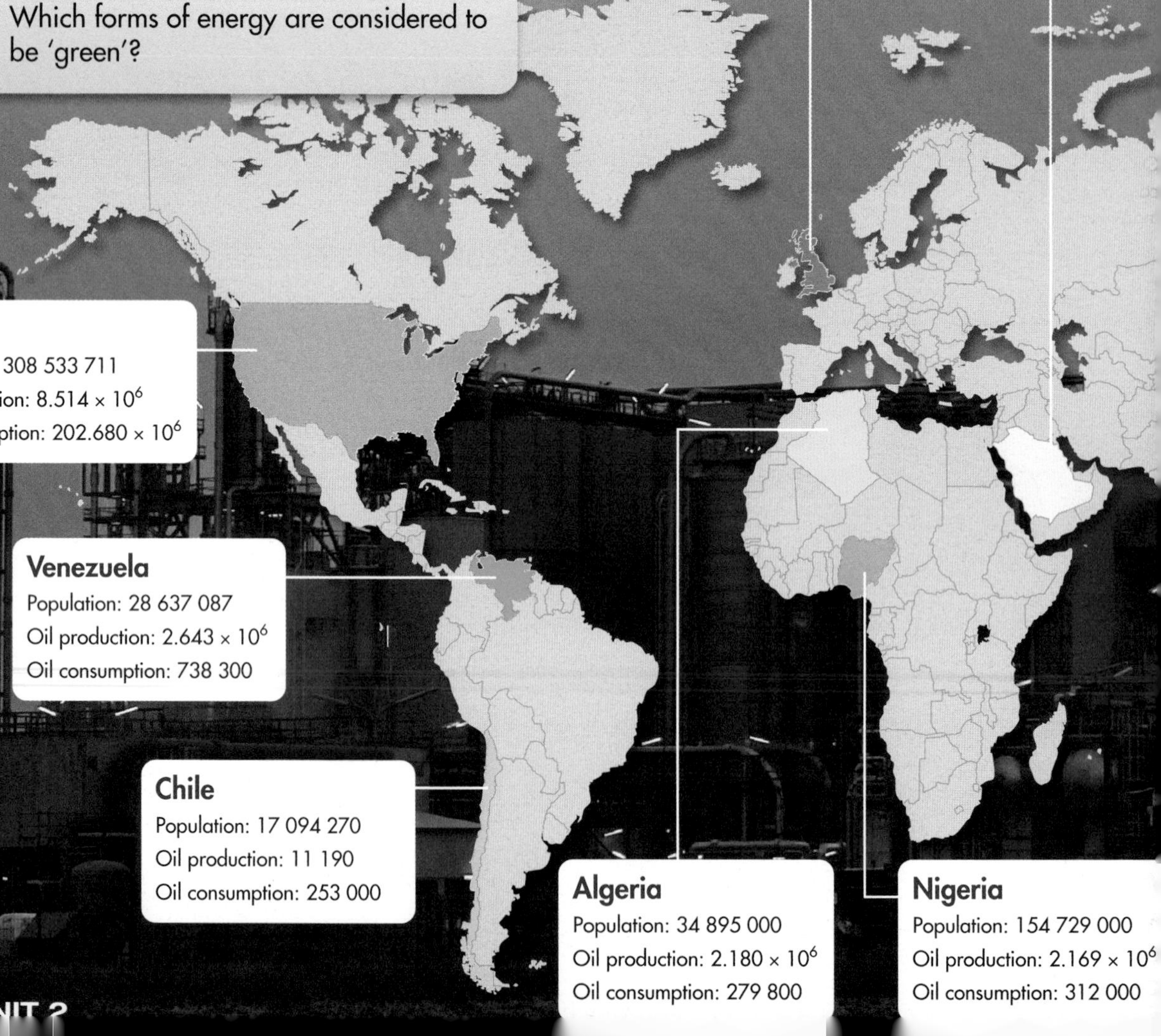

UK
Population: 62 041 708
Oil production: 1.584×10^6
Oil consumption: 1.765×10^6

Saudi Arabia
Population: 25 721 00
Oil production: 10.7×10^6
Oil consumption: 2.34 × 1C

USA
Population: 308 533 711
Oil production: 8.514×10^6
Oil consumption: 202.680×10^6

Venezuela
Population: 28 637 087
Oil production: 2.643×10^6
Oil consumption: 738 300

Chile
Population: 17 094 270
Oil production: 11 190
Oil consumption: 253 000

Algeria
Population: 34 895 000
Oil production: 2.180×10^6
Oil consumption: 279 800

Nigeria
Population: 154 729 000
Oil production: 2.169×10^6
Oil consumption: 312 000

he energy that we get from oil an also be generated from ore environmentally-friendly, ustainable sources.

Your task

A scientist is researching the production and consumption of oil in the world, in order to inform people about the global energy crisis.

She looks at 10 oil-producing countries and, for each country, finds the most recent figures on the country's population, and its oil production and consumption, measured in barrels per day.

The scientist asks you to write a report about the production and consumption of oil throughout the world for a national newspaper.

Your report should use evidence to explain:

- how many barrels of oil are produced per person, per year
- in which year the world is 'greener'
- which country is the 'best' consumer of oil
- which country is the 'worst' consumer of oil.

Year	World population	World oil production, barrels per day
1984	4.77×10^9	5.45×10^7
1989	5.19×10^9	5.99×10^7
1994	5.61×10^9	6.10×10^7
1999	6.01×10^9	6.58×10^7
2004	6.38×10^9	7.25×10^7
2009	6.79×10^9	8.49×10^7

Oil production and oil consumption figures on this map are measured in barrels.

Japan
Population: 127 530 000
Oil production: 133 100
Oil consumption: 5.007×10^6

Indonesia
Population: 234 181 400
Oil production: 1.051×10^6
Oil consumption: 1.219×10^6

Australia
Population: 22 125 030
Oil production: 86 400
Oil consumption: 966 200

Extension

Develop your report by researching the 'green', sustainable energy resources that many countries produce and consume. How do the figures related to 'green' energy compare to those related to oil?

Why this chapter matters

Like most mathematics, quadratic equations have their origins in ancient Egypt.

The Egyptians did not have a formal system of algebra but could solve problems that involved quadratics.This problem was written in hieroglyphics on the Berlin Papyrus which was written some time around 2160–1700BC:

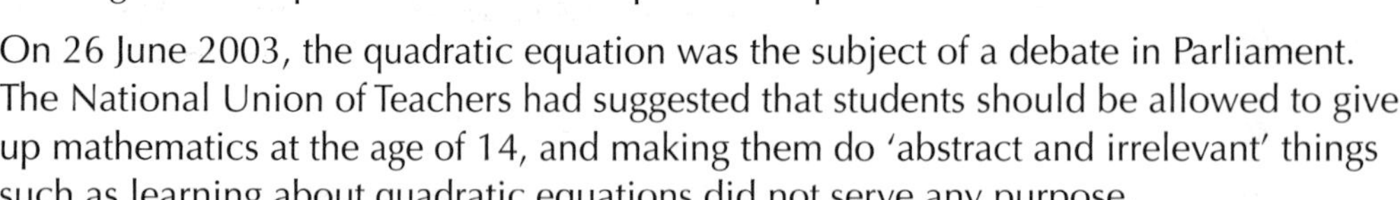
The area of a square of 100 is equal to that of two smaller squares. The side of one is $\frac{1}{2} + \frac{1}{4}$ the side of the other.

Today we would express this as: $x^2 + y^2 = 100$

$$y = \tfrac{3}{4}x$$

In about 300BC, Euclid developed a geometrical method for solving quadratics. This work was developed by Hindu mathematicians, but it was not until much later, in 1145AD that the Arabic mathematician Abraham bar Hiyya Ha-Nasi, published the book *Liber embadorum*, which gave a complete solution of the quadratic equation.

On 26 June 2003, the quadratic equation was the subject of a debate in Parliament. The National Union of Teachers had suggested that students should be allowed to give up mathematics at the age of 14, and making them do 'abstract and irrelevant' things such as learning about quadratic equations did not serve any purpose.

Mr Tony McWalter, the MP for Hemel Hempstead, defending the teaching of quadratic equations, said:

> "Someone who thinks that the quadratic equation is an empty manipulation, devoid of any other significance, is someone who is content with leaving the many in ignorance. I believe that he or she is also pleading for the lowering of standards. A quadratic equation is not like a bleak room, devoid of furniture, in which one is asked to squat. It is a door to a room full of the unparalleled riches of human intellectual achievement. If you do not go through that door, or if it is said that it is an uninteresting thing to do, much that passes for human wisdom will be forever denied you."

Chapter 10 Algebra: Quadratic equations

This chapter will show you …

- **C** how to expand two linear brackets to obtain a quadratic expression
- **B** how to factorise a quadratic expression
- **A** how to solve quadratic equations by factorisation and completing the square

Visual overview

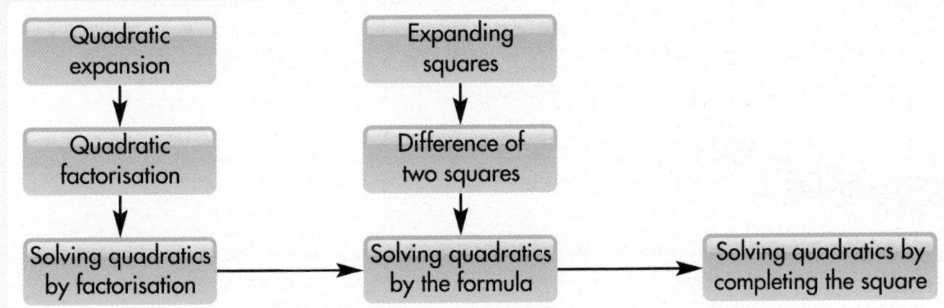

What you should already know

- The basic language of algebra **(KS3 level 5, GCSE grade E)**
- How to collect together like terms **(KS3 level 5, GCSE grade E)**
- How to multiply together two algebraic expressions **(KS3 level 5, GCSE grade E)**
- How to solve simple linear equations **(KS3 level 5 to 6, GCSE grade E to C)**

Quick check

1 Simplify the following.

a $-2x - x$ **b** $3x - x$ **c** $-5x + 2x$

d $2m \times 3m$ **e** $3x \times -2x$ **f** $-4p \times 3p$

2 Solve these equations.

a $x + 6 = 0$ **b** $2x + 1 = 0$ **c** $3x - 2 = 0$

10.1 Expanding brackets

This section will show you how to:

- expand two linear brackets to obtain a quadratic expression

Key words
coefficient
linear
quadratic expression

Quadratic expansion

A **quadratic expression** is one in which the highest power of the variables is 2. For example,

y^2 $\quad$ $3t^2 + 5t$ $\quad$ $5m^2 + 3m + 8$

An expression such as $(3y + 2)(4y - 5)$ can be expanded to give a quadratic expression.

Multiplying out such pairs of brackets is usually called *quadratic expansion*.

The rule for expanding expressions such as $(t + 5)(3t - 4)$ is similar to that for expanding single brackets: multiply everything in one set of brackets by everything in the other set of brackets.

There are several methods for doing this. Examples 1 to 3 show the three main methods: expansion, FOIL and the box method.

EXAMPLE 1

In the expansion method, split the terms in the first set of brackets, make each of them multiply both terms in the second set of brackets, then simplify the outcome.

Expand $(x + 3)(x + 4)$

$$(x + 3)(x + 4) = x(x + 4) + 3(x + 4)$$
$$= x^2 + 4x + 3x + 12$$
$$= x^2 + 7x + 12$$

EXAMPLE 2

FOIL stands for First, Outer, Inner and Last. This is the order of multiplying the terms from each set of brackets.

Expand $(t + 5)(t - 2)$

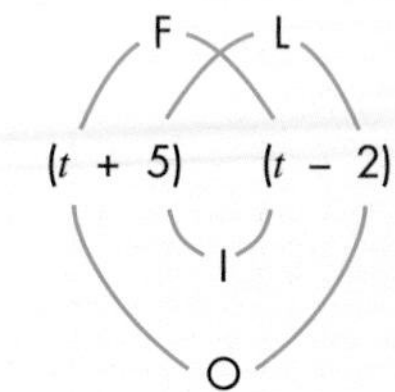

First terms give: $t \times t = t^2$

Outer terms give: $t \times -2 = -2t$.

Inner terms give: $5 \times t = 5t$

Last terms give: $+5 \times -2 = -10$

$$(t + 5)(t - 2) = t^2 - 2t + 5t - 10$$
$$= t^2 + 3t - 10$$

EXAMPLE 3

The box method is similar to that used to do long multiplication.

Expand $(k - 3)(k - 2)$

$$(k - 3)(k - 2) = k^2 - 2k - 3k + 6$$
$$= k^2 - 5k + 6$$

×	k	–3
k	k^2	$-3k$
–2	$-2k$	+6

Warning: Be careful with the signs. This is the main place where mistakes are made in questions involving the expansion of brackets.

EXERCISE 10A

Expand the expressions in questions **1–17**.

HINTS AND TIPS

Use whichever method you prefer. There is no fixed method in GCSE examinations. Examiners give credit for all methods. Whatever method you use, it is important to show the examiner that you know there are four terms in the expansion before it is simplified.

HINTS AND TIPS

A common error is to get minus signs wrong.
$-2x - 3x = -5x$ and
$-2 \times -3 = +6$

1 $(x + 3)(x + 2)$

2 $(t + 4)(t + 3)$

3 $(w + 1)(w + 3)$

4 $(m + 5)(m + 1)$

5 $(k + 3)(k + 5)$

6 $(a + 4)(a + 1)$

7 $(x + 4)(x - 2)$

8 $(t + 5)(t - 3)$

9 $(w + 3)(w - 1)$

10 $(f + 2)(f - 3)$

11 $(g + 1)(g - 4)$

12 $(y + 4)(y - 3)$

13 $(x - 3)(x + 4)$

14 $(p - 2)(p + 1)$

15 $(k - 4)(k + 2)$

16 $(y - 2)(y + 5)$

17 $(a - 1)(a + 3)$

The expansions of the expressions in questions **18–26** follow a pattern. Work out the first few and try to spot the pattern that will allow you immediately to write down the answers to the rest.

18 $(x + 3)(x - 3)$

19 $(t + 5)(t - 5)$

20 $(m + 4)(m - 4)$

21 $(t + 2)(t - 2)$

22 $(y + 8)(y - 8)$

23 $(p + 1)(p - 1)$

24 $(5 + x)(5 - x)$

25 $(7 + g)(7 - g)$

26 $(x - 6)(x + 6)$

PS 27 This rectangle is made up of four parts with areas of x^2, $2x$, $3x$ and 6 square units.

Work out expressions for the sides of the rectangle, in terms of x.

x^2	$2x$
$3x$	6

PS 28 This square has an area of x^2 square units.
It is split into four rectangles.

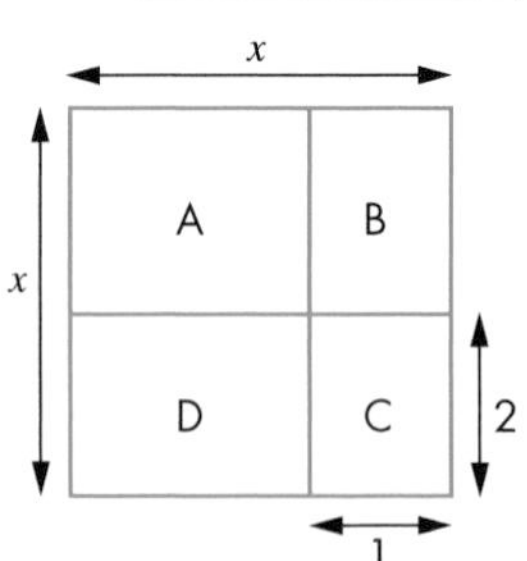

a Fill in the table below to show the dimensions and area of each rectangle.

Rectangle	Length	Width	Area
A	$x - 1$	$x - 2$	$(x - 1)(x - 2)$
B			
C			
D			

b Add together the areas of rectangles B, C and D.

Expand any brackets and collect terms together.

c Use the results to explain why $(x - 1)(x - 2) = x^2 - 3x + 2$.

AU 29 **a** Expand $(x - 3)(x + 3)$

b Use the result in **a** to write down the answers to these. (Do not use a calculator or do a long multiplication.)

i 97×103 **ii** 197×203

Quadratic expansion with non-unit coefficients

All the algebraic terms in x^2 in Exercise 10A have a **coefficient** of 1 or –1. The next two examples show what to do if you have to expand brackets containing terms in x^2 with coefficients that are not 1 or –1.

EXAMPLE 4

Expand $(2t + 3)(3t + 1)$

$$(2t + 3)(3t + 1) = 6t^2 + 2t + 9t + 3$$
$$= 6t^2 + 11t + 3$$

×	$2t$	$+3$
$3t$	$6t^2$	$+9t$
$+1$	$+2t$	$+3$

EXAMPLE 5

Expand $(4x - 1)(3x - 5)$

$$(4x - 1)(3x - 5) = 4x(3x - 5) - (3x - 5)$$ [**Note:** $(3x - 5)$ is the same as $1(3x - 5)$.]
$$= 12x^2 - 20x - 3x + 5$$
$$= 12x^2 - 23x + 5$$

EXERCISE 10B

Expand the expressions in questions **1–21**.

1 $(2x + 3)(3x + 1)$

2 $(3y + 2)(4y + 3)$

3 $(3t + 1)(2t + 5)$

4 $(4t + 3)(2t - 1)$

5 $(5m + 2)(2m - 3)$

6 $(4k + 3)(3k - 5)$

7 $(3p - 2)(2p + 5)$

8 $(5w + 2)(2w + 3)$

9 $(2a - 3)(3a + 1)$

10 $(4r - 3)(2r - 1)$

11 $(3g - 2)(5g - 2)$

12 $(4d - 1)(3d + 2)$

13 $(5 + 2p)(3 + 4p)$

14 $(2 + 3t)(1 + 2t)$

15 $(4 + 3p)(2p + 1)$

16 $(6 + 5t)(1 - 2t)$

17 $(4 + 3n)(3 - 2n)$

18 $(2 + 3f)(2f - 3)$

19 $(3 - 2q)(4 + 5q)$

20 $(1 - 3p)(3 + 2p)$

21 $(4 - 2t)(3t + 1)$

HINTS AND TIPS

Always give answers in the form $\pm ax^2 \pm bx \pm c$ even if the quadratic coefficient is negative.

PS 22 Expand:

a $(x + 1)(x + 1)$

b $(x - 1)(x - 1)$

c $(x + 1)(x - 1)$

d Use the results in parts **a**, **b** and **c** to show that $(p + q)^2 \equiv p^2 + 2pq + q^2$ is an identity.

HINTS AND TIPS

Take $p = x + 1$ and $q = x - 1$.

AU 23 **a** Without expanding the brackets, match each expression on the left with an expression on the right. One is done for you.

$(3x - 2)(2x + 1)$	$4x^2 - 4x + 1$
$(2x - 1)(2x - 1)$	$6x^2 - x - 2$
$(6x - 3)(x + 1)$	$6x^2 + 7x + 2$
$(4x + 1)(x - 1)$ —	$6x^2 + 3x - 3$
$(3x + 2)(2x + 1)$	— $4x^2 - 3x - 1$

b Taking any expression on the left, explain how you can match it with an expression on the right without expanding the brackets.

EXERCISE 10C

B

Try to spot the pattern in each of the expressions in questions **1–15** so that you can immediately write down the expansion.

1 $(2x + 1)(2x - 1)$

2 $(3t + 2)(3t - 2)$

3 $(5y + 3)(5y - 3)$

4 $(4m + 3)(4m - 3)$

5 $(2k - 3)(2k + 3)$

6 $(4h - 1)(4h + 1)$

7 $(2 + 3x)(2 - 3x)$

8 $(5 + 2t)(5 - 2t)$

9 $(6 - 5y)(6 + 5y)$

10 $(a + b)(a - b)$

11 $(3t + k)(3t - k)$

12 $(2m - 3p)(2m + 3p)$

13 $(5k + g)(5k - g)$

14 $(ab + cd)(ab - cd)$

15 $(a^2 + b^2)(a^2 - b^2)$

PS 16 Imagine a square of side a units with a square of side b units cut from one corner.

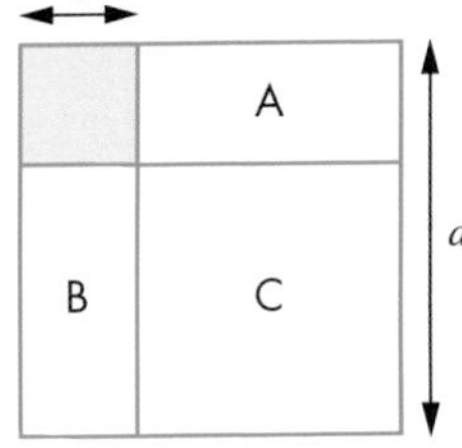

a What is the area remaining after the small square is cut away?

b The remaining area is cut into rectangles, A, B and C, and rearranged as shown.

Write down the dimensions and area of the rectangle formed by A, B and C.

c Explain why $a^2 - b^2 = (a + b)(a - b)$.

AU 17 Explain why the areas of the shaded regions are the same.

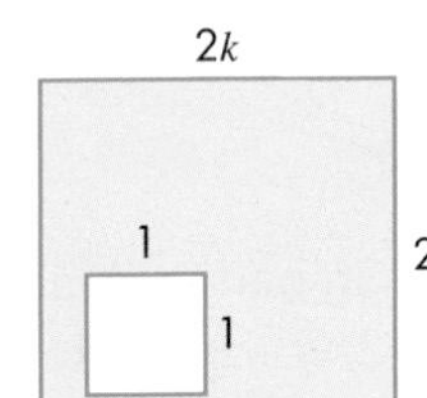

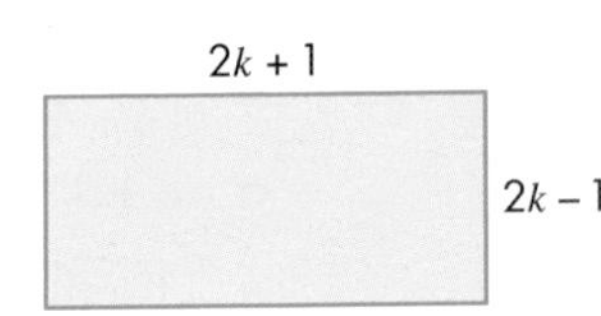

Expanding squares

Whenever you see a **linear** bracketed term squared you must write the brackets down twice and then use whichever method you prefer to expand.

EXAMPLE 6

Expand $(x + 3)^2$

$$(x + 3)^2 = (x + 3)(x + 3)$$
$$= x(x + 3) + 3(x + 3)$$
$$= x^2 + 3x + 3x + 9$$
$$= x^2 + 6x + 9$$

EXAMPLE 7

Expand $(3x - 2)^2$

$(3x - 2)^2 = (3x - 2)(3x - 2)$

$= 9x^2 - 6x - 6x + 4$

$= 9x^2 - 12x + 4$

F L

(3x – 2) (3x – 2)

I

O

EXERCISE 10D

Expand the squares in questions **1–24** and simplify.

> **HINTS AND TIPS**
>
> Remember *always* write down the brackets twice. Do not try to take any short cuts.

C

1 $(x + 5)^2$ **2** $(m + 4)^2$ **3** $(6 + t)^2$

4 $(3 + p)^2$ **5** $(m - 3)^2$ **6** $(t - 5)^2$

7 $(4 - m)^2$ **8** $(7 - k)^2$

B

9 $(3x + 1)^2$ **10** $(4t + 3)^2$ **11** $(2 + 5y)^2$ **12** $(3 + 2m)^2$

13 $(4t - 3)^2$ **14** $(3x - 2)^2$ **15** $(2 - 5t)^2$ **16** $(6 - 5r)^2$

17 $(x + y)^2$ **18** $(m - n)^2$ **19** $(2t + y)^2$ **20** $(m - 3n)^2$

21 $(x + 2)^2 - 4$ **22** $(x - 5)^2 - 25$ **23** $(x + 6)^2 - 36$ **24** $(x - 2)^2 - 4$

PS 25 A teacher asks her class to expand $(3x + 1)^2$.

Bernice's answer is $9x^2 + 1$.

Pete's answer is $3x^2 + 6x + 1$.

a Explain the mistakes that Bernice has made.

b Explain the mistakes that Pete has made.

c Work out the correct answer.

AU 26 Use the diagram to show algebraically and diagrammatically that:

$(2x - 1)^2 = 4x^2 - 4x + 1$

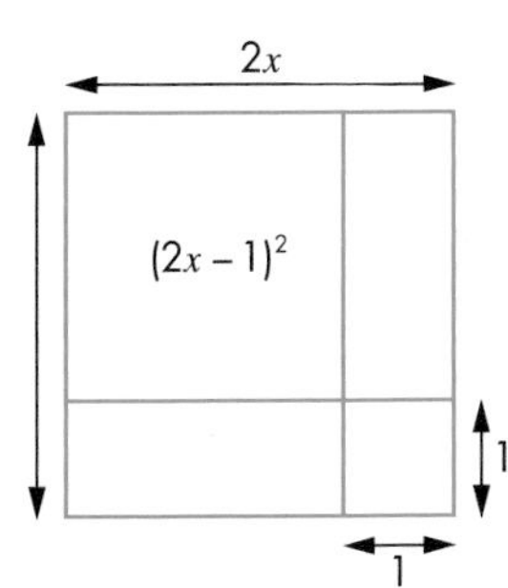

10.2 Quadratic factorisation

This section will show you how to:
- factorise a quadratic expression into two linear brackets

Key words
brackets
coefficient
difference of two squares
factorisation
quadratic expression

Factorisation involves putting a **quadratic expression** back into its **brackets** (if possible). We start with the factorisation of quadratic expressions of the type:

$$x^2 + ax + b$$

where a and b are integers.

Sometimes it is easy to put a quadratic expression back into its brackets, other times it seems hard. However, there are some simple rules that will help you to factorise.

- The expression inside each set of brackets will start with an x, and the signs in the quadratic expression show which signs to put after the xs.
- When the second sign in the expression is a plus, the signs in both sets of brackets are the same as the first sign.

  $x^2 + ax + b = (x + ?)(x + ?)$ Since everything is positive.

  $x^2 - ax + b = (x - ?)(x - ?)$ Since –ve × –ve = +ve
- When the *second* sign is a *minus*, the signs in the brackets are *different*.

  $x^2 + ax - b = (x + ?)(x - ?)$ Since +ve × –ve = –ve

  $x^2 - ax - b = (x + ?)(x - ?)$
- Next, look at the *last* number, b, in the expression. When multiplied together, the two numbers in the brackets must give b.
- Finally, look at the **coefficient** *of* x, a. The *sum* of the two *numbers* in the brackets will give a.

EXAMPLE 8

Factorise $x^2 - x - 6$

Because of the signs we know the brackets must be $(x + ?)(x - ?)$.

Two numbers that have a product of – 6 and a sum of – 1 are – 3 and + 2.

So, $x^2 - x - 6 = (x + 2)(x - 3)$

EXAMPLE 9

Factorise $x^2 - 9x + 20$

Because of the signs we know the brackets must be $(x - ?)(x - ?)$.

Two numbers that have a product of + 20 and a sum of –9 are –4 and –5.

So, $x^2 - 9x + 20 = (x - 4)(x - 5)$

EXERCISE 10E

Factorise the expressions in questions **1–40**.

1 $x^2 + 5x + 6$

2 $t^2 + 5t + 4$

3 $m^2 + 7m + 10$

4 $k^2 + 10k + 24$

5 $p^2 + 14p + 24$

6 $r^2 + 9r + 18$

7 $w^2 + 11w + 18$

8 $x^2 + 7x + 12$

9 $a^2 + 8a + 12$

10 $k^2 + 10k + 21$

11 $f^2 + 22f + 21$

12 $b^2 + 20b + 96$

13 $t^2 - 5t + 6$

14 $d^2 - 5d + 4$

15 $g^2 - 7g + 10$

16 $x^2 - 15x + 36$

17 $c^2 - 18c + 32$

18 $t^2 - 13t + 36$

19 $y^2 - 16y + 48$

20 $j^2 - 14j + 48$

21 $p^2 - 8p + 15$

22 $y^2 + 5y - 6$

23 $t^2 + 2t - 8$

24 $x^2 + 3x - 10$

25 $m^2 - 4m - 12$

26 $r^2 - 6r - 7$

27 $n^2 - 3n - 18$

28 $m^2 - 7m - 44$

29 $w^2 - 2w - 24$

30 $t^2 - t - 90$

31 $h^2 - h - 72$

32 $t^2 - 2t - 63$

33 $d^2 + 2d + 1$

34 $y^2 + 20y + 100$

35 $t^2 - 8t + 16$

36 $m^2 - 18m + 81$

37 $x^2 - 24x + 144$

38 $d^2 - d - 12$

39 $t^2 - t - 20$

40 $q^2 - q - 56$

> **HINTS AND TIPS**
>
> First decide on the signs in the brackets, then look at the numbers.

PS 41 This rectangle is made up of four parts. Two of the parts have areas of x^2 and 6 square units.

The sides of the rectangle are of the form $x + a$ and $x + b$.

There are two possible answers for a and b.

Work out both answers and copy and complete the areas in the other parts of the rectangle.

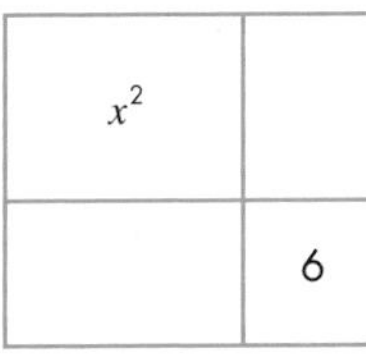

AU 42 **a** Expand $(x + a)(x + b)$

b If $x^2 + 7x + 12 = (x + p)(x + q)$, use your answer to part **a** to write down the values of:

i $p + q$ **ii** pq

c Explain how you can tell that $x^2 + 12x + 7$ will not factorise.

Difference of two squares

In Exercise 10C, you multiplied out, for example, $(a + b)(a - b)$ and obtained $a^2 - b^2$. This type of quadratic expression, with only two terms, both of which are perfect squares separated by a minus sign, is called the **difference of two squares**. You should have found that all the expansions in Exercise 10C involved the differences of two squares.

The exercise illustrates a system of factorisation that will *always* work for the difference of two squares such as these.

$x^2 - 9$ $\quad x^2 - 25$ $\quad x^2 - 4$ $\quad x^2 - 100$

There are three conditions that must be met if the difference of two squares works.

- There must be two terms.
- They must separated by a negative sign.
- Each term must be a perfect square, say x^2 and n^2.

When these three conditions are met, the factorisation is:

$$x^2 - n^2 = (x + n)(x - n)$$

EXAMPLE 10

Factorise $x^2 - 36$

- Recognise the difference of two squares x^2 and 6^2.
- So it factorises to $(x + 6)(x - 6)$.

Expanding the brackets shows that they do come from the original expression.

EXAMPLE 11

Factorise $9x^2 - 169$

- Recognise the difference of two squares $(3x)^2$ and 13^2.
- So it factorises to $(3x + 13)(3x - 13)$.

EXERCISE 10F

Each of the expressions in questions **1–9** is the difference of two squares. Factorise them.

HINTS AND TIPS

Learn how to spot the difference of two squares as it occurs a lot in GCSE examinations.

1. $x^2 - 9$
2. $t^2 - 25$
3. $m^2 - 16$
4. $9 - x^2$
5. $49 - t^2$
6. $k^2 - 100$
7. $4 - y^2$
8. $x^2 - 64$
9. $t^2 - 81$

B

PS 10 **a** A square has a side of x units.

What is the area of the square?

b A rectangle, A, 2 units wide, is cut from the square and placed at the side of the remaining rectangle, B.

A square, C, is then cut from the bottom of rectangle A to leave a final rectangle, D.

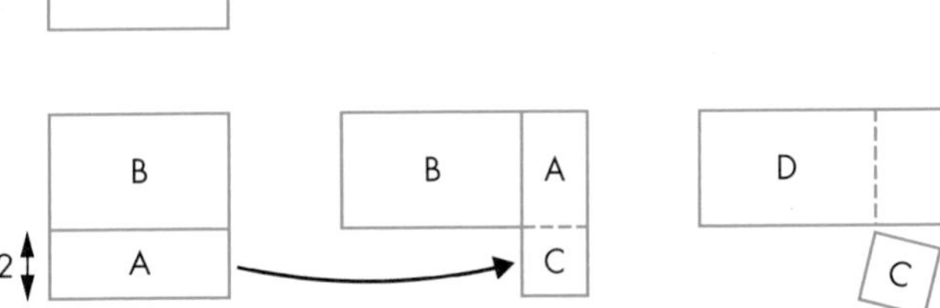

i What is the height of rectangle B?

ii What is the width of rectangle D?

iii What is the area of rectangle B plus rectangle A?

iv What is the area of square C?

c By working out the area of rectangle D, explain why $x^2 - 4 = (x + 2)(x - 2)$.

AU 11 **a** Expand and simplify: $(x + 2)^2 - (x + 1)^2$

b Factorise: $a^2 - b^2$

c In your answer for part **b**, replace a with $(x + 2)$ and b with $(x + 1)$.
Expand and simplify the answer.

d What can you say about the answers to parts **a** and **c**?

e Simplify: $(x + 1)^2 - (x - 1)^2$

Each of the expressions in questions **12–20** is the difference of two squares. Factorise them.

12 $x^2 - y^2$ **13** $x^2 - 4y^2$ **14** $x^2 - 9y^2$ **15** $9x^2 - 1$ **16** $16x^2 - 9$

17 $25x^2 - 64$ **18** $4x^2 - 9y^2$ **19** $9t^2 - 4w^2$ **20** $16y^2 - 25x^2$

Factorising $ax^2 + bx + c$

We can adapt the method for factorising $x^2 + ax + b$ to take into account the factors of the coefficient of x^2.

EXAMPLE 12

Factorise $3x^2 + 8x + 4$

- First, note that both signs are positive. So the signs in the brackets must be $(?x + ?)(?x + ?)$.
- As 3 has only 3×1 as factors, the brackets must be $(3x + ?)(x + ?)$.
- Next, note that the factors of 4 are 4×1 and 2×2.
- Now find which pair of factors of 4 combine with 3 and 1 to give 8.

You can see that the combination 3×2 and 1×2 adds up to 8.

- So, the complete factorisation becomes $(3x + 2)(x + 2)$.

EXAMPLE 13

Factorise $6x^2 - 7x - 10$

- First, note that both signs are negative. So the signs in the brackets must be $(?x + ?)(?x - ?)$.
- As 6 has 6×1 and 3×2 as factors, the brackets could be $(6x \pm ?)(x \pm ?)$ or $(3x \pm ?)(2x \pm ?)$.
- Next, note that the factors of 10 are 5×2 and 1×10.
- Now find which pair of factors of 10 combine with the factors of 6 to give -7.

3	(6)		±1	(±2)
2	(1)		±10	(±5)

  You can see that the combination 6×-2 and 1×5 adds up to -7.
- So, the complete factorisation becomes $(6x + 5)(x - 2)$.

Although this seems to be very complicated, it becomes quite easy with practice and experience.

EXERCISE 10G

Factorise the expressions in questions **1–12**.

1 $2x^2 + 5x + 2$

2 $7x^2 + 8x + 1$

3 $4x^2 + 3x - 7$

4 $24t^2 + 19t + 2$

5 $15t^2 + 2t - 1$

6 $16x^2 - 8x + 1$

7 $6y^2 + 33y - 63$

8 $4y^2 + 8y - 96$

9 $8x^2 + 10x - 3$

10 $6t^2 + 13t + 5$

11 $3x^2 - 16x - 12$

12 $7x^2 - 37x + 10$

PS 13 This rectangle is made up of four parts, with areas of $12x^2$, $3x$, $8x$ and 2 square units.

Work out expressions for the sides of the rectangle, in terms of x.

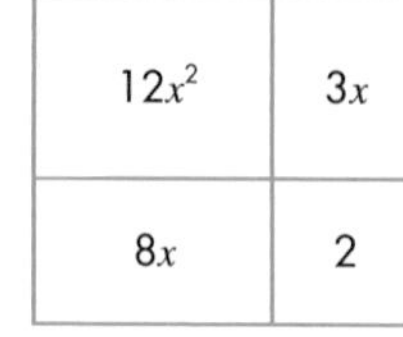

AU 14 Three students are asked to factorise the expression $6x^2 + 30x + 36$. These are their answers.

Adam	**Bertie**	**Cara**
$(6x + 12)(x + 3)$	$(3x + 6)(2x + 6)$	$(2x + 4)(3x + 9)$

All the answers are correctly factorised.

a Explain why one quadratic expression can have three different factorisations.

b Which of the following is the most complete factorisation?

$2(3x + 6)(x + 3)$ $\quad$ $6(x + 2)(x + 3)$ $\quad$ $3(x + 2)(2x + 6)$

Explain your choice.

10.3 Solving quadratic equations by factorisation

This section will show you how to:

- solve a quadratic equation by factorisation

Key words
factors
solve

Solving the quadratic equation $x^2 + ax + b = 0$

To **solve** a quadratic equation such as $x^2 - 2x - 3 = 0$, you first have to be able to factorise it. Work through Examples 14 to 16 below to see how this is done.

EXAMPLE 14

Solve $x^2 + 6x + 5 = 0$

This factorises into $(x + 5)(x + 1) = 0$.

The only way this expression can ever equal 0 is if the value of one of the brackets is 0.
Hence either $(x + 5) = 0$ or $(x + 1) = 0$

$\Rightarrow x + 5 = 0$ or $x + 1 = 0$

$\Rightarrow x = -5$ or $x = -1$

So the solution is $x = -5$ or $x = -1$.

EXAMPLE 15

Solve $x^2 + 3x - 10 = 0$

This factorises into $(x + 5)(x - 2) = 0$.

Hence either $(x + 5) = 0$ or $(x - 2) = 0$

$\Rightarrow x + 5 = 0$ or $x - 2 = 0$

$\Rightarrow x = -5$ or $x = 2$.

So the solution is $x = -5$ or $x = 2$.

EXAMPLE 16

Solve $x^2 - 6x + 9 = 0$

This factorises into $(x - 3)(x - 3) = 0$.

The equation has repeated roots.

That is: $(x - 3)^2 = 0$

Hence, there is only one solution, $x = 3$.

EXERCISE 10H

Solve the equations in questions **1–12**.

C

1 $(x + 2)(x + 5) = 0$

2 $(t + 3)(t + 1) = 0$

3 $(a + 6)(a + 4) = 0$

4 $(x + 3)(x - 2) = 0$

5 $(x + 1)(x - 3) = 0$

6 $(t + 4)(t - 5) = 0$

7 $(x - 1)(x + 2) = 0$

8 $(x - 2)(x + 5) = 0$

9 $(a - 7)(a + 4) = 0$

10 $(x - 3)(x - 2) = 0$

11 $(x - 1)(x - 5) = 0$

12 $(a - 4)(a - 3) = 0$

First factorise, then solve the equations in questions **13–26**.

B

13 $x^2 + 5x + 4 = 0$

14 $x^2 + 11x + 18 = 0$

15 $x^2 - 6x + 8 = 0$

16 $x^2 - 8x + 15 = 0$

17 $x^2 - 3x - 10 = 0$

18 $x^2 - 2x - 15 = 0$

19 $t^2 + 4t - 12 = 0$

20 $t^2 + 3t - 18 = 0$

21 $x^2 - x - 2 = 0$

22 $x^2 + 4x + 4 = 0$

23 $m^2 + 10m + 25 = 0$

24 $t^2 - 8t + 16 = 0$

25 $t^2 + 8t + 12 = 0$

26 $a^2 - 14a + 49 = 0$

A

PS 27 A woman is x years old. Her husband is three years younger.
The product of their ages is 550.

a Set up a quadratic equation to represent this situation.

b How old is the woman?

> **HINTS AND TIPS**
>
> If one solution to a real-life problem is negative, reject it and only give the positive answer.

PS 28 A rectangular field is 40 m longer than it is wide.
The area is 48 000 square metres.

The farmer wants to place a fence all around the field.

How long will the fence be?

> **HINTS AND TIPS**
>
> Let the width be x, set up a quadratic equation and solve it to get x.

First rearrange the equations in questions **29–37**, then solve them.

> **HINTS AND TIPS**
>
> You cannot solve a quadratic equation by factorisation unless it is in the form $x^2 + ax + b = 0$

29 $x^2 + 10x = -24$

30 $x^2 - 18x = -32$

31 $x^2 + 2x = 24$

32 $x^2 + 3x = 54$

33 $t^2 + 7t = 30$

34 $x^2 - 7x = 44$

35 $t^2 - t = 72$

36 $x^2 = 17x - 72$

37 $x^2 + 1 = 2x$

A

AU **38** A teacher asks her class to solve $x^2 - 3x = 4$.

This is Mario's answer.

$x^2 - 3x - 4 = 0$

$(x - 4)(x + 1) = 0$

Hence $x - 4 = 0$ or $x + 1 = 0$

$x = 4$ or -1

This is Sylvan's answer.

$x(x - 3) = 4$

Hence $x = 4$ or $x - 3 = 4 \Rightarrow x = -3 + 4 = -1$

When the teacher reads out the answer of $x = 4$ or -1, both students mark their work as correct.

Who used the correct method and what mistakes did the other student make?

Solving the general quadratic equation by factorisation

The general quadratic equation is of the form $ax^2 + bx + c = 0$ where a, b and c are positive or negative whole numbers. (It is easier to make sure that a is always positive.) Before any quadratic equation can be solved by factorisation, it must be rearranged to this form.

The method is similar to that used to solve equations of the form $x^2 + ax + b = 0$. That is, you have to find two **factors** of $ax^2 + bx + c$ with a product of 0.

EXAMPLE 17

Solve these quadratic equations. **a** $12x^2 - 28x = -15$ **b** $30x^2 - 5x - 5 = 0$

a First, rearrange the equation to the general form.

$12x^2 - 28x + 15 = 0$

This factorises into $(2x - 3)(6x - 5) = 0$.

The only way this product can equal 0 is if the value of one of the brackets is 0. Hence:

either $2x - 3 = 0$ or $6x - 5 = 0$

$\Rightarrow 2x = 3$ or $6x = 5$

$\Rightarrow x = \frac{3}{2}$ or $x = \frac{5}{6}$

So the solution is $x = 1\frac{1}{2}$ or $x = \frac{5}{6}$

Note: It is almost always the case that if a solution is a fraction which is then changed into a rounded-off decimal number, the original equation cannot be evaluated exactly, using that decimal number. So it is preferable to leave the solution in its fraction form. This is called the *rational form* (see pages 284–288).

b This equation is already in the general form and it will factorise to $(15x + 5)(2x - 1) = 0$ or $(3x + 1)(10x - 5) = 0$.

Look again at the equation. There is a common factor of 5 which can be taken out to give:

$5(6x^2 - x - 1 = 0)$

This is much easier to factorise to $5(3x + 1)(2x - 1) = 0$, which can be solved to give $x = -\frac{1}{3}$ or $x = \frac{1}{2}$

Special cases

Sometimes the values of b and c are zero. (Note that if a is zero the equation is no longer a quadratic equation but a linear equation. These were covered in Chapter 8.)

EXAMPLE 18

Solve these quadratic equations. **a** $3x^2 - 4 = 0$ **b** $4x^2 - 25 = 0$ **c** $6x^2 - x = 0$

a Rearrange to get $3x^2 = 4$.

Divide both sides by 3: $x^2 = \frac{4}{3}$

Take the square root on both sides: $x = \pm\sqrt{\frac{4}{3}} = \pm\frac{2}{\sqrt{3}} = \pm\frac{2\sqrt{3}}{3}$

Note: A square root can be positive or negative. The answer is in *surd form* (see Chapter 9).

b You can use the method of part **a** or you should recognise this as the difference of two squares (page 310). This can be factorised to $(2x - 5)(2x + 5) = 0$.

Each set of brackets can be put equal to zero.

$2x - 5 = 0 \Rightarrow x = +\frac{5}{2}$

$2x + 5 = 0 \Rightarrow x = -\frac{5}{2}$ So the solution is $x = \pm\frac{5}{2}$

c There is a common factor of x, so factorise as $x(6x - 1) = 0$.

There is only one set of brackets this time but each factor can be equal to zero, so $x = 0$ or $6x - 1 = 0$.

Hence, $x = 0$ or $\frac{1}{6}$

EXERCISE 10I

Give your answers either in rational form or as mixed numbers.

1 Solve these equations.

a $3x^2 + 8x - 3 = 0$ **b** $6x^2 - 5x - 4 = 0$

c $5x^2 - 9x - 2 = 0$ **d** $4t^2 - 4t - 35 = 0$

e $18t^2 + 9t + 1 = 0$ **f** $3t^2 - 14t + 8 = 0$

g $6x^2 + 15x - 9 = 0$ **h** $12x^2 - 16x - 35 = 0$ **i** $15t^2 + 4t - 35 = 0$

j $28x^2 - 85x + 63 = 0$ **k** $24x^2 - 19x + 2 = 0$ **l** $16t^2 - 1 = 0$

m $4x^2 + 9x = 0$ **n** $25t^2 - 49 = 0$ **o** $9m^2 - 24m - 9 = 0$

HINTS AND TIPS

Look out for the special cases where b or c is zero.

2 Rearrange these equations into the general form and then solve them.

a $x^2 - x = 42$ **b** $8x(x + 1) = 30$

c $(x + 1)(x - 2) = 40$ **d** $13x^2 = 11 - 2x$

A

A

e $(x + 1)(x - 2) = 4$

f $10x^2 - x = 2$

g $8x^2 + 6x + 3 = 2x^2 + x + 2$

h $25x^2 = 10 - 45x$

i $8x - 16 - x^2 = 0$

j $(2x + 1)(5x + 2) = (2x - 2)(x - 2)$

k $5x + 5 = 30x^2 + 15x + 5$

l $2m^2 = 50$

m $6x^2 + 30 = 5 - 3x^2 - 30x$

n $4x^2 + 4x - 49 = 4x$

o $2t^2 - t = 15$

AU 3 Here are three equations.

A: $(x - 1)^2 = 0$ B: $3x + 2 = 5$ C: $x^2 - 4x = 5$

a Give some mathematical fact that equations A and B have in common.

b Give a mathematical reason why equation B is different from equations A and C.

PS 4 Pythagoras' theorem states that the sum of the squares of the two short sides of a right-angled triangle equals the square of the long side (hypotenuse).

A right-angled triangle has sides $5x - 1$, $2x + 3$ and $x + 1$ cm.

a Show that $20x^2 - 24x - 9 = 0$

b Find the area of the triangle.

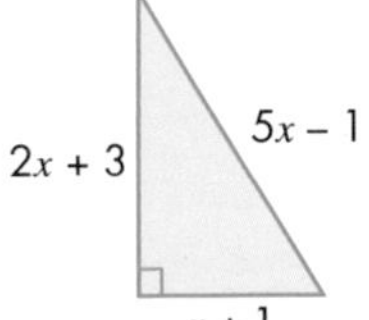

10.4 Solving a quadratic equation by completing the square

This section will show you how to:

- solve a quadratic equation by completing the square

Key words
completing the square
square root
surd

Another method for solving quadratic equations is **completing the square**. This method can be used to give answers to a specified number of decimal places or to leave answers in **surd** form.

You will remember that:

$$(x + a)^2 = x^2 + 2ax + a^2$$

which can be rearranged to give:

$$x^2 + 2ax = (x + a)^2 - a^2$$

This is the basic principle behind completing the square.

There are three basic steps in rewriting $x^2 + px + q$ in the form $(x + a)^2 + b$.

Step 1: Ignore q and just look at the first two terms, $x^2 + px$.

Step 2: Rewrite $x^2 + px$ as $\left(x + \frac{p}{2}\right)^2 - \left(\frac{p}{2}\right)^2$.

Step 3: Bring q back to get $x^2 + px + q = \left(x + \frac{p}{2}\right)^2 - \left(\frac{p}{2}\right)^2 + q$.

Note: p is always even so the numbers involved are whole numbers.

EXAMPLE 19

Rewrite the following in the form $(x \pm a) \pm b$.

a $x^2 + 6x - 7$

b $x^2 - 8x + 3$

a Ignore −7 for the moment.
Rewrite $x^2 + 6x$ as $(x + 3)^2 - 9$
(Expand $(x + 3)^2 - 9 = x^2 + 6x + 9 - 9 = x^2 + 6x$. The 9 is subtracted to get rid of the constant term when the brackets are expanded.)
Now bring the −7 back, so $x^2 + 6x - 7 = (x + 3)^2 - 9 - 7$
Combine the constant terms to get the final answer: $x^2 + 6x - 7 = (x + 3)^2 - 16$

b Ignore +3 for the moment.
Rewrite $x^2 - 8x$ as $(x - 4)^2 - 16$
(Note that you still subtract $(-4)^2$, as $(-4)^2 = +16$)
Now bring the +3 back, so $x^2 - 8x + 3 = (x - 4)^2 - 16 + 3$
Combine the constant terms to get the final answer: $x^2 - 8x + 3 = (x - 4)^2 - 13$

EXAMPLE 20

Rewrite $x^2 + 4x - 7$ in the form $(x + a)^2 - b$. Hence solve the equation $x^2 + 4x - 7 = 0$, giving your answers to 2 decimal places.

Note that:

$$x^2 + 4x = (x + 2)^2 - 4$$

So:

$$x^2 + 4x - 7 = (x + 2)^2 - 4 - 7 = (x + 2)^2 - 11$$

When $x^2 + 4x - 7 = 0$, you can rewrite the equations completing the square as: $(x + 2)^2 - 11 = 0$

Rearranging gives $(x + 2)^2 = 11$

Taking the **square root** of both sides gives:

$x + 2 = \pm\sqrt{11}$ This answer is in surd form and could be left like this, but you
$\Rightarrow x = -2 \pm \sqrt{11}$ are asked to evaluate it to 2 decimal places.
$\Rightarrow x = 1.32$ or -5.32 (to 2 decimal places)

EXAMPLE 21

Solve $x^2 - 6x - 1 = 0$ by completing the square. Leave your answer in the form $a \pm \sqrt{b}$.

$x^2 - 6x = (x - 3)^2 - 9$

So $x^2 - 6x - 1 = (x - 3)^2 - 9 - 1 = (x - 3)^2 - 10$

When $x^2 - 6x - 1 = 0$, then $(x - 3)^2 - 10 = 0$

$\Rightarrow (x - 3)^2 = 10$

Taking the square root of both sides gives:

$x - 3 = \pm\sqrt{10}$

$\Rightarrow x = 3 \pm\sqrt{10}$

EXERCISE 10J

1 Write an equivalent expression in the form $(x \pm a)^2 - b$.

a $x^2 + 4x$ **b** $x^2 + 14x$ **c** $x^2 - 6x$ **d** $x^2 + 6x$

e $x^2 - 4x$ **f** $x^2 - 10x$ **g** $x^2 + 20x$ **h** $x^2 + 10x$

i $x^2 + 8x$ **j** $x^2 - 2x$ **k** $x^2 + 2x$

2 Write an equivalent expression in the form $(x \pm a)^2 - b$.

Question **1** will help with **a** to **h**.

a $x^2 + 4x - 1$ **b** $x^2 + 14x - 5$ **c** $x^2 - 6x + 3$ **d** $x^2 + 6x + 7$

e $x^2 - 4x - 1$ **f** $x^2 + 6x + 3$ **g** $x^2 - 10x - 5$ **h** $x^2 + 20x - 1$

i $x^2 + 8x - 6$ **j** $x^2 + 2x - 1$ **k** $x^2 - 2x - 7$ **l** $x^2 + 2x - 9$

3 Solve the following equations by completing the square. Leave your answers in surd form where appropriate. The answers to question **2** will help.

a $x^2 + 4x - 1 = 0$ **b** $x^2 + 14x - 5 = 0$ **c** $x^2 - 6x + 3 = 0$

d $x^2 + 6x + 7 = 0$ **e** $x^2 - 4x - 1 = 0$ **f** $x^2 + 6x + 3 = 0$

g $x^2 - 10x - 5 = 0$ **h** $x^2 + 20x - 1 = 0$ **i** $x^2 + 8x - 6 = 0$

j $x^2 + 2x - 1 = 0$ **k** $x^2 - 2x - 7 = 0$ **l** $x^2 + 2x - 9 = 0$

4 Solve by completing the square. Give your answers to 2 decimal places.

a $x^2 + 2x - 5 = 0$ **b** $x^2 - 4x - 7 = 0$ **c** $x^2 + 2x - 9 = 0$

5 Prove that the solutions to the equation $x^2 + bx + c = 0$ are:

$$-\frac{b}{2} \pm \sqrt{\left(\frac{b^2}{4} - c\right)}$$

A

A*

A*

AU 6 Dave rewrites the expression $x^2 + px + q$ by completing the square.
He correctly does this and gets $(x - 7)^2 - 52$.

What are the values of p and q?

PS 7 **a** Frankie writes the steps to solve $x^2 + 6x + 7 = 0$ by completing the square on sticky notes. Unfortunately he drops them and they get out of order. Can you put the notes in the correct order?

Take –2 over the equals sign	Take +3 over the equals sign	Write $x^2 + 6x + 7 = 0$ as $(x + 3)^2 - 2 = 0$	Take the square root of both sides

b Write down the stages as in part **a** needed to solve the equation $x^2 - 4x - 3 = 0$

c Solve the equations below, giving the answers in surd form.

i $x^2 + 6x + 7 = 0$ **ii** $x^2 - 4x - 3 = 0$

PS 8 Rearrange the following statements to give the complete solution, using the method of completing the square to the equation: $ax^2 + bx + c = 0$

A: $x = -\frac{b}{2a} \pm \sqrt{\frac{b^2}{4a^2} - \frac{c}{a}}$

B: $\left(\left(x + \frac{b}{2a}\right)^2 - \frac{b^2}{4a^2}\right) + \frac{c}{a} = 0$

C: $a\left(\left(x + \frac{b}{2a}\right)^2 - \frac{b^2}{4a^2}\right) + c = 0$

D: $\left(x + \frac{b}{2a}\right)^2 - \frac{b^2}{4a^2} + \frac{c}{a}$

E: $\left(x + \frac{b}{2a}\right)^2 - \frac{b^2}{4a^2} + \frac{c}{a} = 0$

F: $x = -\frac{b}{2a} \pm \sqrt{\frac{b^2}{4a^2} - \frac{4ac}{4a^2}}$

G: $x = -\frac{b}{2a} \pm \frac{1}{2a}\sqrt{b^2 - 4ac}$

H: $a\left(x^2 + \frac{b}{a}x\right) + c = 0$

I: $x = \frac{-b \pm \sqrt{b^2 - 4ac}}{2a}$

J: $x + \frac{b}{2a} = \pm\sqrt{\frac{b^2}{4a^2} - \frac{c}{a}}$

GRADE BOOSTER

- **C** You can expand a pair of linear brackets to get a quadratic expression
- **B** You can factorise a quadratic expression of the form $x^2 + ax + b$
- **B** You can solve a quadratic equation of the form $x^2 + ax + b = 0$
- **A** You can factorise a quadratic expression of the form $ax^2 + bx + c$
- **A** You can solve a quadratic equation of the form $ax^2 + bx + c = 0$ by factorisation
- **A*** You can solve a quadratic equation by completing the square

What you should know now

- How to expand linear brackets
- How to solve quadratic equations by factorisation and completing the square

EXAMINATION QUESTIONS

1 **a** **i** Factorise $y^2 - 5y + 6$ *(2 marks)*

ii Hence solve the equation

$y^2 - 5y + 6 = 0$ *(1 mark)*

b Simplify $\frac{2(x + 3)^2}{8(x + 3)}$ *(2 marks)*

c Simplify $(2m^3p)^4$ *(2 marks)*

AQA, June 2006, Paper 1 Higher, Question 2 (c), (d) and (e)

2 **a** Find the values of a and b such that:

$x^2 + 8x - 5 = (x + a)^2 + b$ *(2 marks)*

b Hence, or otherwise, solve the equation:

$x^2 + 8x - 5 = 0$

Give your answers to 2 decimal places. *(2 marks)*

AQA, June 2006, Paper 2 Higher, Question 11

3 Make x the subject of $\sqrt{\frac{a}{x + b}} = c$ *(4 marks)*

AQA, November 2007, Paper 1 Higher, Question 20 (a)

4 **a** Factorise $2n^2 + 9n + 9$ *(2 marks)*

b Hence, or otherwise, write 299 as the product of two prime factors. *(1 mark)*

AQA, November 2008, Paper 1 Higher, Question 18

5 **a** Factorise $8p - 6$

b Factorise $r^2 + 6r$

c Simplify $s^2 \times s^4$

6 Find, using trial and improvement, an exact solution of:

$3x^2 - 2x = 96$

x	$3x^2 - 2x$	Comment
1	1	Too small

(3 marks)

AQA, June 2005, Paper 1 Intermediate, Question 12

7 **a** Factorise $x^5 - 4x^2$

b **i** Factorise $x^2 - 3x - 10$

ii Hence solve the equation:

$x^2 - 3x - 10 = 0$

8 Multiply and simplify $(2p - 5q)(3p - q)$ *(3 marks)*

AQA, November 2004, Paper 1 Intermediate, Question 15

9 **a** Expand and simplify $(a + b)(a - b)$

b **i** Factorise $x^2 - 20x + 36$

ii Hence solve the equation:

$x^2 - 20x + 36 = 0$

10 The perimeter of a rectangle is 25 cm.

The length of the rectangle is x cm.

a Write down an expression for the width of the rectangle in terms of x. *(1 mark)*

b The area of the rectangle is 38 cm^2. Show that $2x^2 - 25x + 76 = 0$ *(2 marks)*

c Solve the equation given in part **b** to find the value of x. Give your answer to 2 decimal places. *(3 marks)*

AQA, June 2005, Module 5, Paper 2 Higher, Question 12

11 **a** Find the values of a and b such that

$x^2 + 10x + 40 = (x + a)^2 + b$ *(2 marks)*

b Hence, or otherwise, write down the minimum value of $x^2 + 10x + 40$ *(1 mark)*

AQA, June 2005, Module 5, Paper 1 Higher, Question 14

12 Factorise fully $3x^2 - 12y^2$

13 **a** Factorise $2n^2 + 5n + 3$ *(2 marks)*

b Hence, or otherwise, write 253 as the product of two prime factors. *(2 marks)*

AQA, June 2004, Paper 1 Higher, Question 16

14 Solve the equation $x^2 + 4x - 10 = 0$ *(2 marks)*

Give your answers to 2 decimal places.
You *must* show your working. *(2 marks)*

AQA, June 2003, Paper 2 Intermediate, Question 10

15 **a** Find the values of a and b such that:

$x^2 + 6x - 3 = (x + a)^2 + b$ *(2 marks)*

b Hence, or otherwise, solve the equation:

$x^2 + 6x - 3 = 0$ *(3 marks)*

giving your answers in surd form.

AQA, June 2004, Paper 1 Higher, Question 20

16 **a** Factorise $x^2 - 8x + 12$ *(2 marks)*

b Hence, or otherwise, solve the equation:

$(y + 1)^2 - 8(y + 1) + 12 = 0$ *(2 marks)*

AQA, June 2004, Paper 1 Higher, Question 18a

Worked Examination Questions

1 You are given that:

$$(2x + b)^2 + c = ax^2 - 4x - 5$$

Calculate the values a, b and c

1 $4x^2 + 4bx + b^2 + c = ax^2 - 4x - 5$

Expand and simplify the left-hand side. This scores 1 mark for method and 1 mark for accuracy.

$4x^2 = ax^2 \Rightarrow a = 4$

$4bx = -4x \Rightarrow b = -1$

$b^2 + c = -5 \Rightarrow c = -6$

Equate the terms in x^2, x and the constant term. Solve the resulting equations. This scores 1 mark for method and 1 mark for accuracy.

Total: 4 marks

2 **a** Factorise: $2n^2 + 9n + 9$

b Hence, or otherwise, write 299 as the product of two prime factors.

2 a $(2n + 3)(n + 3)$

Factorise in the normal way. This scores 1 mark for method and 1 mark for accuracy.

b Let $n = 10$

$2 \times 10^2 + 9 \times 10 + 9 = 299$

$(2 \times 10 + 3)(10 + 3) = 23 \times 13$

Substitute $n = 10$ to find the prime factors. This scores 1 mark for method and 1 mark for accuracy.

Total: 4 marks

10 Functional Maths
Stopping distances

You may have seen signs on the motorway saying 'Keep your distance'. These signs advise drivers to keep a safe distance between their car and the car in front, so that they have time to stop if, for example, the car in front comes to a rapid stop or if the engine fails. The distance that should be left between cars is commonly known as the 'stopping distance'.

The stopping distance is made up of two parts. The first part is the 'thinking distance', which is the time it takes for the brain to react and for you to apply the brakes. The second part is the braking distance, which is the distance it takes for the car to come to a complete stop, once the brakes have been applied.

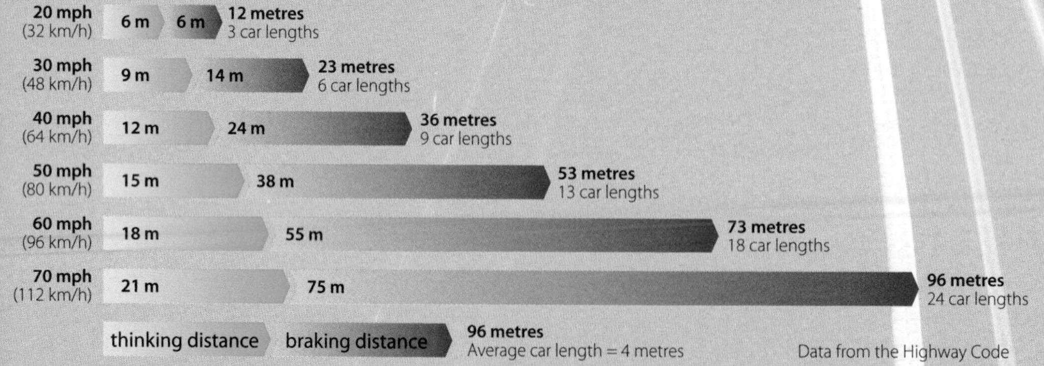

Notice that this diagram is based on 'typical' stopping distances. There are many factors that affect the stopping distance, such as road conditions, how good the brakes are and how heavy the car is, and so the stopping distance will never be the same in every situation.

Your task

This table shows the probability of a crash being fatal at certain speeds.

Speed at which crash happens (mph)	Probability of crash being fatal
70	0.60
60	0.50
50	0.42
40	0.34
30	0.26
20	0.17
10	0.09
5	0.05

James is learning to drive. His driving instructor has been teaching him about typical stopping distances, but James is not convinced that the distances given by his instructor, which are taken from the *Highway Code*, are right.

His instructor sets him a challenge: show whether the distances given in the *Highway Code* are correct.

James finds this formula for calculating stopping distances:

$$d = \frac{s^2}{20} + s$$

where d is the stopping distance (in feet) and s is the speed (in miles per hour).

Remember: 1 foot = 30 cm.

Does he prove his instructor to be right or wrong?

Getting started

Consider the following points to help you complete this task.

- How could you represent thinking, braking and stopping distances as a graph?
- Can you apply James's formula to real-life scenarios?
  - For example:
    If you are driving down a straight road and suddenly, 175 feet in front of you, a pallet falls off a lorry, what is the maximum speed from which you would be able to stop safely?
- How might the weather affect James's formula?
- What are the risks of fatality?

Why this chapter matters

Graphs are to be found in a host of different media, including newspapers and the textbooks of most of the subjects that you learn in school.

Graphs are used to show the relationship between two variables. Very often, one of these variables is time. Then the graph shows how the other variable changes over time.

For example, this graph shows how the exchange rate between the dollar and the pound changed over five months in 2009.

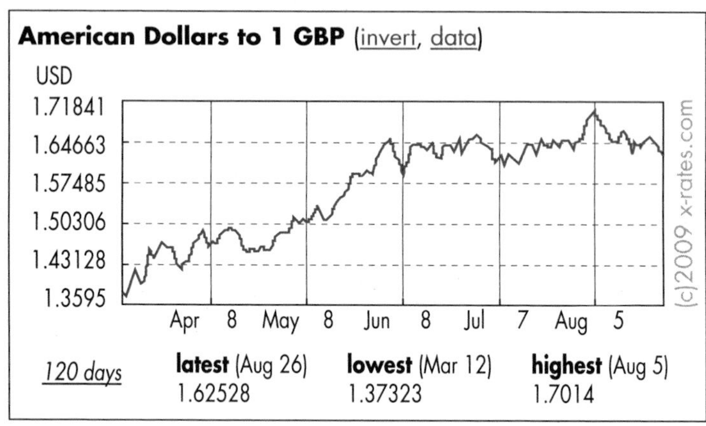

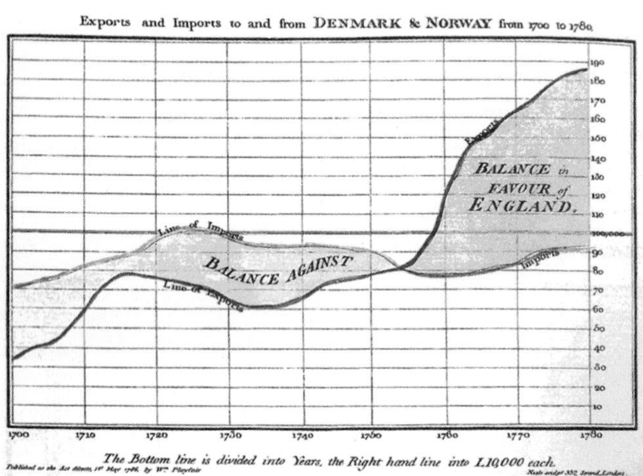

The earliest line graphs, such as the one shown here, appeared in the book *A Commercial and Political Atlas*, written in 1786 by Henry Playfair, who also used bar charts and pie charts for the first time. Playfair argued that charts and graphs communicated information to an audience better than tables of data.

Do you think that this is true?

This graph shows all the data from a racing car going around a circuit. Engineers can use this to fine-tune parts of the car to give the best performance. It illustrates that graphs give a visual representation of how variables change and can be used to compare data in a way that looking at lists of data cannot.

Think about instances in school and everyday life where a line graph would help you to communicate information more effectively.

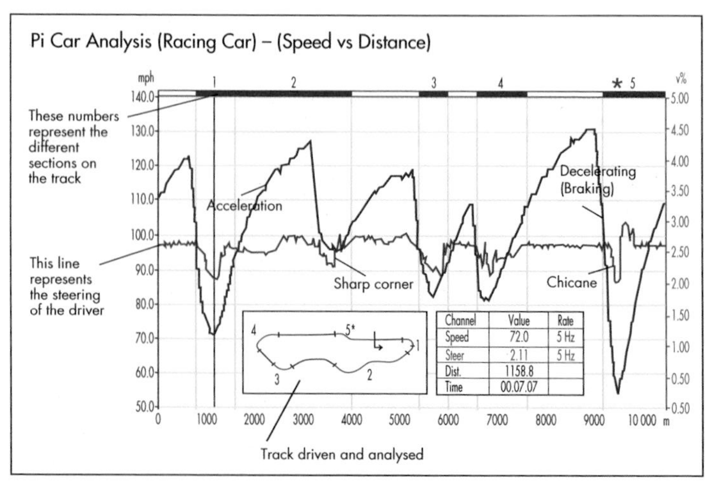

Algebra: Real-life graphs

This chapter will show you …

D how to interpret distance–time graphs

C to A how to interpret other types of graphs associated with real-life situations

Visual overview

Distance–time graphs

Other types of graphs

What you should already know

- How to plot coordinate points **(KS3 level 4, GCSE grade F)**
- How to read scales **(KS3 level 4, GCSE grade F)**

Quick check

1 Give the coordinates of points A, B and C.

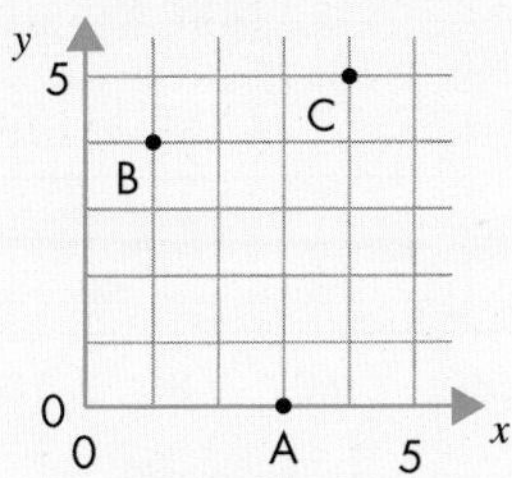

2 What are the values shown on the following scales?

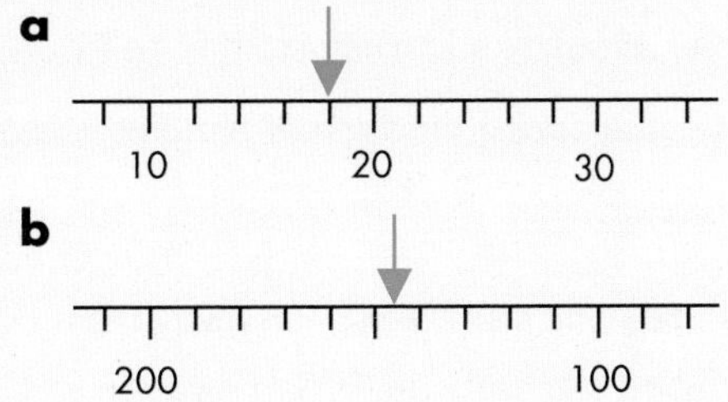

11.1 Straight-line distance–time graphs

This section will show you how to:

- interpret distance–time graphs

Key words
average speed
distance
distance–time graph
gradient
speed
time

As the name suggests, a **distance–time graph** gives information about how far someone or something has travelled over a given **time** period.

A travel graph is read in a similar way to the conversion graphs you have just done. But you can also find the **average speed** from a distance–time graph, using the formula:

$$\text{average speed} = \frac{\text{total distance travelled}}{\text{total time taken}}$$

EXAMPLE 1

The distance–time graph below represents a car journey from Barnsley to Nottingham, a distance of 50 km, and back again.

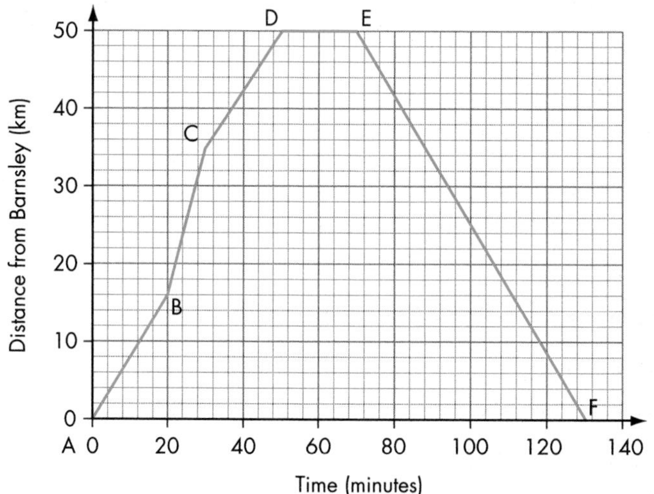

a What can you say about points B, C and D?

b What can you say about the journey from D to F?

c Work out the average speed for each of the five stages of the journey.

From the graph:

a B: After 20 minutes the car was 16 km away from Barnsley.
C: After 30 minutes the car was 35 km away from Barnsley.
D: After 50 minutes the car was 50 km away from Barnsley, so at Nottingham.

b D–F: The car stayed at Nottingham for 20 minutes, and then took 60 minutes for the return journey.

c The average speeds over the five stages of the journey are worked out as follows.

A to B represents 16 km in 20 minutes.

20 minutes is $\frac{1}{3}$ of an hour, so we need to multiply by 3 to give distance/hour. Multiplying both numbers by 3 gives 48 km in 60 minutes, which is 48 km/h.

B to C represents 19 km in 10 minutes.

Multiplying both numbers by 6 gives 114 km in 60 minutes, which is 114 km/h.

C to D represents 15 km in 20 minutes.

Multiplying both numbers by 3 gives 45 km in 60 minutes, which is 45 km/h.

D to E represents a stop: no further distance travelled.

E to F represents the return journey of 50 km in 60 minutes, which is 50 km/h.

So, the return journey was at an average speed of 50 km/h.

EXERCISE 11A

FM 1 Paul was travelling in his car to a meeting. This distance–time graph illustrates his journey.

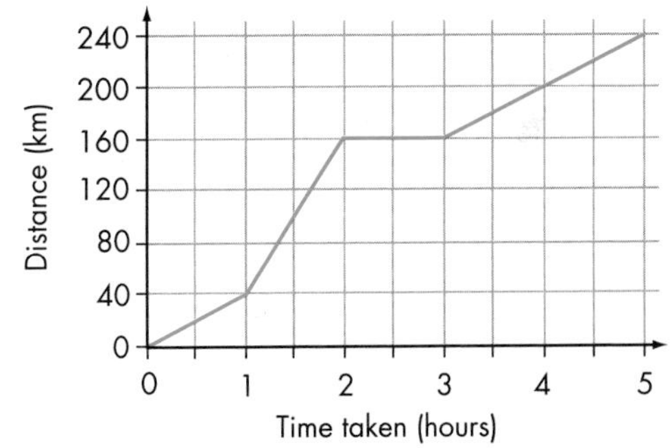

a How long after he set off did he:

i stop for his break

ii set off after his break

iii get to his meeting place?

b At what average speed was he travelling:

i over the first hour

ii over the second hour

iii for the last part of his journey?

c The meeting was scheduled to start at 10.30 am. What is the latest time he should have left home?

HINTS AND TIPS

If a part of a journey takes 30 minutes, just double the distance to get the average speed.

FM 2 James was travelling to Cornwall on his holiday. This distance–time graph illustrates his journey.

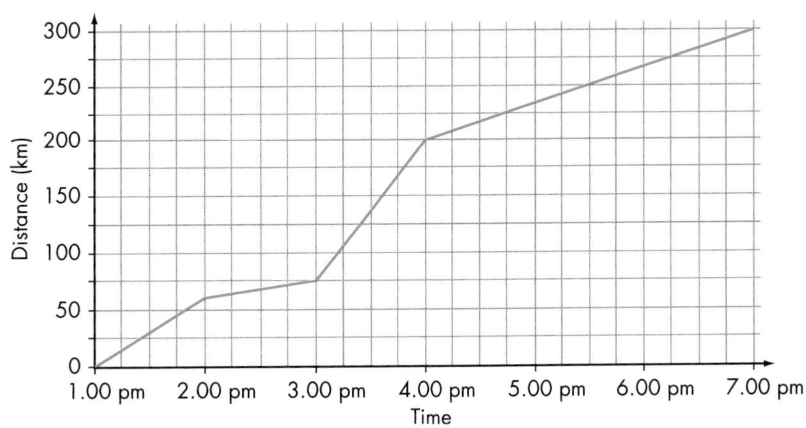

a His greatest speed was on the motorway.

i How far did he travel on the motorway?

ii What was his average speed on the motorway?

b **i** When did he travel the most slowly? **ii** What was his lowest average speed?

D

FM 3 A small bus set off from Leeds to pick up Mike and his family. It then went on to pick up Mike's parents and grandparents. It then travelled further, dropping them all off at a hotel. The bus then went on a further 10 km to pick up another party and it took them back to Leeds. This distance–time graph illustrates the journey.

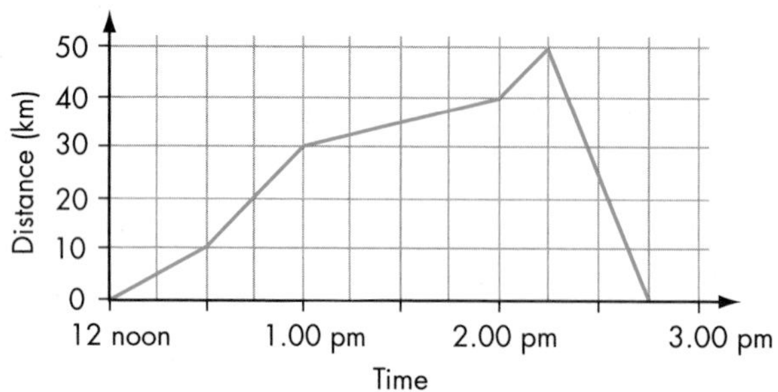

a How far from Leeds did Mike's parents and grandparents live?

b How far from Leeds is the hotel at which they all stayed?

c What was the average speed of the bus on its way back to Leeds?

PS 4 Richard and Paul took part in a 5000-m race. It is illustrated in this graph.

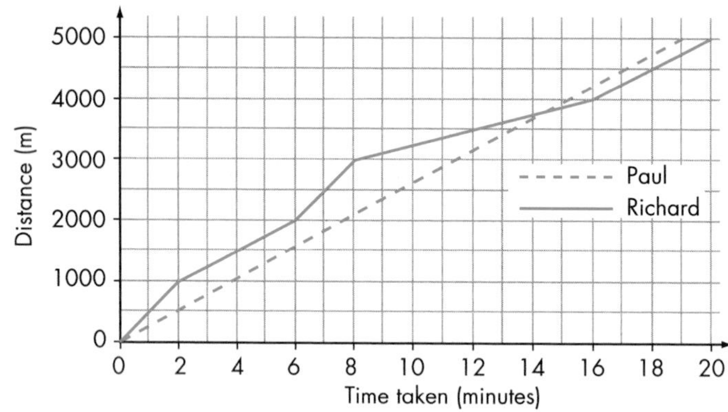

a Paul ran a steady race. What is his average speed in:

i metres per minute

ii kilometres per hour?

b Richard ran in spurts. What was his highest average speed?

c Who won the race and by how much?

FM PS 5 Three friends, Patrick, Araf and Sean, ran a 1000-m race. The race is illustrated on the distance–time graph shown here.

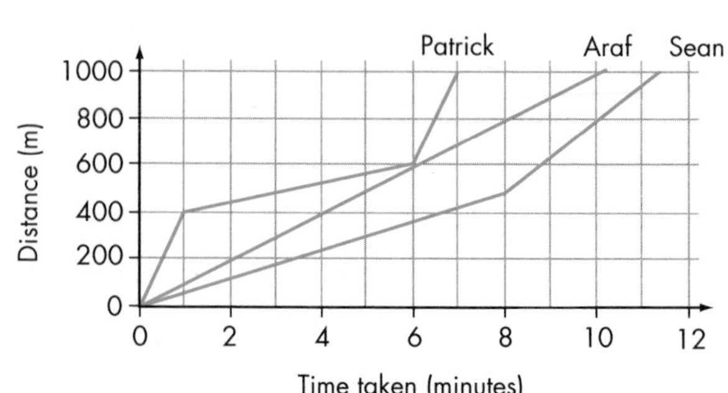

a Describe how each of them completed the race.

b **i** What is Araf's average speed in m/s?

ii What is this speed in km/h?

PS 6 A walker sets off at 9.00 am from point P to walk along a trail at a steady pace of 6 km per hour.

90 minutes later, a cyclist sets off from P on the same trail at a steady pace of 15 km per hour.

At what time did the cyclist overtake the walker?

You may use a graph to help you solve this question.

HINTS AND TIPS

This question can be done by many methods, but drawing a distance–time graph is the easiest. Mark a grid with a horizontal axis as time from 9 am to 1 pm, and the vertical axis as distance from 0 to 24. Draw lines for both walker and cyclist. Remember that the cyclist doesn't start until 10.30.

D

AU 7 Three school friends set off from school at the same time, 3.45 pm. They all lived 12 km away from the school. The distance–time graph illustrates their journeys.

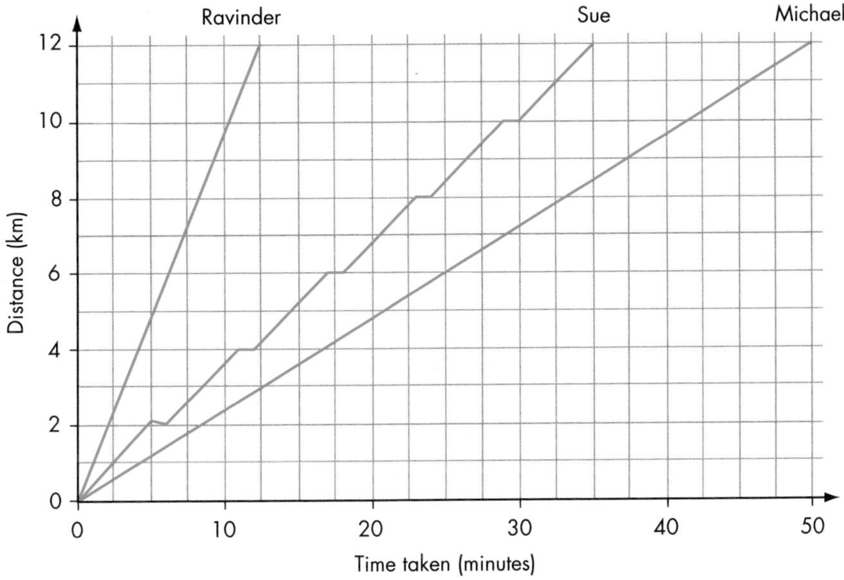

One of them went by bus, one cycled and one was taken by car.

a **i** Explain how you know that Sue used the bus.

ii Who went by car?

b At what times did each of them get home?

c **i** When the bus was moving, it covered 2 km in 5 minutes. What is this speed in kilometres per hour?

ii Overall, the bus covered 12 km in 35 minutes. What is this speed, in kilometres per hour?

iii How many stops did the bus make before Sue got off?

C

Gradient of straight-line distance–time graphs

The **gradient** of a straight line is a measure of its slope.

You can find the gradient of this line by constructing a right-angled triangle of which the hypotenuse (sloping side) is on the line. Then:

$$\text{average speed} = \frac{\text{distance measured vertically}}{\text{distance measured horizontally}} = \frac{6}{4} = 1.5$$

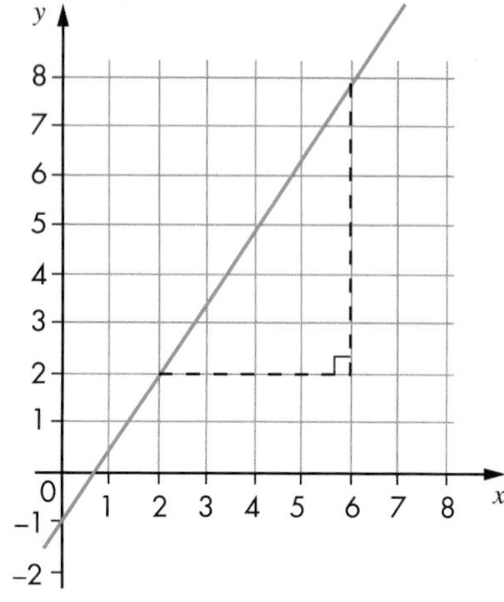

Look at the following examples of straight lines and their gradients.

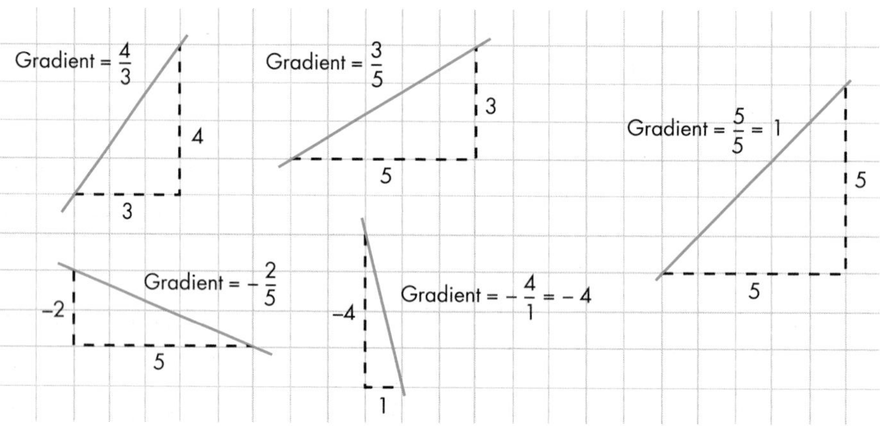

Note: Lines which slope downwards from left to right have *negative gradients*.

You can only count squares to find the gradient if the scale on both axes is one square to one unit. For a straight-line graph that compares two quantities, you must find the gradient by using the *scales* on its axes, *not* the actual number of grid squares. The gradient usually represents a third quantity, the value of which you want to know. For example, look at the next graph.

The gradient on this distance–time graph represents average speed.

$$\text{Gradient} = \frac{500 \text{ km}}{2 \text{ h}} = 250 \text{ km/h}$$

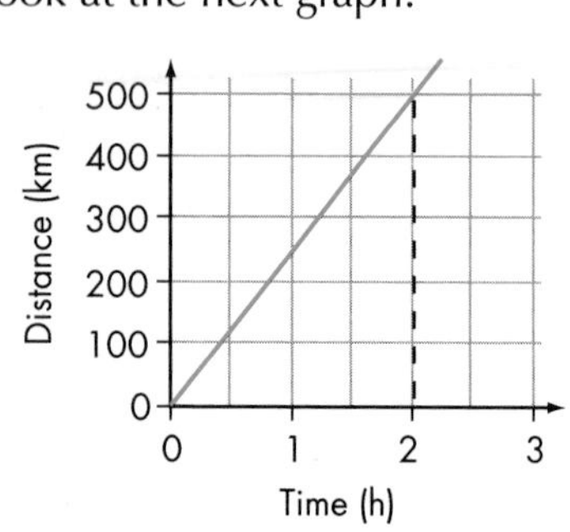

EXERCISE 11B

FM **1** Ravi was ill in hospital.

This is his temperature chart for the two weeks he was in hospital.

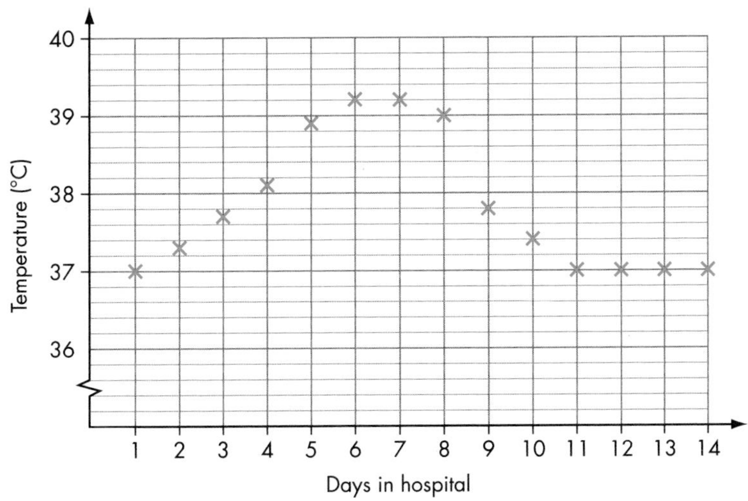

a What was Ravi's highest temperature?

b Between which days did Ravi's temperature increase the fastest? Explain how you can tell.

c Between which days did Ravi's temperature fall the fastest? Explain how you can tell.

d When Ravi's temperature went over 38.5 °C he was put on an antibiotic drip.

i On what day did Ravi go on the drip?

ii How many days did it take for the antibiotics to work before Ravi's temperature was below 38.5 again?

e Once Ravi's temperature had returned to normal and was stable for four days, he was allowed home. What is the normal body temperature?

2 Calculate the gradient of each line, using the scales on the axes.

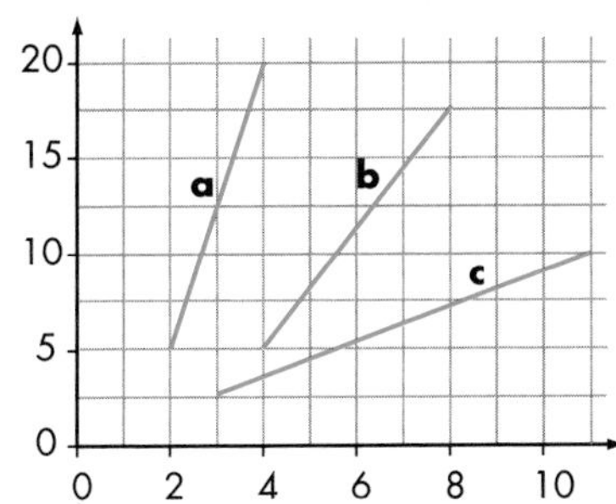

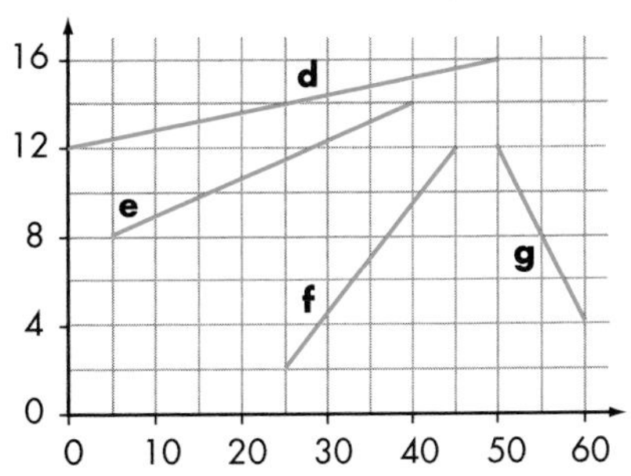

C

3 Calculate the average speed of the journey represented by the line in each of the following diagrams.

a

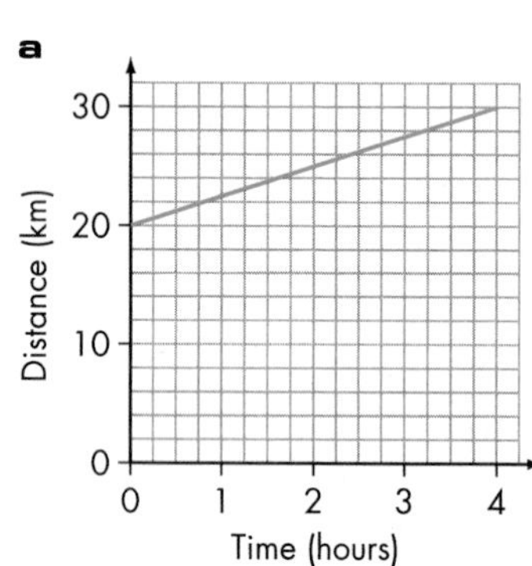

b

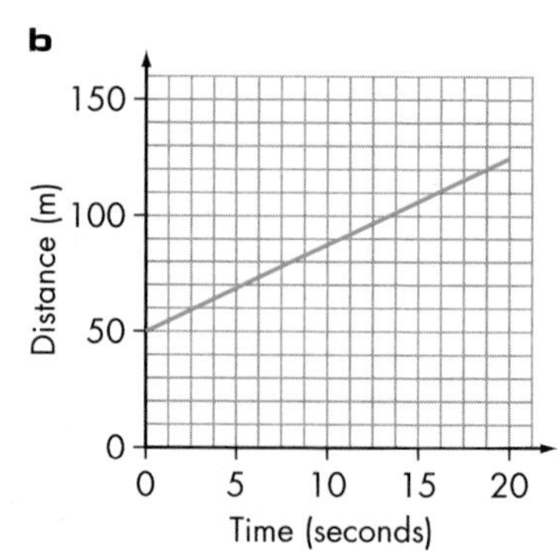

c

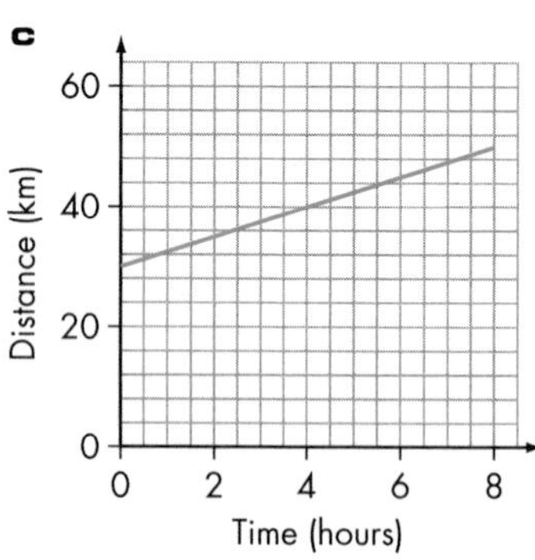

4 From the diagrams below, calculate the speed for each stage of each journey.

a

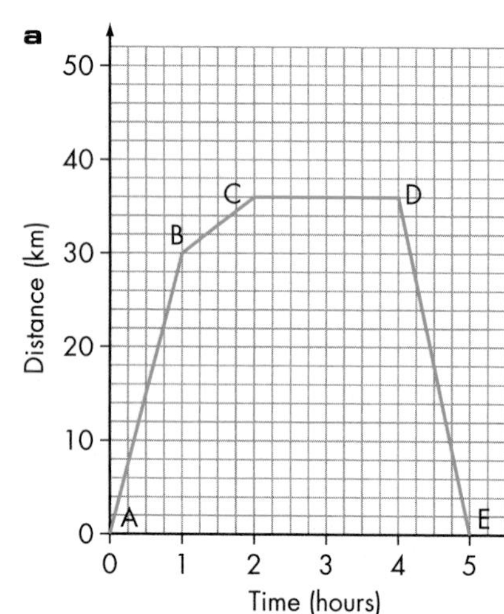

b

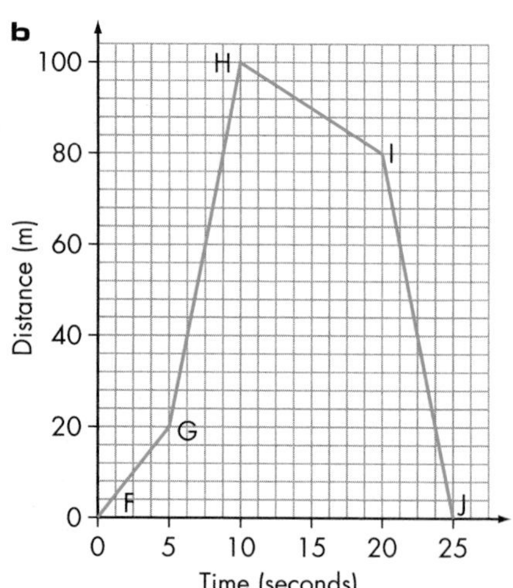

AU 5 Students in a class were asked to predict the y-value for an x-value of 10 for this line.

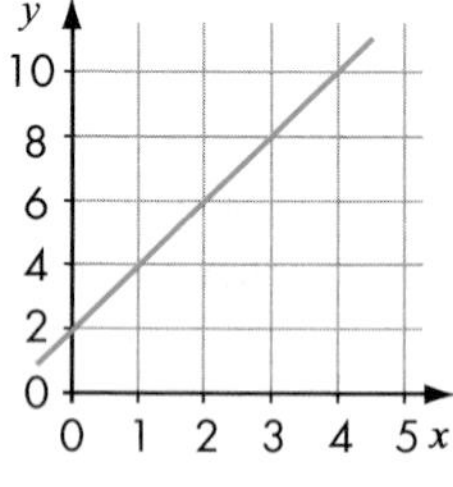

> Rob says, "The gradient is 1, so the line is $y = x + 2$. When $x = 10$, $y = 12$."

Rob is wrong.

Explain why and work out the correct y-value.

FM PS 6 The Health and Safety regulations for vent pipes from gas appliances state that the minimum height depends on the pitch (gradient) of the roof.

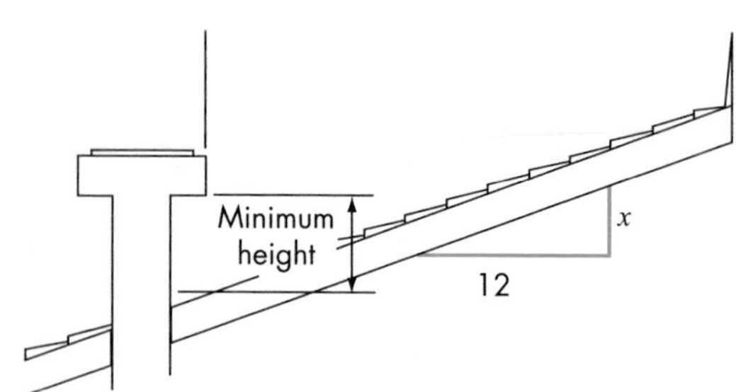

This is the rule:

> minimum height = 1 m or twice the pitch in metres, whichever is greater

a What is the minimum height for a roof with a pitch of 2?

b What is the minimum height for a roof with a pitch of 0.4?

C

c What is the minimum height for these two roofs?

i

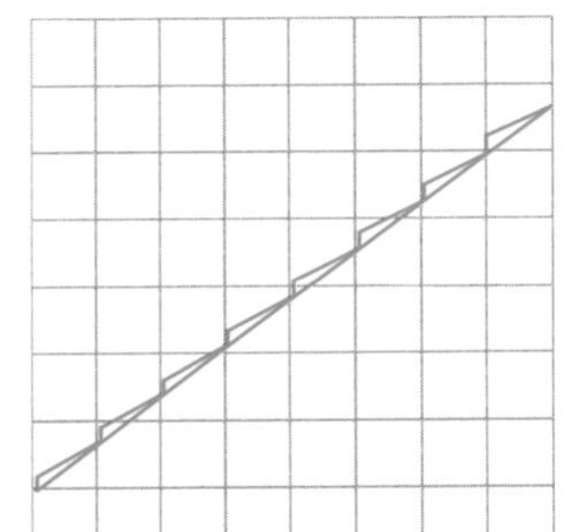

ii

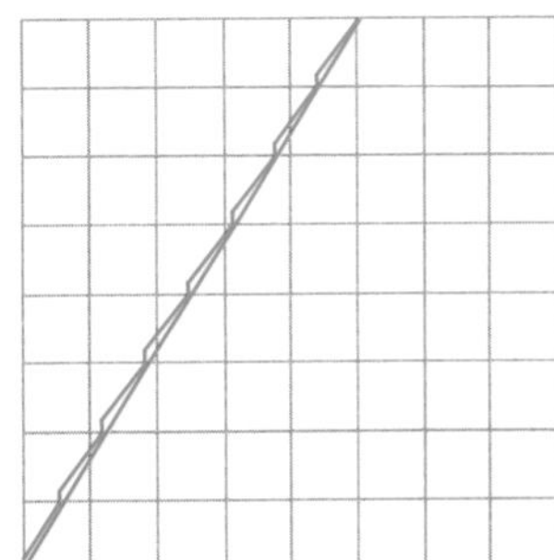

11.2 Other types of graphs

This section will show you how to:

- identify and draw some of the more unusual types of real-life graphs

Key words
curved
depth
gradient
measure

Some situations can lead to unusual graphs. For example, this graph represents the cost of postage of a first-class letter against its weight.

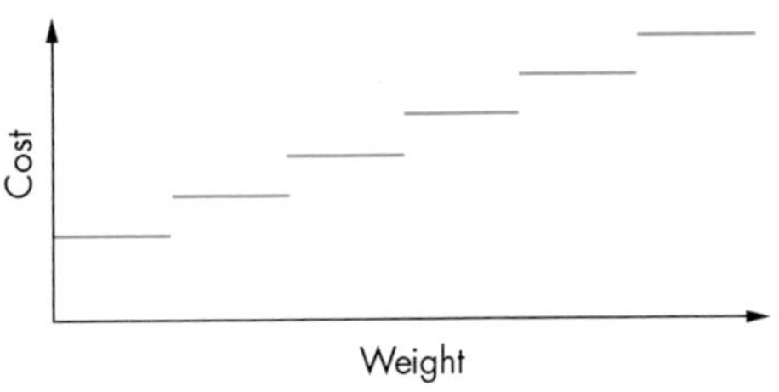

This next graph shows the change in the depth of water in a flat-bottomed flask, as it is filled from a tap delivering water at a steady rate. The graph shows that at first the depth of water increases quickly then slows down as the flask gets wider. As the flask gets narrower, the depth increases at a faster rate. Finally, when the water reaches the neck, which has a constant cross-section, the depth increases at a constant rate to the top of the neck.

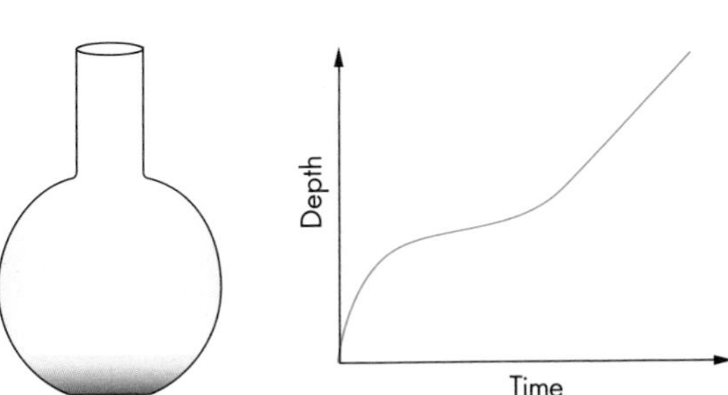

The application of graphs to describe the rate of change of depth as a container is filled with water is also covered in question **1** (Exercise 11C).

Another example of the use of graphs is set out in question **3** of Exercise 11C, in the calculation of personal income tax.

Further practical applications of graphs, with special reference to finding the formulae or rules governing them, are featured in Chapter 12.

EXERCISE 11C

AU 1 **a** Liquid is poured at a steady rate into the bottle shown in the diagram.

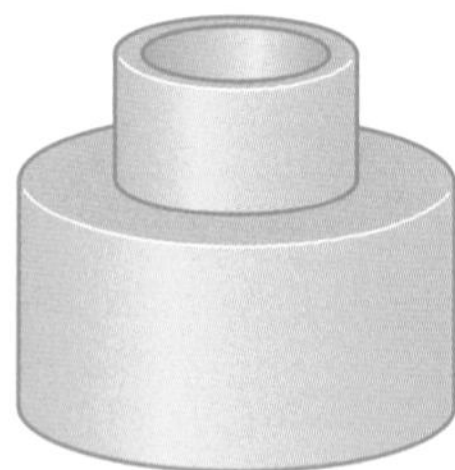

As the bottle is filled, the depth, d, of the liquid in the bottle changes.

Which of the four graphs below shows the change in depth?

A d Time

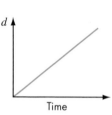

B d Time

C

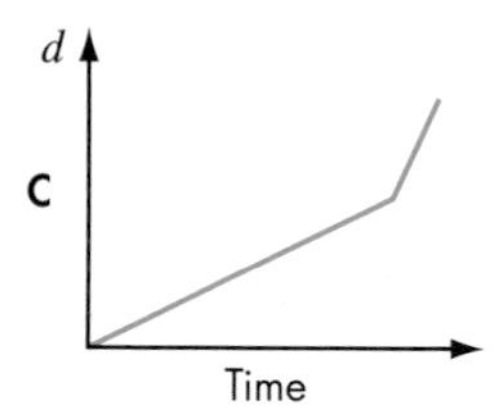

D d Time

b Liquid is poured at a steady rate into another container.

The graph shows how the depth, d, changes.

Sketch a picture of this container.

d Time

PS 2 Draw a graph of the depth of water in each of these containers as it is filled steadily.

a

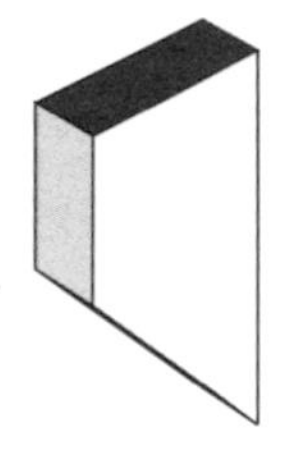

b

c

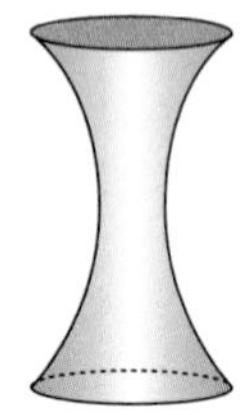

d

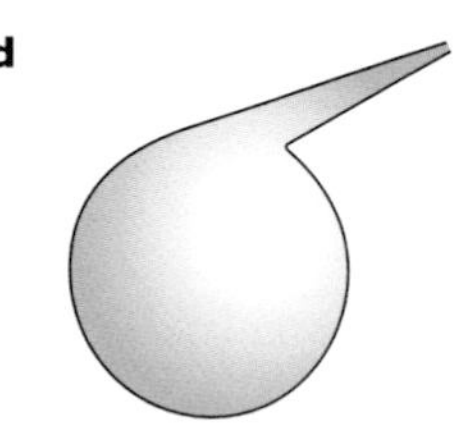

e

f

FM 3 The following is a simplified model of how income tax is calculated for an individual.

The first £5000 earned is tax free. Any income over £5000 up to £35 000 is taxed at 20%.

For example, a person who earns £20 000 per year would pay 20% of £15 000 i.e. £3000.

Any income over £35 000 is taxed at 40%.

Draw a graph to show the amount of tax paid by people who earn up to £50 000 per year.

Take the horizontal axis as 'income' from £0 to £50 000. Take the vertical axis as 'tax paid' from £0 to £12 000.

GRADE BOOSTER

D You can draw and read information from a distance–time graph

C You can calculate the gradient of a straight line and use this to find speed from a distance–time graph

B You can interpret real-life graphs

A You can interpret and draw more complex real-life graphs

What you should know now

- How to find the speed from a distance–time graph
- How to interpret real-life graphs

1 Mr Smith leaves home at 10 am to go to the shopping mall. He walks to the station where he catches a train. He gets off at the mall. The travel graph shows his journey.

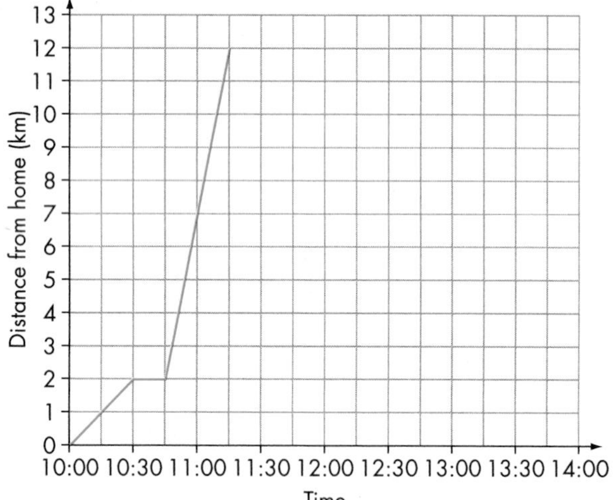

After shopping Mr Smith goes home by taxi. The taxi leaves the mall at 1 pm and arrives at his home at 1:45 pm.

a Complete the travel graph. *(2 marks)*

b Calculate the average speed of the taxi. *(2 marks)*

AQA, June 2005, Paper 2 (2-tier trial), Question 1

2 Kevin drove from Leeds to Luton.

The distance–time graph shows his journey.

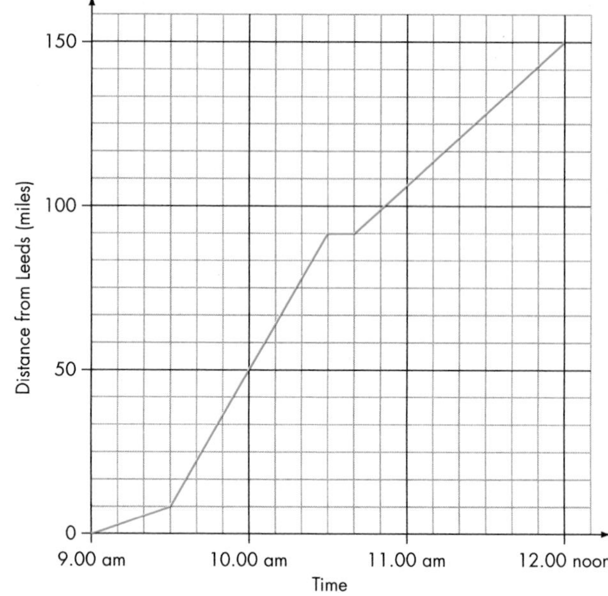

a How far is it from Leeds to Luton? *(1 mark)*

b Kevin stopped at a service station for petrol.

How long did he stop for? *(1 mark)*

c What was Kevin's average speed for the whole journey? *(2 marks)*

AQA, June 2008, Paper 2 Foundation, Question 20

3 A train travels from Glasgow to London in $4\frac{3}{4}$ hours. The distance travelled is 323 miles. Find the average speed of the train in miles per hour.

4 A motorbike drives from Sheffield to Plymouth. The journey is 468 kilometres in total. 372 kilometres are on motorway and 96 kilometres on normal roads. On normal roads the bike does 15 kilometres to a litre of petrol. In total the bike uses 25 litres of petrol on the journey. How many kilometres per litre does the bike do on average on motorways?

5 Grant and Mark race each other over two lengths of a 50 metre swimming pool.

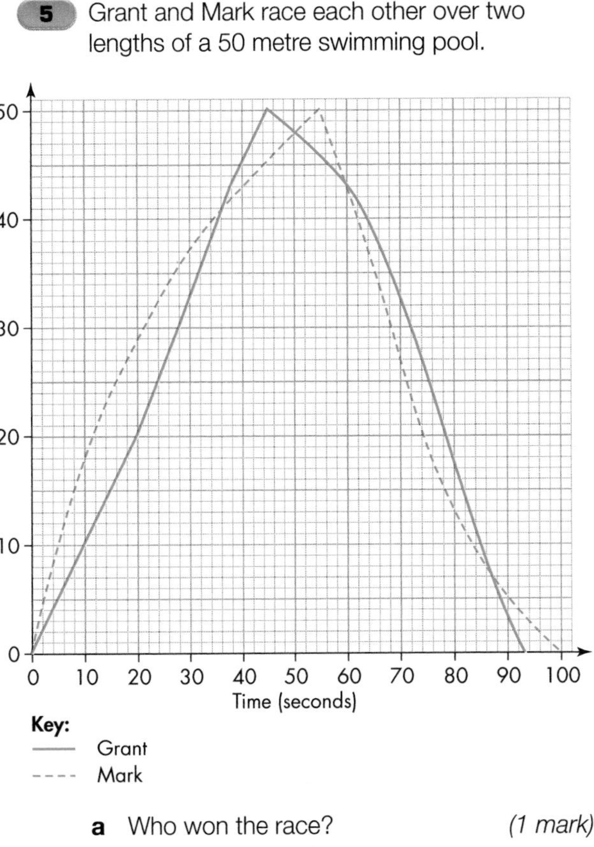

a Who won the race? *(1 mark)*

b What was the winning time? *(1 mark)*

c What was Grant's average speed during the first 30 seconds of the race? *(2 marks)*

d **i** Who was swimming faster at 60 seconds? *(1 mark)*

ii How can you tell from the graph? *(1 mark)*

AQA, November 2007, Paper 2 Intermediate, Question 10

6 A cyclist sets off on a ride over the moors at 9 am. The climb up to the highest point is 25 km. It takes the cyclist 1 hour 30 minutes to do this. She rests at the highest point for 15 minutes then sets off back. She arrives home at 11:45 am.

a Show this information on a travel graph with a horizontal axis showing time from 9 am to 12 pm and a vertical axis showing distance from home from 0 to 40 km. *(2 marks)*

b Calculate the average speed of the return journey in km per hour. *(2 marks)*

AQA, June 2005, Paper 2 Higher, Question 8

Worked Examination Questions

1 The distance–time graph shows the journey of a train between two stations. The stations are 6 km apart.

a During the journey the train stopped at a signal. For how long was the train stopped?

b What was the average speed of the train for the whole journey? Give your answer in kilometres per hour.

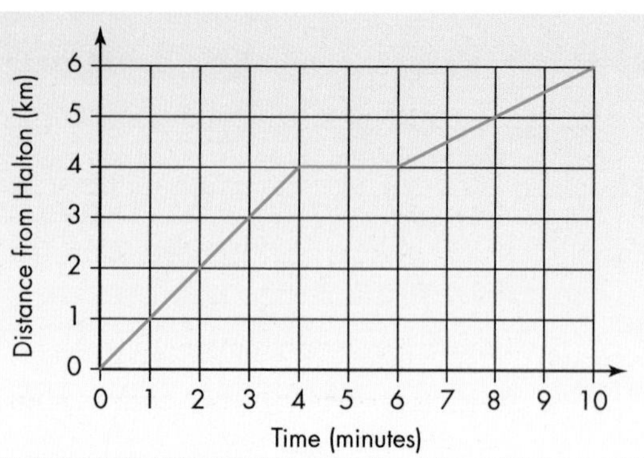

1 a *The train stopped for 2 minutes (where the line is horizontal).*

This gets 1 mark.

b *The train travels 6 km in 10 minutes.*
This is 36 km in 60 minutes.
So the average speed is 36 km/h.

Multiply both numbers by 6. This gets 1 mark for writing down any distance and an equivalent time, and 1 mark for the answer.

Total: 3 marks

FM **2** The graph shows the increase in rail fares as a percentage of the fares in 1997 since the railways were privatised in 1997.

a In what year did first-class fares double in price from 1997?

b Approximately how much would a regulated standard-class fare that cost £20 in 1997 cost in 2002?

c Approximately how much would a first-class fare that cost £100 in 1997 cost in 2010?

d During which period did first-class fares rise the most? How can you tell?

e An unregulated standard-class fare cost £35 in 2008. Approximately how much would this fare have been in 1997?

2 a *2007*

Read when the fares were 200%. This gets 1 mark for method.

b *£22.50*

Read the percentage increase in 2002 and multiply the fare by this figure (about 12.5%). This gets 1 mark for method and 1 mark for accuracy.

c *£245*

Read the percentage increase in 2010. This gets 1 mark for method.

d *2005–2010*

This is the steepest part of the graph. This gets 1 mark.

e *£20*

Unregulated fares have gone up by 75%. 75% of £20 is £15. This gets 1 mark for accuracy.

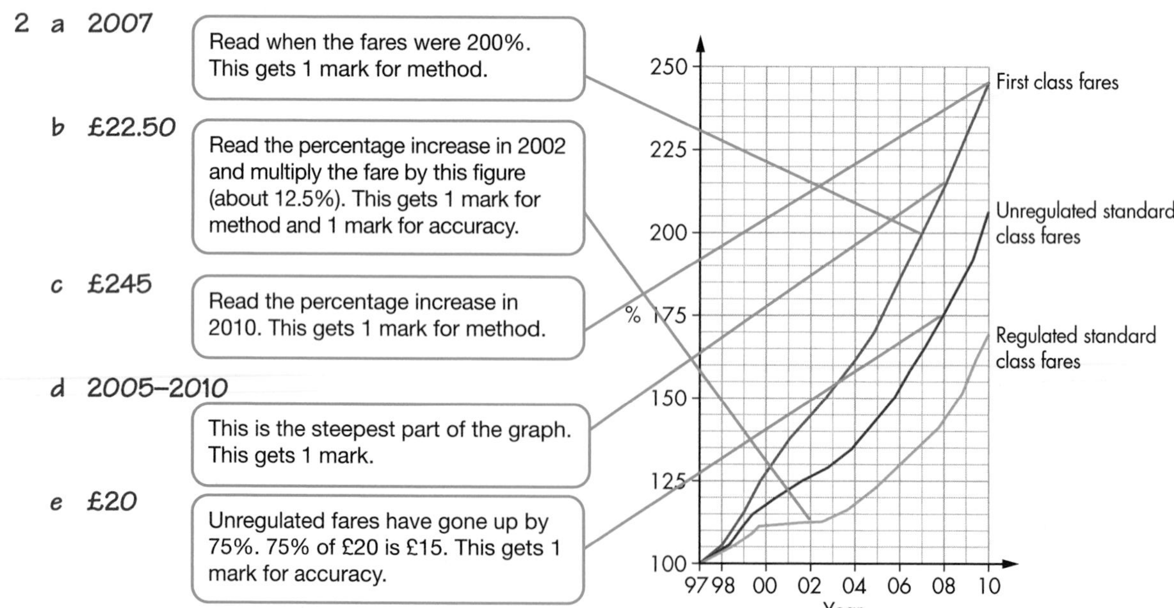

Total: 6 marks

Worked Examination Questions

PS **3** A cyclist sets off at midday from a point P and cycles at a steady speed of 20 km/h for 90 minutes. She then rests for 30 minutes and continues at a steady speed of 15 km/h.

A car sets off from P on the same road. The car drives at a steady speed of 45 km/h and overtakes the cyclist at 4 pm.

What time did the car set off from P?

You may use a copy of the axes shown here to help you with your answer.

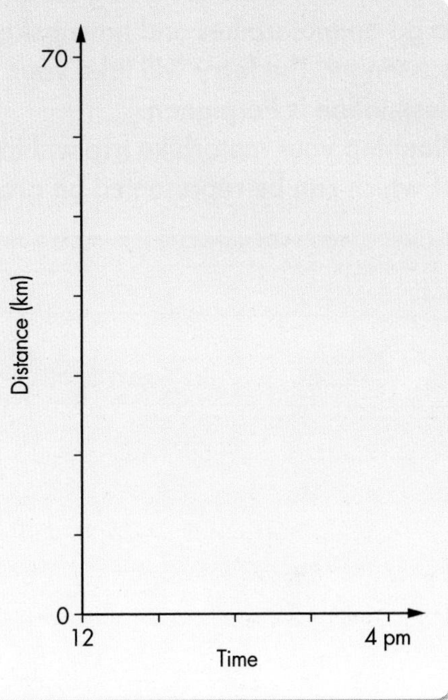

3 Line from (12, 0) to (1.30, 30)

Line from (1.30, 30) to (2, 30)

Line from (2, 30) to (4, 60)

60 km ÷ 45 km/hour = 1 h 20 m

Line from (4, 60) with a gradient of 45 km/h.

4pm – 1 h 20 m = 2.40 pm

> Draw a distance–time graph of the cyclist's journey. This gets 1 mark for method and 1 mark for accuracy.

> There are two methods to calculate the time it takes the car to overtake the cyclist. Either is OK. This gets 1 mark for method.

> Work out the time the motorist set off. This gets 1 mark for accuracy.

Total: 4 marks

Functional Maths
Planning a motorbike trip to France

A group of friends are going on a holiday to France. They have decided to go on motorbikes and have asked you to join them as a pillion passenger. The ferry will take your group to Boulogne and the destination is Perpignan.
Planning your motorbike trip will involve a range of mathematics, much of which can be represented on graphs.

Your task

The following task will require you to work in groups of 2–3.

Using all the information that you gather from these pages and your own knowledge, investigate the key mathematical elements of your motorbike trip.

Remember, sometimes events outside our control can change our travel plans. Take the following scenarios into account when planning your motorbike trip.

There is a problem at the ferry port and you must use the Channel Tunnel instead.

Just prior to travelling, the British pound drops against the euro, giving a new exchange rate of 1 euro to 98p.

One friend would like to extend the trip to Barcelona.

You must draw at least three graphs and use as many different mathematical methods as possible when drawing up your final travel plans and your contingency recommendations.

Getting started

Start by thinking about the mathematics that you use when you go on holiday. Here are a few questions to get you going.

- What information do you need before you travel?
- How many euros (€) are there in one British pound (£)?
- What differences might you find when you travel abroad?
- What are the differences between metric and imperial units of measure? (It may help to list the conversion facts that you know.)
- After approximately how long would you need to stop to rest when travelling?

Handy hints

There are a number of measures and units in France that will need converting when you get there. Two of the most noticeable are:

- **Currency:** in France the currency is in euros.
- **Distances:** in France, distances are measured in kilometres, so speeds are in kilometres per hour.

1 euro ≈ £0.90

1 gallon ≈ 4 litres

1 mile ≈ 1.6 km

A motorbike fuel tank holds 3 gallons and travels about 45 miles per gallon.

The cost of petrol in France is €1.2 per litre.

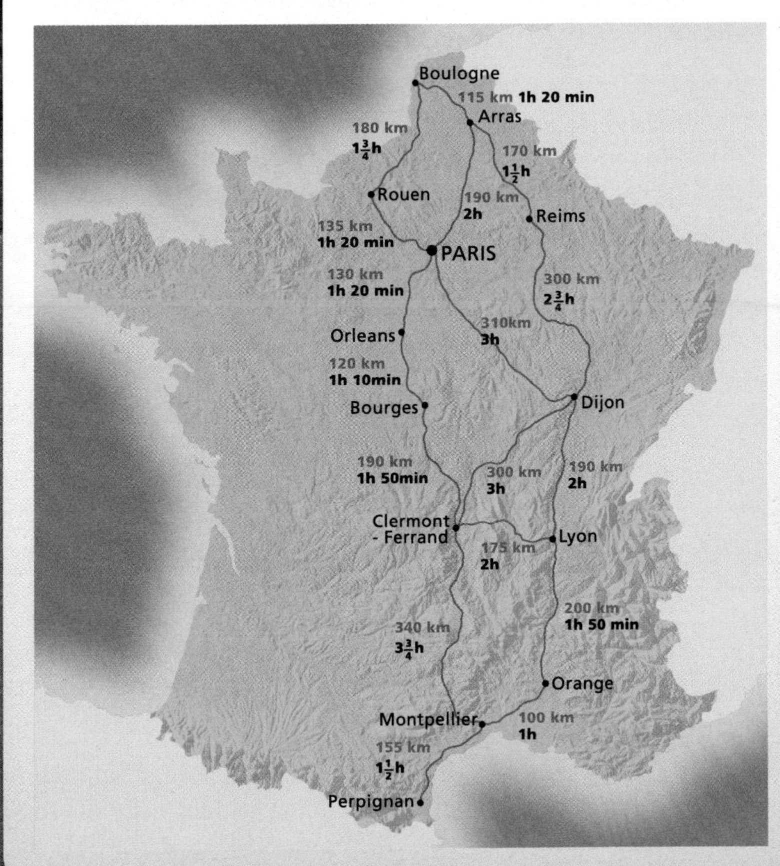

Why this chapter matters

A famous saying is 'A picture is worth a thousand words' and graphs in mathematics are worth many lines of algebra as they are a visual way of showing the relationship between two variables. This chapter deals with linear graphs, which are straight line graphs. You will meet many different types of non-linear graphs in later chapters.

Many years ago the city of Konigsberg (now known as Kalingrad) had seven bridges joining the four separate parts of the city.

The citizens had a challenge to see if anyone could walk across all seven bridges without crossing any of them twice.

The problem is the same as trying to draw this diagram without taking your pencil off the paper.

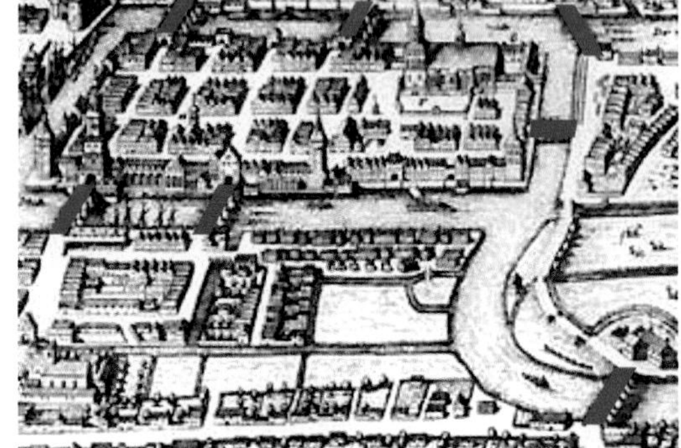

Bridges of Konigsberg

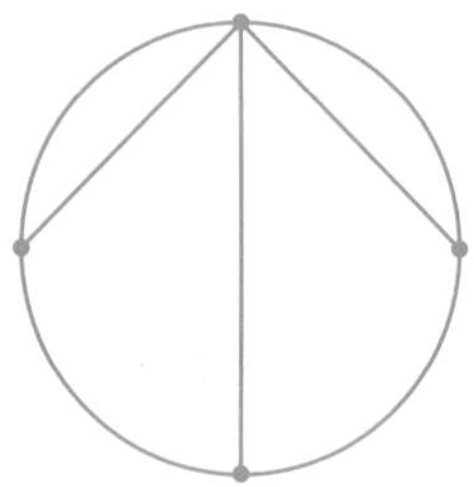

Copy the diagram and see if it can be done.

Like the citizens of Konigsberg and their problem with the bridges, you will find that it is impossible.

This problem was investigated by the Swiss mathematician Leonard Euler (1707–1783).

Leonard Euler

He proved that it was not possible and started a new branch of mathematics called 'Graph theory'. This is not the same as the study of linear graphs, but is more concerned with where lines meet (vertices) and the lines joining them (arcs).

Copy the following diagrams and see if you can draw any of them without taking your pencil off the paper.

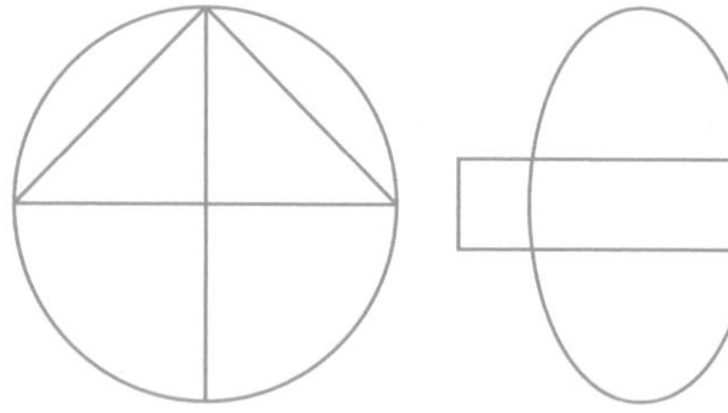

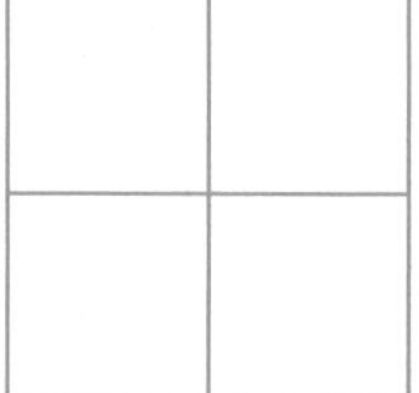

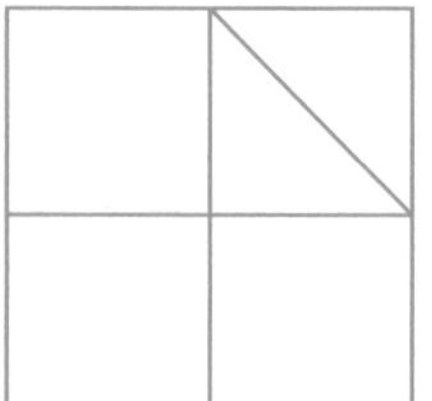

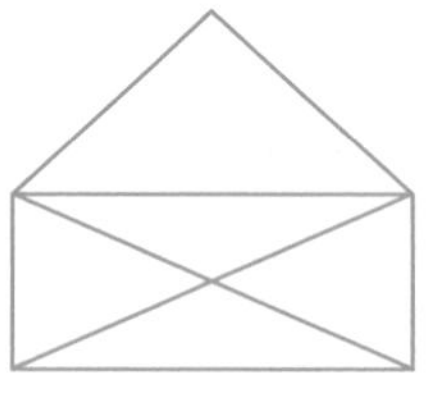

There is a way of telling if this can be done, which you can investigate at the end of this chapter.

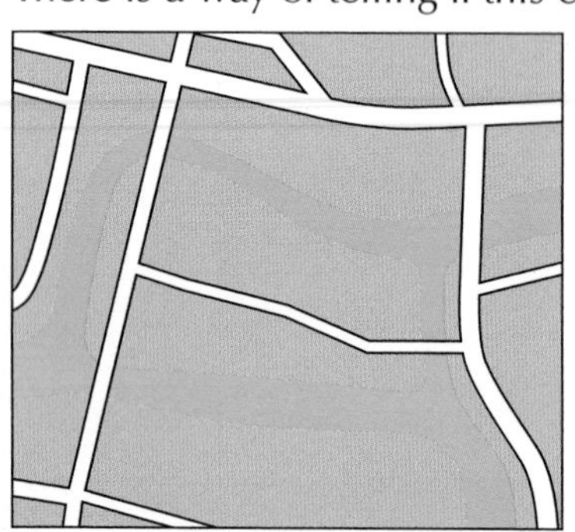

Layout of Kalingrad

In the Second World War, Konigsberg was badly damaged and many of the bridges were destroyed. This is a rough layout of Kalingrad (Konigsberg) as it is today:

Can you trace a route, starting from the island, that crosses all the remaining bridges without crossing a bridge twice?

Chapter 12 Algebra: Linear graphs and equations

This chapter will show you ...

- **C** how to draw graphs of linear equations
- **C** how to use graphs to find the solution to linear equations
- **B** how to find the equation of a linear graph
- **B** how to use graphs to find exact or approximate solutions to simultaneous equations

Visual overview

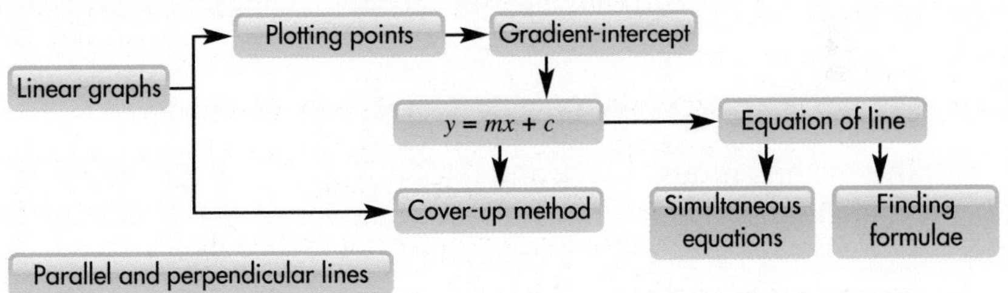

What you should already know

- How to read and plot coordinates **(KS3 level 4, GCSE grade F)**
- How to substitute into simple algebraic functions **(KS3 level 4, GCSE grade F)**
- How to plot a graph from a given table of values **(KS3 level 5, GCSE grade E)**

Quick check

1 This table shows values of $y = 2x + 3$ for $-2 \leqslant x \leqslant 5$.

x	−2	−1	0	1	2	3	4	5
y	−1	1	3	5	7	9	11	

a Complete the table for $x = 5$.

b Copy these axes and plot the points to draw the graph of $y = 2x + 3$.

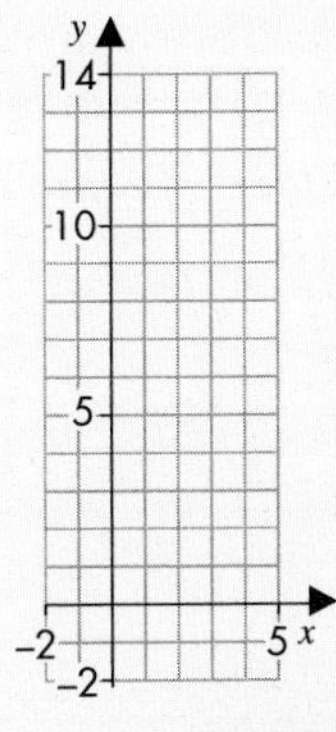

12.1 Linear graphs

This section will show you how to:
- draw linear graphs without using flow diagrams

Key words
axis (pl: axes)
linear graphs
scale

This chapter is concerned with drawing straight-line graphs. These are usually referred to as **linear graphs**.

The minimum number of points needed to draw a linear graph is two but it is better to use three or more because that gives at least one point to act as a check. There is no rule about how many points to plot but here are some tips.

- Use a sharp pencil and mark each point with an accurate cross.
- Position yourself so that your eyes are directly over the graph. If you look from the side, you will not be able to line up your ruler accurately.

Drawing graphs by finding points

This method is quite quick and does not need flow diagrams. However, if you prefer flow diagrams, use them. Work through Example 1 to see how to draw a graph by finding points.

EXAMPLE 1

Draw the graph of $y = 4x - 5$ for values of x from 0 to 5. This is usually written as $0 \leqslant x \leqslant 5$.

Choose three values for x: these should be the highest and lowest x-values and one in between.

Work out the y-values by substituting the x-values into the equation.

When $x = 0$, $y = 4(0) - 5 = -5$. This gives the point $(0, -5)$.
When $x = 3$, $y = 4(3) - 5 = 7$. This gives the point $(3, 7)$.
When $x = 5$, $y = 4(5) - 5 = 15$. This gives the point $(5, 15)$.

Keep a record of your calculations in a table. You now have to decide the extent (range) of the **axes**. You can find this out by looking at the coordinates that you have so far.
The smallest x-value is 0, the largest is 5.
The smallest y-value is -5, the largest is 15.

x	0	3	5
y	–5	7	15

Now draw the axes, plot the points and complete the graph.
It is usually a good idea to choose 0 as one of the x-values.
In an examination, the range for the x-values will usually be given and the axes already drawn.

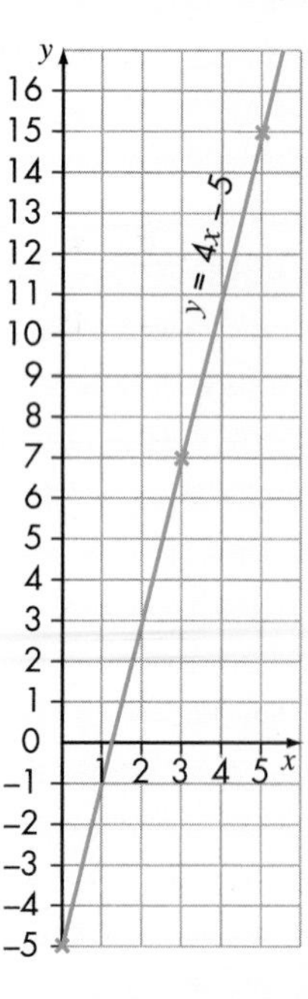

Read through these hints before drawing the linear graphs required in Exercise 12A.

- Use the highest and lowest values of x given in the range.
- Don't pick x-values that are too close together, for example, 1 and 2. Try to space them out so that you can draw a more accurate graph.
- Always label your graph with its equation. This is particularly important when you are drawing two graphs on the same set of axes.
- If you want to use a flow diagram, use one.
- Create a table of values. You will often have to complete these in your examinations.

EXERCISE 12A

D

1 Draw the graph of $y = 3x + 4$ for x-values from 0 to 5 ($0 \leqslant x \leqslant 5$).

2 Draw the graph of $y = 2x - 5$ for $0 \leqslant x \leqslant 5$.

3 Draw the graph of $y = \frac{x}{2} - 3$ for $0 \leqslant x \leqslant 10$.

4 Draw the graph of $y = 3x + 5$ for $-3 \leqslant x \leqslant 3$.

5 Draw the graph of $y = \frac{x}{3} + 4$ for $-6 \leqslant x \leqslant 6$.

6 **a** On the same set of axes, draw the graphs of $y = 3x - 2$ and $y = 2x + 1$ for $0 \leqslant x \leqslant 5$.

b At which point do the two lines intersect?

7 **a** On the same axes, draw the graphs of $y = 4x - 5$ and $y = 2x + 3$ for $0 \leqslant x \leqslant 5$.

b At which point do the two lines intersect?

8 **a** On the same axes, draw the graphs of $y = \frac{x}{3} - 1$ and $y = \frac{x}{2} - 2$ for $0 \leqslant x \leqslant 12$.

b At which point do the two lines intersect?

9 **a** On the same axes, draw the graphs of $y = 3x + 1$ and $y = 3x - 2$ for $0 \leqslant x \leqslant 4$.

b Do the two lines intersect? If not, why not?

10 **a** Copy and complete the table to draw the graph of $x + y = 5$ for $0 \leqslant x \leqslant 5$.

x	0	1	2	3	4	5
y	5		3		1	

b Now draw the graph of $x + y = 7$ for $0 \leqslant x \leqslant 7$ on the same axes.

D

11 Ian the electrician used this formula to work out how much to charge for a job:

$C = 25 + 30H$

where C is the charge and H is how long the job takes.

John the electrician uses this formula:

$C = 35 + 27.5H$

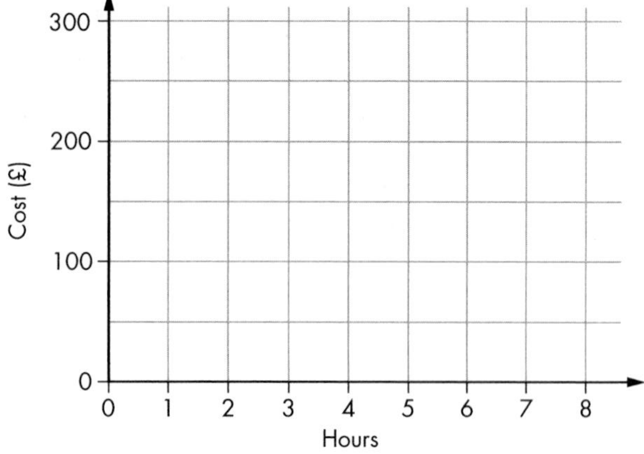

a On a copy of the grid, draw lines to represent these formulae.

FM **b** Who would you hire for a job that takes 2 hours?

C

AU **12** **a** Draw the graphs $y = 4$, $y = x$ and $x = 1$ on a copy of the grid shown on the right.

b What is the area of the triangle formed by the three lines?

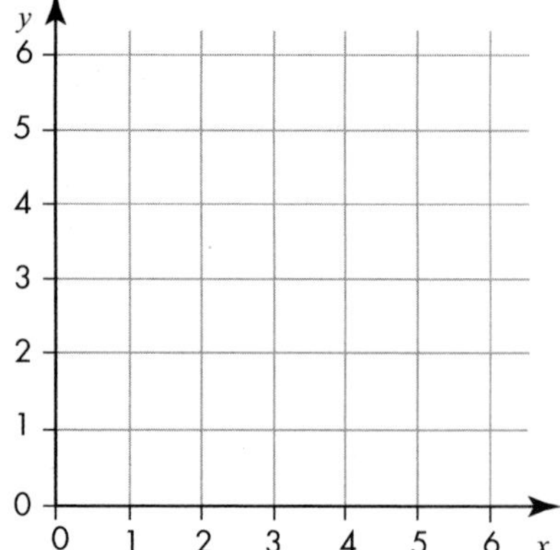

PS **13** These two graphs show y against x and y against z.

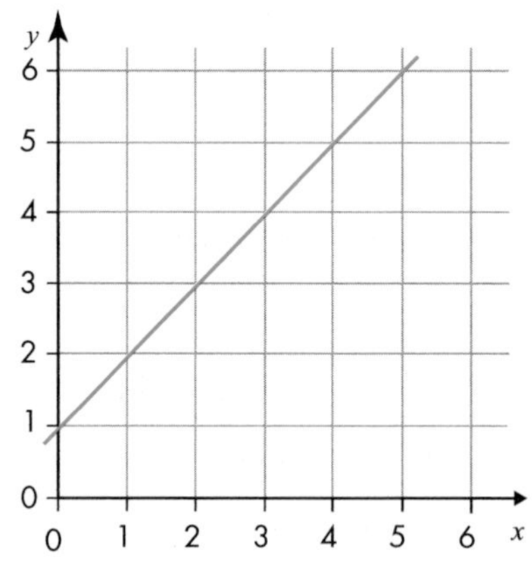

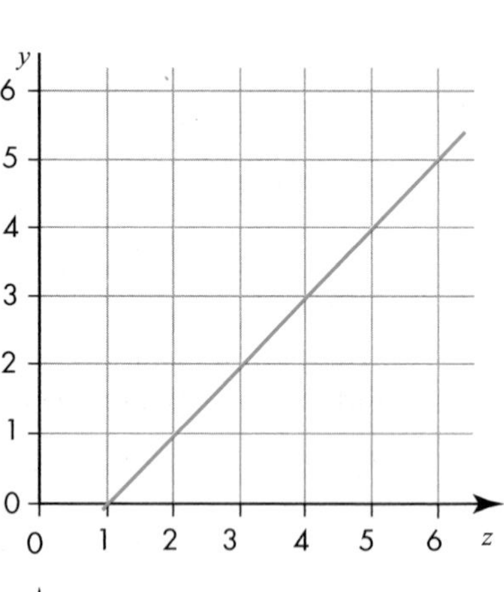

On a copy of this blank grid, show the graph of x against z.

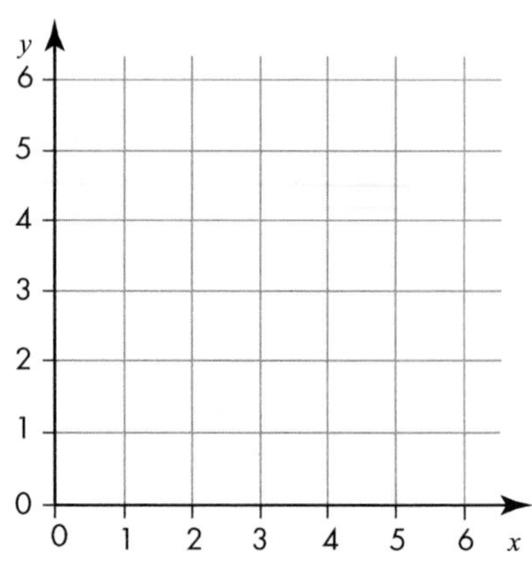

Gradient

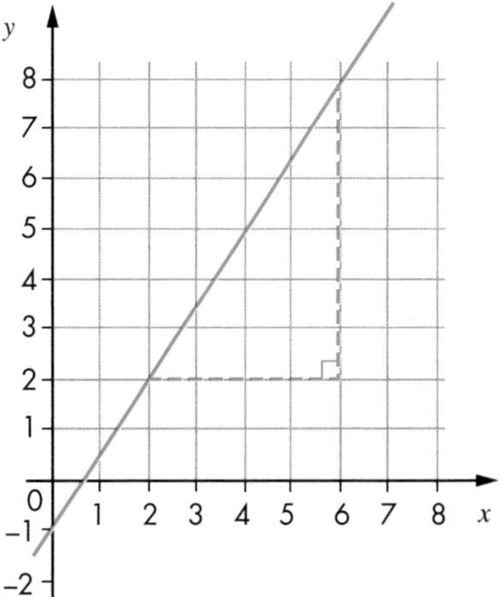

The slope of a line is called its gradient. The steeper the slope of the line, the larger the value of the gradient.

The gradient of the line shown here can be measured by drawing, as large as possible, a right-angled triangle that has part of the line as its hypotenuse (sloping side). The gradient is then given by:

$$\text{gradient} = \frac{\text{distance measured up}}{\text{distance measured along}}$$

$$= \frac{\text{difference on } y\text{-axis}}{\text{difference on } x\text{-axis}}$$

For example, to measure the steepness of the line in the next figure, you first draw a right-angled triangle of which the hypotenuse is part of this line. It does not matter where you draw the triangle but it makes the calculations much easier if you choose a sensible place. This usually means using existing grid lines, so that you avoid fractional values.

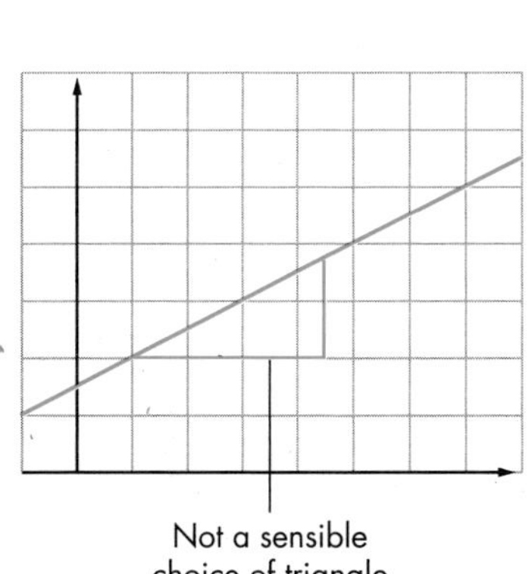

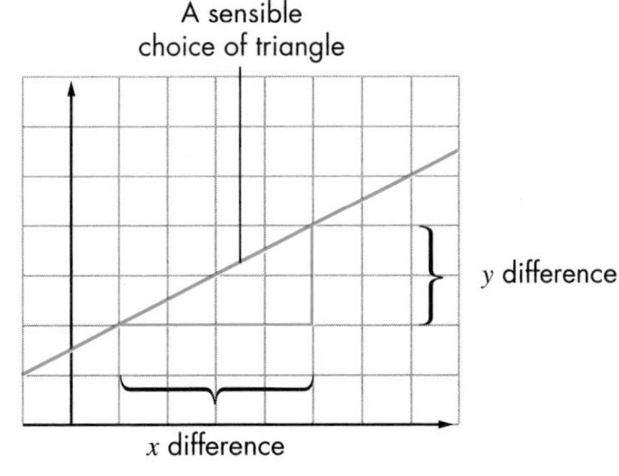

After you have drawn the triangle, you measure (or count) how many squares there are on the vertical side. This is the difference between your y-coordinates. In the case above, this is 2.

You then measure (or count) how many squares there are on the horizontal side. This is the difference between your x-coordinates. In the case above, this is 4.

To work out the gradient, you do the following calculation.

$$\text{gradient} = \frac{\text{difference of the } y\text{-coordinates}}{\text{difference of the } x\text{-coordinates}} = \frac{2}{4} = \frac{1}{2} \text{ or } 0.5$$

Note that the value of the gradient is not affected by where the triangle is drawn. As you are calculating the ratio of two sides of the triangle, the gradient will always be the same wherever you draw the triangle.

You can use the method of counting squares in cases like this, where the **scale** is one square to one unit.

Remember: When a line slopes down from left to right, the gradient is negative, so you must place a minus sign in front of the calculated fraction.

EXAMPLE 2

Find the gradient of each of these lines.

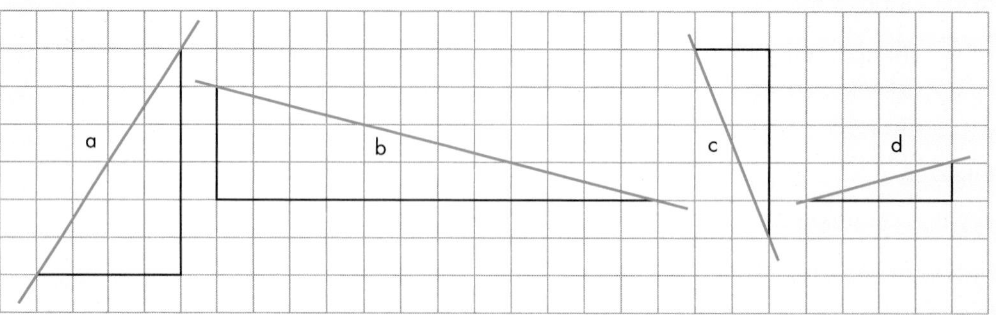

In each case, a sensible choice of triangle has already been made.

a y difference = 6, x difference = 4 Gradient $= 6 \div 4 = \frac{3}{2} = 1.5$

b y difference = 3, x difference = 12 Line slopes down from left to right, so gradient $= -(3 \div 12) = -\frac{1}{4} = -0.25$

c y difference = 5, x difference = 2 Line slopes down from left to right, so gradient $= -(5 \div 2) = -\frac{5}{2} = -2.5$

d y difference = 1, x difference = 4 Gradient $= 1 \div 4 = \frac{1}{4} = 0.25$

Drawing a line with a certain gradient

To draw a line with a certain gradient, you reverse the process described above. That is, you first draw the right-angled triangle, using the given gradient. For example, take a gradient of 2.

Start at a convenient point (A in the diagrams below). A gradient of 2 means that for an x-step of 1 the y-step must be 2 (because 2 is the fraction $\frac{2}{1}$). So, move one square across and two squares up, and mark a dot.

Repeat this as many times as you like and draw the line. You can also move one square back and two squares down, which gives the same gradient, as the third diagram shows.

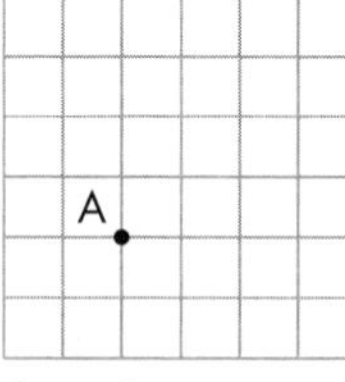

Stage 1

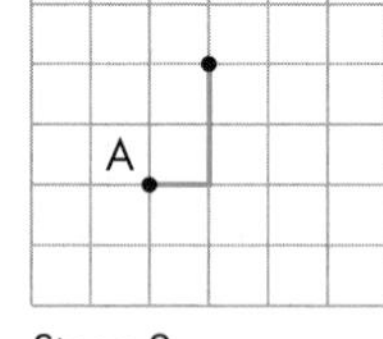

Stage 2

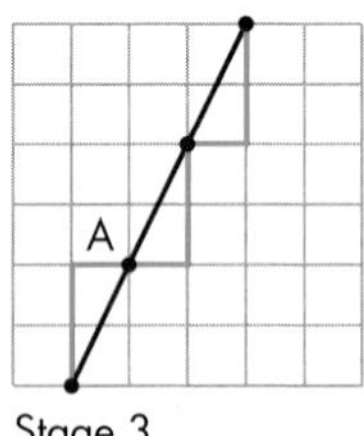

Stage 3

EXAMPLE 3

Draw lines with these gradients. **a** $\frac{1}{3}$ **b** -3 **c** $-\frac{1}{4}$

a This is a fractional gradient which has a y-step of 1 and an x-step of 3. Move three squares across and one square up every time.

b This is a negative gradient, so for every one square across, move three squares down.

c This is also a negative gradient and it is a fraction. So for every four squares across, move one square down.

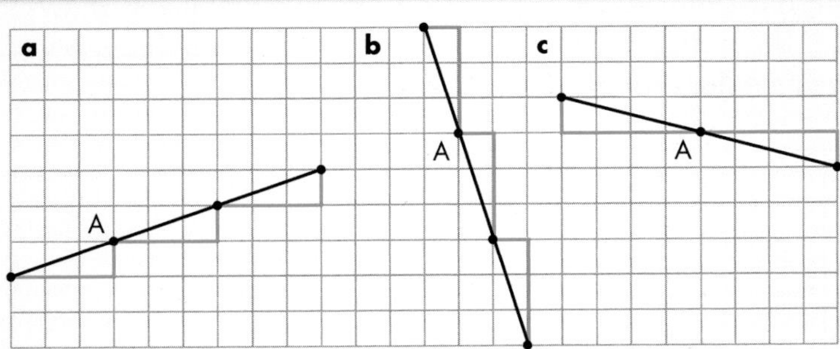

EXERCISE 12B

1 Find the gradient of each of these lines.

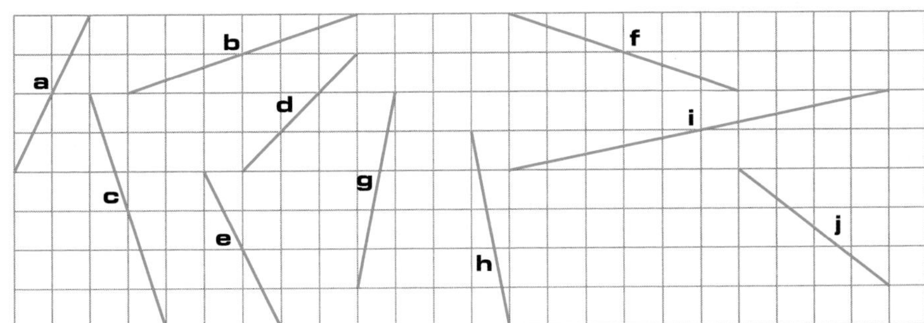

2 Draw lines with these gradients.

a 4 **b** $\frac{2}{3}$ **c** –2 **d** $-\frac{4}{5}$ **e** 6 **f** –6

3 Find the gradient of each of these lines. What is special about these lines?

a

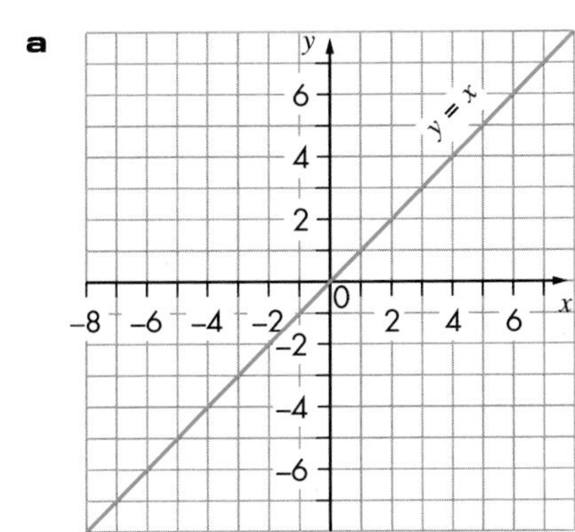

b

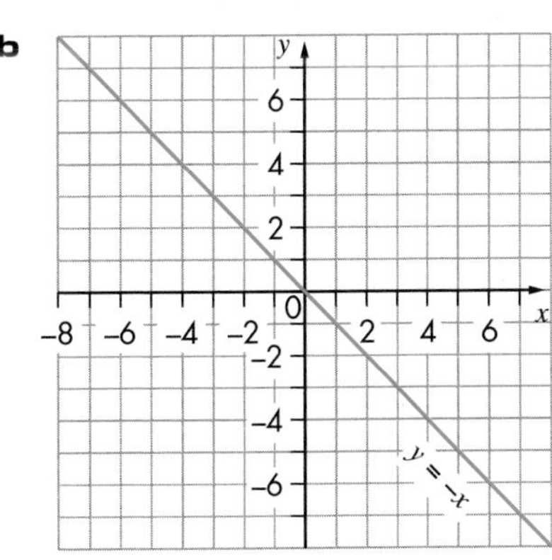

C

FM 4 This graph shows the profile of a fell race. The horizontal axis shows the distance, in miles, of the race. The vertical axis is the height above sea level throughout the race. There are 5280 feet in a mile.

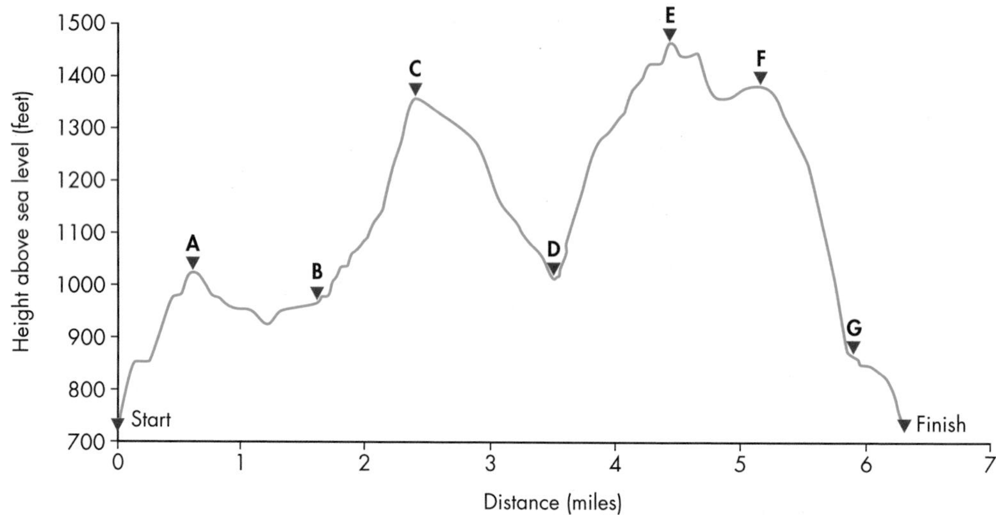

a Work out the approximate gradient of the race from the start to point A.

b The steepest part of the race is from F to G.

  i How can you tell this from the graph?

  ii Work out the approximate gradient from F to G.

c Fell races are classified in terms of distance and amount of ascent.

Distance:	Short (S)	Less than 6 miles
	Medium (M)	Between 6 and 12 miles
	Long (L)	Over 12 miles
Ascent	C	An average of 100 to 125 feet per mile
	B	An average of 125 to 250 feet per mile
	A	An average of 250 or more feet per mile

So, for example, an AL race would be over 12 miles and have at least 250 feet of ascent, on average, per mile.

What category is the race above?

5 The line on grid **e** is horizontal. The lines on grids **a** to **d** get nearer and nearer to the horizontal.

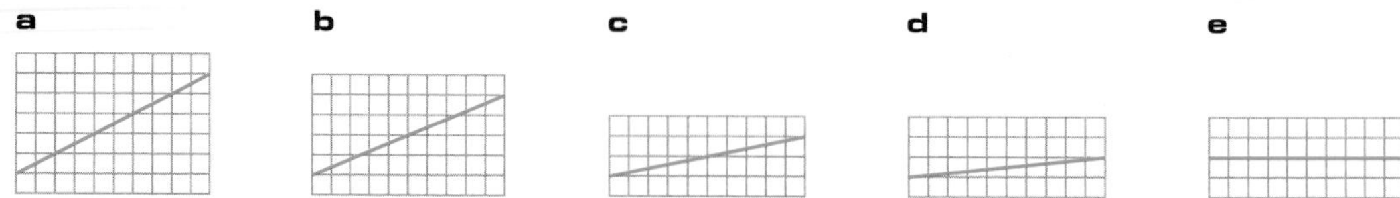

Find the gradient of each line in grids **a** to **d**. By looking at the values you obtain, what do you think the gradient of a horizontal line is?

6 The line on grid **e** is vertical. The lines on grids **a** to **d** get nearer and nearer to the vertical.

a **b** **c** **d** **e**

Find the gradient of each line in grids **a** to **d**. By looking at the values you obtain, what do you think the gradient of a vertical line is?

AU 7 Raisa says the gradients of these two lines are the same.

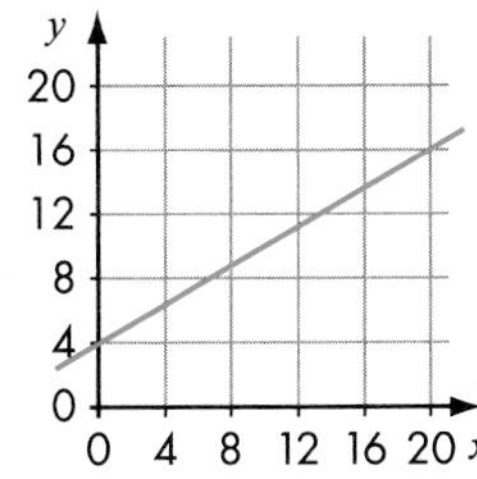

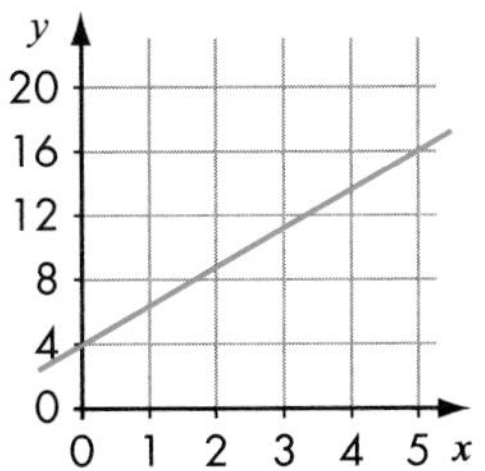

Why is Raisa wrong?

PS 8 Put the following gradients in order of steepness, starting with the shallowest.

1 horizontal, 2 vertical 2 horizontal, 5 vertical 3 horizontal, 5 vertical
4 horizontal, 6 vertical 5 horizontal, 8 vertical 6 horizontal, 11 vertical

12.2 Drawing graphs by the gradient-intercept method

This section will show you how to:

- draw graphs using the gradient-intercept method

Key words
coefficient
constant term
cover-up method
gradient-intercept
$y = mx + c$

The ideas that you have discovered in the last activity lead to another way of plotting lines, known as the **gradient-intercept** method.

EXAMPLE 4

Draw the graph of $y = 3x - 1$, using the gradient-intercept method.

- Because the **constant term** is –1, you know that the graph goes through the y-axis at –1. Mark this point with a dot or a cross (**A** on diagram **i**).
- The number in front of x (called the **coefficient** of x) gives the relationship between y and x. 3 is the coefficient of x and this tells you that the y-value is 3 times the x-value, so the gradient of the line is 3. For an x-step of one unit, there is a y-step of three. Starting at –1 on the y-axis, move one square across and three squares up and mark this point with a dot or a cross (**B** on diagram **i**).

Repeat this from every new point. You can also move one square back and three squares down. When enough points have been marked, join the dots (or crosses) to make the graph (diagram **ii**). Note that if the points are not in a straight line, you have made a mistake.

i

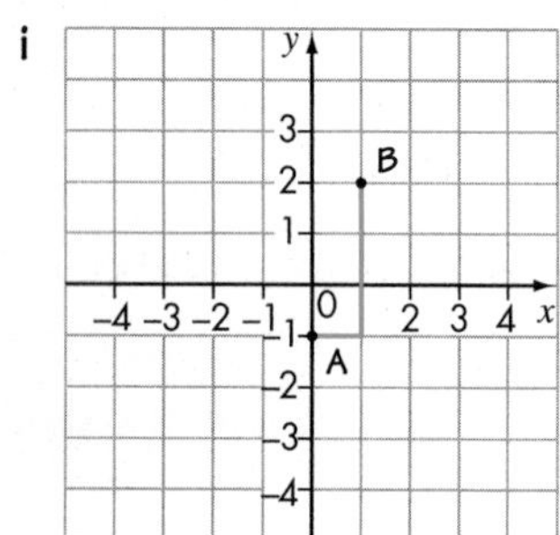

ii

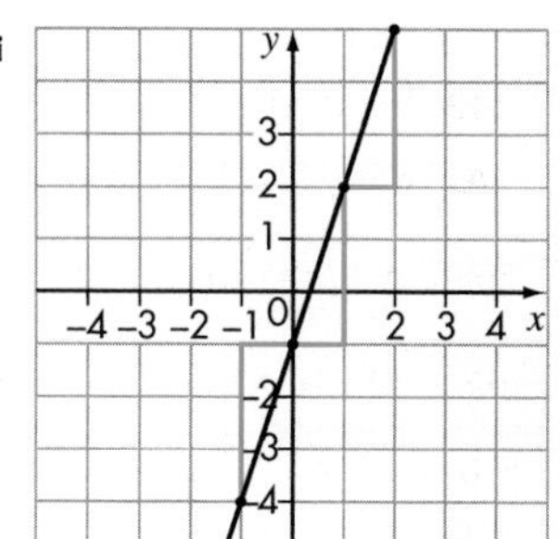

In any equation of the focus $\boldsymbol{y = mx + c}$, the constant term, c, is the intercept on the y-axis and the coefficient of x, m, is the gradient of the line.

EXERCISE 12C

C

1 Draw these lines, using the gradient-intercept method. Use the same grid, taking x from –10 to 10 and y from –10 to 10. If the grid gets too 'crowded', draw another one.

a $y = 2x + 6$ **b** $y = 3x - 4$ **c** $y = \frac{1}{2}x + 5$

d $y = x + 7$ **e** $y = 4x - 3$ **f** $y = 2x - 7$

g $y = \frac{1}{4}x - 3$ **h** $y = \frac{2}{3}x + 4$ **i** $y = 6x - 5$

j $y = x + 8$ **k** $y = \frac{4}{5}x - 2$ **l** $y = 3x - 9$

2 **a** Using the gradient-intercept method, draw the following lines on the same grid. Use axes with ranges $-6 \leqslant x \leqslant 6$ and $-8 \leqslant y \leqslant 8$.

i $y = 3x + 1$ **ii** $y = 2x + 3$

b Where do the lines cross?

C

3 **a** Using the gradient-intercept method, draw the following lines on the same grid. Use axes with ranges $-14 \leqslant x \leqslant 4$ and $-2 \leqslant y \leqslant 6$.

i $y = \frac{x}{3} + 3$

ii $y = \frac{x}{4} + 2$

b Where do the lines cross?

4 **a** Using the gradient-intercept method, draw the following lines on the same grid. Use axes with ranges $-4 \leqslant x \leqslant 6$ and $-6 \leqslant y \leqslant 8$.

i $y = x + 3$

ii $y = 2x$

b Where do the lines cross?

AU 5 Here are the equations of three lines.

A: $y = 3x - 1$ B: $2y = 6x - 4$ C: $y = 2x - 2$

a State a mathematical property that lines A and B have in common.

b State a mathematical property that lines B and C have in common.

c Which of the following points is the intersection of lines A and C?

(1, –4) (–1, –4) (1, 4)

B

PS 6 **a** What is the gradient of line A?

b What is the gradient of line B?

c What angle is there between lines A and B?

d What relationship do the gradients of A and B have with each other?

e Another line C has a gradient of 3.

What is the gradient of a line perpendicular to C?

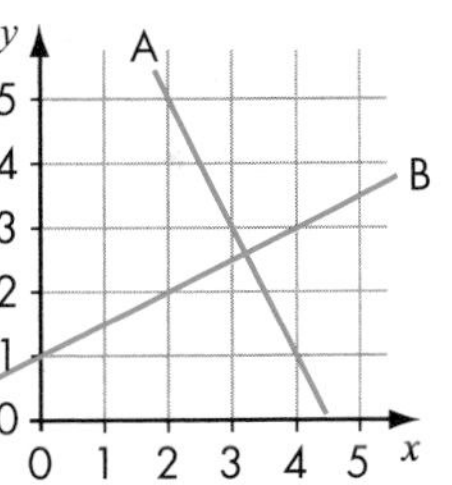

Cover-up method for drawing graphs

The x-axis has the equation $y = 0$. This means that all points on the x-axis have a y-value of 0.

The y-axis has the equation $x = 0$. This means that all points on the y-axis have an x-value of 0.

You can use these facts to draw any line that has an equation of the form:

$$ax + by = c$$

EXAMPLE 5

Draw the graph of $4x + 5y = 20$.

Because the value of x is 0 on the y-axis, you can solve the equation for y:

$$4(0) + 5y = 20$$
$$5y = 20$$
$$\Rightarrow y = 4$$

Hence, the line passes through the point (0, 4) on the y-axis (diagram **A**).

Because the value of y is 0 on the x-axis, you can also solve the equation for x:

$$4x + 5(0) = 20$$
$$4x = 20$$
$$\Rightarrow x = 5$$

Hence, the line passes through the point (5, 0) on the x-axis (diagram **B**). You need only two points to draw a line. (Normally, you would like a third point but in this case you can accept two.) Draw the graph by joining the points (0, 4) and (5, 0) (diagram **C**).

A
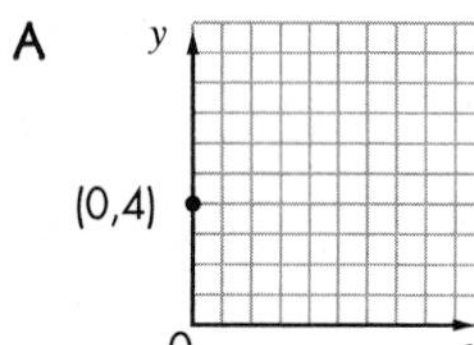

B
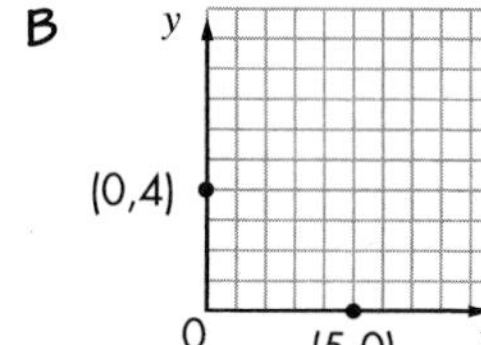

C
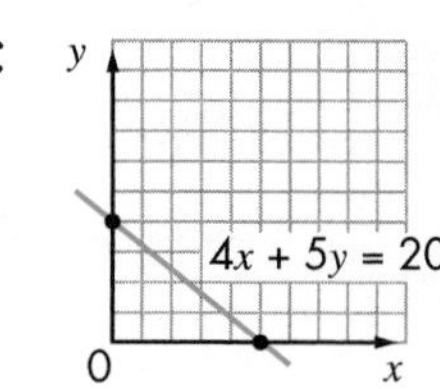

This type of equation can be drawn very easily, without much working at all, using the **cover-up method**.

Start with the equation:	$4x + 5y = 20$
Cover up the x-term:	$\square + 5y = 20$
Solve the equation (when $x = 0$):	$y = 4$
Now cover up the y-term:	$4x + \square = 20$
Solve the equation (when $y = 0$):	$x = 5$

This gives the points (0, 4) on the y-axis and (5, 0) on the x-axis.

EXAMPLE 6

Draw the graph of $2x - 3y = 12$.

Start with the equation:	$2x - 3y = 12$
Cover up the x-term:	$\square - 3y = 12$
Solve the equation (when $x = 0$):	$y = -4$
Now cover up the y-term:	$2x +$  $=12$
Solve the equation (when $y = 0$):	$x = 6$

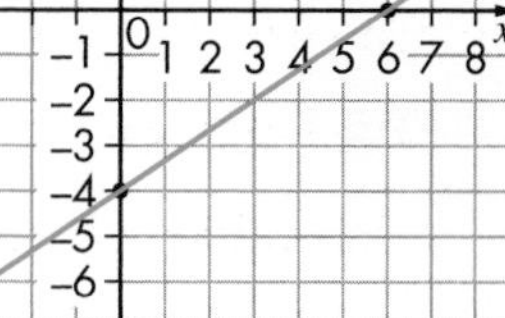

This gives the points (0, –4) on the y-axis and (6, 0) on the x-axis.

EXERCISE 12D

B

1 Draw these lines using the cover-up method. Use the same grid, taking x from –10 to 10 and y from –10 to 10. If the grid gets too 'crowded', draw another.

a $3x + 2y = 6$ **b** $4x + 3y = 12$ **c** $4x - 5y = 20$

d $x + y = 10$ **e** $3x - 2y = 18$ **f** $x - y = 4$

g $5x - 2y = 15$ **h** $2x - 3y = 15$ **i** $6x + 5y = 30$

j $x + y = -5$ **k** $x + y = 3$ **l** $x - y = -4$

2 **a** Using the cover-up method, draw the following lines on the same grid. Use axes with ranges $-2 \leqslant x \leqslant 6$ and $-2 \leqslant y \leqslant 6$.

i $2x + y = 4$

ii $x - 2y = 2$

b Where do the lines cross?

3 **a** Using the cover-up method, draw the following lines on the same grid.

Use axes with ranges $-2 < x < 6$ and $-3 < y < 6$.

i $x + 2y = 6$

ii $2x - y = 2$

b Where do the lines cross?

4 **a** Using the cover-up method, draw the following lines on the same grid.

Use axes with ranges $-6 \leqslant x \leqslant 8$ and $-2 \leqslant y \leqslant 8$.

i $x + y = 6$

ii $x - y = 2$

b Where do the lines cross?

AU **5** Here are the equations of three lines.

A: $2x + 6y = 12$ B: $x - 2y = 6$ C: $x + 3y = -9$

a State a mathematical property that lines A and B have in common.

b State a mathematical property that lines B and C have in common.

c State a mathematical property that lines A and C have in common.

d The line A crosses the y-axis at (0, 2).

The line C crosses the x-axis at (–9, 0).

Find values of a and b so that this line passes through these two points.

$ax + by = 18$

B

PS 6 The diagram shows an octagon ABCDEFGH.

The equation of the line through A and B is $y = 3$.

The equation of the line through B and C is $x + y = 4$.

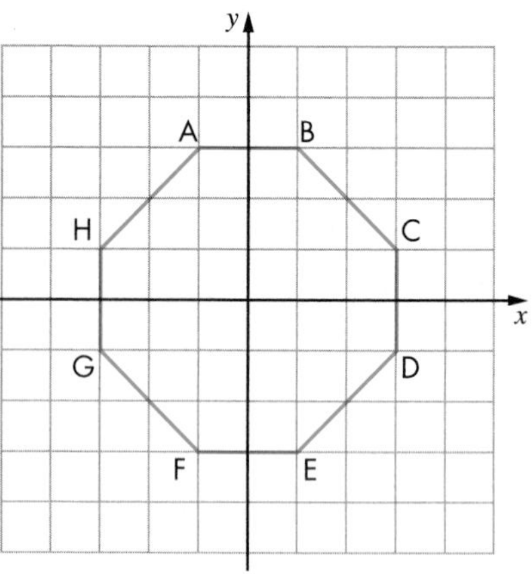

a Write down the equation of the lines through:

i C and D **ii** D and E **iii** E and F

iv F and G **v** G and H **vi** H and A

b The gradient of the line through F and B is 3.

Write down the gradient of the lines through:

i A and E **ii** G and C **iii** H and D

12.3 Finding the equation of a line from its graph

This section will show you how to:

- find the equation of a line, using its gradient and intercept

Key words
coefficient
gradient
intercept

The equation $y = mx + c$

When a graph can be expressed in the form $y = mx + c$, the **coefficient** of x, m, is the **gradient**, and the constant term, c, is the **intercept** on the y-axis.

This means that if you know the gradient, m, of a line and its intercept, c, on the y-axis, you can write down the equation of the line immediately.

For example, if $m = 3$ and $c = -5$, the equation of the line is $y = 3x - 5$.

All linear graphs can be expressed in the form $y = mx + c$.

This gives a method of finding the equation of any line drawn on a pair of coordinate axes.

EXAMPLE 7

Find the equation of the line shown in diagram **A**.

A

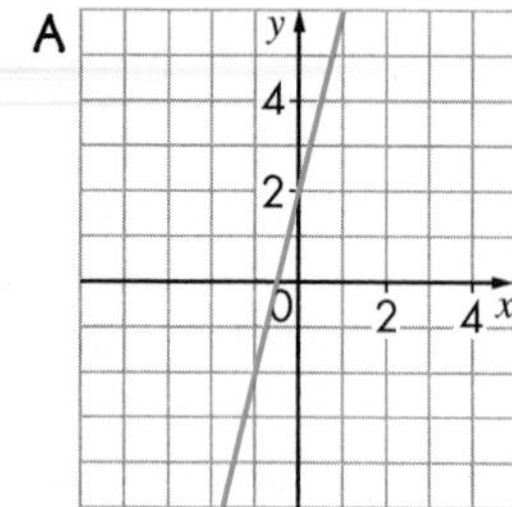

B

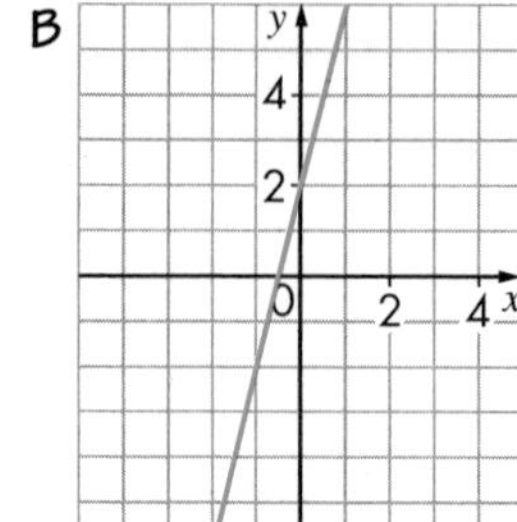

C

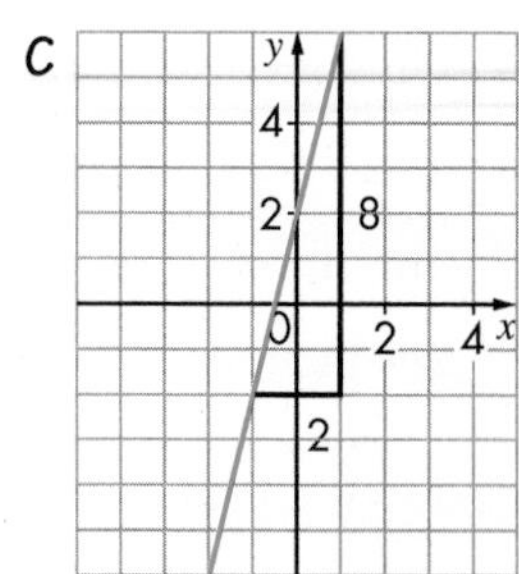

First, find where the graph crosses the y-axis (diagram **B**).

So $c = 2$

Next, measure the gradient of the line (diagram **C**).

y-step = 8

x-step = 2

gradient = $8 \div 2 = 4$

So $m = 4$

Finally, write down the equation of the line: $y = 4x + 2$

EXERCISE 12E

B

1 Give the equation of each of these lines, all of which have positive gradients. (Each square represents one unit.)

a

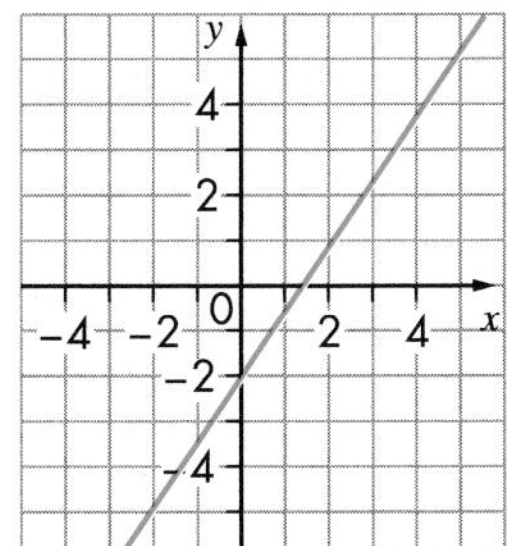

b

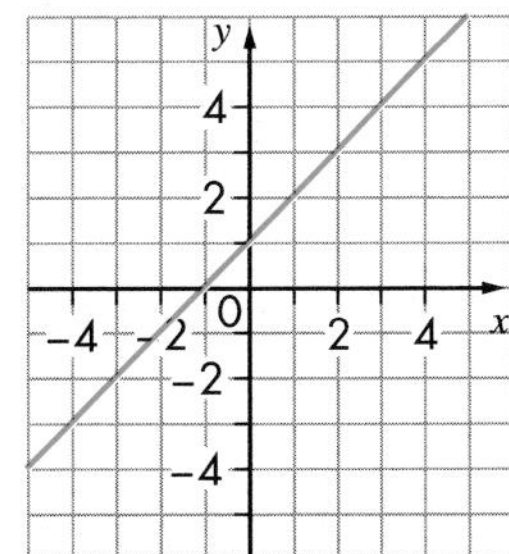

c

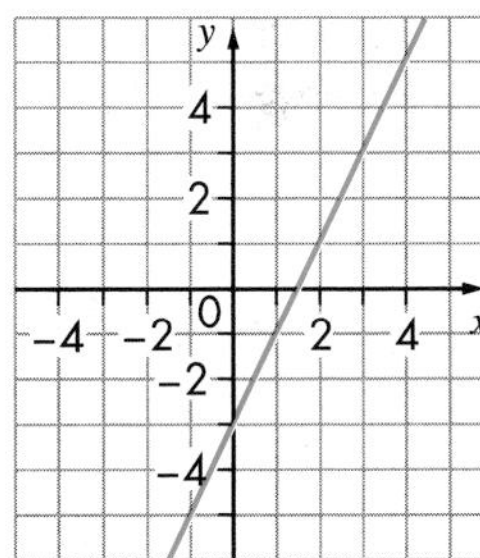

d

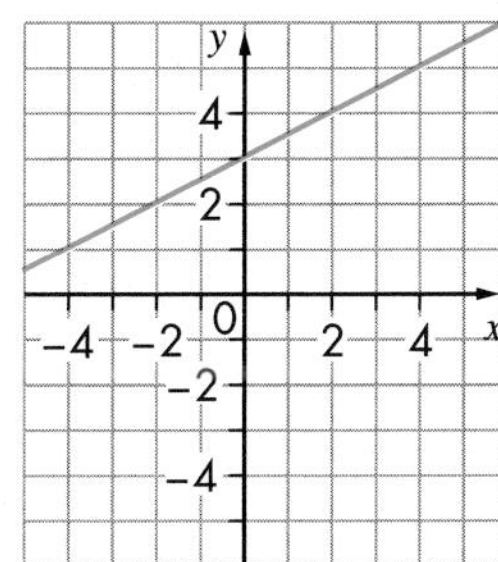

e

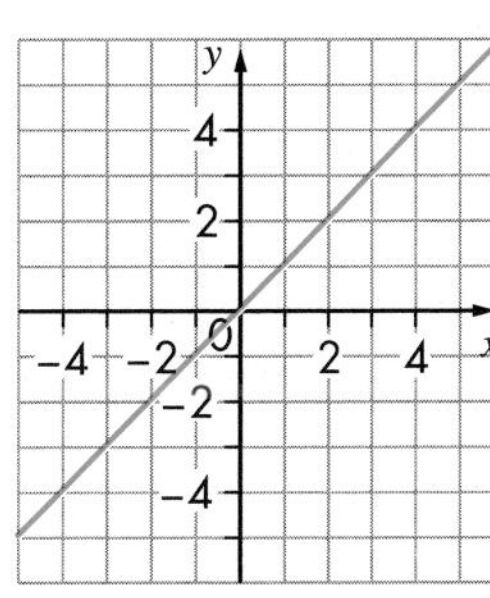

f

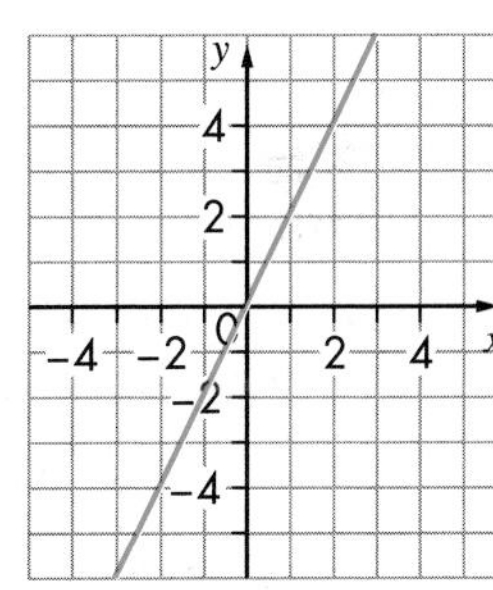

PS 2 In each of these grids, there are two lines. (Each square represents one unit.)

a

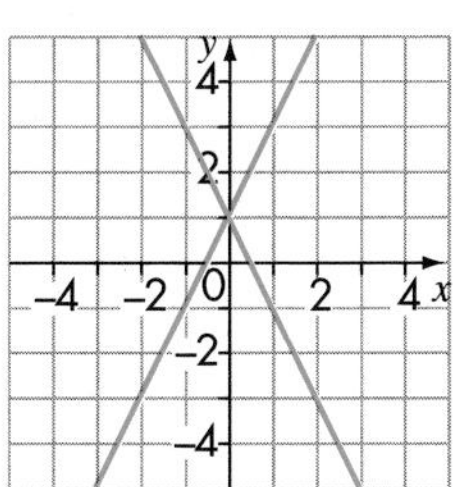

b

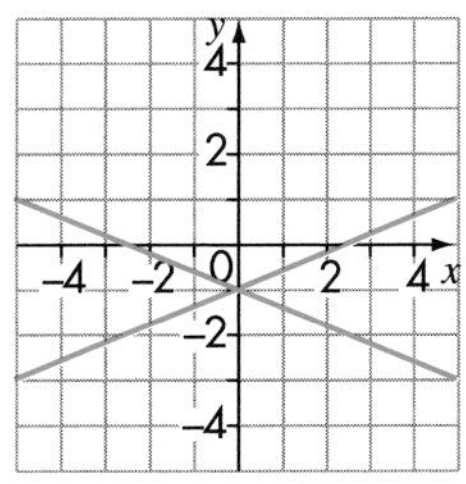

c

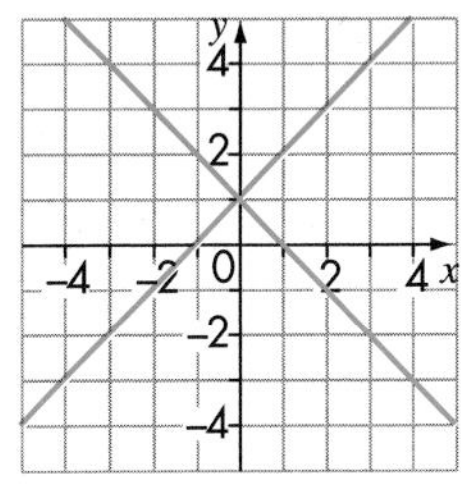

For each grid:

i find the equation of each of the lines **ii** describe any symmetries that you can see

iii describe any connection between the gradients of each pair of lines.

B

AU **3** A straight line passes through the points (1, 3) and (2, 5).

a Explain how you can tell that the line also passes through (0, 1).

b Explain how you can tell that the line has a gradient of 2.

c Work out the equation of the line that passes through (1, 5) and (2, 8).

4 Give the equation of each of these lines, all of which have negative gradients. (Each square represents one unit.)

a

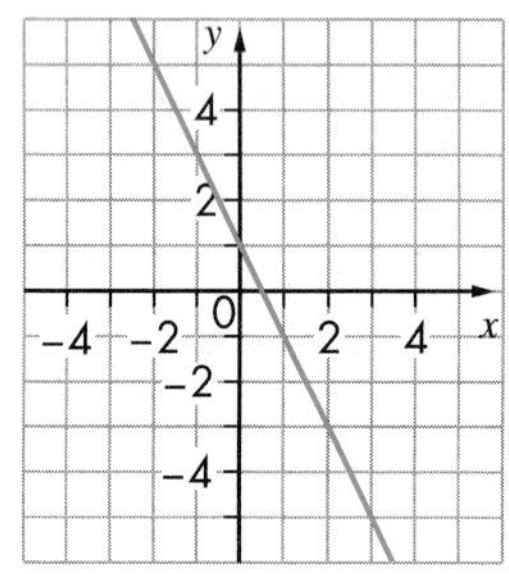

b

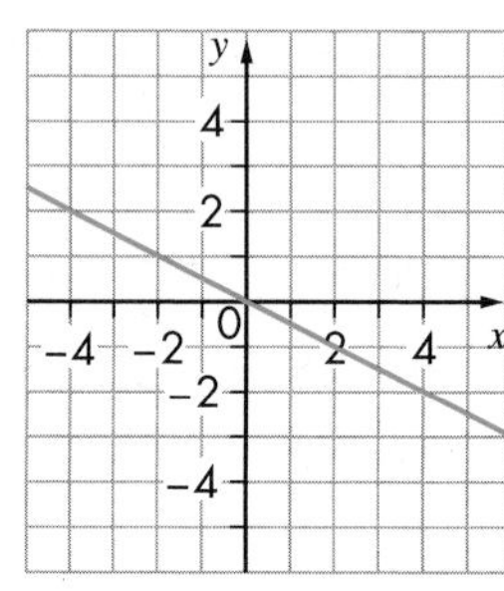

c

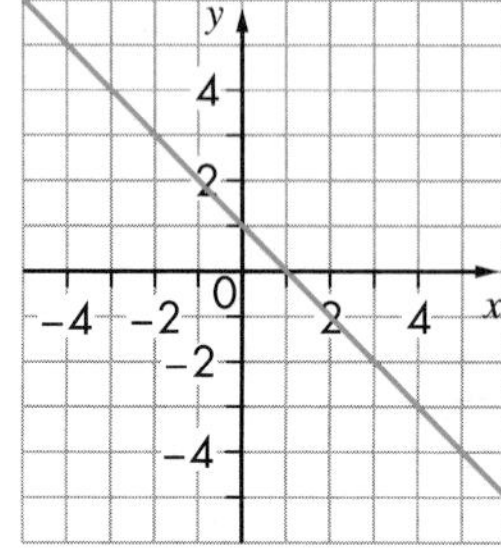

d

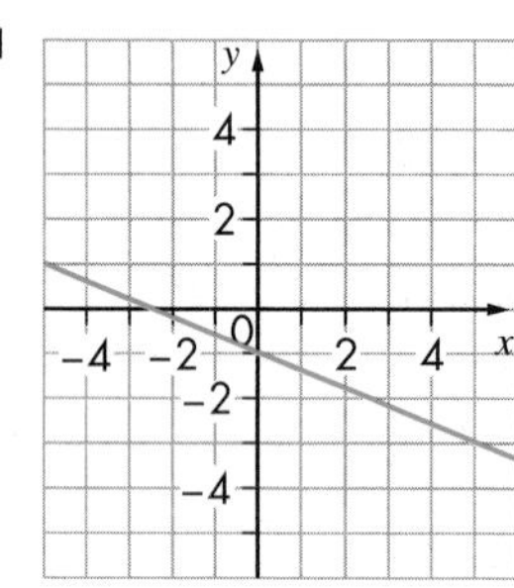

e

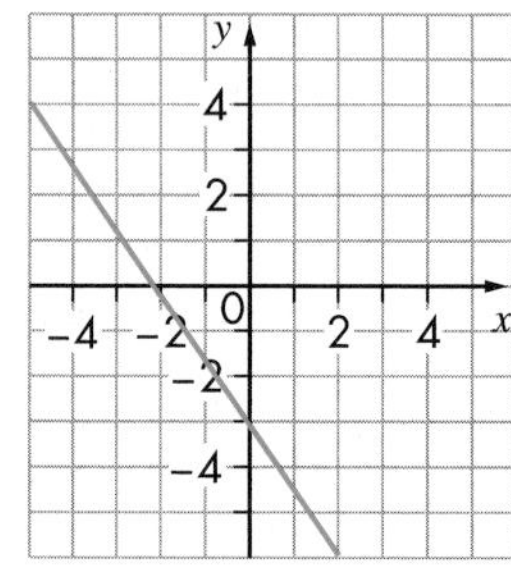

PS **5** In each of these grids, there are three lines. One of them is $y = x$. (Each square represents one unit.)

a

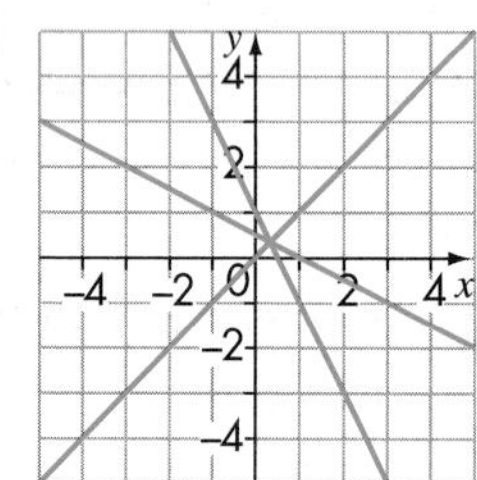

b

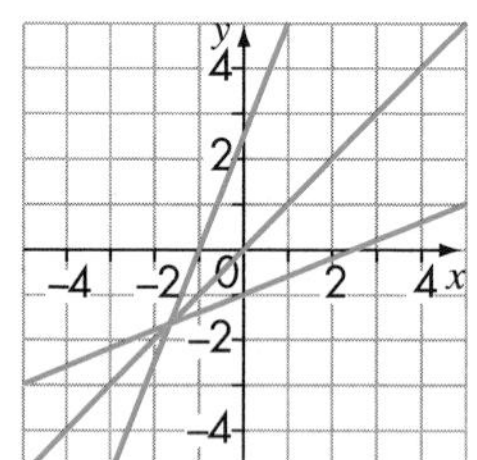

c

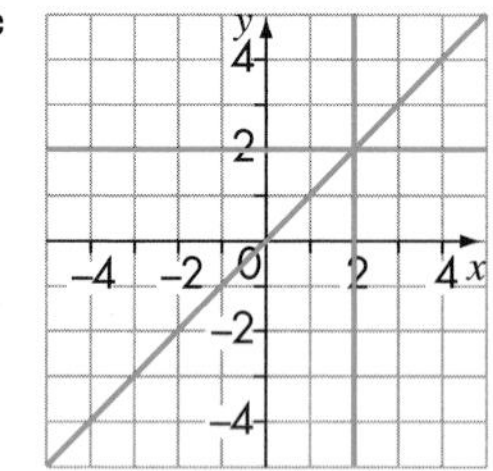

For each grid:

i find the equation of each of the other two lines

ii describe any symmetries that you can see

iii describe any connection between the gradients of each group of lines.

12.4 Uses of graphs

This section will show you how to:

- use straight-line graphs to find formulae
- solve simultaneous linear equations, using graphs

Key words
formula
(pl: formulae)
rule

In Chapter 11 you met two uses of graphs in kinematics, and the use of graphs to represent mortgage repayments and the rate of change of depth as a container is filled with water. Two other uses of graphs that you will now consider are finding **formulae** and solving simultaneous equations. Solving quadratic and other equations by graphical methods is covered later in this course.

Finding formulae or rules

EXAMPLE 8

A taxi fare will cost more, the further you go.
The graph below illustrates the fares in one part of England.

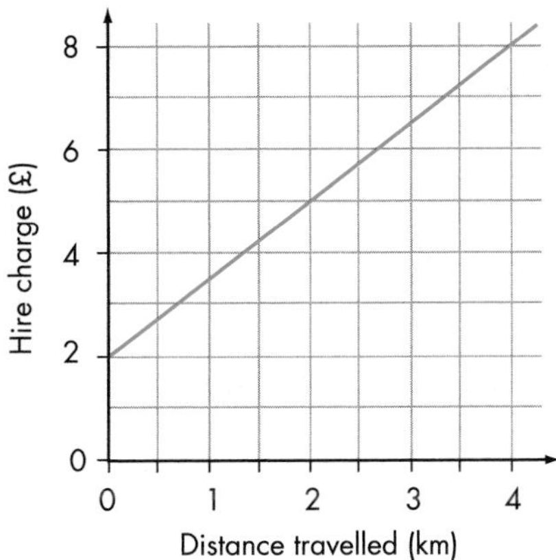

The taxi company charges a basic hire fee to start with of £2.00. This is shown on the graph as the point where the line cuts through the hire-charge axis (when distance travelled is 0).

The gradient of the line is:

$$\frac{8-2}{4} = \frac{6}{4} = 1.5$$

This represents the hire charge per kilometre travelled.

So the total hire charge is made up of two parts: a basic hire charge of £2.00 and an additional charge of £1.50 per kilometre travelled. This can be put in a formula as

hire charge = £2.00 + £1.50 per kilometre

In this example, £2.00 is the constant term in the formula (the equation of the graph).

EXERCISE 12F

FM **1** This graph is a conversion graph between temperatures in °C and °F.

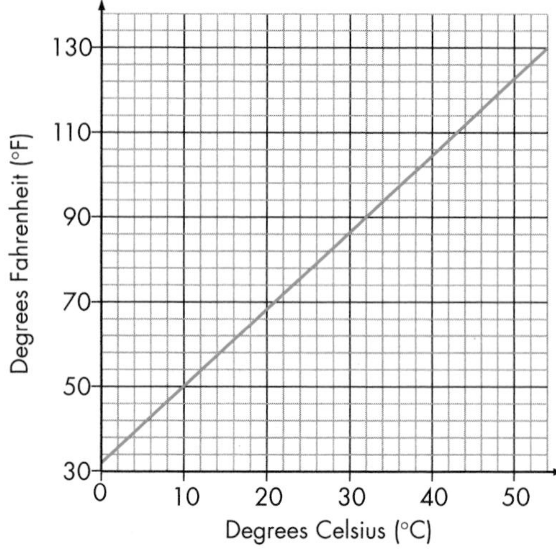

a What temperature in °F is equivalent to a temperature of 0 °C?

b What is the gradient of the line?

c From your answers to parts **a** and **b**, write down a **rule** that can be used to convert °C to °F.

FM **2** This graph illustrates charges for fuel.

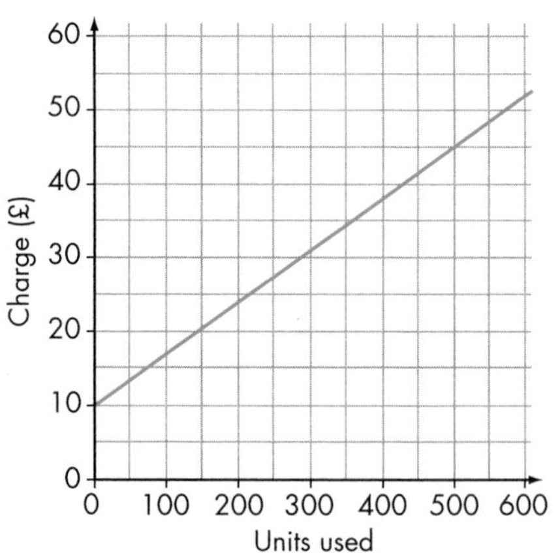

a What is the gradient of the line?

b The standing charge is the basic charge before the cost per unit is added. What is the standing charge?

c Write down the rule used to work out the total charge for different amounts of units used.

FM **3** In 2008, the exchange rate between the American dollar and the British pound changed.

The graph shows the exchange rate for three different months of the year.

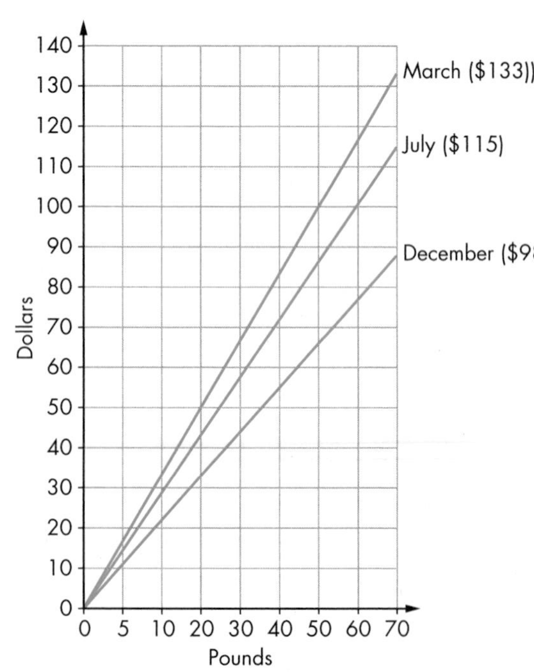

a If Mr Bush changed £1000 into dollars in March and another £1000 into dollars in December, approximately how much less did he get in December than in March?

b George went to America in March and stayed until July. In March, he changed £5000 into dollars. In July, he still had $2000 dollars left and he changed them back into pounds.

i How much, in dollars, did George spend between March and July?

ii How much, in pounds, did George actually spend between March and July?

AU 4 This graph is a sketch of the rate charged for taxi journeys by a firm during weekdays from 6 am to 8 pm.

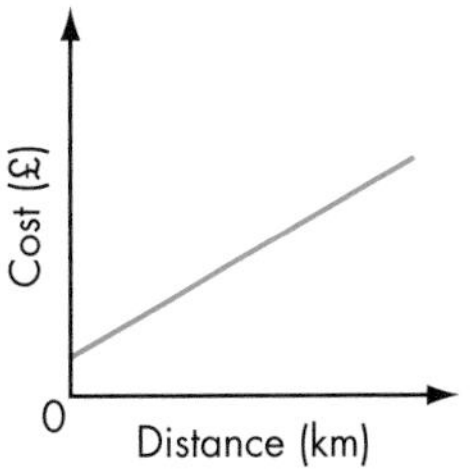

a At weekends from 6 am to 8 am, the company charges the same rate per kilometre but increases the basic charge.

Sketch a graph to show this. Mark it with A.

b During weekdays from 8 pm to 6 am, the company charges the same basic charge but an increased charge per kilometre.

On the same axes as in part **a**, sketch a graph to show this. Mark it with B.

c During weekends from 8 pm to 6 am, the company increases the basic charge and increases the charge per kilometre.

On the same axes as in part **a**, sketch a graph to show this. Mark it with C.

PS 5 A motorcycle courier will deliver packages, up to a weight of 22 pounds, within a city centre.

The courier has three charging bands: packages up to 5 pounds, packages from 5 to 12 pounds and packages over 12 pounds.

This graph shows how much he charges.

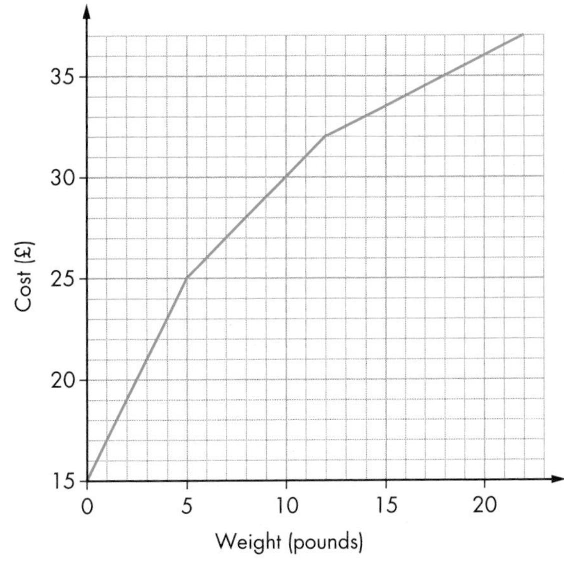

Work out the values of a, b, c, d, e and f to show his charges as equations.

$y = ax + b \qquad 0 < x \leqslant 5$

$y = cx + d \qquad 5 < x \leqslant 12$

$y = ex + f \qquad 12 < x \leqslant 25$

FM 6 This graph shows the hire charge for heaters over a number of days.

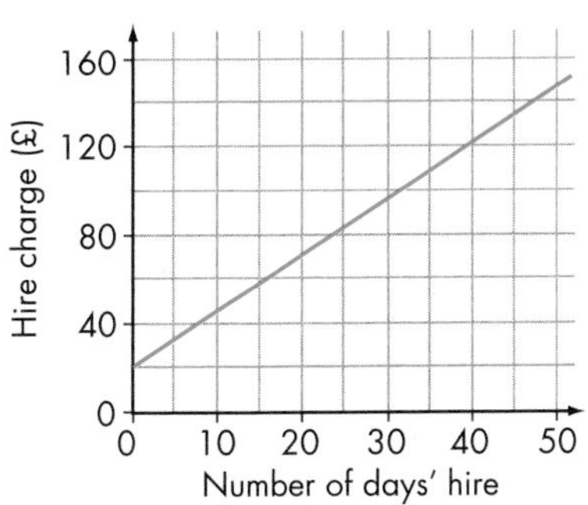

a Calculate the gradient of the line.

b What is the basic charge before the daily hire charge is added on?

c Write down the rule used to work out the total hire charge.

B

FM **7** This graph shows the hire charge for a conference centre, depending on the number of people at the conference.

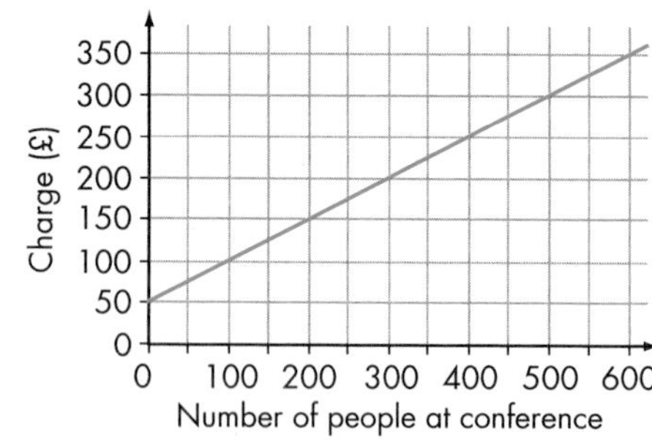

a Calculate the gradient of the line.

b What is the basic fee for hiring the conference centre?

c Write down the rule used to work out the total hire charge for the centre.

FM **8** This graph shows the length of a spring when different weights are attached to it.

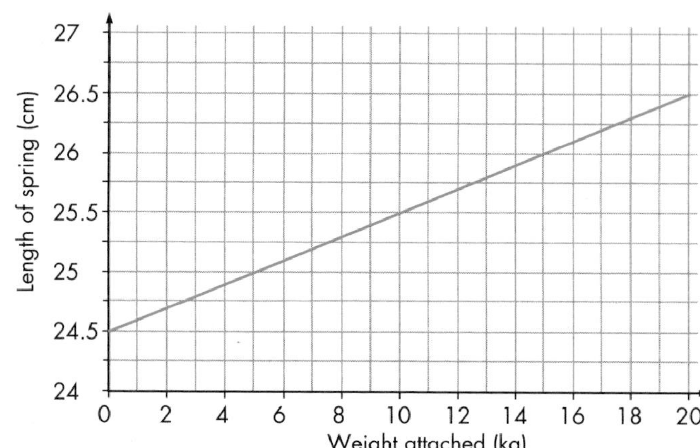

a Calculate the gradient of the line.

b How long is the spring when no weight is attached to it?

c By how much does the spring extend per kilogram?

d Write down the rule for finding the length of the spring for different weights.

Solving simultaneous equations

EXAMPLE 9

By drawing their graphs on the same grid, find the solution of these simultaneous equations.

a $3x + y = 6$ **b** $y = 4x - 1$

a The first graph is drawn using the cover-up method. It crosses the x-axis at (2, 0) and the y-axis at (0, 6).

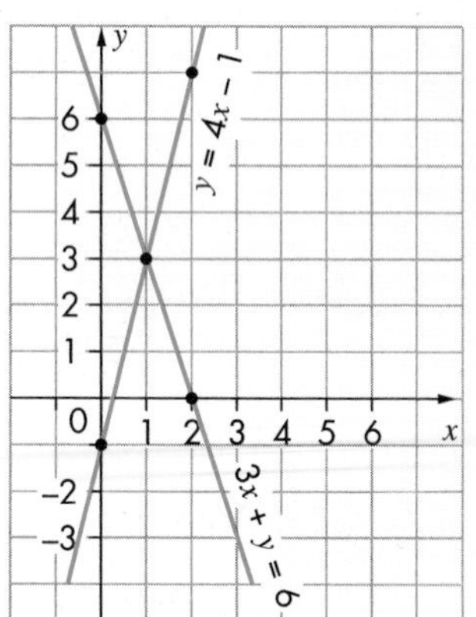

b This graph can be drawn by finding some points or by the gradient-intercept method. If you use the gradient-intercept method, you find the graph crosses the y-axis at –1 and has a gradient of 4.

The point where the graphs intersect is (1, 3). So the solution to the simultaneous equations is $x = 1$, $y = 3$.

EXERCISE 12G

In questions **1–12**, draw the graphs to find the solution of each pair of simultaneous equations.

1 $x + 4y = 8$
$x - y = 3$

2 $y = 2x - 1$
$3x + 2y = 12$

3 $y = 2x + 4$
$y = x + 7$

4 $y = x$
$x + y = 10$

5 $y = 2x + 3$
$5x + y = 10$

6 $y = 5x + 1$
$y = 2x + 10$

7 $y = x + 8$
$x + y = 4$

8 $y - 3x = 9$
$y = x - 3$

9 $y = -x$
$y = 4x - 5$

10 $3x + 2y = 18$
$y = 3x$

11 $y = 3x + 2$
$y + x = 10$

12 $y = \dfrac{x}{3} + 1$
$x + y = 11$

13 One cheesecake and two chocolate gateaux cost £9.50.

Two cheesecakes and one chocolate gateau cost £8.50.

Using x to represent the price of a cheesecake and y to represent the cost of a gateau, set up a pair of simultaneous equations.

On a set of axes with the x-axis numbered from 0 to 20 and the y-axis numbered from 0 to 10, draw the graphs of the two equations.

Use the graphs to write down the cost of a cheesecake and the cost of a gateau.

PS 14 The graph shows four lines.

P: $y = 4x + 1$ Q: $y = 2x + 2$

R: $y = x - 2$ S: $x + y + 1 = 0$

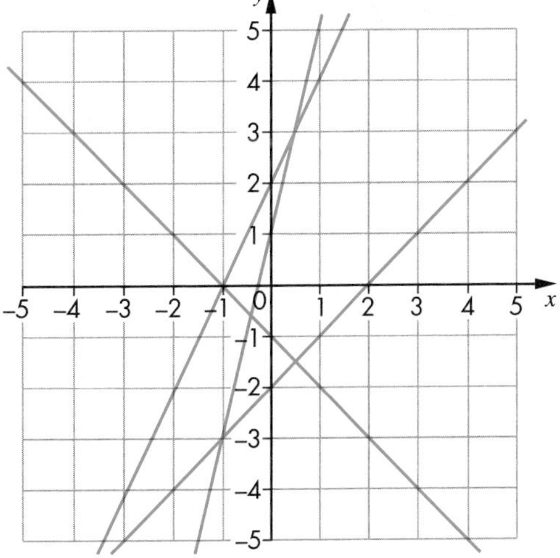

Which pairs of lines intersect at the following points?

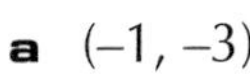

a $(-1, -3)$ **b** $(\frac{1}{2}, -1\frac{1}{2})$

c $(\frac{1}{2}, 3)$ **d** $(-1, 0)$

e Solve the simultaneous equations P and S to find the exact solution.

AU 15 Four lines have the following equations.

A: $y = x$ B: $y = 2$

C: $x = -3$ D: $y = -x$

These lines intersect at six different points.

Without drawing the lines accurately, write down the coordinates of the six intersection points.

HINTS AND TIPS

Sketch the lines.

12.5 Parallel and perpendicular lines

This section will show you how to:

- draw linear graphs parallel or perpendicular to other lines and passing through a specific point

Key words
negative reciprocal
parallel
perpendicular

EXAMPLE 10

In each of these grids, there are two lines.

a

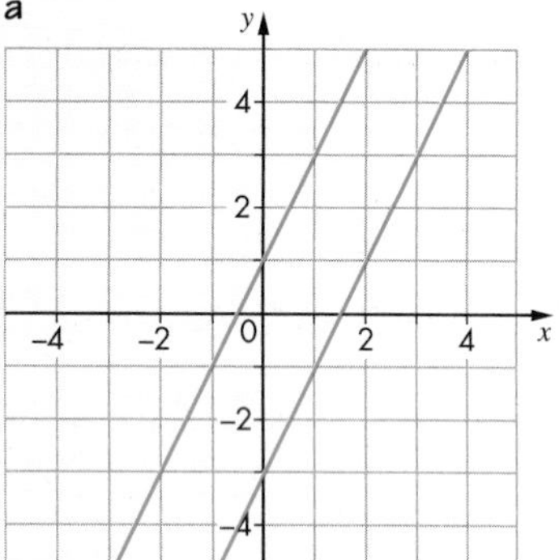

b

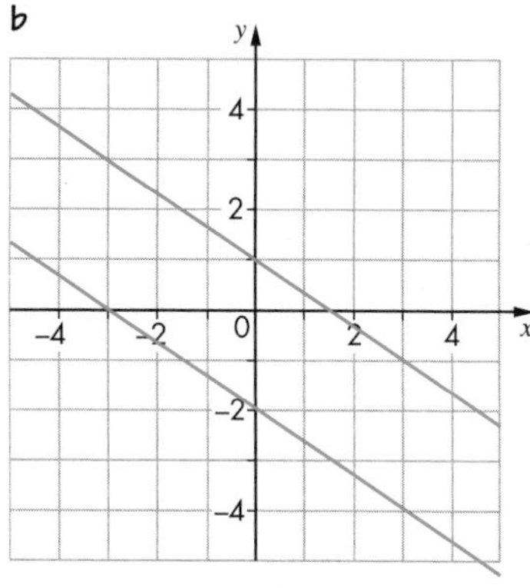

c

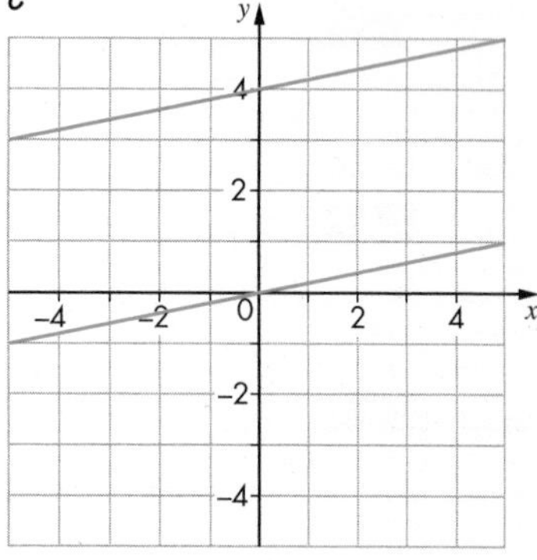

For each grid:

i find the equation of each line

ii describe the geometrical relationship between the lines

iii describe the numerical relationships between their gradients.

i Grid **a**: the lines have equations $y = 2x + 1$, $y = 2x - 3$

Grid **b**: the lines have equations $y = -\frac{2}{3}x + 1$, $y = -\frac{2}{3}x - 2$

Grid **c**: the lines have equations $y = \frac{1}{5}x$, $y = \frac{1}{5}x + 4$

ii In each case, the lines are parallel.

iii In each case, the gradients are equal.

EXAMPLE 11

In each of these grids, there are two lines.

a

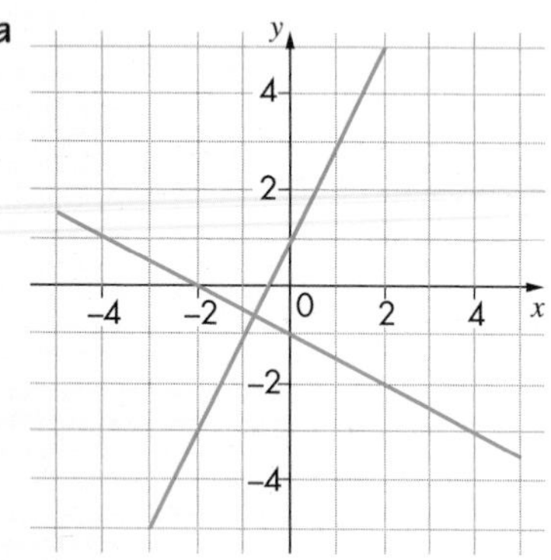

b

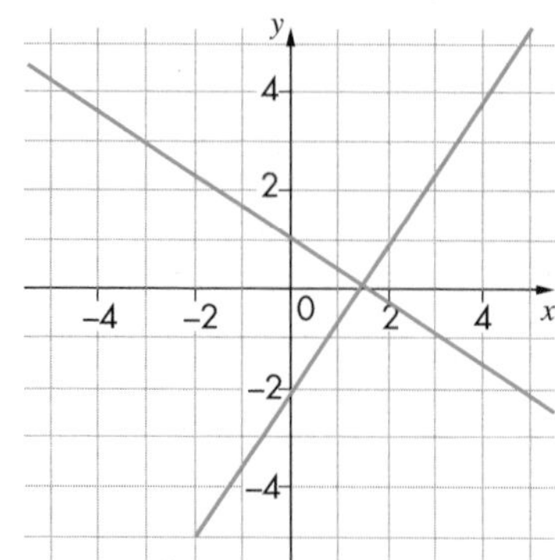

c

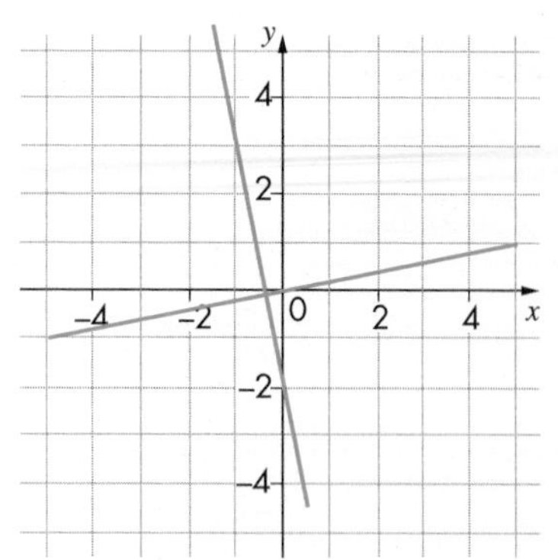

For each grid:

i find the equation of each line

ii describe the geometrical relationship between the lines

iii describe the numerical relationships between their gradients.

i Grid a: the lines have equations $y = 2x + 1$, $y = -\frac{1}{2}x - 1$
Grid b: the lines have equations $y = \frac{3}{2}x - 2$, $y = -\frac{2}{3}x + 1$
Grid c: the lines have equations $y = \frac{1}{5}x$, $y = -5x - 2$

ii In each case the lines are perpendicular (at right angles).

iii In each case the gradients are reciprocals of each other but with different signs.

Note: If two lines are **parallel**, then their gradients are equal.

If two lines are **perpendicular**, their gradients are **negative reciprocals** of each other.

EXAMPLE 12

Two points A and B are A (0, 1) and B (2, 4).

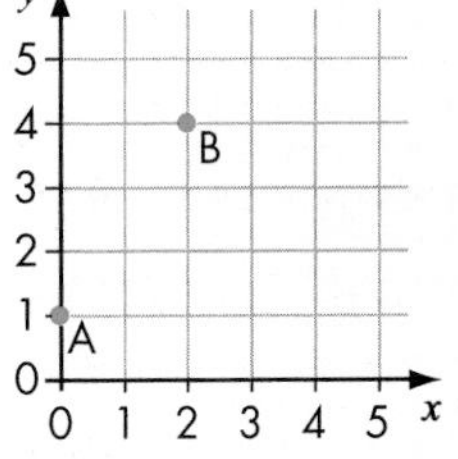

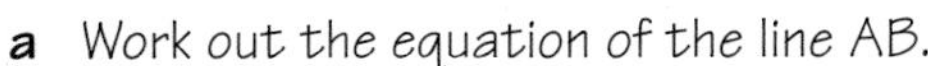

a Work out the equation of the line AB.

b Write down the equation of the line parallel to AB and passing through the point (0, 5).

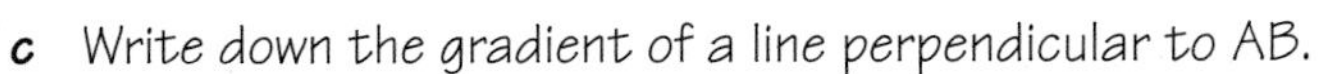

c Write down the gradient of a line perpendicular to AB.

d Write down the equation of a line perpendicular to AB and passing through the point (0, 2).

a The gradient of AB is $\frac{3}{2}$ and passes through (0, 1) so the equation is $y = \frac{3}{2}x + 1$.

b The gradient is the same and the intercept is (0, 5) so the equation is $y = \frac{3}{2}x + 5$.

c The perpendicular gradient is the negative reciprocal $-\frac{2}{3}$.

d The gradient is $-\frac{2}{3}$ and the intercept is (0, 2) so the equation is $y = -\frac{2}{3}x + 2$.

EXAMPLE 13

Find the line that is perpendicular to the line $y = \frac{1}{2}x - 3$ and passes through (0, 5).

The gradient of the new line will be the negative reciprocal of $\frac{1}{2}$ which is -2.

The point (0, 5) is the intercept on the y-axis so the equation of the line is:
$y = -2x + 5$

EXAMPLE 14

The point A is (2, 1) and the point B is (4, 4).

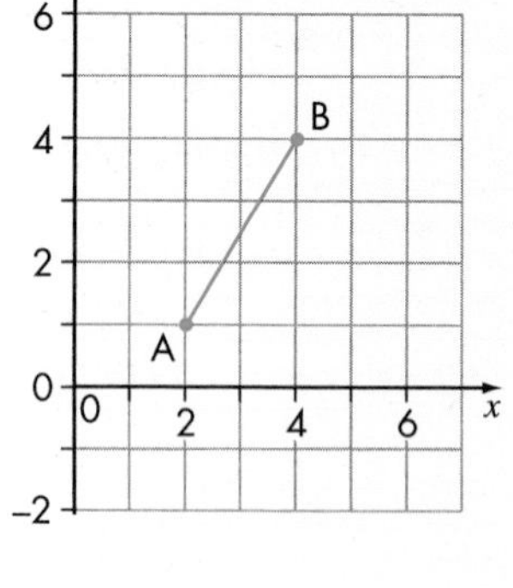

a Find the equation of the line parallel to AB and passing through (6, 11).

b Find the equation of the line parallel to AB and passing through (8, 0).

a The gradient of AB is $\frac{3}{2}$, so the new equation is of the form $y = \frac{3}{2}x + c$

The new line passes through (6, 11), so $11 = \frac{3}{2} \times 6 + c$

$$\Rightarrow c = 2$$

Hence the new line is $y = \frac{3}{2}x + 2$

b The gradient of AB is $\frac{3}{2}$, so the new equation is of the form $y = \frac{3}{2}x + c$.

The new line passes through (8, 0), so $0 = \frac{3}{2} \times 8 + c$

$$\Rightarrow c = -12$$

Hence the new line is $y = \frac{3}{2}x - 12$

EXAMPLE 15

The point A is (2, −1) and the point B is (4, 5).

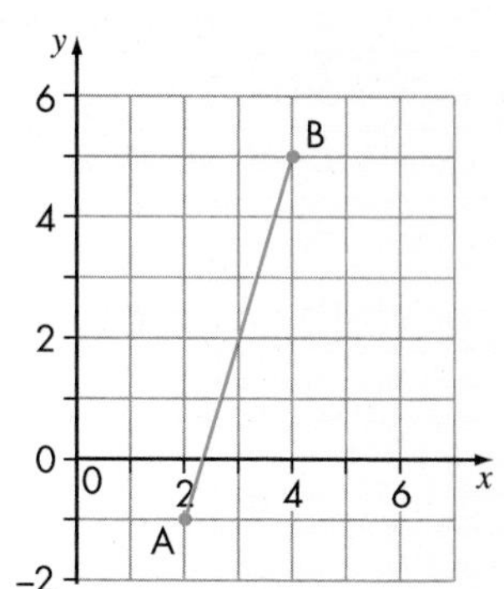

a Find the equation of the line parallel to AB and passing through (2, 8).

b Find the equation of the line perpendicular to the midpoint of AB.

a The gradient of AB is 3, so the new equation is of the form

$y = 3x + c$

The new line passes through (2, 8), so $8 = 3 \times 2 + c$

$$\Rightarrow c = 2$$

Hence the line is $y = 3x + 2$

b The midpoint of AB is (3, 2).

The gradient of the perpendicular line is the negative reciprocal of 3, which is $-\frac{1}{3}$.

We could find c as in part **a** but we can also do a sketch on the grid. This will show that the perpendicular line passes through (0, 3).

Hence the equation of the line is $y = -\frac{1}{3}x + 3$

EXERCISE 12H

FM **1** Two plumbers, Dwayne Pipes and Ivor Wrench, use the same graph to charge for jobs. A sketch of this graph is shown.

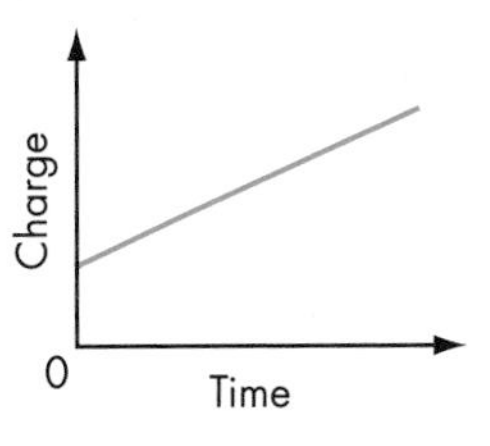

a Dwayne decides to increase his fixed charge and leave his charge per hour the same.

Sketch the new graph for Dwayne on a copy of the original graph.

b Ivor decides to leave his fixed charge the same and increase his charge per hour.

Sketch the new graph for Ivor on a copy of the original graph.

AU **2** Here are the equations of three lines.

Line A: $y = 3x - 2$

Line B: $y = 3x + 1$

Line C: $y = -\frac{1}{3}x + 1$

a Give a reason why line A is the odd one out of the three.

b Give a reason why line C is the odd one out of the three.

c Which of the following would be a reason why line B is the odd one out of the three?

i Line B is the only one that intersects the negative x-axis.

ii Line B is not parallel to either of the other two lines.

iii Line B does not pass through (0, –2).

3 Write down the negative reciprocals of the following numbers.

a 2 **b** –3 **c** 5 **d** –1

e $\frac{1}{2}$ **f** $\frac{1}{4}$ **g** $-\frac{1}{3}$ **h** $-\frac{2}{3}$

i 1.5 **j** 10 **k** –6 **l** $\frac{4}{3}$

4 Write down the equation of the line perpendicular to each of the following lines and which passes through the same point on the y-axis.

a $y = 2x - 1$ **b** $y = -3x + 1$ **c** $y = x + 2$ **d** $y = -x + 2$

e $y = \frac{1}{2}x + 3$ **f** $y = \frac{1}{4}x - 3$ **g** $y = -\frac{1}{3}x$ **h** $y = -\frac{2}{3}x - 5$

5 Write down the equations of these lines.

a Parallel to $y = 4x - 5$ and passes through (0, 1)

b Parallel to $y = \frac{1}{2}x + 3$ and passes through (0, –2)

c Parallel to $y = -x + 2$ and passes through (0, 3)

A

6 Write down the equations of these lines.

a Perpendicular to $y = 3x + 2$ and passes through (0, –1)

b Perpendicular to $y = -\frac{1}{3}x - 2$ and passes through (0, 5)

c Perpendicular to $y = x - 5$ and passes through (0, 1)

A*

7 A is the point (1, 5). B is the point (3, 3).

a Find the equation of the line parallel to AB and passing through (5, 9).

b Find the equation of the line perpendicular to AB and passing through the midpoint of AB.

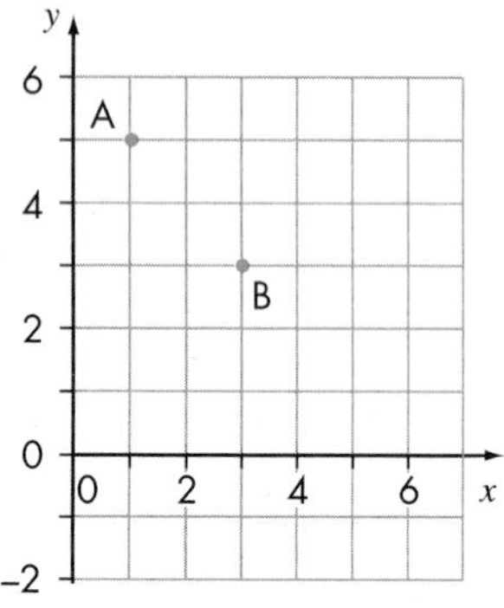

8 Find the equation of the line that passes through the midpoint of AB, where A is (–5, –3) and B is (–1, 3), and has a gradient of 2.

9 Find the equation of the line perpendicular to $y = 4x - 3$, passing though (–4, 3).

10 A is the point (0, 6), B is the point (5, 5) and C is the point (4, 0).

a Write down the point where the line BC intercepts the y-axis.

b Work out the equation of the line AB.

c Write down the equation of the line BC.

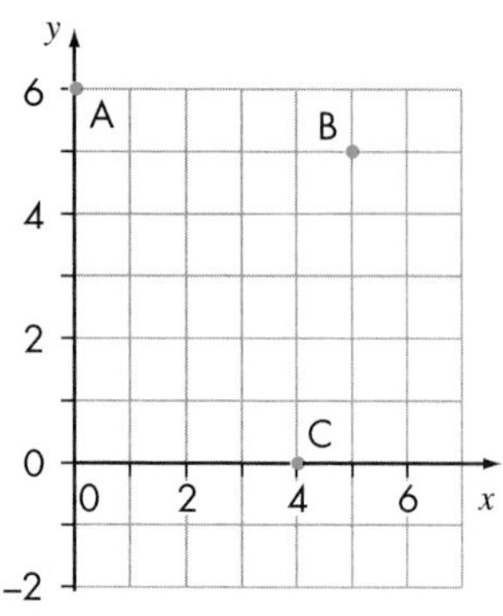

PS 11 Find the equation of the perpendicular bisector of the points A (1, 2) and B (3, 6).

12 A is the point (0, 4), B is the point (4, 6) and C is the point (2, 0).

a Find the equation of the line BC.

b Show that the point of intersection of the perpendicular bisectors of AB and AC is (3, 3).

c Show algebraically that this point lies on the line BC.

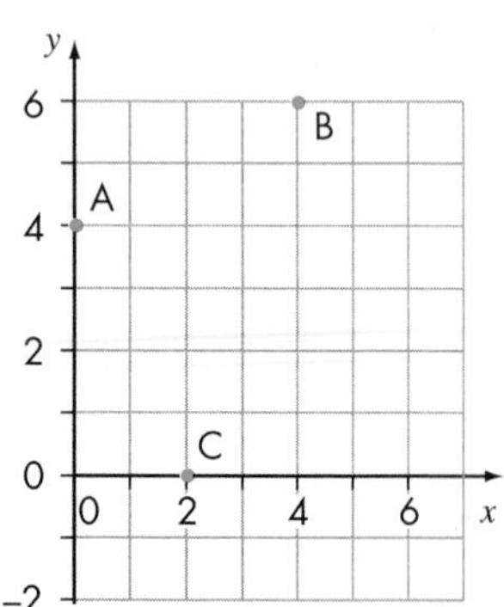

PS 13 A is the point (–2, 3) and B is the point (0, 2). Find the equation of the line that is perpendicular to AB and passes through the midpoint of AB.

GRADE BOOSTER

D You can draw straight lines by plotting points

C You can draw straight lines using the gradient-intercept method

B You can solve a pair of linear simultaneous equations from their graphs

A You can find the equations of linear graphs parallel and perpendicular to other linear graphs, that pass through specific points

What you should know now

- How to draw linear graphs
- How to solve simultaneous linear equations by finding the intersection point of the graphs of the equations or other related equations
- How to use gradients to find equations of parallel and perpendicular graphs

EXAMINATION QUESTIONS

1 **a** Draw the graph of $y = 2x + 3$ for values of x from 0 to 5. Use a grid with axes covering $0 \leqslant x \leqslant 6$ and $0 \leqslant y \leqslant 14$.

b Use your graph to solve $6.5 = 2x + 3$.

2 The diagram shows a sketch of the graph of $y = 3x + 1$.

Copy the diagram, and draw and label sketch graphs of these.

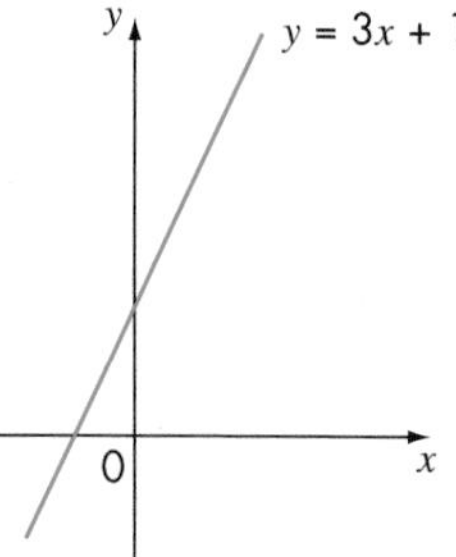

a $y = 1$

b $y = x + 1$

3 **a** Find the equation of the line AB.

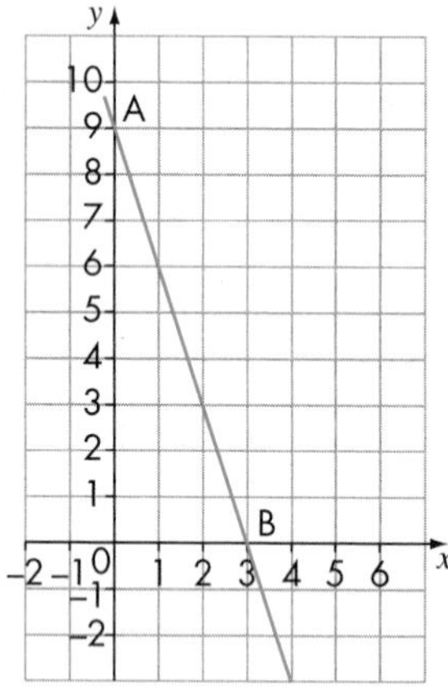

b Give the y-coordinate of the point on the line with an x-coordinate of 6. *(2 marks)*

c Write down the gradient of a line perpendicular to AB. *(1 mark)*

AQA, November 2004, Paper 2 Higher, Question 7

4 Here are the equations of six lines.

i	$y = 2x + 1$	**ii**	$y = -\frac{1}{3}x - 3$
iii	$y = \frac{1}{3}x - 1$	**iv**	$y = 2x - 2$
v	$y = 3x + 2$	**vi**	$y = \frac{1}{2}x - 2$

a Which two lines are parallel?

b Which pair of lines are perpendicular?

c Which two lines intersect on the y-axis?

5 The diagram shows the points A(–1, 7), B(0, 5) and C(4, –3).

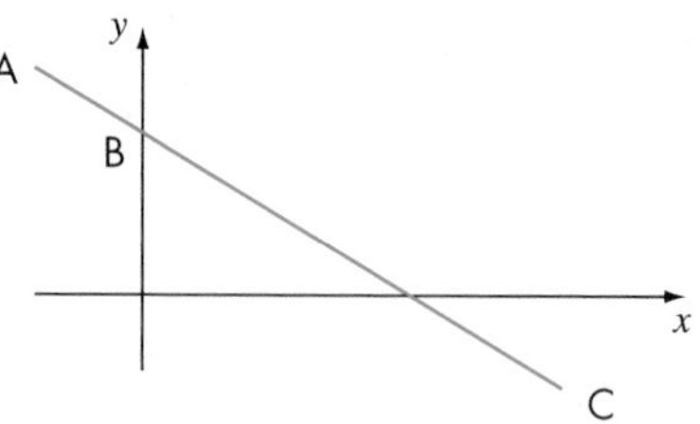

Find the equation of the straight line which passes through A, B and C.

6 Find the equation of the straight line through the point (0, 3) which is perpendicular to the line $y = \frac{3}{5}x + 5$.

7 A is the point (5, 5). B is the point (3, 1). Find the equation of the line perpendicular to AB and passing through the midpoint of AB.

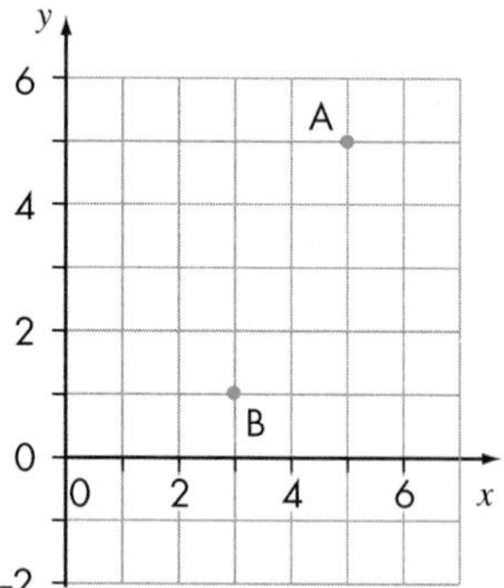

8 Find the equation of the line parallel to the line $y = 3x + 5$ passing through the point (2, 9).

9 Find the equation of the perpendicular bisector of the points A(4, 3) and B(8, 5).

10 A is the point (6, 3), B is the point (0, 5). Find algebraically, the point of intersection of the line perpendicular to AB passing through the midpoint and the line $2y + x = 4$.

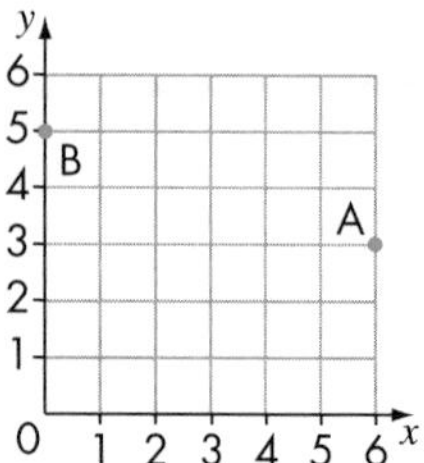

A*  A  B D

Worked Examination Questions

1 Three burgers and a portion of chips cost £4.

One burger and three portions of chips cost £3.

Using x for the cost of a burger and y as the cost of a portion of chips, use a graphical method to find the values of x and y.

1 $3x + y = 5$

$x + 3y = 3$

Use the given information to set up the equations. This scores 1 mark for method and 1 mark for accuracy.

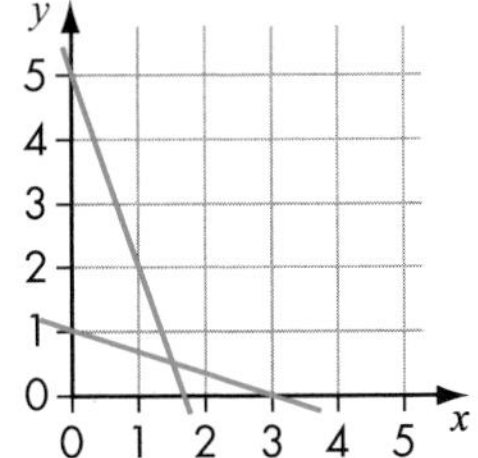

Draw the graphs using the cover-up rule. This scores 1 mark for method and 1 mark for accuracy.

$x = £1.50$ and $y = £0.50$

Read off the values of x and y and change them to values in pounds and pence. This scores 1 mark for accuracy. Remember to check that the values work in the original problem.

Total: 5 marks

2 Three corners of a square A(0, 4), B(4, 5) and D(1, 0) are shown on the grid.

Show algebraically that the point C is at (5, 1).

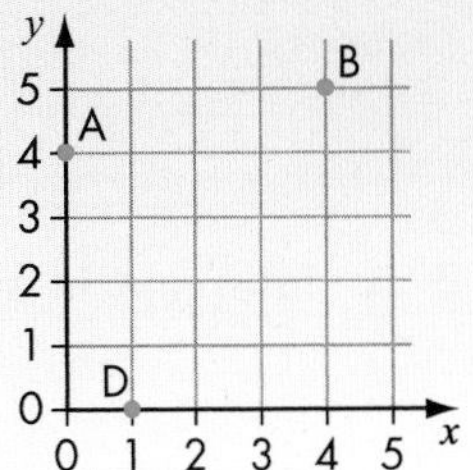

2 Line AB has gradient and intercept (0, 4).

So has equation $y = \frac{1}{4}x + 4$

Line AD is $y = -4x + 4$

Find the equations of lines AB and AD. This scores 1 mark for method and 1 mark for accuracy.

Line BC is of the form $y = -4y + y$ and passes through (4, 5).

Substituting, $5 = -4 \times 4 + c \Rightarrow c = 21$

Line DC is of the form $y = \frac{1}{4}x + c$ and passes through (1, 0).

Substituting, $0 = 1 \times \frac{1}{4} + c \Rightarrow c = -\frac{1}{4}$

Find the equations of lines through B and D parallel to AD and AB. This scores 1 mark for method and 1 mark for accuracy.

Point C is the intersection of $y = -4x + 21$ and $y = \frac{1}{4}x - \frac{1}{4}$

Find the intersection point of the lines. This scores 1 mark for method and 1 mark for accuracy.

So $\frac{1}{4}x - \frac{1}{4} = -4x + 21, \Rightarrow 4\frac{1}{4}x = 21\frac{1}{4} \Rightarrow x = 5, y = 1.$

Total: 6 marks

Worked Examination Questions

AU **3** **a** Find the equation of the line shown.

b Find the equation of the line parallel to the line shown and passing through (0, –5).

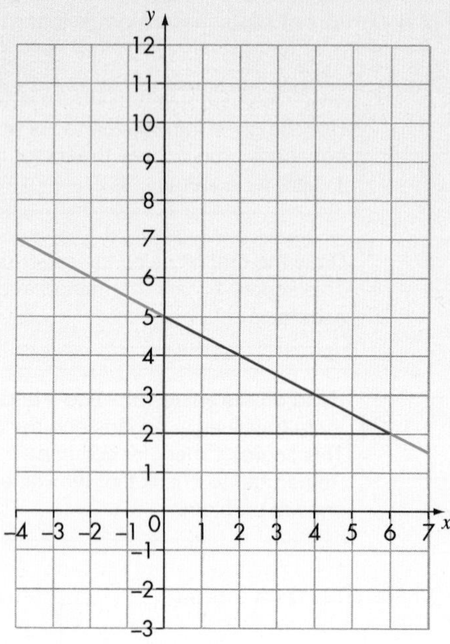

3 a Intercept is at (0, 5)

First identify the point where the line crosses the y-axis. This is the intercept, c. This gets 1 mark.

Gradient $= -\frac{3}{6} = -\frac{1}{2}$

Draw a right-angled triangle using grid lines as two sides of the triangle and part of the line as the hypotenuse. (Shown in red on diagram.) This gets 1 mark for method. Measure the y-step and the x-step of the triangle and divide the y-step by the x-step to get the gradient, m. As the line slopes down from left to right the gradient is negative.

Equation of the line is $y = -\frac{1}{2}x + 5$

Put the two numbers into the equation $y = mx + c$ to get the equation of the line. This gets 1 mark for accuracy.

b Gradient is same as in **a**: $-\frac{1}{2}$

This is a follow-through mark, so whatever gradient was found in **a** gets the mark. This gets 1 mark.

Intercept is (0, –5)

Equation is $y = -y\frac{1}{2} - 5$

Point given is on the y-axis, so just give the equation in the form $y = mx + c$. This gets 1 mark.

Total: 5 marks

Square numbers

The square numbers are 1, 4, 9, 16, 25, 36, …
The nth term of this sequence is n^2.

Triangular numbers

The triangular numbers are 1, 3, 6, 10, 15, 21, …
The nth term of this sequence is $\frac{1}{2}n(n + 1)$.

Powers of 2

The powers of 2 are 2, 4, 8, 16, 32, 64, …
The nth term of this sequence is 2^n.

Powers of 10

The powers of 10 are 10, 100, 1000, 10 000, 100 000, 1 000 000, …
The nth term of this sequence is 10^n.

Prime numbers

The first 20 prime numbers are 2, 3, 5, 7, 11, 13, 17, 19, 23, 29, 31, 37, 41, 43, 47, 53, 59, 61, 67, 71.

A prime number is a number that only has two factors, 1 and itself.

There is no pattern to the prime numbers so they do not have a formula for the nth term.

One important fact that you should remember is that there is only one even prime number, 2.

EXAMPLE 7

p is a prime number, q is an odd number and r is an even number.

Say if the following are always odd (O), always even (E) or could be either odd or even (X).

a pq **b** $p + q + r$ **c** pqr **d** $q^2 + r^2$

a The easiest way to do this question is to substitute numbers and see whether the outcome is odd or even.

For example, let $p = 2$ and $q = 3$, then $pq = 6$ and is even; but p could also be 3 or 5, which are odd, so $pq = 3 \times 5 = 15$ which is odd.

So pq could be either (X).

b Let $p = 2$ or 3, $q = 5$ and $r = 4$; so $p + q + r = 2 + 5 + 4 = 11$, or $3 + 5 + 4 = 12$

So $p + q + r$ could be either (X).

c Let $p = 2$ or 3, $q = 5$ and $r = 4$; so $pqr = 2 \times 5 \times 4 = 40$ or $3 \times 5 \times 4 = 60$

Both are even, so pqr is always even (E).

d Let $q = 5$ and $r = 4$; $q^2 + r^2 = 5^2 + 4^2 = 21 + 16 = 37$

This is odd, so $q^2 + r^2$ is always odd (O).

C

FM 9 This chart is used by an online CD retailer for the charges for buying n CDs including any postage and packing charges.

n	1	2	3	4	5	6	7	8	9	10	11	12	13	14	15
Charge (£)	10	18	26	34	42	49	57	65	73	81	88	96	104	112	120

a Using the charges for one to five CDs, work out an expression for the nth term.

b Using the charges for six to 10 CDs, work out an expression for the nth term.

c Using the charges for 11 to 15 CDs, work out an expression for the nth term.

d What is the basic charge for a CD?

PS 10 Look at this series of fractions.

$\frac{31}{109}, \frac{33}{110}, \frac{35}{111}, \frac{37}{112}, \frac{39}{113}, \ldots$

a Explain why the nth term of the numerators is $2n + 29$.

b Write down the nth term of the denominators.

c Explain why the terms of the series will eventually get very close to 2.

d Which term of the series has a value equal to 1?

HINTS AND TIPS

Use algebra to set up an equation.

13.3 Special sequences

This section will show you how to:

- recognise and continue some special number sequences

Key words

even, odd, powers of 2, powers of 10, prime, square, triangular

There are some number sequences that occur frequently. It is useful to know these as they are very likely to occur in examinations.

Even numbers

The even numbers are 2, 4, 6, 8, 10, 12, …

The nth term of this sequence is $2n$.

Odd numbers

The odd numbers are 1, 3, 5, 7, 9, 11, …

The nth term of this sequence is $2n - 1$.

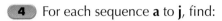

C

4 For each sequence **a** to **j**, find:

i the nth term **ii** the 100th term **iii** the term closest to 100.

a 5, 9, 13, 17, 21, …
b 3, 5, 7, 9, 11, 13, …
c 4, 7, 10, 13, 16, …
d 8, 10, 12, 14, 16, …
e 9, 13, 17, 21, …
f 6, 11, 16, 21, …
g 0, 3, 6, 9, 12, …
h 2, 8, 14, 20, 26, …
i 7, 15, 23, 31, …
j 25, 27, 29, 31, …

5 A sequence of fractions is $\frac{3}{4}, \frac{5}{7}, \frac{7}{10}, \frac{9}{13}, \frac{11}{16}, \ldots$

a Find the nth term in the sequence.

b By changing each fraction to a decimal, can you see a pattern?

c What, as a decimal, will be the value of:

i the 100th term **ii** the 1000th term?

d Use your answers to part **c** to predict what the 10 000th term and the millionth term are. (Check these on your calculator.)

6 Repeat question **5** for $\frac{3}{6}, \frac{7}{11}, \frac{11}{16}, \frac{15}{21}, \frac{19}{26}, \ldots$

FM 7 A haulage company uses this formula to calculate the cost of transporting n pallets.

For $n \leqslant 5$, the cost will be £$(40n + 50)$.

For $6 \leqslant n \leqslant 10$, the cost will be £$(40n + 25)$.

For $n \geqslant 11$, the cost will be £$40n$.

a How much will the company charge to transport seven pallets?

b How much will the company charge to transport 15 pallets?

c A company is charged £170 for transporting pallets. How many pallets did they transport?

d Another haulage company uses the formula £$50n$ to calculate the costs for transporting n pallets.

At what value of n do the two companies charge the same amount?

PS 8 The formula for working out a series of fractions is $\frac{2n + 1}{3n + 1}$.

a Work out the first three fractions in the series.

b **i** Work out the value of the fraction as a decimal when $n = 1\,000\,000$.

ii What fraction is equivalent to this decimal?

c How can you tell this from the original formula?

EXAMPLE 6

From the sequence 5, 12, 19, 26, 33, … find the following.

a the nth term **b** the 50th term **c** the first term that is greater than 1000

a The difference between consecutive terms is 7. So the first part of the nth term is $7n$.

Subtract the difference 7 from the first term 5, which gives $5 - 7 = -2$.

So the nth term is given by $7n - 2$.

b The 50th term is found by substituting $n = 50$ into the rule, $7n - 2$.

So 50th term $= 7 \times 50 - 2 = 350 - 2$

$= 348$

c The first term that is greater than 1000 is given by:

$$7n - 2 > 1000$$

$$\Rightarrow 7n > 1000 + 2$$

$$\Rightarrow n > \frac{1002}{7}$$

$$n > 143.14$$

So the first term (which has to be a whole number) over 1000 is the 144th.

EXERCISE 13B

1 Find the next two terms and the nth term in each of these linear sequences.

HINTS AND TIPS

Remember to look at the differences and the first term.

a 3, 5, 7, 9, 11, … **b** 5, 9, 13, 17, 21, …
c 8, 13, 18, 23, 28, … **d** 2, 8, 14, 20, 26, …
e 5, 8, 11, 14, 17, … **f** 2, 9, 16, 23, 30, …
g 1, 5, 9, 13, 17, … **h** 3, 7, 11, 15, 19, … **i** 2, 5, 8, 11, 14, …
j 2, 12, 22, 32, … **k** 8, 12, 16, 20, … **l** 4, 9, 14, 19, 24, …

2 Find the nth term and the 50th term in each of these linear sequences.

a 4, 7, 10, 13, 16, … **b** 7, 9, 11, 13, 15, … **c** 3, 8, 13, 18, 23, …
d 1, 5, 9, 13, 17, … **e** 2, 10, 18, 26, … **f** 5, 6, 7, 8, 9, …
g 6, 11, 16, 21, 26, … **h** 3, 11, 19, 27, 35, … **i** 1, 4, 7, 10, 13, …
j 21, 24, 27, 30, 33, … **k** 12, 19, 26, 33, 40, … **l** 1, 9, 17, 25, 33, …

3 **a** Which term of the sequence 5, 8, 11, 14, 17, … is the first one to be greater than 100?

b Which term of the sequence 1, 8, 15, 22, 29, … is the first one to be greater than 200?

c Which term of the sequence 4, 9, 14, 19, 24, … is the closest to 500?

C

13.2 Finding the nth term of a linear sequence

This section will show you how to:
- find the nth term of a linear sequence

Key words
nth term

A linear sequence has the same *difference* between each term and the next.

For example:

2, 5, 8, 11, 14, … difference of 3

The ***n*th term** of this sequence is given by $3n - 1$.

Here is another linear sequence:

5, 7, 9, 11, 13, … difference of 2

The nth term of this sequence is given by $2n + 3$.

So, you can see that the nth term of a linear sequence is *always* of the form $An + b$, where:

- A, the coefficient of n, is the difference between each term and the next term (consecutive terms)
- b is the difference between the first term and A.

EXAMPLE 4

Find the nth term of the sequence 5, 7, 9, 11, 13, …

The difference between consecutive terms is 2. So the first part of the nth term is $2n$.

Subtract the difference, 2, from the first term, 5, which gives $5 - 2 = 3$.

So the nth term is given by $2n + 3$.

(You can test it by substituting $n = 1, 2, 3, 4, \dots$.)

EXAMPLE 5

Find the nth term of the sequence 3, 7, 11, 15, 19, …

The difference between consecutive terms is 4. So the first part of the nth term is $4n$.

Subtract the difference 4 from the first term 3, which gives $3 - 4 = -1$.

So the nth term is given by $4n - 1$.

AU **8** On the first day of Christmas my true love sent to me:

a partridge in a pear tree

On the second day of Christmas my true love sent to me:

two turtle doves
and a partridge in a pear tree

and so on until…

On the twelfth day of Christmas my true love sent to me:

twelve drummers drumming
eleven pipers piping
ten lords a-leaping
nine ladies dancing
eight maids a-milking
seven swans a-swimming
six geese a-laying
five golden rings
four calling birds
three French hens
two turtle doves
and a partridge in a pear tree

How many presents were given, in total, on the 12 days of Christmas?

HINTS AND TIPS

Work out the pattern for the number of presents each day. For example, on day 1 there was 1 present, on day 2 there were 2 + 1 = 3 presents, and so on. Total the presents after each day, so after 1 day there was a total of 1 present, after 2 days a total of 4 presents, and so on. Also, try to spot any patterns.

PS **9** The first term that these two sequences have in common is 17:

8, 11, 14, 17, 20, …
1, 5, 9, 13, 17, …

What are the next two terms that the two sequences have in common?

AU **10** Two sequences are:

2, 5, 8, 11, 14, …
3, 6, 9, 12, 15, …

Will the two sequences ever have a term in common?

Show how you decided.

AU **11** The nth term of a sequence is $3n + 7$.

The nth term of another sequence is $4n - 2$.

These two sequences have several terms in common but only one term that is common *and* has the same position in the sequence.

Without writing out the sequences, show how you can tell, using the expressions for the nth term, that this is the 9th term.

C

Chapter 13 Algebra: Algebraic methods

This chapter will show you ...

- **C** How to express a rule for a sequence in words and algebraically
- **B** Some common sequences of numbers
- **A to A*** How to rearrange a formula where the subject appears twice
- **B to A*** How to combine fractions algebraically and solve equations with algebraic fractions
- **A** How to solve linear and non-linear simultaneous equations
- **B to A*** How to prove results, using rigorous and logical mathematical arguments

Visual overview

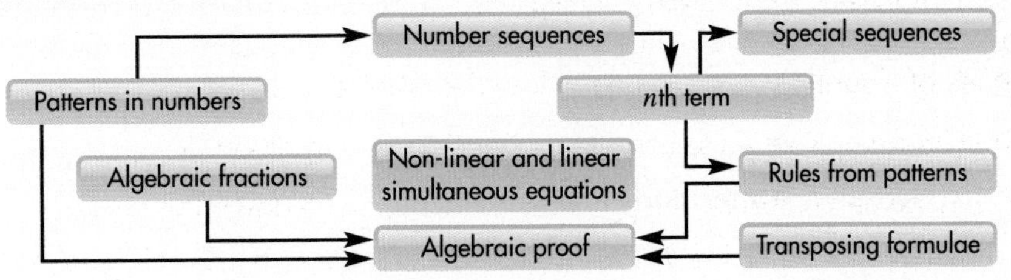

What you should already know

- How to substitute numbers into an algebraic expression **(KS3 level 5, GCSE grade E)**
- How to state a rule for a simple linear sequence in words **(KS3 level 6, GCSE grade D)**
- How to factorise simple linear expressions **(KS3 level 6, GCSE grade D)**
- How to expand a pair of linear brackets to get a quadratic equation **(KS3 level 7, GCSE grade C)**

Quick check

1 Write down the next three terms of these sequences.
a 2, 5, 8, 11, 14, … **b** 1, 4, 9, 16, 25, 36, ….

2 Work out the value of the expression $3n - 2$ for:
a $n = 1$ **b** $n = 2$ **c** $n = 3$

3 Factorise: **a** $2x + 6$ **b** $x^2 - x$ **c** $10x^2 + 2x$

4 Expand: **a** $(x + 6)(x + 2)$ **b** $(2x + 1)(x - 3)$ **c** $(x - 2)^2$

5 Make x the subject of: **a** $2y + x = 3$ **b** $x - 3y = 4$ **c** $4y - x = 3$

13.1 Number sequences

This section will show you how to:

- recognise how number sequences are built up
- generate sequences, given the nth term

Key words

coefficient
consecutive
difference
nth term
sequence
term
term-to-term

A number **sequence** is an ordered set of numbers with a rule to find every number in the sequence. The rule that takes you from one number to the next could be a simple addition or multiplication, but often it is more tricky than that. So you need to look most carefully at the pattern of a sequence.

Each number in a sequence is called a **term** and is in a certain position in the sequence.

Look at these sequences and their rules.

3, 6, 12, 24, ... doubling the last term each time ... 48, 96, ...

2, 5, 8, 11, ... adding 3 to the last term each time ... 14, 17, ...

1, 10, 100, 1000, ... multiplying the last term by 10 each time ... 10 000, 100 000, ...

1, 8, 15, 22, ... adding 7 to the last term each time ... 29, 36, ...

These are all quite straightforward once you have looked for the link from one term to the next (**consecutive** terms). A pattern in which each term (apart from the first) is derived from the term before it is a **term-to-term** sequence.

Differences

For some sequences you need to look at the **differences** between consecutive terms to determine the pattern.

EXAMPLE 1

Find the next two terms of the sequence 1, 3, 6, 10, 15, ...

Looking at the differences between each pair of consecutive terms, you notice:

```
1    3    6    10    15
   ↑    ↑    ↑     ↑
   2    3    4     5
```

So, you can continue the sequence as follows:

```
1    3    6    10    15    21    28
   ↑    ↑    ↑     ↑
   2    3    4     5    +6    +7
```

The differences usually form a number sequence of their own, so you need to find out the sequence of the differences before you can expand the original sequence.

Generalising to find the rule

When using a number sequence, you sometimes need to know, say, its 50th term, or even a later term in the sequence. To do so, you need to find the rule that produces the sequence in its general form.

Let's first look at the problem backwards. That is, take a rule and see how it produces a sequence.

EXAMPLE 2

A sequence is formed by the rule $3n + 1$, where $n = 1, 2, 3, 4, 5, 6, \ldots$. Write down the first five terms of the sequence.

Substituting $n = 1, 2, 3, 4, 5$ in turn:

$$(3 \times 1 + 1), (3 \times 2 + 1), (3 \times 3 + 1), (3 \times 4 + 1), (3 \times 5 + 1), \ldots$$
$$4 \qquad 7 \qquad 10 \qquad 13 \qquad 16$$

So the sequence is 4, 7, 10, 13, 16, …

Notice that the difference between each term and the next is always 3, which is the **coefficient** of n (the number attached to n). The constant term is the difference between the first term and the coefficient (in this case, $4 - 3 = 1$).

EXAMPLE 3

The ***n*th term** of a sequence is $4n - 3$. Write down the first five terms of the sequence.

Substituting $n = 1, 2, 3, 4, 5$ in turn:

$$(4 \times 1 - 3), (4 \times 2 - 3), (4 \times 3 - 3), (4 \times 4 - 3), (4 \times 5 - 3)$$
$$1 \qquad 5 \qquad 9 \qquad 13 \qquad 17$$

So the sequence is 1, 5, 9, 13, 17, …

Notice that the difference between each term and the next is always 4, which is the coefficient of n. The constant term is the difference between the first term and the coefficient ($1 - 4 = -3$).

EXERCISE 13A

1 Look carefully at each number sequence below. Find the next two numbers in the sequence and try to explain the pattern.

a 1, 1, 2, 3, 5, 8, 13, …

b 1, 4, 9, 16, 25, 36, …

c 3, 4, 7, 11, 18, 29, …

HINTS AND TIPS

These patterns do not go up by the same value each time so you will need to find another connection between the terms.

D

2 Triangular numbers are found as follows.

Find the next four triangular numbers.

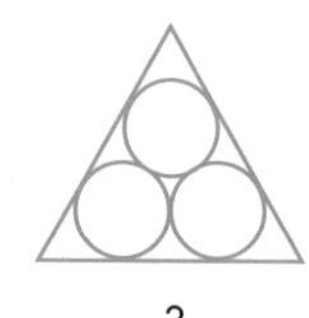

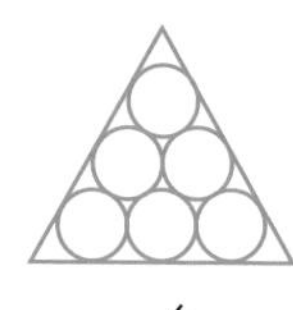

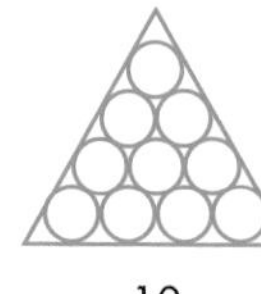

3 Hexagonal numbers are found as follows.

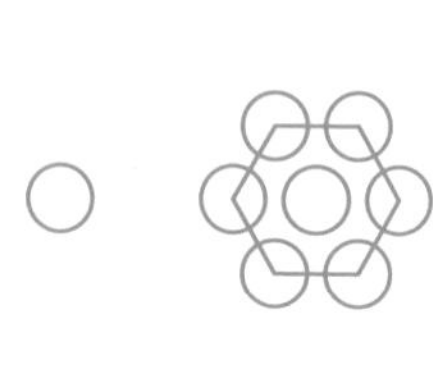

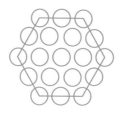

Find the next three hexagonal numbers.

4 The first two terms of the sequence of fractions $\frac{n-1}{n+1}$ are:

$n = 1 : \frac{1-1}{1+1} = \frac{0}{2} = 0 \qquad n = 2 : \frac{2-1}{2+1} = \frac{1}{3}$

Work out the next five terms of the sequence.

5 A sequence is formed by the rule $\frac{1}{2} \times n \times (n + 1)$ for $n = 1, 2, 3, 4, \ldots$

The first term is given by $n = 1 : \frac{1}{2} \times 1 \times (1 + 1) = 1$

The second term is given by $n = 2 : \frac{1}{2} \times 2 \times (2 + 1) = 3$

a Work out the next five terms of this sequence.

b This is a well-known sequence you have met before. What is it?

6 5! means 'factorial 5', which is $5 \times 4 \times 3 \times 2 \times 1 = 120$

In the same way 7! means $7 \times 6 \times 5 \times 4 \times 3 \times 2 \times 1 = 5040$

a Calculate 2!, 3!, 4! and 6!

b If your calculator has a factorial button, check that it gives the same answers as you get for part **a**. What is the largest factorial you can work out with your calculator before you get an error?

PS 7 The letters of the alphabet are written as the pattern:

ABBCCCDDDDEEEEEFFFFFFGGGGGGG …

so that the number of each times the letter is written matches its place in the alphabet.

So, for example, as J is the 10th letter in the alphabet, there will be 10 Js in the list.

When the pattern gets to the 26th Z, it repeats.

What letter will be the 1000th in the list?

HINTS AND TIPS

Work out how many letters there are in the sequence from ABB … to … ZZZ, then work out how many of these sequences are needed to get past 1000.

Why this chapter matters

We have already seen that patterns appear in numbers — prime numbers, square numbers and multiples — all form patterns. Number patterns are not only of mathematical value, they also make the study of nature and geometric patterns a little more interesting.

There are many mathematical patterns that appear in nature. The most famous of these is probably the Fibonacci series.

1 1 2 3 5 8 13 21 ...

This is formed by adding the two previous terms to get the next term.

The sequence was discovered by the Italian, Leonardo Fibonacci, in 1202, when he was investigating the breeding patterns of rabbits!

Since then, the pattern has been found in many other places in nature. The spirals found in a nautilus shell and in the seed heads of a sunflower plant also follow the Fibonacci series.

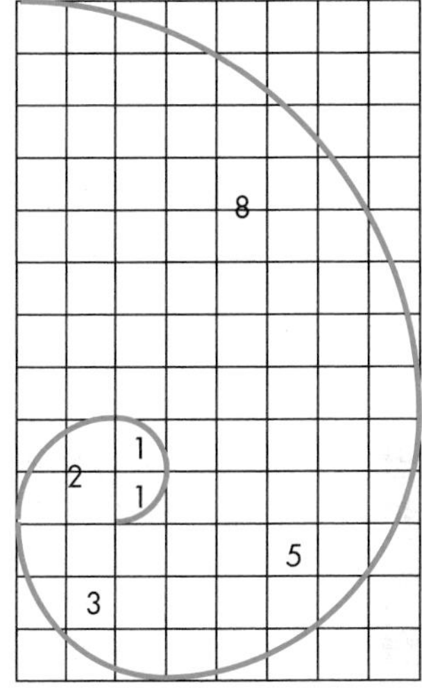

The Fibonnaci sequence has some other interesting properties.

- Divide each term by the previous term and write down the results.

  $1 \div 1 = 1$, $2 \div 1 = 2$, $3 \div 2 = 1.5$, $5 \div 3 = 1.66$, $8 \div 5 = 1.6$, $13 \div 8 = 1.625$, ...
- Set up a spreadsheet to do this for 100 terms.
- Then look up the *Golden ratio* on the internet.

Fractals form another kind of pattern.

Fractals are geometric patterns that are continuously repeated on a smaller and smaller scale.

A good example of a fractal is this: start with an equilateral triangle and draw an equilateral triangle, a third the size of the original, on the middle of each side. Keep on repeating this and you will get an increasingly complex-looking shape.

The pattern shown here is called the Koch snowflake. It is named after the Swedish mathematician, Helge von Koch (1870–1924).

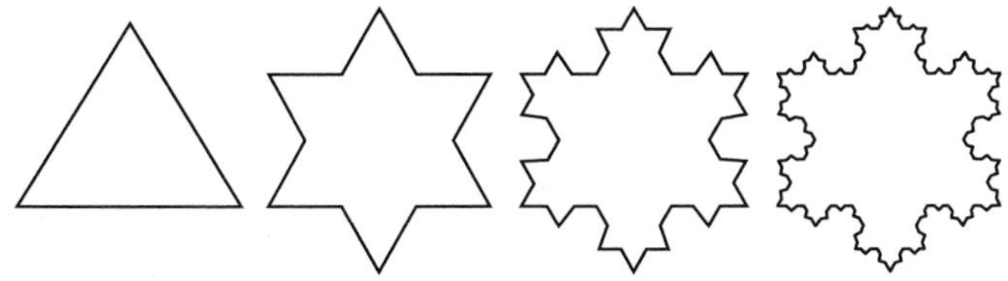

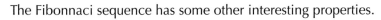

Fractals are commonly found in nature, a good example being the complex patterns found in plants, such as the leaves of a fern.

Your task

1 Investigate the number of odd nodes and even nodes that each of these shapes has, and whether they are traversable networks. Find the rule that makes a network traversable.

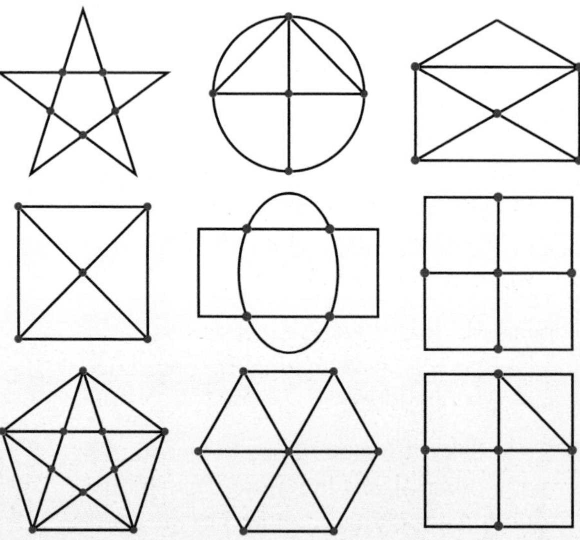

Prove your rule by creating networks of your own.

2 This is a plan of a building

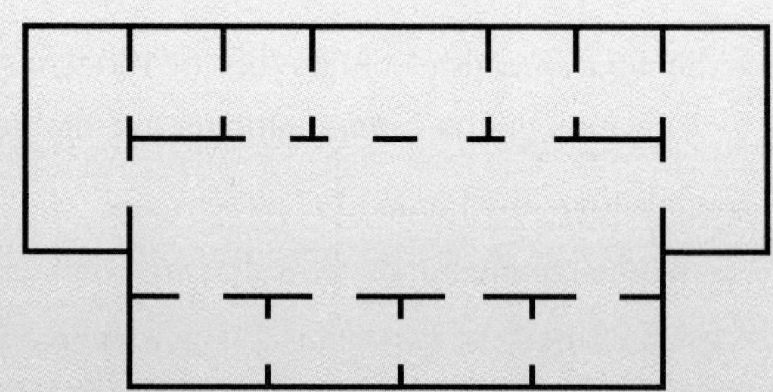

Using your rule, trace a route through the house so that you pass through each door once, and only once.

Extension

Research the Königsberg Bridge problem (which you first learnt about on page 344), and Leonhard Euler. Use your research to check the rule you found in your task and to find out more about networks.

12 Problem Solving
Traverse the network

Graph theory is the study of mathematical structures that model the relationship between objects from one collection. Just think about the 3D molecular structures that you see in chemistry – these are an example of how graph theory can be used.

Graph theory is also used to create networks. You can often 'traverse' a network. Effectively, this means that you can draw them without taking your pen off the page. In this task you will look for a rule for working out when it is possible to traverse a network.

Getting started

Draw these networks, without taking your pen off the page if possible.

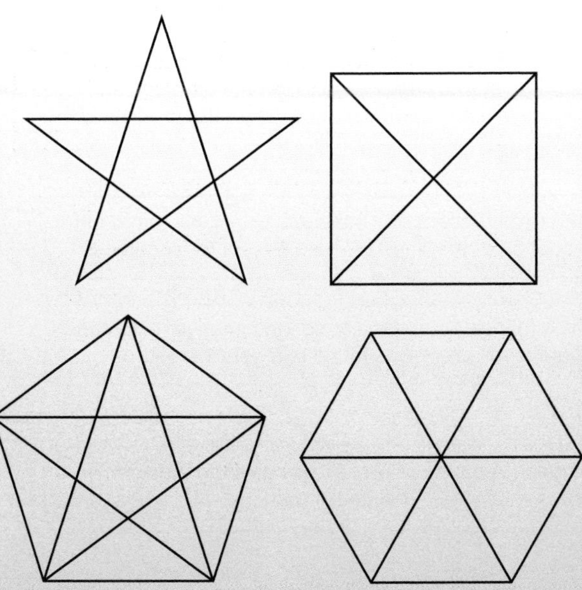

Facts

Arcs and nodes

A **node** is a point where **arcs** meet. This shape has 5 nodes and 10 arcs.

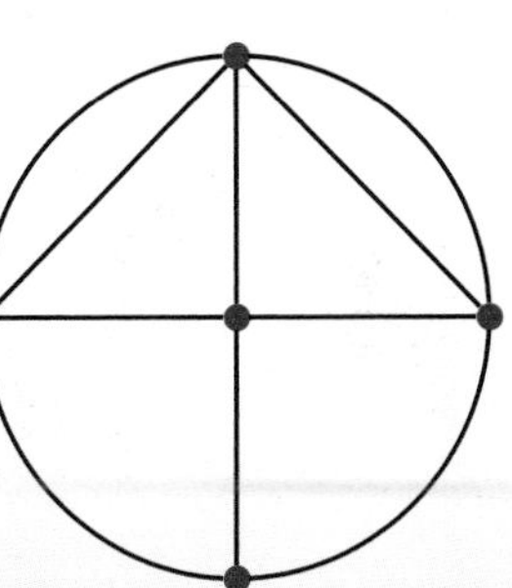

The degree of a node

The degree of a node is how many arcs intersect at that node.

This shape has one node of degree 5, one node of degree 3 and three nodes of degree 4

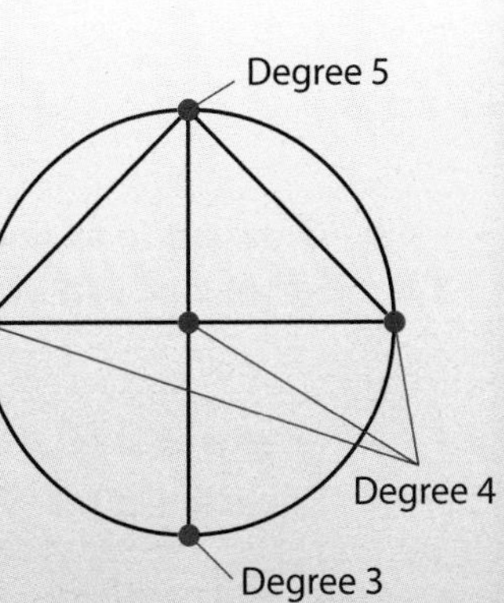

Worked Examination Questions

AU **4** **a** Find the equation of the line shown.

b Find the equation of the line perpendicular to the line shown and passing through (0, –5).

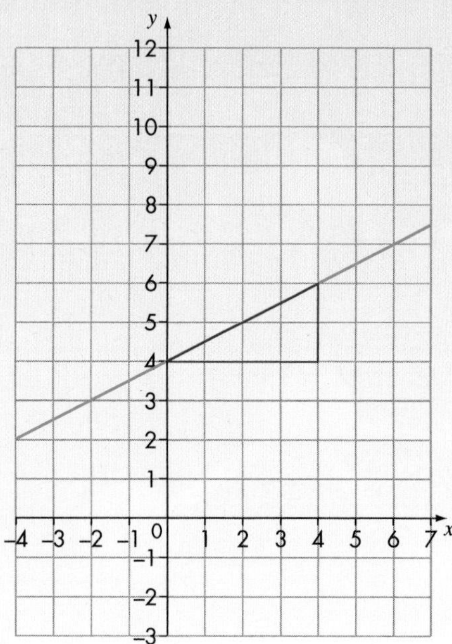

4 a Intercept is at (0, 4)

First identify the point where the line crosses the y-axis. This is the intercept, c. This gets 1 mark.

Gradient = $\frac{2}{4} = \frac{1}{2}$

Equation of the line is $y = \frac{1}{2}x + 4$

Draw a right-angled triangle using grid lines as two sides of the triangle and part of the line as the hypotenuse. (Shown in red on diagram.) This gets 1 mark for method. Measure the y-step and the x-step of the triangle and divide the y-step by the x-step to get the gradient, m. As the line slopes down from left to right the gradient is negative.

Put the two numbers into the equation $y = mx + c$ to get the equation of the line. This gets 1 mark for accuracy.

b Gradient is the negative reciprocal of the one in **a** so is: –2

This is a follow-through mark, so the negative reciprocal of whatever gradient was found in **a** gets 1 mark.

Intercept is (0, –1)
Equation is $y = -2x - 1$

Point given is on the y-axis, so just give the equation in the form $y = mx + c$. This gets 1 mark.

Total: 5 marks

EXERCISE 13C

C

1 The powers of 2 are $2^1, 2^2, 2^3, 2^4, 2^5, \ldots$

This gives the sequence 2, 4, 8, 16, 32, …

The *n*th term is given by 2^n.

a Continue the sequence for another five terms.

b Give the *n*th term of these sequences.

i 1, 3, 7, 15, 31, … **ii** 3, 5, 9, 17, 33, … **iii** 6, 12, 24, 48, 96, …

2 The powers of 10 are $10^1, 10^2, 10^3, 10^4, 10^5, \ldots$

This gives the sequence 10, 100, 1000, 10 000, 100 000, …

The *n*th term is given by 10^n.

a Describe the connection between the number of zeros in each term and the power of the term.

b If $10^n = 1\,000\,000$, what is the value of *n*?

c Give the *n*th term of these sequences.

i 9, 99, 999, 9 999, 99 999, … **ii** 20, 200, 2000, 20 000, 200 000, …

3 a Pick any odd number. Pick any other odd number.

Add the two numbers together. Is the answer odd or even?

Complete this table.

+	**Odd**	**Even**
Odd	Even	
Even		

b Pick any odd number. Pick any other odd number.

Multiply the two numbers together. Is the answer odd or even?

Complete this table.

×	**Odd**	**Even**
Odd	Odd	
Even		

AU 4 a Write down the next two lines of this number pattern.

$$1 = 1 = 1^2$$
$$1 + 3 = 4 = 2^2$$
$$1 + 3 + 5 = 9 = 3^2$$

b Use the pattern in part **a** to write down the total of.

i 1 + 3 + 5 + 7 + 9 + 11 + 13 + 15 + 17 + 19

ii 2 + 4 + 6 + 8 + 10 + 12 + 14

C

5 The triangular numbers are 1, 3, 6, 10, 15, 21, …

a Continue the sequence for another five terms.

b The nth term of this sequence is given by $\frac{1}{2}n(n + 1)$.

Use the formula to find:

i the 20th triangular number

ii the 100th triangular number.

c Add consecutive terms of the triangular number sequence.

For example, $1 + 3 = 4$, $3 + 6 = 9$, …

What do you notice?

PS 6 p is an odd number, q is an even number. State if the following are odd or even.

a $p + 1$ **b** $q + 1$ **c** $p + q$

d p^2 **e** $qp + 1$ **f** $(p + q)(p - q)$

g $q^2 + 4$ **h** $p^2 + q^2$ **i** p^3

PS 7 p is a prime number, q is an even number.

State if the following are odd or even, or could be either odd or even.

a $p + 1$ **b** $p + q$ **c** p^2

d $qp + 1$ **e** $(p + q)(p - q)$ **f** $2p + 3q$

AU 8 **a** p is an odd number, q is an even number and r is an odd number.

Are the following expressions odd or even?

i $pq + r$ **ii** pqr **iii** $(p + q)^2 + r$

b x is a prime number and both y and z are odd.

Write an expression using all of x, y, and z, and no other numbers or letters, so that the answer is always even.

PS 9 A palindromic number is one that reads the same forwards as backwards, e.g. 242, 1001.

In the triangular number series 1, 3, 6, 10, 15, …, the first palindromic number is the 10th term: 55.

Find the next two palindromic triangular numbers.

AU 10 The square numbers are 1, 4, 9, 16, 25, …

The nth term of this sequence is n^2.

a Continue the sequence for another five terms.

b Give the nth term of these sequences.

i 2, 5, 10, 17, 26, … **ii** 2, 8, 18, 32, 50, … **iii** 0, 3, 8, 15, 24, …

13.4 General rules from given patterns

This section will show you how to:

- find the nth term from practical problems

Key words
difference
pattern
rule

Many problem-solving situations that you are likely to meet involve number sequences. So you need to be able to formulate general **rules** from given number **patterns**.

EXAMPLE 8

The diagram shows a pattern of squares building up.

a How many squares will be in the nth pattern?

b Which pattern has 99 squares in it?

a First, build up the following table for the patterns.

Pattern number	1	2	3	4	5
No. of squares	1	3	5	7	9

Looking at the difference between consecutive patterns, you can see it is always two squares. So, use $2n$.

Subtract the difference 2 from the first number, which gives $1 - 2 = -1$.

So the number of squares on the base of the nth pattern is $2n - 1$.

b Now find n when $2n - 1 = 99$:

$$2n - 1 = 99$$
$$2n = 99 + 1 = 100$$
$$n = 100 \div 2 = 50$$

The pattern with 99 squares is the 50th.

When you are trying to find a general rule from a sequence of diagrams, always set up a table to connect the pattern number with the number of the variable (squares, matches, seats, etc.) that you are trying to find the rule for. Once the table is set up, it is easy to find the nth term.

EXERCISE 13D

C

1 A pattern of squares is built up from matchsticks as shown.

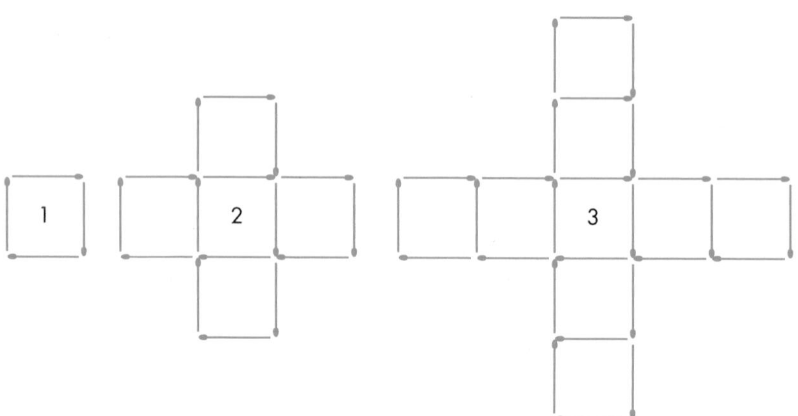

a Draw the fourth diagram.

b How many squares are in the nth diagram?

c How many squares are in the 25th diagram?

d With 200 squares, which is the biggest diagram that could be made?

> **HINTS AND TIPS**
>
> Write out the number sequences to help you see the patterns.

2 A pattern of triangles is built up from matchsticks.

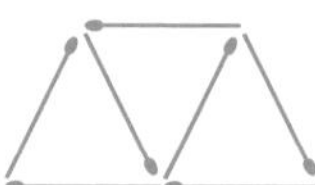
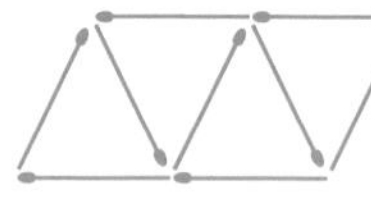

1 2 3 4

a Draw the fifth set of triangles in this pattern.

b How many matchsticks are needed for the nth set of triangles?

c How many matchsticks are needed to make the 60th set of triangles?

d If there are only 100 matchsticks, which is the largest set of triangles that could be made?

FM 3 A conference centre had tables each of which could sit six people. When put together, the tables could seat people as shown.

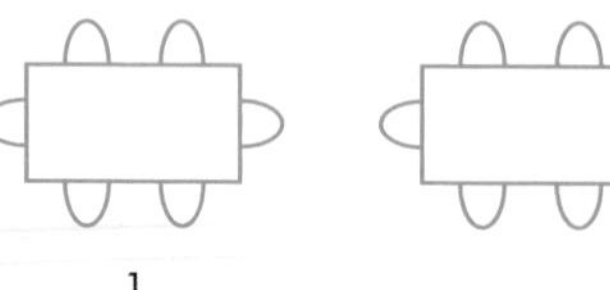
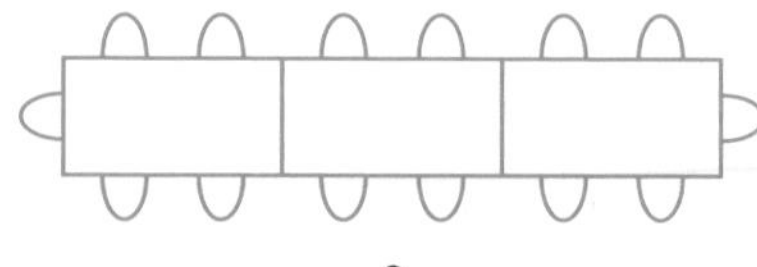

1 2 3

a How many people could be seated at four tables put together this way?

b How many people could be seated at n tables put together in this way?

c A conference had 50 people who wished to use the tables in this way. How many tables would they need?

4 Prepacked fencing units come in the shape shown on the right, made of four pieces of wood. When you put them together in stages to make a fence, you also need joining pieces, so the fence will start to build up as shown below.

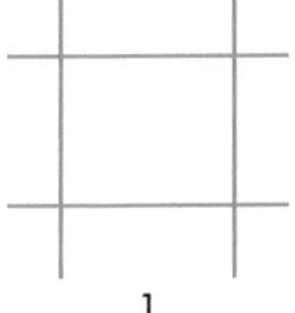

1

2

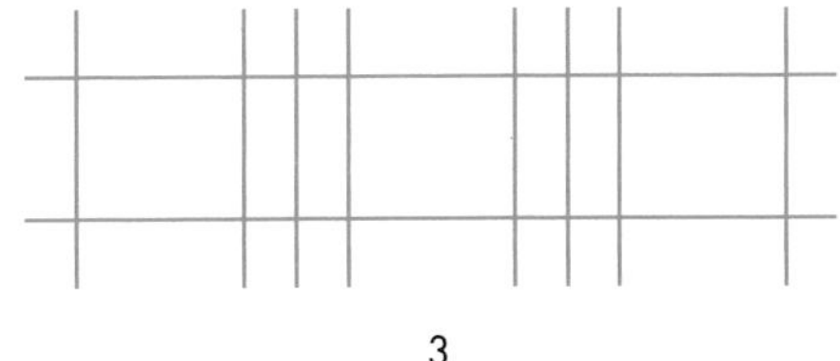

3

a How many pieces of wood would you have in a fence made up in:

i five stages

ii n stages

iii 45 stages?

b I made a fence out of 124 pieces of wood. How many stages did I use?

5 Regular pentagons of side length 1 cm are joined together to make a pattern, as shown.

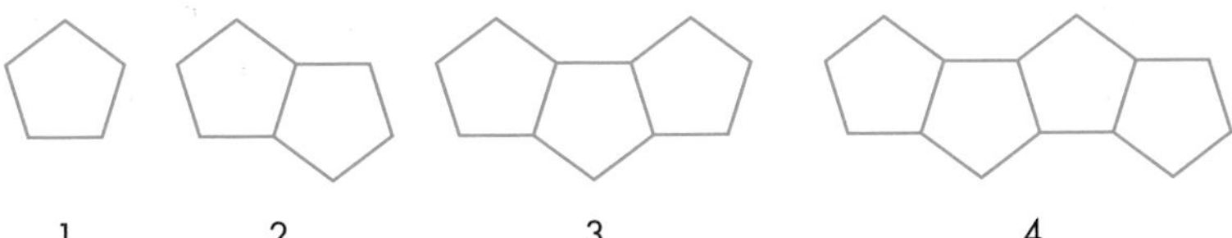

1 2 3 4

Copy this pattern and write down the perimeter of each shape.

a What is the perimeter of patterns like this made from:

i six pentagons

ii n pentagons

iii 50 pentagons?

b What is the largest number of pentagons that can be put together like this to have a perimeter less than 1000 cm?

FM 6 Lamp-posts are put at the end of every 100-m stretch of a motorway, as shown.

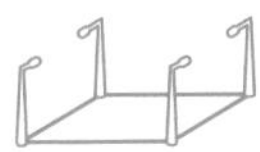

1

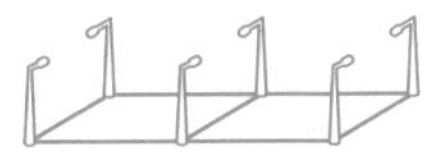

2

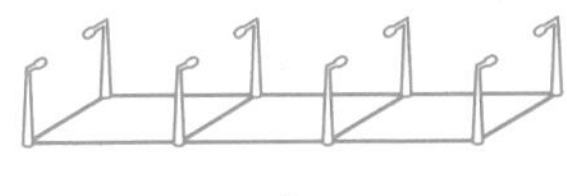

3

a How many lamp-posts are needed for:

i 900 m of this motorway

ii 8 km of this motorway?

b The M99 motorway is being built. The contractor has ordered 1598 lamp-posts. How long is this motorway?

C

FM 7 A school dining hall had trapezium-shaped tables. Each table could seat five people, as shown on the right. When the tables were joined together, as shown below, each table could not seat as many people.

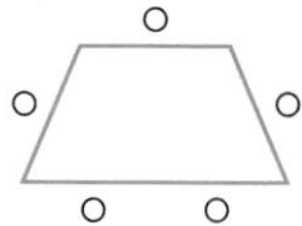

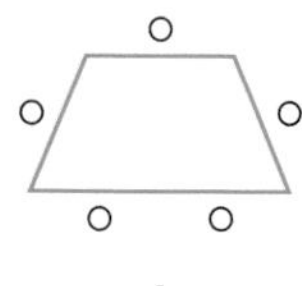

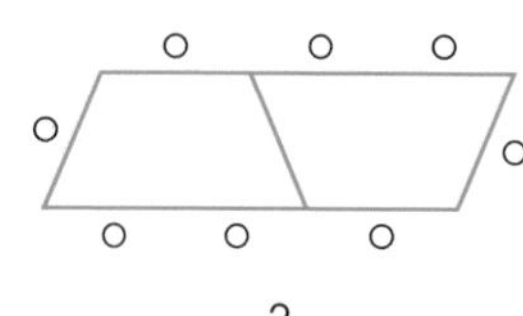

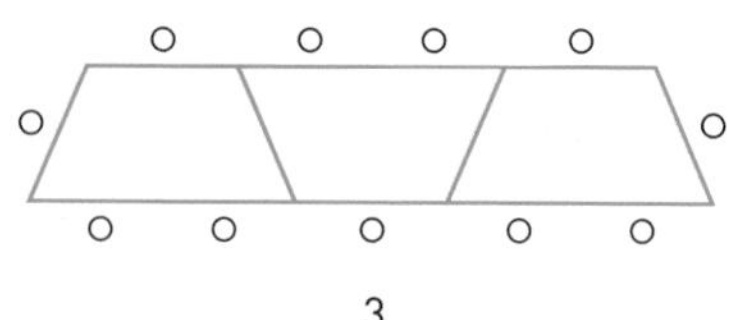

1 2 3

a In this arrangement, how many could be seated if there were:

i four tables **ii** n tables **iii** 13 tables?

b For an outside charity event, up to 200 people had to be seated. How many tables arranged like this did they need?

FM 8 When setting out tins to make a display of a certain height, you need to know how many tins to start with at the bottom.

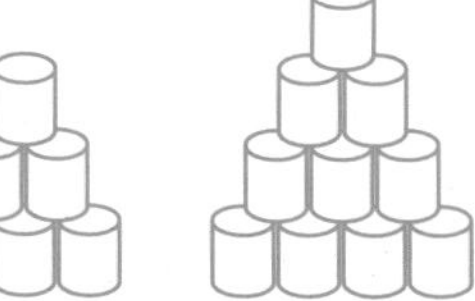

a How many tins are needed on the bottom if you wish the display to be:

i five tins high **ii** n tins high **iii** 18 tins high?

b I saw a shop assistant starting to build a display, and noticed he was starting with 20 tins on the bottom. How high was the display when it was finished?

9 **a** The values of 2 raised to a positive whole-number power are 2, 4, 8, 16, 32, …

What is the nth term of this sequence?

b A supermarket sells four different-sized bottles of water: pocket size, 100 ml; standard size, 200 ml; family size, 400 ml; giant size, 800 ml.

i Describe the number pattern that the contents follow.

ii The supermarket introduces a super giant size, which is the next-sized bottle in the pattern. How much does this bottle hold?

PS 10 Draw an equilateral triangle.

Mark the midpoints of each side and draw and shade in the equilateral triangle formed by these points.

Repeat this with the three unshaded triangles remaining.

Keep on doing this with the unshaded triangles that are left.

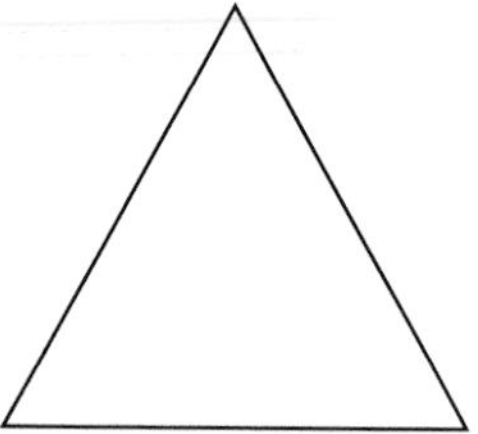

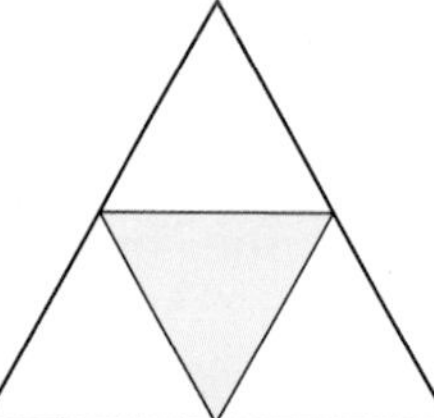

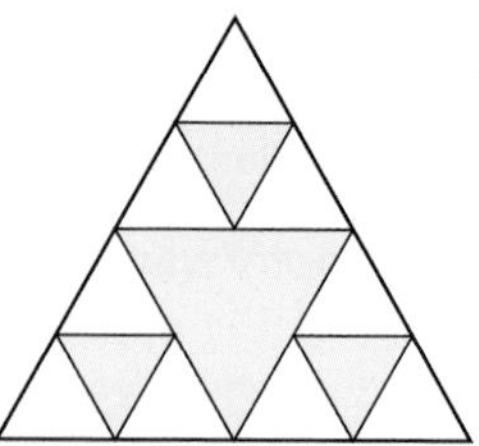

The pattern is called a Sierpinski triangle and is one of the earliest examples of a fractal type pattern.

The shaded areas in each triangle are $\frac{1}{4}$, $\frac{7}{16}$, $\frac{37}{64}$, $\frac{175}{256}$.

It is very difficult to work out an nth term for this series of fractions.

Use your calculator to work out the **unshaded** area, e.g. $\frac{3}{4}$, $\frac{9}{16}$,…

You should be able to write down a formula for the nth term of this pattern.

Pick a large value for n.

Will the shaded area ever cover all of the original triangle?

AU 11 Thom is building three different patterns with matches.

He builds the patterns in steps.

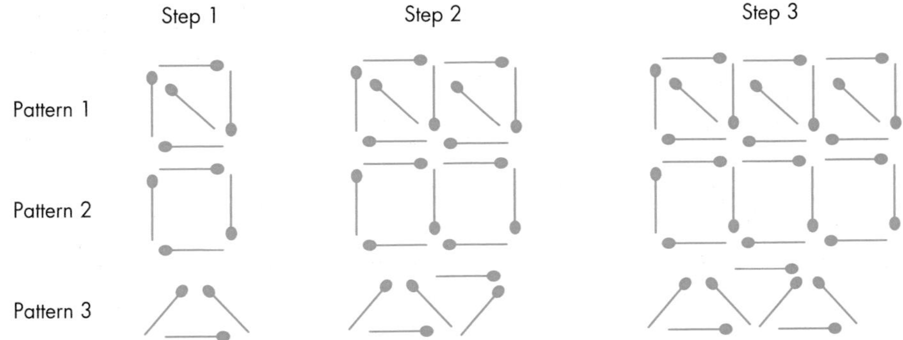

Thom has five boxes of matches that are labelled 'Average contents 42 matches'.

Will Thom have enough matches to get to step 20?

Show your working.

FM 12 For a display of grapefruit, a supermarket manager stacks them in layers, each of which is a triangle.

These are the first four layers.

a If the display is four layers deep, how many grapefruit will be in the display?

b The manager tells her staff that there should not be any more than eight layers, as the fruit will get squashed otherwise.

What is the most grapefruit that could be stacked?

13.5 Changing the subject of a formula

This section will show you how to:

- change the subject of a formula where the subject occurs more than once

Key words
subject

You have already considered changing the **subject** of a formula in which the subject appears only once. This is like solving an equation but using letters. You have also solved equations in which the unknown appears on both sides of the equation. This requires you to collect the terms in the unknown (usually x) on one side and the numbers on the other.

You can do something similar, to rearrange formulae in which the subject appears more than once. The principle is the same. Collect all the subject terms on the same side and everything else on the other side. Most often, you then need to factorise the subject out of the resulting expression.

EXAMPLE 9

Make x the subject of this formula.

$$ax + b = cx + d$$

First, rearrange the formula to get all the x-terms on the left-hand side and all the other terms on the right-hand side. (The rule 'change sides – change signs' still applies.)

$$ax - cx = d - b$$

Factorise x out of the left-hand side to get:

$$x(a - c) = d - b$$

Divide by the expression in brackets, which gives:

$$x = \frac{d - b}{a - c}$$

EXAMPLE 10

Make p the subject of this formula.

$$5 = \frac{ap + b}{cp + d}$$

First, multiply both sides by the denominator of the algebraic fraction, which gives:

$$5(cp + d) = ap + b$$

Expand the brackets to get:

$$5cp + 5d = ap + b$$

Now continue as in Example 9:

$$5cp - ap = b - 5d$$

$$p(5c - a) = b - 5d$$

$$p = \frac{b + 5d}{5c - a}$$

EXERCISE 13E

In questions **1** to **10**, make the letter in brackets the subject of the formula.

1 $3(x + 2y) = 2(x - y)$ (x)

2 $3(x + 2y) = 2(x - y)$ (y)

3 $5 = \dfrac{a + b}{a - c}$ (a)

4 $p(a + b) = q(a - b)$ (a)

5 $p(a + b) = q(a - b)$ (b)

6 $A = 2\pi rh + \pi rk$ (r)

7 $v^2 = u^2 + av^2$ (v)

8 $s(t - r) = 2r - 3$ (r)

9 $s(t - r) = 2(r - 3)$ (r)

10 $R = \dfrac{x - 3}{x - 2}$ (x)

11 **a** The perimeter of the shape shown on the right is given by the formula $P = \pi r + 2kr$. Make r the subject of this formula.

b The area of the same shape is given by $A = \frac{1}{2}[\pi r^2 + r^2\sqrt{(k^2 - 1)}]$ Make r the subject of this formula.

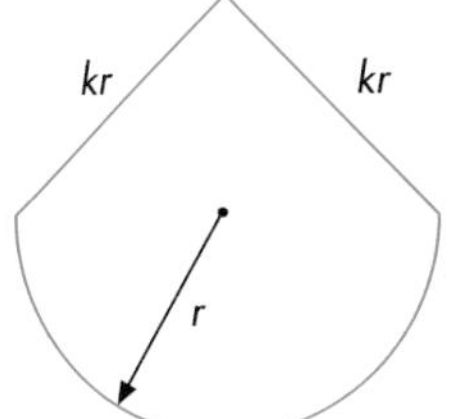

12 When £P is invested for Y years at a simple interest rate of R, the following formula gives the amount, A, at any time.

$$A = P + \frac{PRY}{100}$$

Make P the subject of this formula.

13 When two resistors with values a and b are connected in parallel, the total resistance is given by:

$$R = \frac{ab}{a + b}$$

a Make b the subject of the formula.

b Write the formula when a is the subject.

AU **14** **a** Make x the subject of this formula.

$$y = \frac{x + 2}{x - 2}$$

b Show that the formula $y = 1 + \dfrac{4}{x - 2}$ can be rearranged to give:

$$x = 2 + \frac{4}{y - 1}$$

c Combine the right-hand sides of each formula in part **b** into single fractions and simplify as much as possible.

d What do you notice?

A*

15 The volume of the solid shown is given by:

$V = \frac{2}{3}\pi r^3 + \pi r^2 h$

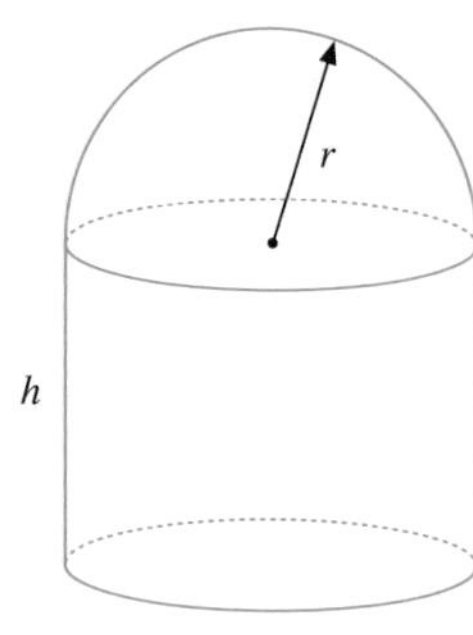

a Explain why it is not possible to make r the subject of this formula.

b Make π the subject.

c If $h = r$, can the formula be rearranged to make r the subject? If so, rearrange it to make r the subject.

16 Make x the subject of this formula.

$W = \frac{1}{2}z(x + y) + \frac{1}{2}y(x + z)$

PS 17 The following formulae in y can be rearranged to give the formulae in terms of x as shown.

$y = \dfrac{x + 1}{x + 2}$ gives $x = \dfrac{1 - 2y}{y - 1}$

$y = \dfrac{2x + 1}{x + 2}$ gives $x = \dfrac{1 - 2y}{y - 2}$

$y = \dfrac{3x + 2}{4x + 1}$ gives $x = \dfrac{2 - y}{4y - 3}$

$y = \dfrac{x + 5}{3x + 2}$ gives $x = \dfrac{5 - 2y}{3y - 1}$

Without rearranging the formula, write down $y = \dfrac{5x + 1}{2x + 3}$ as $x = \ldots$ and explain how you can do this without any algebra.

AU 18 A formula used in GCSE mathematics is the cosine rule, which relates the three sides of any triangle with the angle between two of the sides.

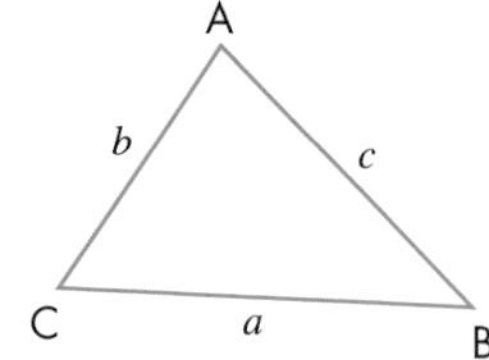

The formula is $a^2 = b^2 + c^2 - 2bc \cos A$.

This formula is known as an algebraic, cyclically symmetric formula.

That means that the various letters can be swapped with each other in a cycle, i.e. a becomes b, b becomes c and c becomes a.

a Write the formula so that it starts $b^2 = \ldots$

b When the formula is rearranged to make $\cos A$ the subject, then it becomes

$$\cos A = \frac{b^2 + c^2 - a^2}{2bc}$$

Write an equivalent formula that starts $\cos C = \ldots$

13.6 Algebraic fractions

This section will show you how to:

- simplify algebraic fractions
- solve equations containing algebraic fractions

Key words
brackets
cancel
cross-multiply
expression
factorise

The following four rules are used to work out the value of fractions.

Addition: $\frac{a}{b} + \frac{c}{d} = \frac{ad + bc}{bd}$

Subtraction: $\frac{a}{b} - \frac{c}{d} = \frac{ad - bc}{bd}$

Multiplication: $\frac{a}{b} \times \frac{c}{d} = \frac{ac}{bd}$

Division: $\frac{a}{b} \div \frac{c}{d} = \frac{ad}{bc}$

Note that a, b, c and d can be numbers, other letters or algebraic **expressions**. Remember:

- use **brackets**, if necessary
- **factorise** if you can
- **cancel** if you can.

EXAMPLE 11

Simplify **a** $\frac{1}{x} + \frac{x}{2y}$ **b** $\frac{2}{b} - \frac{a}{2b}$

a Using the addition rule: $\frac{1}{x} + \frac{x}{2x} = \frac{(1)(2y) + (x)(x)}{(x)(2y)} = \frac{2y + x^2}{2xy}$

b Using the subtraction rule: $\frac{2}{b} - \frac{a}{2b} = \frac{(2)(2b) - (a)(b)}{(b)(2b)} = \frac{4b - ab}{2b^2}$

$$= \frac{\not{b}(4 - a)}{2b^{\not{2}}} = \frac{4 - a}{2b}$$

Note: There are different ways of working out fraction calculations. Part **b** could have been done by making the denominator of each fraction the same.

$$\frac{(2)2}{(2)b} - \frac{a}{2b} = \frac{4 - a}{2b}$$

EXAMPLE 12

Simplify **a** $\frac{x}{3} \times \frac{x+2}{x-2}$ **b** $\frac{x}{3} \div \frac{2x}{7}$

a Using the multiplication rule: $\frac{x}{3} \times \frac{x+2}{x-2} = \frac{(x)(x+2)}{(2)(x-2)} = \frac{x^2+2x}{3x-6)}$

Remember that the line that separates the top from the bottom of an algebraic fraction acts as brackets as well as a division sign. Note that it is sometimes preferable to leave an algebraic fraction in a factorised form.

b Using the division rule: $\frac{x}{3} \div \frac{2x}{7} = \frac{(x)(7)}{(3)(2x)} = \frac{7}{6}$

EXAMPLE 13

Solve this equation. $\frac{x+1}{3} - \frac{x-3}{2} = 1$

Use the rule for combining fractions, and then **cross-multiply** to take the denominator of the left-hand side to the right-hand side.

$$\frac{(2)(x+1) - (3)(x-3)}{(2)(3)} = 1$$

$$2(x+1) - 3(x-3) = 6 \ (= 1 \times 2 \times 3)$$

Note the brackets. These will avoid problems with signs and help you to expand to get a linear equation.

$$2x + 2 - 3x + 9 = 6 \Rightarrow -x = -5 \Rightarrow x = 5$$

EXAMPLE 14

Solve this equation. $\frac{3}{x-1} - \frac{2}{x+1} = 1$

Use the rule for combining fractions, and cross-multiply to take the denominator of the left-hand side to the right-hand side, as in Example 13. Use brackets to help with expanding and to avoid problems with minus signs.

$$3(x+1) - 2(x-1) = (x-1)(x+1)$$

$$3x + 3 - 2x + 2 = x^2 - 1$$ (Right-hand side is the difference of two squares.)

Rearrange into the general quadratic form (see Chapter 10).

$$x^2 - x - 6 = 0$$

Factorise and solve $(x-3)(x+2) = 0 \Rightarrow x = 3$ or -2

Note that when your equation is rearranged into the quadratic form it should factorise. If it doesn't, then you have almost certainly made a mistake. If the question required an answer as a decimal or a surd it would say so.

EXAMPLE 15

Simplify this expression. $\frac{2x^2 + x - 3}{4x^2 - 9}$

Factorise the numerator and denominator: $\frac{(2x + 3)(x - 1)}{(2x + 3)(2x - 3)}$

Denominator is the difference of two squares.

Cancel any common factors: $\frac{\cancel{(2x + 3)}(x - 1)}{\cancel{(2x + 3)}(3x - 3)}$

If at this stage there isn't a common factor on top and bottom, you should check your factorisations.

The remaining fraction is the answer: $\frac{(x - 1)}{(2x - 3)}$

EXERCISE 13F

1 Simplify each of these.

a $\frac{x}{2} + \frac{x}{3}$ b $\frac{3x}{4} + \frac{x}{5}$ c $\frac{3x}{4} + \frac{2x}{5}$

d $\frac{x}{2} + \frac{y}{3}$ e $\frac{xy}{4} + \frac{2}{x}$ f $\frac{x + 1}{2} + \frac{x + 2}{3}$

g $\frac{2x + 1}{2} + \frac{3x + 1}{4}$ h $\frac{x}{5} + \frac{2x + 1}{3}$ i $\frac{x - 2}{2} + \frac{x - 3}{4}$

j $\frac{x - 4}{4} + \frac{2x - 3}{2}$

2 Simplify each of these.

a $\frac{x}{2} - \frac{x}{3}$ b $\frac{3x}{4} - \frac{x}{5}$ c $\frac{3x}{4} - \frac{2x}{5}$

d $\frac{x}{2} - \frac{y}{3}$ e $\frac{xy}{4} - \frac{2}{y}$ f $\frac{x + 1}{2} - \frac{x + 2}{3}$

g $\frac{2x + 1}{2} - \frac{3x + 1}{4}$ h $\frac{x}{5} - \frac{2x + 1}{3}$ i $\frac{x - 2}{2} - \frac{x - 3}{4}$

j $\frac{x - 4}{4} - \frac{2x - 3}{2}$

3 Solve the following equations.

a $\frac{x + 1}{2} + \frac{x + 2}{5} = 3$ b $\frac{x + 2}{4} + \frac{x + 1}{7} = 3$ c $\frac{4x + 1}{3} - \frac{x + 2}{4} = 2$

d $\frac{2x - 1}{3} + \frac{3x + 1}{4} = 7$ e $\frac{2x + 1}{2} - \frac{x + 1}{7} = 1$ f $\frac{3x + 1}{5} - \frac{5x - 1}{7} = 0$

B

B

4 Simplify each of these.

a $\frac{x}{2} \times \frac{x}{3}$ **b** $\frac{2x}{7} \times \frac{3y}{4}$ **c** $\frac{4x}{3y} \times \frac{2y}{x}$

d $\frac{4y^2}{9x} \times \frac{3x^2}{2y}$ **e** $\frac{x}{2} \times \frac{x-2}{5}$ **f** $\frac{x-3}{15} \times \frac{5}{2x-6}$

g $\frac{2x+1}{2} \times \frac{3x+1}{4}$ **h** $\frac{x}{5} \times \frac{2x+1}{3}$ **i** $\frac{x-2}{2} \times \frac{4}{x-3}$

j $\frac{x-5}{10} \times \frac{5}{x^2-5x}$

A

5 Simplify each of these.

a $\frac{x}{2} \div \frac{x}{3}$ **b** $\frac{2x}{7} \div \frac{4y}{14}$ **c** $\frac{4x}{3y} \div \frac{x}{2y}$

d $\frac{4y^2}{9x} \div \frac{2y}{3x^2}$ **e** $\frac{x}{2} \div \frac{x-2}{5}$ **f** $\frac{x-3}{15} \div \frac{5}{2x-6}$

g $\frac{2x+1}{2} \div \frac{4x+2}{4}$ **h** $\frac{x}{6} \div \frac{2x^2+x}{3}$ **i** $\frac{x-2}{12} \div \frac{4}{x-3}$

j $\frac{x-5}{10} \div \frac{x^2-5x}{5}$

6 Simplify each of these. Factorise and cancel where appropriate.

a $\frac{3x}{4} + \frac{x}{4}$ **b** $\frac{3x}{4} - \frac{x}{4}$ **c** $\frac{3x}{4} \times \frac{x}{4}$

d $\frac{3x}{4} \div \frac{x}{4}$ **e** $\frac{3x+1}{2} + \frac{x-2}{5}$ **f** $\frac{3x+1}{2} - \frac{x-2}{5}$

g $\frac{3x+1}{2} \times \frac{x-2}{5}$ **h** $\frac{x^2-9}{10} \times \frac{5}{x-3}$ **i** $\frac{2x+3}{5} \div \frac{6x+9}{10}$

j $\frac{2x^2}{9} - \frac{2y^2}{3}$

7 Show that each algebraic fraction simplifies to the given expression.

a $\frac{2}{x+1} + \frac{5}{x+2} = 3$ simplifies to $3x^2 + 2x - 3 = 0$

b $\frac{4}{x-2} + \frac{7}{x+1} = 3$ simplifies to $3x^2 - 14x + 4 = 0$

c $\frac{3}{4x+1} - \frac{4}{x+2} = 2$ simplifies to $8x^2 + 31x + 2 = 0$

d $\frac{2}{2x-1} - \frac{6}{x+1} = 11$ simplifies to $22x^2 + 21x - 19 = 0$

e $\frac{3}{2x-1} - \frac{4}{3x-1} = 1$ simplifies to $x^2 - x = 0$

A*

PS 8 For homework a teacher asks her class to simplify the expression $\frac{x^2 - x - 2}{x^2 + x - 6}$.

This is Tom's answer:

$$\frac{\cancel{x^2} - x - \cancel{2}^{-1}}{\cancel{x^2} + x - \cancel{6}_{+3}}$$

$$= \frac{-x - 1}{x + 3} = \frac{x + 1}{x + 3}$$

When she marked the homework, the teacher was in a hurry and only checked the answer, which was correct.

Tom made several mistakes. What are they?

AU 9 An expression of the form $\frac{ax^2 + bx - c}{dx^2 - e}$ simplifies to $\frac{x - 1}{2x - 3}$.

What was the original expression?

10 Solve the following equations.

a $\frac{4}{x + 1} + \frac{5}{x + 2} = 2$ **b** $\frac{18}{4x - 1} - \frac{1}{x + 1} = 1$ **c** $\frac{2x - 1}{2} - \frac{6}{x + 1} = 1$

d $\frac{3}{2x - 1} - \frac{4}{3x - 1} = 1$

11 Simplify the following expressions.

a $\frac{x^2 + 2x - 3}{2x^2 + 7x + 3}$ **b** $\frac{4x^2 - 1}{2x^2 + 5x - 3}$ **c** $\frac{6x^2 + x - 2}{9x^2 - 4}$

d $\frac{4x^2 + x - 3}{4x^2 - 7x + 3}$ **e** $\frac{4x^2 - 25}{8x^2 - 22x + 5}$

13.7 Linear and non-linear simultaneous equations

This section will show you how to:

- solve linear and non-linear simultaneous equations

Key words

linear
non-linear
substitute

You have already seen the method of substitution for solving **linear** simultaneous equations (Chapter 8, page 251). Example 16 is a reminder.

EXAMPLE 16

Solve these simultaneous equations.

$$2x + 3y = 7 \qquad (1)$$
$$x - 4y = 9 \qquad (2)$$

First, rearrange equation (2) to obtain:

$$x = 9 + 4y$$

Substitute the expression for x into equation (1), which gives:

$$2(9 + 4y) + 3y = 7$$

Expand and solve this equation to obtain:

$$18 + 8y + 3y = 7$$
$$\Rightarrow 11y = -11$$
$$\Rightarrow y = -1$$

Now substitute for y into either equation (1) or (2) to find x. Using equation (1),

$$\Rightarrow 2x - 3 = 7$$
$$\Rightarrow x = 5$$

You can use a similar method when you need to solve a pair of equations, one of which is linear and the other of which is **non-linear**. But you must always **substitute** from the linear into the non-linear.

EXAMPLE 17

Solve these simultaneous equations.

$$x^2 + y^2 = 5$$
$$x + y = 3$$

Call the equations (1) and (2):

$$x^2 + y^2 = 5 \qquad (1)$$
$$x + y = 3 \qquad (2)$$

Rearrange equation (2) to obtain:

$$x = 3 - y$$

Substitute this into equation (1), which gives:

$$(3 - y)^2 + y^2 = 5$$

Expand and rearrange into the general form of the quadratic equation:

$$9 - 6y + y^2 + y^2 = 5$$
$$2y^2 - 6y + 4 = 0$$

Cancel by 2:

$$y^2 - 3y + 2 = 0$$

Factorise:

$$(y - 1)(y - 2) = 0$$
$$\Rightarrow y = 1 \text{ or } 2$$

Substitute for y in equation (2):

When $y = 1$, $x = 2$ and when $y = 2$, $x = 1$

Note that you should always give answers as a pair of values in x and y.

EXAMPLE 18

Find the solutions of the pair of simultaneous equations: $y = x^2 + x - 2$ and $y = 2x + 4$

This example is slightly different, as both equations are given in terms of y, so substituting for y gives:

$2x + 4 = x^2 + x - 2$

Rearranging into the general quadratic:

$x^2 - x - 6 = 0$

Factorising and solving gives:

$(x + 2)(x - 3) = 0$

$x = -2$ or 3

Substituting back to find y:

When $x = -2$, $y = 0$

When $x = 3$, $y = 10$

So the solutions are $(-2, 0)$ and $(3, 10)$.

EXERCISE 13G

1 Solve these pairs of linear simultaneous equations using the substitution method.

a $2x + y = 9$
$x - 2y = 7$

b $3x - 2y = 10$
$4x + y = 17$

c $x - 2y = 10$
$2x + 3y = 13$

2 Solve these pairs of simultaneous equations.

a $xy = 2$
$y = x + 1$

b $xy = -4$
$2y = x + 6$

3 Solve these pairs of simultaneous equations.

a $x^2 + y^2 = 25$
$x + y = 7$

b $x^2 + y^2 = 9$
$y = x + 3$

c $x^2 + y^2 = 13$
$5y + x = 13$

4 Solve these pairs of simultaneous equations.

a $y = x^2 + 2x - 3$
$y = 2x + 1$

b $y = x^2 - 2x - 5$
$y = x - 1$

c $y = x^2 - 2x$
$y = 2x - 3$

5 Solve these pairs of simultaneous equations.

a $y = x^2 + 3x - 3$ and $y = x$

b $x^2 + y^2 = 13$ and $x + y = 1$

c $x^2 + y^2 = 5$ and $y = x + 1$

d $y = x^2 - 3x + 1$ and $y = 2x - 5$

e $y = x^2 - 3$ and $y = x + 3$

f $y = x^2 - 3x - 2$ and $y = 2x - 6$

g $x^2 + y^2 = 41$ and $y = x + 1$

A

A*

A*

AU 6 **a** Solve the simultaneous equations: $y = x^2 + 3x - 4$ and $y = 5x - 5$

b Which of the sketches below represents the graphs of the equations in part **a**?

Explain your choice.

i

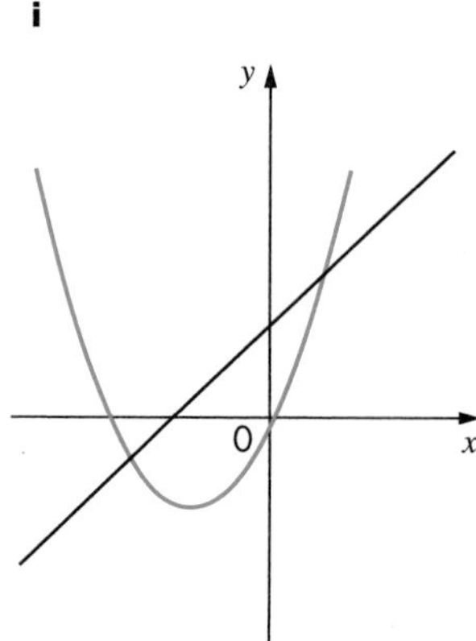

ii

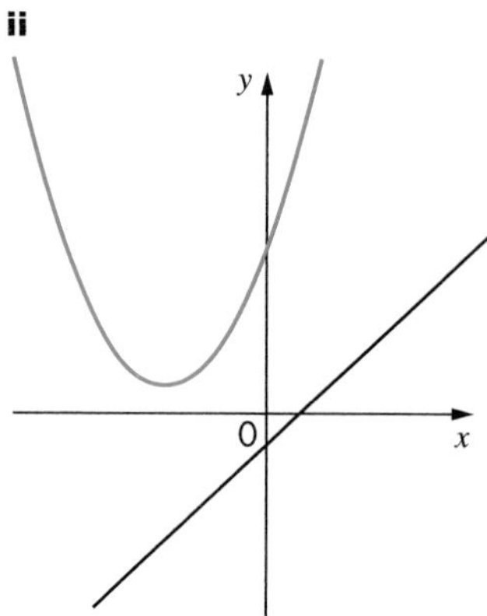

iii

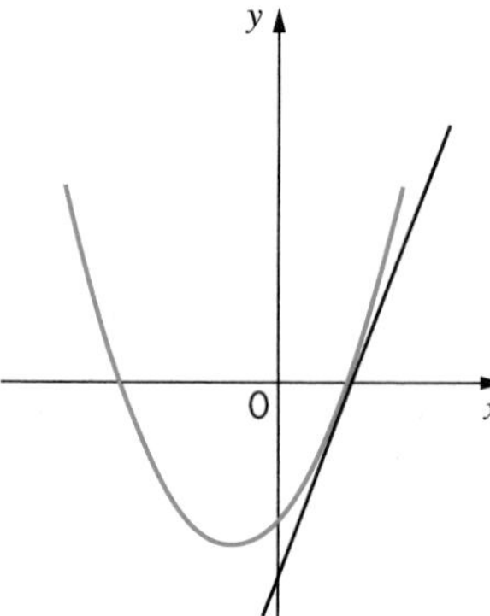

PS 7 The simultaneous equations $x^2 + y^2 = 5$ and $y = 2x + 5$ only has one solution.

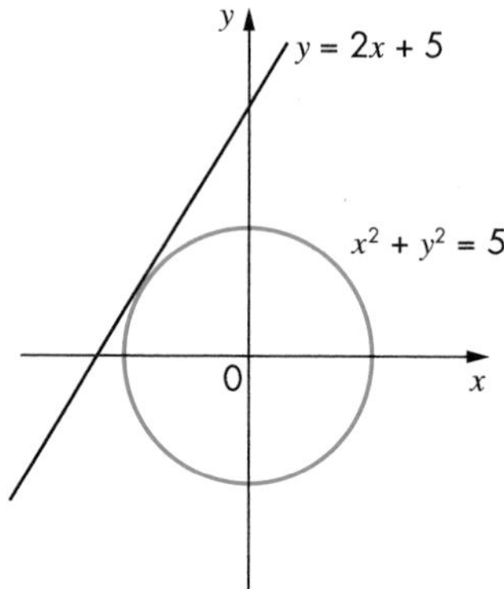

a Find the solution.

b Write down the intersection of each pair of graphs.

i $x^2 + y^2 = 5$ and $y = -2x + 5$

ii $x^2 + y^2 = 5$ and $y = -2x - 5$

iii $x^2 + y^2 = 5$ and $y = 2x - 5$

PS 8 Solve these pairs of simultaneous equations.

a $y = x^2 + x - 2$
$y = 5x - 6$

b $y = x^2 + 2x - 3$
$y = 4x - 4$

c What is the geometrical significance of the answers to parts **a** and **b**?

13.8 Algebraic proof

This section will show you how to:

- recognise and continue some special number sequences

Key words
proof
show
verify

You will have met the fact that the sum of any two odd numbers is always an even number before, but can you prove it?

You can take any two odd numbers, add them together and get a number that divides exactly by 2. This does not prove the result, even if everyone in your class, or your school, or the whole of Britain, did this for a different pair of starting odd numbers. Unless you tried every pair of odd numbers (and there is an infinite number of them) you cannot be 100% certain this result is always true.

This is how to prove the result.

Let n be any whole number.

Whatever whole number is represented by n, $2n$ has to be even. So, $2n + 1$ represents any odd number.

Let one odd number be $2n + 1$, and let the other odd number be $2m + 1$.

The sum of these is:

$$\begin{aligned}(2n + 1) + (2m + 1) &= 2n + 2m + 1 + 1\\ &= 2n + 2m + 2\\ &= 2(n + m + 1), \text{ which must be even.}\end{aligned}$$

This proves the result, as n and m can be any numbers.

In an algebraic **proof**, every step must be shown clearly and the algebra must be done properly.

There are three levels of 'proof': **Verify** that …, **Show** that …, and Prove that …

- At the lowest level (verification), all you have to do is substitute numbers into the result to show that it works.
- At the middle level, you have to show that both sides of the result are the same algebraically.
- At the highest level (proof), you have to manipulate the left-hand side of the result to become its right-hand side.

The following example demonstrates these three different procedures.

EXAMPLE 19

You are given that $n^2 + (n + 1)^2 - (n + 2)^2 = (n - 3)(n + 1)$.

a Verify that this result is true.

b Show that this result is true.

c Prove that this result is true.

a Choose a number for n, say $n = 5$. Put this value into both sides of the expression, which gives:

$$5^2 + (5 + 1)^2 - (5 + 2)^2 = (5 + 3)(5 + 1)$$
$$25 + 36 - 49 = 2 \times 6$$
$$12 = 12$$

Hence, the result is true.

b Expand the LHS and RHS of the expression to get:

$$n^2 + n^2 + 2n + 1 - (n^2 + 4n + 4) = n^2 - 2n - 3$$
$$n^2 - 2n - 3 = n^2 - 2n - 3$$

That is, both sides are algebraically the same.

c Expand the LHS of the expression to get: $n^2 + n^2 + 2n + 1 - (n^2 + 4n + 4)$

Collect like terms, which gives $n^2 + n^2 - n^2 + 2n - 4n + 1 - 4 = n^2 - 2n - 3$

Factorise the collected result: $n^2 - 2n - 3 = (n - 3)(n + 1)$, which is the RHS of the original expression.

EXERCISE 13H

a Choose any odd number and any even number. Add these together. Is the result odd or even? Does this always work for any odd number and even number you choose?

b Let any odd number be represented by $2n + 1$. Let any even number be represented by $2m$, where m and n are integers. Prove that the sum of an odd number and an even number always gives an odd number.

AU 2 Prove the following results.

a The sum of two even numbers is even.

b The product of two even numbers is even.

c The product of an odd number and an even number is even.

d The product of two odd numbers is odd.

e The sum of four consecutive numbers is always even.

f Half the sum of four consecutive numbers is always odd.

A*

AU 3 A Fibonacci sequence is formed by adding the previous two terms to get the next term. For example, starting with 3 and 4, the series is:

3, 4, 7, 11, 18, 29, 47, 76, 123, 199, …

a Continue the Fibonacci sequence 1, 1, 2, … up to 10 terms.

b Continue the Fibonacci sequence a, b, $a + b$, $a + 2b$, $2a + 3b$, … up to 10 terms.

c Prove that the difference between the 8th term and the 5th term of any Fibonacci sequence is twice the 6th term.

AU 4 The nth term in the sequence of triangular numbers 1, 3, 6, 10, 15, 21, 28, … is given by $\frac{1}{2}n\,(n + 1)$.

a Show that the sum of the 11th and 12th terms is a perfect square.

b Explain why the $(n + 1)$th term of the triangular number sequence is given by $\frac{1}{2}(n + 1)(n + 2)$.

c Prove that the sum of any two consecutive triangular numbers is always a square number.

AU 5 The diagram shows part of a 10 × 10 'hundred square'.

12	13	14	15
22	23	24	25
32	33	34	35
42	43	44	45

a One 2 × 2 square is marked.

i Work out the difference between the product of the bottom-left and top-right values and the product of the top-left and bottom-right values:

$22 \times 13 - 12 \times 23$

ii Repeat this for any other 2 × 2 square of your choosing.

b Prove that this will always give an answer of 10 for any 2 × 2 square chosen.

c The diagram shows a calendar square (where the numbers are arranged in rows of seven).

Prove that you always get a value of 7 if you repeat the procedure in part **a i**.

1	2	3	4	5	6	7
8	9	10	11	12	13	14
15	16	17	18	19	20	21
22	23	24	25	26	27	28
29	30	31				

d Prove that in a number square that is arranged in rows of n numbers then the difference is always n if you repeat the procedure in part **a i**.

AU 6 Prove that if you add any two-digit number from the 9 times table to the reverse of itself (that is, swap the tens digit and units digit), the result will always be 99.

A*

AU **7** Speed Cabs charges 45 pence per kilometre for each journey. Evans Taxis has a fixed charge of 90p plus 30p per kilometre.

a **i** Verify that Speed Cabs is cheaper for a journey of 5 km.

ii Verify that Evans Taxis is cheaper for a journey of 7 km.

b Show clearly why both companies charge the same for a journey of 6 km.

c Show that if Speed Cabs charges a pence per kilometre, and Evans Taxis has a fixed charge of £b plus a charge of c pence per kilometre, both companies charge the same for a journey of $\frac{4}{3x - 1}$ kilometres.

AU **8** You are given that:

$$(a + b)^2 + (a - b)^2 = 2(a^2 + b^2)$$

a Verify that this result is true for $a = 3$ and $b = 4$.

b Show that the LHS is the same as the RHS.

c Prove that the LHS can be simplified to the RHS.

AU **9** Prove that: $(a + b)^2 - (a - b)^2 = 4ab$

AU **10** The rule for converting from degrees Fahrenheit to degrees Celsius is to subtract 32° and then to multiply by $\frac{5}{9}$.

Prove that the temperature that has the same value in both scales is –40°.

AU **11** The sum of the series $1 + 2 + 3 + 4 + \dots + (n - 2) + (n - 1) + n$ is given by $\frac{1}{2}n(n + 1)$.

a Verify that this result is true for $n = 6$.

b Write down a simplified value, in terms of n, for the sum of these two series.

$$1 + 2 + 3 + \dots + (n - 2) + (n - 1) + n$$

and $$n + (n - 1) + (n - 2) + \dots + 3 + 2 + 1$$

c Prove that the sum of the first n integers is $\frac{1}{2}n(n + 1)$.

AU **12** The following is a 'think of a number' trick.

- Think of a number.
- Multiply it by 2.
- Add 10.
- Divide the result by 2.
- Subtract the original number.

The result is always 5.

a Verify that the trick works when you pick 7 as the original number.

b Prove why the trick always works.

AU 13 You are told that 'when two numbers have a difference of 2, the difference of their squares is twice the sum of the two numbers'.

a Verify that this is true for 5 and 7.

b Prove that the result is true.

c Prove that when two numbers have a difference of n, the difference of their squares is n times the sum of the two numbers.

AU 14 Four consecutive numbers are 4, 5, 6 and 7.

a Verify that their product plus 1 is a perfect square.

b Complete the multiplication square and use it to show that:

$$(n^2 - n - 1)^2 = n^4 - 2n^3 - n^2 + 2n + 1$$

	n^2	$-n$	-1
n^2	n^4		$-n^2$
$-n$		n^2	
-1			

c Let four consecutive numbers be $(n - 2)$, $(n - 1)$, n, $(n + 1)$. Prove that the product of four consecutive numbers plus 1 is a perfect square.

AU 15 Here is another mathematical trick to try on a friend.

- Think of two single-digit numbers.
- Multiply one number (your choice) by 2.
- Add 5 to this answer.
- Multiply this answer by 5.
- Add the second number.
- Subtract 4.
- Ask your friend to state the final answer.
- Mentally subtract 21 from this answer.

The two digits you get are the two digits your friend first thought of.

Prove why this works.

EXERCISE 13I

You may not be able algebraically to prove all of these results. Some of them can be disproved by a counter-example. You should first try to verify each result, then attempt to prove it — or at least try to demonstrate that the result is probably true by trying lots of examples.

AU 1 T represents any triangular number. Prove the following.

a $8T + 1$ is always a square number.

b $9T + 1$ is always another triangular number.

A*

AU **2** Lewis Carroll, who wrote *Alice in Wonderland*, was also a mathematician. In 1890, he suggested the following results.

a For any pair of numbers, x and y, if $x^2 + y^2$ is even, then $\frac{1}{2}(x^2 + y^2)$ is the sum of two squares.

b For any pair of numbers, x and y, $2(x^2 + y^2)$ is always the sum of two squares.

c Any number of which the square is the sum of two squares is itself the sum of two squares.

Can you prove these statements to be true or false?

AU **3** For all values of n, $n^2 - n + 41$ gives a prime number. True or false?

AU **4** Pythagoras' theorem says that for a right-angled triangle with two short sides a and b and a long side c, $a^2 + b^2 = c^2$. For any integer n, $2n$, $n^2 - 1$ and $n^2 + 1$ form three numbers that obey Pythagoras' theorem. Can you prove this?

AU **5** Waring's theorem states that: "Any whole number can be written as the sum of not more than four square numbers".

For example, $27 = 3^2 + 3^2 + 3^2$ and $23 = 3^2 + 3^2 + 2^2 + 1^2$

Is this always true?

AU **6** Take a three-digit multiple of 37, for example, $7 \times 37 = 259$. Write these digits in a cycle.

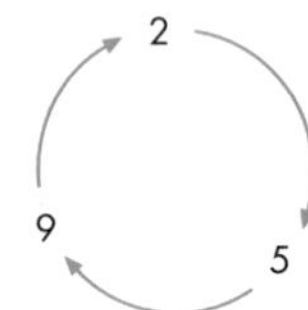

Take all possible three-digit numbers from the cycle, for example, 259, 592 and 925.

Divide each of these numbers by 37 to find that:

$259 = 7 \times 37 \quad 592 = 16 \times 37 \quad 925 = 25 \times 37$

Is this true for all three-digit multiples of 37?

Is it true for a five-digit multiple of 41?

AU **7** Prove that the sum of the squares of two consecutive integers is an odd number.

8 The difference of two squares is an identity, i.e.,

$$a^2 - b^2 \equiv (a + b)(a - b)$$

which means that it is true for all values of a and b whether they are numeric or algebraic.

Prove that $a^2 - b^2 \equiv (a + b)(a - b)$ is true when $a = 2x + 1$ and $b = x - 1$

9 The square of the sum of the first n consecutive whole numbers is equal to the sum of the cubes of the first n consecutive whole numbers.

a Verify that $(1 + 2 + 3 + 4)^2 = 1^3 + 2^3 + 3^3 + 4^3$

b The sum of the first n consecutive whole numbers is $\frac{1}{2}n(n + 1)$

Write down a formula for the sum of the cubes of the first n whole numbers.

c Test your formula for $n = 6$

GRADE BOOSTER

- **D** You can substitute numbers into an nth-term rule
- **D** You can understand how odd and even numbers interact in addition, subtraction and multiplication problems
- **C** You can give the nth term of a linear sequence
- **C** You can give the nth term of a sequence of powers of 2 or 10
- **B** You can solve linear equations involving algebraic fractions where the subject appears as the numerator
- **B** You can verify results by substituting numbers into them
- **B** You can understand the proofs of simple theorems, such as an exterior angle of a triangle is the sum of the two opposite interior angles
- **A** You can rearrange a formula where the subject appears twice
- **A** You can combine fractions, using the four algebraic rules of addition, subtraction, multiplication and division
- **A** You can show that an algebraic statement is true, using both sides of the statement to justify your answer
- **A*** You can rearrange more complicated formulae where the subject may appear twice or as a power
- **A*** You can solve a quadratic equation obtained from algebraic fractions where the variable appears in the denominator
- **A*** You can simplify algebraic fractions by factorisation and cancellation
- **A*** You can solve a pair of simultaneous equations where one is linear and the other is non-linear
- **A*** You can prove algebraic results with rigorous and logical mathematical arguments

What you should know now

- How to manipulate algebraic fractions and solve equations resulting from the simplified fractions
- How to solve a pair of simultaneous equations where one is linear and one is non-linear
- How to recognise a linear sequence and find its nth term
- How to recognise a sequence of powers of 2 or 10
- How to rearrange a formula where the subject appears twice
- The meaning of the terms 'verify that', 'show that' and 'prove'
- How to prove some standard results in mathematics
- How to use your knowledge of proof to answer the questions throughout the book that are flagged with the proof icon

EXAMINATION QUESTIONS

1 Solve the equations.

a $5y + 11 = 3(y + 7)$ *(3 marks)*

b $\dfrac{x+1}{3} + \dfrac{x+2}{5} = 1$

You **must** show your working. *(4 marks)*

AQA, November 2005, Paper 2 Higher, Question 7

2 **a** Write down the nth term of the sequence.

4, 9, 14, 19, 24, … *(? marks)*

b The nth term of a sequence is given by

$\dfrac{2n-1}{n+1}$

The first three terms are $\frac{1}{2} = 0.5$, $\frac{3}{3} = 1$ and $\frac{5}{4} = 1.25$

Show that the 6th term of the sequence is the first one that is not a terminating decimal. *(3 marks)*

AQA, June 2009, Paper 2 Higher, Question 11

3 Make u the subject of the formula:

$s = \frac{1}{2}(u + v)t$ *(3 marks)*

AQA, June 2006, Paper 1 Higher, Question 9

4 Solve the equation $\dfrac{x+4}{5} + \dfrac{x-2}{3} = 3$

(4 marks)

AQA, November 2008, Paper 2 Higher, Question 10 (b)

5 Solve the equation $\dfrac{x+3}{2} - \dfrac{x-2}{3} = 4$ *(4 marks)*

AQA, June 2009, Paper 2 Higher, Question 16

6 **a** Make x the subject of $\sqrt{\dfrac{a}{x+b}} = c$ *(4 marks)*

b Find the values of p and q such that $x^2 + px + 17 \equiv (x - 5)^2 + q$

(3 marks)

AQA, November 2007, Paper 1 Higher, Question 20

7 Make x the subject of the formula:

$a(x - b) = a^2 + bx$ *(4 marks)*

AQA, June 2005, Paper 2 Higher, Question 18

8 **a** Factorise fully $8a^2 - 50$ *(2 marks)*

b Simplify fully $\dfrac{12x^2 - 36x + 15}{12x^2 - 3}$ *(4 marks)*

AQA, November 2007, Paper 2 Higher, Question 16

9 Solve the equation.

$\dfrac{4}{2x+1} - \dfrac{1}{3x-1} = 5$ *(6 marks*

AQA, June 2005, Paper 2 Higher, Question 1

10 A shape is made from two trapezia.

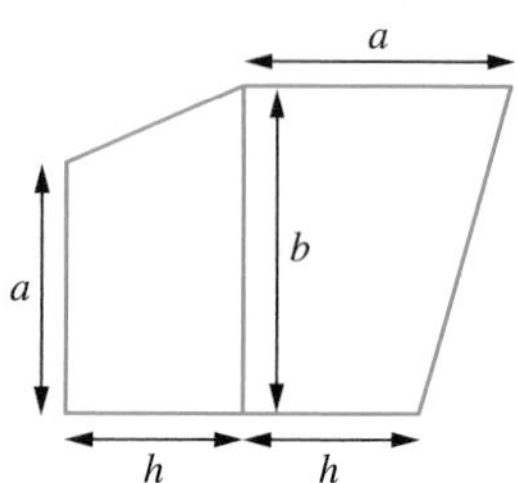

The area of this shape is given by:

$A = \dfrac{h}{2}(a + b) + \dfrac{b}{2}(a + h)$

Rearrange the formula to make a the subject. *(4 marks*

AQA, November 2005, Paper 2 Higher, Question 2

11 Rearrange $y = \dfrac{xy + 2}{3x - 4}$ to make x the subject.

Simplify your answer as much as possible. *(4 marks*

AQA, June 2006, Paper 2 Higher, Question 1

12 Simplify: $\dfrac{2x^2 - 9x - 18}{x^2 - 36}$ *(4 marks*

AQA, November 2006, Paper 1 Higher, Question 1

13 The diagram shows the circle $x^2 + y^2 = 26$ and the line $y = x + 4$.

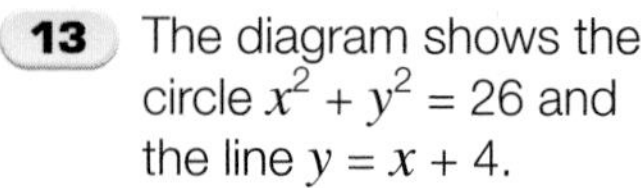

The line and the circle intersect at the points A and B.

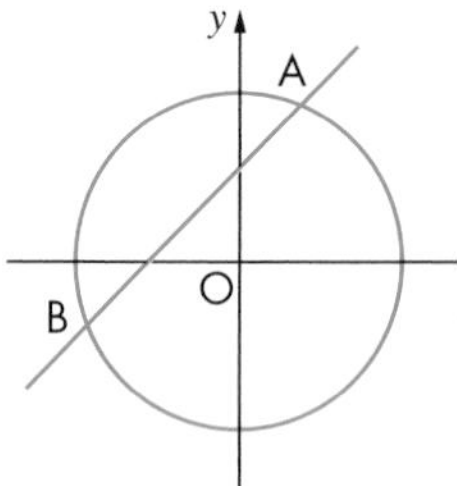

a Show that the x-coordinates of A and B satisfy the equation $x^2 + 4x - 5 = 0$. *(3 marks*

b Hence find the coordinates of A and B. *(2 marks*

AQA, May 2008, Paper 1 Higher, Question 2

14 Solve the simultaneous equations.

$x = 3 + 2y$

$x^2 + 2y^2 = 27$

Do **not** use trial and improvement.

You **must** show your working. *(6 marks*

AQA, June 2009, Paper 2 Higher, Question 2

A* A B C

Worked Examination Questions

1 Make g the subject of the following formula.

$$\frac{t(3+g)}{8-g} = 2$$

1 $t(3 + g) = 2(8 - g)$ — Cross multiply to get rid of the fraction. This scores 1 mark for method.

$3t + gt = 16 - 2g$ — Expand the brackets. This scores 1 mark for accuracy.

$gt + 2g = 16 - 3t$ — Collect all the g terms on the left-hand side and other terms on the right-hand side. This scores 1 mark for method.

$g(t + 2) = 16 - 3t$

$g = \frac{16 - 3t}{t + 2}$ — Simplify, $gt + 2g = g(t + 2)$, and divide by $(t + 2)$. This scores 1 mark for accuracy.

Total: 4 marks

2 Tom is building fences using posts and rails.

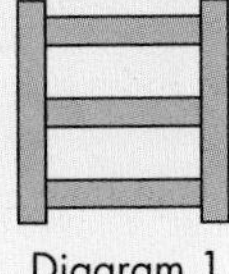

Diagram 1
2 posts, 3 rails

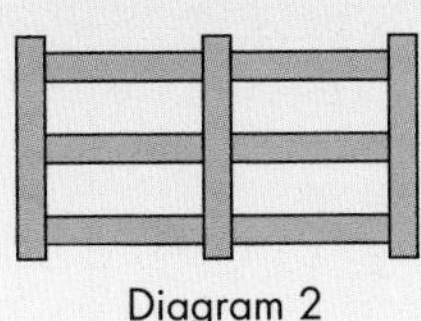

Diagram 2
3 posts, 6 rails

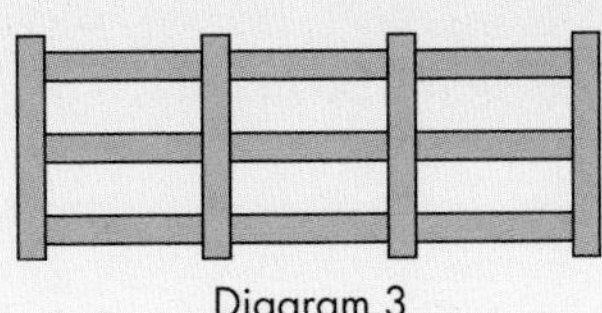

Diagram 3
4 posts, 9 rails

a How many rails will be in a fence with 6 posts?

b How many posts will be needed for a fence with 27 rails?

c Posts cost £12 and rails costs £5.

Write down a formula for the cost of a fence with n posts.

2 a 15 rails — This answer can be found by 'counting on', i.e. 5 posts, 12 rails 6 posts, 15 rails. This scores 1 mark.

b 10 posts — This could be found by 'counting on' but it is better to find a rule. The number of rails is in the 3 times table and is the multiple that is 1 less than the number of posts.

$27 = 9 \times 3$, so number of posts is $9 + 1$.

This scores 1 mark.

c £$(27n - 15)$ — Once the formula is found in part **b** this is a matter of putting the costs and the nth terms together.

Cost $= 12n + 3 \times 5 \times (n - 1)$

... which can be simplified. This scores 1 mark for accuracy.

It is very important that once you find a formula, you check it. This is a fundamental part of functional maths. So take one of the given examples at the start of the question.

Diagram 2 is 3 posts and 6 rails, which is $3 \times 12 + 6 \times 5 = £66$.

The formula gives $27 \times 3 - 15 = 81 - 15 = 66$.

Total: 3 marks

Worked Examination Questions

AU **3** Here are formulae for the nth terms of three sequences.

Formula 1: $4n + 1$
Formula 2: $5n - 2$
Formula 3: $5n + 10$

Say if the sequences generated by the nth terms always (A) give multiples of 5, never (N) give multiples of 5 or sometimes (S) give multiples of 5.

3 Formula 1: Sometimes (S)
Formula 2: Never (N)
Formula 3: Always (A)

Total: 3 marks

Substitute $n = 1, 2, 3$, etc. until you can be sure of the sequences.
These are:
5, 9, 13 17, 21, 25, 29, …
3, 8, 13, 18, 23, 28, …
15, 20, 25, 30, 35, 40, …
This gives 1 mark each.

PS **4** The grid shows the graph of $y = x^2 - x - 6$ and the straight line $y = x + 3$.

Find the values of the points of intersection of the graph to two decimal places.

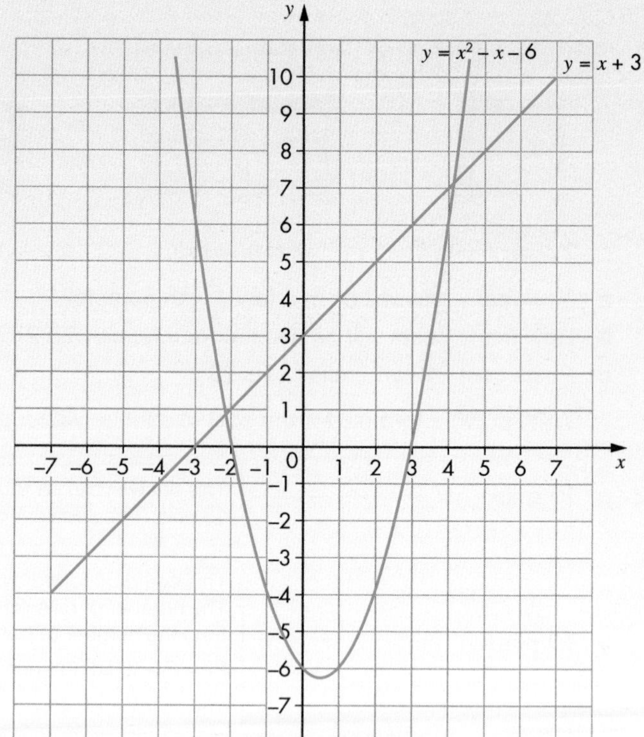

4 $x + 3 = x^2 - x - 6$

Substitute the linear equation into the non-linear. This gives 1 mark for method.

$x^2 - 2x - 9 = 0$

Rearrange into the general quadratic. This gives 1 mark for method.

$x^2 - 2x + 1 = 10$
$(n - 1)^2 = 10$
$n - 1 = \pm\sqrt{10} = \pm 3.1622$

Use the method of completing the square to find the solution for x to 2 decimal places. This gives 1 mark for method and 1 mark for accuracy.

$x = 4.16$ or -2.16 (2 dp)

Substitute the x values back into the linear equation to find the y values. This gives 1 mark for accuracy.

Total: 5 marks

Worked Examination Questions

PS **5** **a** n is a positive integer.

i Explain why $n(n + 1)$ must be an even number.

ii Explain why $2n + 1$ must be an odd number.

b Expand and simplify $(2n + 1)^2$.

c Prove that the square of any odd number is always 1 more than a multiple of 8.

5 a i If n is odd, $n + 1$ is even.
If n is even, $n + 1$ is odd.
Even times odd is always even.

This is a lead-in to the rest of the task. An explanation in words is good enough. Keep the words to a minimum. This gives 1 mark.

ii $2n$ must be even, so $2n + 1$ must be odd.

An explanation in words is good enough. This gives 1 mark.

b $(2n + 1)^2 = (2n + 1)(2n + 1) =$
$4n^2 + 2n + 2n + 1 = 4n^2 + 4n + 1$

Always write down a squared bracket twice, then expand it by whichever method you prefer. This gives 1 mark.

c $(2n + 1)^2 = 4n^2 + 4n + 1$

Use the fact that $2n + 1$ is odd, and it has been 'squared' in part **b**.

$4n^2 + 4n + 1 = 4n(n + 1) + 1$

The 'one more than' is taken care of with the +1. This gives 1 mark for method.

$4 \times n(n + 1) + 1 = 4 \times$ even $+ 1$,
which must be a multiple of 8 plus 1.

Show that the $4n^2 + 4n$ is a multiple of 8 using the result in part **a i**. This gives 1 mark for accuracy.

Total: 5 marks

13 Problem Solving
Patterns in the pyramids

Some sets of square numbers have a special connection. For example:

$$3^2 + 4^2 = 5^2$$

The set (3, 4, 5) is called a Pythagorean triple. (In Book 2, you will learn about Pythagoras' theorem, which is connected with right-angled triangles. Pythagorean triples, however, were well known before Pythagoras himself!)

Pythagorean triples were used by ancient people in the construction of great monuments such as Stonehenge and the Egyptian pyramids. They are just one example of how we can use patterns.

Getting started

Many patterns, including Pythagorean triples, can be found, using diagrams.

1 Working in pairs, start with the smallest odd number and, going up in consecutive odd numbers, draw diagrams to represent the numbers. Extend your diagrams using a rule.

Have a look at what another group has done. Have they found the same rule as yours? Is there more than one way to represent odd numbers diagrammatically?

Getting started (continued)

2 Represent a square number diagrammatically – the clue is in the name.

One representation of odd numbers can be used to show how consecutive odd numbers add together to make square numbers. See if you can find this and show it in a diagram of 3^2.

3 Use the pattern from the diagrams to complete this sequence:

$1 = 1^2 = 1$

$1 + 3 = 2^2 = 4$

$1 + 3 + 5 =$ ..... = ...

$1 + 3 + 5 + 7 =$ ..... = ...

= ..... = ...

Look for connections between the last odd number and the square number.

Use these connections to fill in the missing numbers in this sequence:

$1 + 3 + 5 +$ ..... $+ 19 =$ ..... = ...

$1 + 3 + 5 +$ ..... + ... $= 12^2 = 144$

$1 + 3 + 5 +$ ..... $+ 99 =$ ..... = ...

$1 + 3 + 5 +$ ..... + ... $= 200^2 = 40\ 000$

Your task

It is your task to use diagrams to find patterns, and make and test generalisations.

1 Draw accurate diagrams to show that (5, 12, 13) is a Pythagorean triple. Find at least three more Pythagorean triples.

2 Here are some sequences which are seen in everyday life, for example nature and science.

1, 3, 6, 10, 28, 36, 45, ...

1, 8, 27, 64, 125, 216, 343, 512, 729, ...

2, 8, 18, 32, 50, 72, 98, 162, ...

0, 1, 1, 2, 3, 4, 8, 13, 21, 34, ...

Investigate the sequences, looking for patterns, diagrammatical representations and nth terms.

3 Now see if you can generate some sequences of your own. Can you think where they may apply in real-life situations?

Extension

Use the internet to find out about Pythagoras, his theorem and Euler's Formula.

PITAGORA

Why this chapter matters

The theory of linear programming has been used by many companies to reduce their costs and increase productivity.

The theory of linear programming, which uses inequalities in two dimensions, was developed at the start of the Second World War in 1939.

It was used to work out ways to get armaments as efficiently as possible and to increase the effectiveness of resources. It was so powerful an analytical tool that the Allies did not want the Germans to know about it, so it was not made public until 1947.

George Dantzig, who was one of the inventors of linear programming, came late to a lecture at University one day and saw two problems written on the blackboard. He copied them, thinking they were the homework assignment. He solved both problems, but had to apologise to the lecturer as he found them a little harder than the usual homework, so he took a few days to solve them and was late handing them in.

The lecturer was astonished. The problems he had written on the board were not homework but examples of 'impossible problems'. Not any more!

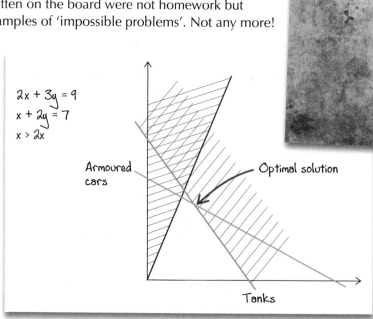

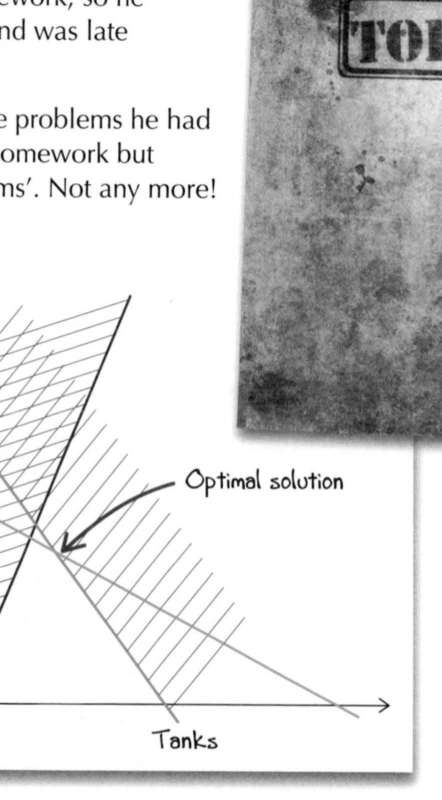

Chapter

14 Algebra: Inequalities and regions

1 Solving inequalities

2 Graphical inequalities

This chapter will show you ...

C how to solve a linear inequality

B how to find a region on a graph that obeys a linear inequality in two variables

Visual overview

Linear inequalities → Inequalities in two variables

What you should already know

- How to solve linear equations **(KS3 level 6, GCSE grade D)**
- How to draw linear graphs **(KS3 level 6, GCSE grade D)**

Quick check

1 Solve these equations.

a $\frac{2x + 5}{3} = 7$ **b** $2x - 7 = 13$

2 On a grid with x- and y-axes from 0 to 10, draw the graphs of these equations.

a $y = 3x + 1$ **b** $2x + 3y = 12$

14.1 Solving inequalities

This section will show you how to:
- solve a simple linear inequality

Key words
inclusive inequality
inequality
number line
strict inequality

Inequalities behave similarly to equations, which you have already met. In the case of linear inequalities, you use the same rules to solve them as you use for linear equations. There are four inequality signs, $<$ which means 'less than', $>$ which means 'greater than', $\leqslant$ which means 'less than or equal to' and $\geqslant$ which means 'greater than or equal to'.

Be careful. Never replace the inequality sign with an equals sign or you could end up getting no marks in an examination.

EXAMPLE 1

Solve $2x + 3 < 14$

Rewrite this as: $2x < 14 - 3$

$2x < 11$

Divide both sides by 2: $\frac{2x}{2} < \frac{11}{2}$

$\Rightarrow x < 5.5$

This means that x can take any value below 5.5 but *not* the value 5.5.

$<$ and $>$ are called **strict inequalities**.

Note: The inequality sign given in the problem is the sign to use in the answer.

EXAMPLE 2

Solve $\frac{x}{2} + 4 \geqslant 13$

Solve just like an equation but leave the inequality sign in place of the equals sign.

Subtract 4 from both sides: $\frac{x}{2} \geqslant 9$

Multiply both sides by 2: $x \geqslant 18$

This means that x can take any value above and including 18.

$\leqslant$ and $\geqslant$ are called **inclusive inequalities**.

EXAMPLE 3

Solve $\frac{3x + 7}{2} < 14$

Rewrite this as: $3x + 7 < 14 \times 2$

That is: $3x + 7 < 28$

$\Rightarrow \quad 3x < 28 - 7$

$\Rightarrow \quad 3x < 21$

$\Rightarrow \quad x < 21 \div 3$

$\Rightarrow \quad x < 7$

EXAMPLE 4

Solve $1 < 3x + 4 \leqslant 13$

Divide the inequality into two parts, and treat each part separately.

$1 < 3x + 4$	$3x + 4 \leqslant 13$
$\Rightarrow \quad 1 - 4 < 3x$	$\Rightarrow \quad 3x \leqslant 13 - 4$
$\Rightarrow \quad -3 < 3x$	$\Rightarrow \quad 3x \leqslant 9$
$\Rightarrow \quad -\frac{3}{3} < x$	$\Rightarrow \quad x \leqslant \frac{9}{3}$
$\Rightarrow \quad -1 < x$	$\Rightarrow \quad x \leqslant 3$

Hence, $-1 < x \leqslant 3$

EXERCISE 14A

1 Solve the following linear inequalities.

a $x + 4 < 7$ **b** $t - 3 > 5$ **c** $p + 2 \geqslant 12$

d $2x - 3 < 7$ **e** $4y + 5 \leqslant 17$ **f** $3t - 4 > 11$

g $\frac{x}{2} + 4 < 7$ **h** $\frac{y}{5} + 3 \leqslant 6$ **i** $\frac{t}{3} - 2 \geqslant 4$

j $3(x - 2) < 15$ **k** $5(2x + 1) \leqslant 35$ **l** $2(4t - 3) \geqslant 34$

2 Write down the largest integer value of x that satisfies each of the following.

a $x - 3 \leqslant 5$, where x is positive

b $x + 2 < 9$, where x is positive and even

c $3x - 11 < 40$, where x is a square number

d $5x - 8 \leqslant 15$, where x is positive and odd

e $2x + 1 < 19$, where x is positive and prime

C

C

3 Write down the smallest integer value of x that satisfies each of the following.

a $x - 2 \geqslant 9$, where x is positive

b $x - 2 > 13$, where x is positive and even

c $2x - 11 \geqslant 19$, where x is a square number

FM 4 Ahmed went to town with £20 to buy two CDs. His bus fare was £3. The CDs were both the same price. When he reached home he still had some money in his pocket. What was the most each CD could cost?

HINTS AND TIPS

Set up an inequality and solve it.

AU 5 **a** Explain why you cannot make a triangle with three sticks of length 3 cm, 4 cm and 8 cm.

b Three sides of a triangle are x, $x + 2$ and 10 cm.

x is a whole number.

What is the smallest value x can take?

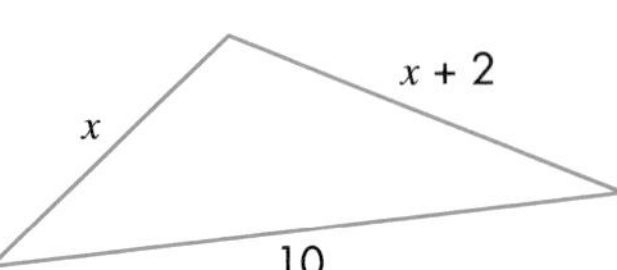

B

PS 6 Five cards have inequalities and equations marked on them.

$x > 0$	$x < 3$	$x \geqslant 4$	$x = 2$	$x = 6$

The cards are shuffled and then turned over, one at a time.
If two consecutive cards have any numbers in common, then a point is scored.
If they do not have any numbers in common, then a point is deducted.

a The first two cards below score –1 because $x = 6$ and $x < 3$ have no numbers in common.
Explain why the total for this combination scores 0.

$x = 6$	$x < 3$	$x > 0$	$x = 2$	$x \geqslant 4$

b What does this combination score?

$x > 0$	$x = 6$	$x \geqslant 4$	$x = 2$	$x < 3$

c Arrange the cards to give a maximum score of 4.

7 Solve the following linear inequalities.

a $4x + 1 \geqslant 3x - 5$

b $5t - 3 \leqslant 2t + 5$

c $3y - 12 \leqslant y - 4$

d $2x + 3 \geqslant x + 1$

e $5w - 7 \leqslant 3w + 4$

f $2(4x - 1) \leqslant 3(x + 4)$

8 Solve the following linear inequalities.

a $\frac{x + 4}{2} \leqslant 3$

b $\frac{x - 3}{5} > 7$

c $\frac{2x + 5}{3} < 6$

d $\frac{4x - 3}{5} \geqslant 5$

e $\frac{2t - 2}{7} > 4$

f $\frac{5y + 3}{5} \leqslant 2$

9 Solve the following linear inequalities.

a $7 < 2x + 1 < 13$

b $5 < 3x - 1 < 14$

c $-1 < 5x + 4 \leqslant 19$

d $1 \leqslant 4x - 3 < 13$

e $11 \leqslant 3x + 5 < 17$

f $-3 \leqslant 2x - 3 \leqslant 7$

The number line

The solution to a linear inequality can be shown on the **number line** by using the following conventions.

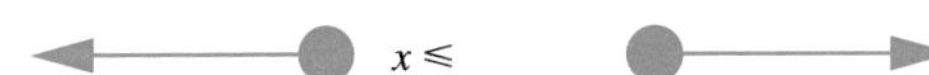

A strict inequality does not include the boundary point but an inclusive inequality does include the boundary point.

Below are five examples.

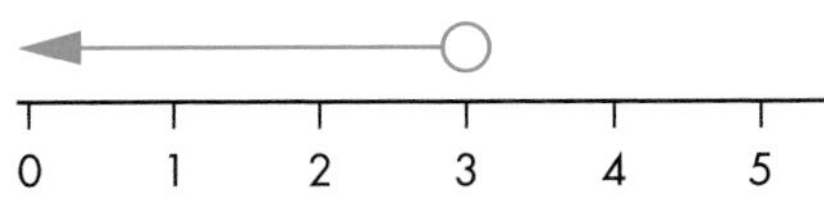

represents $x < 3$

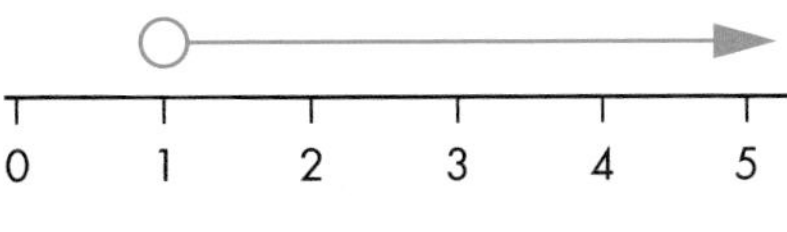

represents $x > 1$

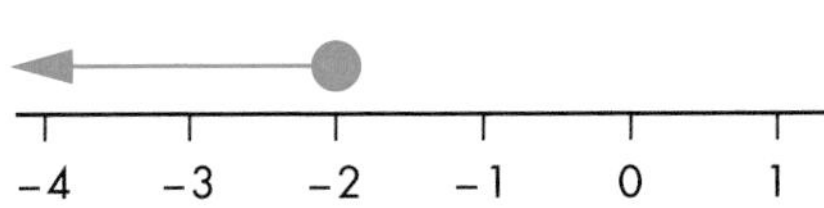

represents $x \leqslant -2$

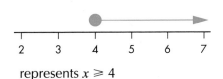

represents $x \geqslant 4$

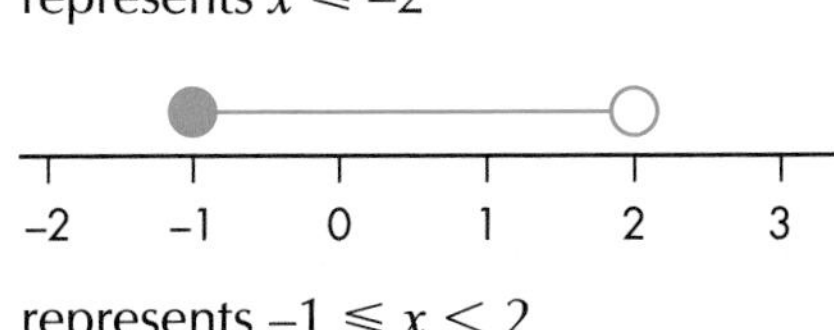

represents $-1 \leqslant x < 2$

This is a 'between' inequality. It can be written as $x \geqslant -1$ and $x < 2$, but the notation $-1 \leqslant x < 2$ is much neater.

EXAMPLE 5

a Write down the inequality shown by this diagram.

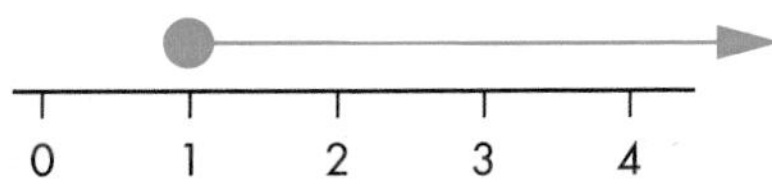

b **i** Solve the inequality $2x + 3 < 11$.

ii Mark the solution on a number line.

c Write down the integers that satisfy both the inequalities in **a** and **b**.

a The inequality shown is $x \geqslant 1$.

b **i** $2x + 3 < 11$

$\Rightarrow 2x < 8$

$\Rightarrow x < 4$

ii

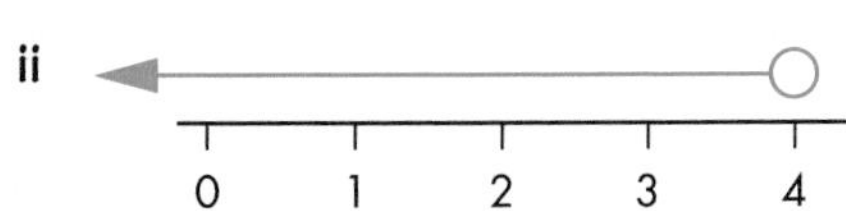

c The integers that satisfy both inequalities are 1, 2 and 3.

EXERCISE 14B

1 Write down the inequality that is represented by each diagram below.

a

b

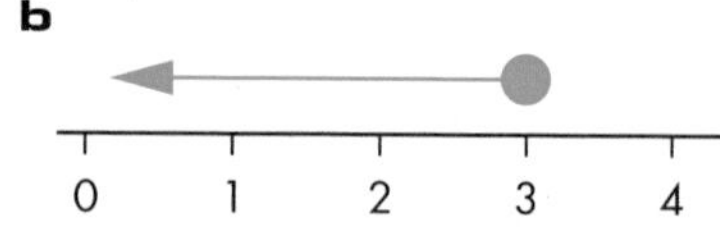

c

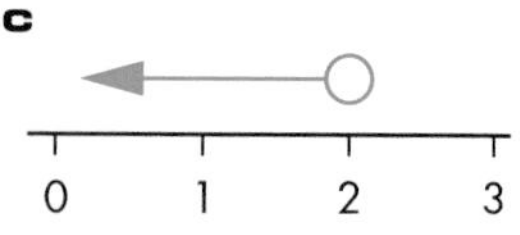

d

e

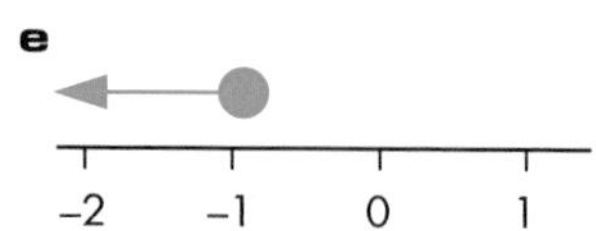

f

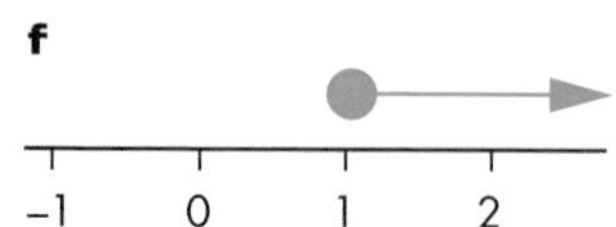

2 Draw diagrams to illustrate these inequalities.

a $x \leqslant 3$ **b** $x > -2$ **c** $x \geqslant 0$ **d** $x < 5$

e $x \geqslant -1$ **f** $2 < x \leqslant 5$ **g** $-1 \leqslant x \leqslant 3$ **h** $-3 < x < 4$

3 Solve the following inequalities and illustrate their solutions on number lines.

a $x + 4 \geqslant 8$ **b** $x + 5 < 3$ **c** $4x - 2 \geqslant 12$ **d** $2x + 5 < 3$

e $2(4x + 3) < 18$ **f** $\frac{x}{2} + 3 \leqslant 2$ **g** $\frac{x}{5} - 2 > 8$ **h** $\frac{x}{3} + 5 \geqslant 3$

FM 4 Max went to the supermarket with £1.20. He bought three apples costing x pence each and a chocolate bar costing 54p. When he got to the till, he found he didn't have enough money.

Max took one of the apples back and paid for two apples and the chocolate bar. He counted his change and found he had enough money to buy a 16p chew.

a Explain why $3x + 54 > 120$ and solve the inequality.

b Explain why $2x + 54 \leqslant 104$ and solve the inequality.

c Show the solution to both of these inequalities on a number line.

d What is the possible price of an apple?

AU 5 On copies of the number lines below, draw two inequalities so that only the integers {–1, 0, 1, 2} are common to both inequalities.

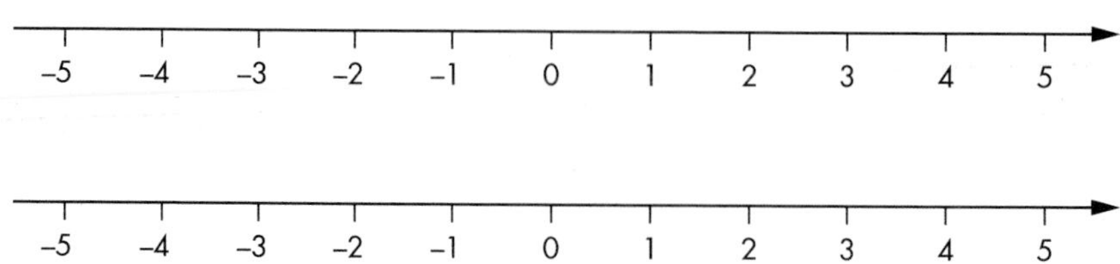

PS 6 What numbers are being described?

x is a square number.

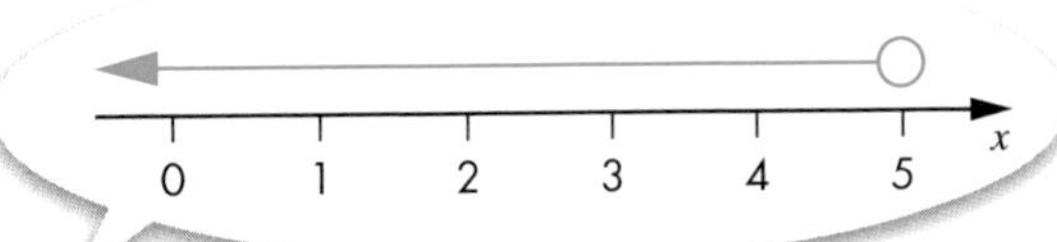

$2x + 3 > 5$

7 Solve the following inequalities and illustrate their solutions on number lines.

a $\frac{2x + 5}{3} > 3$ **b** $\frac{3x + 4}{2} \geqslant 11$ **c** $\frac{2x + 8}{3} \leqslant 2$ **d** $\frac{2x - 1}{3} \geqslant -3$

14.2 Graphical inequalities

This section will show you how to:

- show a graphical inequality
- how to find regions that satisfy more than one graphical inequality

Key words
boundary
included
origin
region

A linear inequality can be plotted on a graph. The result is a **region** that lies on one side or the other of a straight line. You will recognise an inequality by the fact that it looks like an equation but instead of the equals sign it has an inequality sign: $<$, $>$, $\leqslant$, or $\geqslant$.

The following are examples of linear inequalities that can be represented on a graph.

$y < 3$ $x > 7$ $-3 \leqslant y < 5$ $y \geqslant 2x + 3$ $2x + 3y < 6$ $y \leqslant x$

The method for graphing an inequality is to draw the **boundary** line that defines the inequality. This is found by replacing the inequality sign with an equals sign. When a strict inequality is stated ($<$ or $>$), the boundary line should be drawn as a *dashed* line to show that it is not included in the range of values. When $\leqslant$ or $\geqslant$ is used to state the inequality, the boundary line should be drawn as a *solid* line to show that the boundary is **included**.

After the boundary line has been drawn, shade the *required region*.

To confirm on which side of the line the region lies, choose any point that is not on the boundary line and test it in the inequality. If it satisfies the inequality, that is the side required. If it doesn't, the other side is required.

Work through the six inequalities in the following example to see how the procedure is applied.

EXAMPLE 6

Show each of the following inequalities on a graph.

a $y \leqslant 3$ **b** $x > 7$ **c** $-3 \leqslant y < 5$

d $y \leqslant 2x + 3$ **e** $2x + 3y < 6$ **f** $y \leqslant x$

a Draw the line $y = 3$. Since the inequality is stated as $\leqslant$, the line is *solid*. Test a point that is not on the line. The **origin** is always a good choice if possible, as 0 is easy to test.

Putting 0 into the inequality gives $0 \leqslant 3$. The inequality is satisfied and so the region containing the origin is the side we want.

Shade it in.

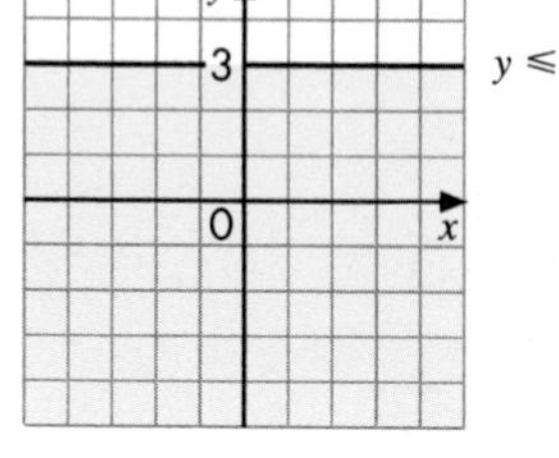

b Since the inequality is stated as $>$, the line is *dashed*. Draw the line $x = 7$.

Test the origin (0, 0), which gives $0 > 7$. This is not true, so you want the other side of the line from the origin.

Shade it in.

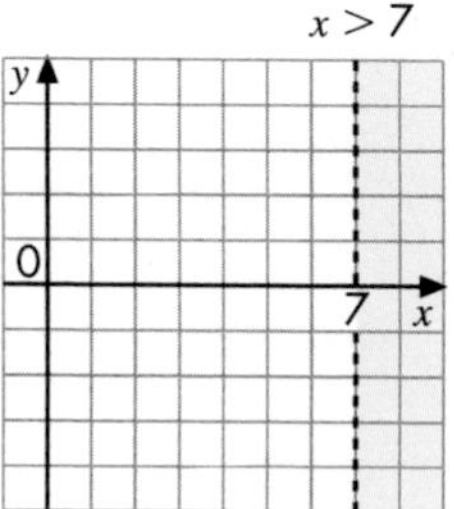

c Draw the lines $y = -3$ (solid for $\leqslant$) and $y = 5$ (dashed for $<$).

Test a point that is not on either line, say (0, 0). Zero is between –3 and 5, so the required region lies between the lines.

Shade it in.

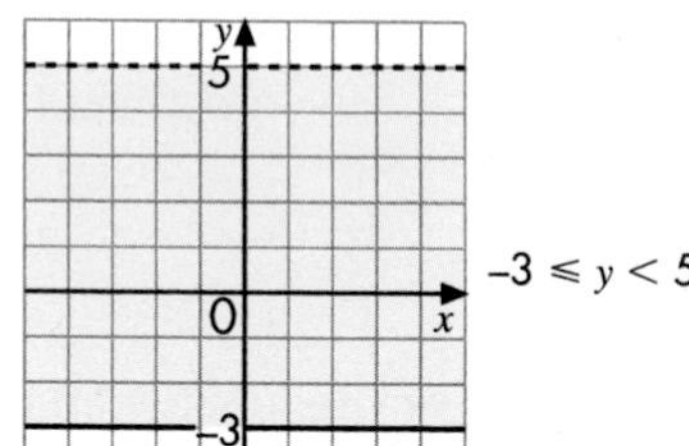

d Draw the line $y = 2x + 3$. Since the inequality is stated as $\leqslant$, the line is solid.

Test a point that is not on the line, (0, 0). Putting these x- and y-values in the inequality gives $0 \leqslant 2(0) + 3$, which is true. So the region that includes the origin is what you want.

Shade it in.

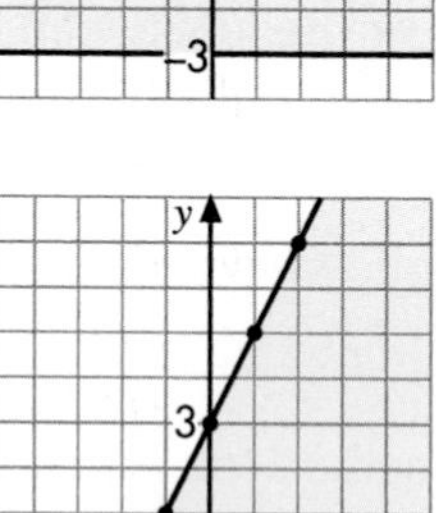

e Draw the line $2x + 3y = 6$. Since the inequality is stated as $<$, the line is dashed.

Test a point that is not on the line, say (0, 0). Is it true that $2(0) + 3(0) < 6$? The answer is yes, so the origin is in the region that you want.

Shade it in.

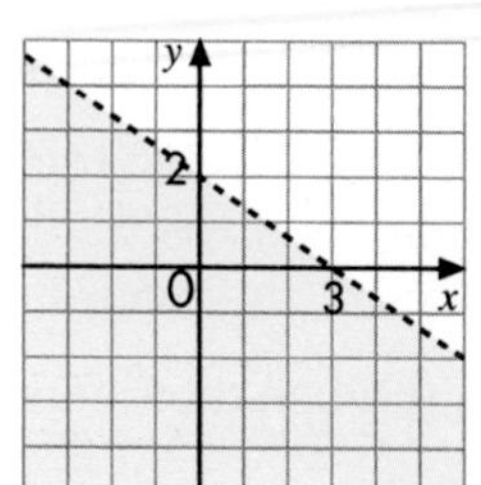

f Draw the line $y = x$. Since the inequality is stated as $\leqslant$, the line is solid.

This time the origin is on the line, so pick any other point, say (1, 3). Putting $x = 1$ and $y = 3$ in the inequality gives $3 \leqslant 1$. This is not true, so the point (1, 3) is not in the region you want.

Shade in the other side to (1, 3)

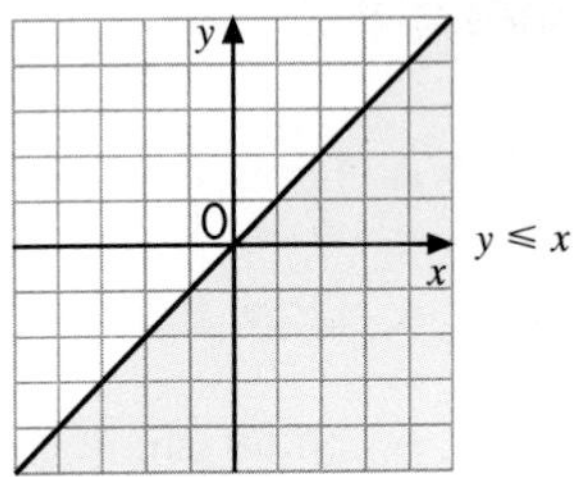

More than one inequality

When you have to show a region that satisfies more than one inequality, it is clearer to *shade* the regions *not required,* so that the *required region* is left *blank*.

EXAMPLE 7

a On the same grid, show the regions that represent the following inequalities by shading the unwanted regions.

i $x > 2$ **ii** $y \geqslant x$ **iii** $x + y < 8$

b Are these points

i (3, 4) **ii** (2, 6) **iii** (3, 3)

in the region that satisfies all three inequalities?

a **i**

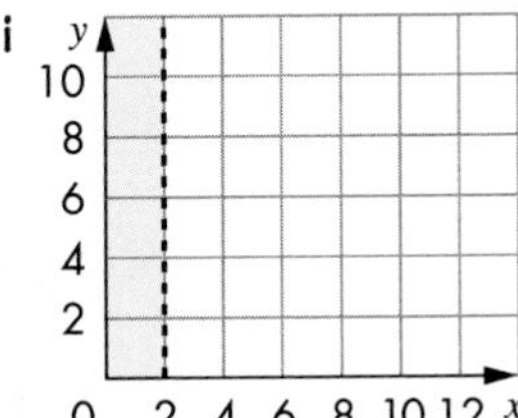

ii

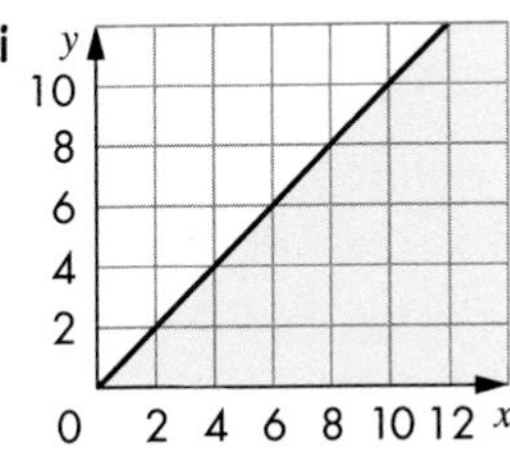

iii

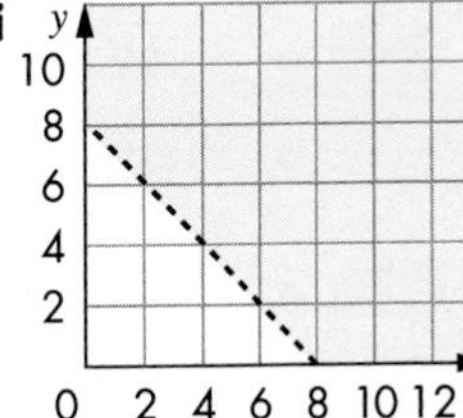

i The region $x > 2$ is shown unshaded in diagram **i**. The boundary line is $x = 2$ (dashed).

ii The region $y \geqslant x$ is shown unshaded in diagram **ii**. The boundary line is $y = x$ (solid).

iii The region $x + y < 8$ is shown unshaded in diagram **iii**.
The boundary line is $x + y = 8$ (dashed). The regions have first been drawn separately so that each may be clearly seen. The diagram on the right shows all three regions on the same grid. The white triangular area defines the region that satisfies all three inequalities.

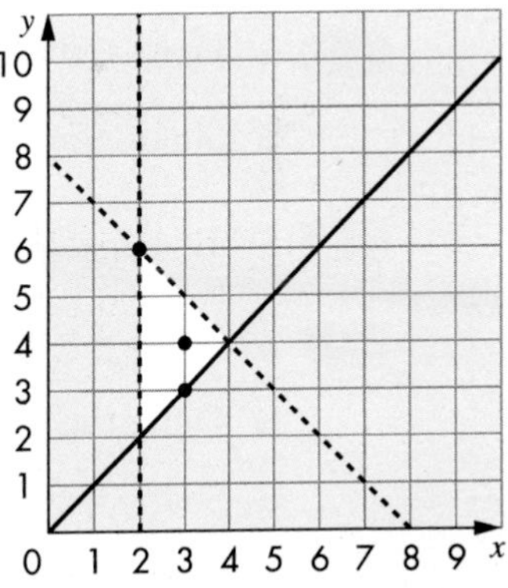

b **i** The point (3, 4) is clearly within the region that satisfies all three inequalities.

ii The point (2, 6) is on the boundary lines $x = 2$ and $x + y = 8$. As these are dashed lines, they are not included in the region defined by all three inequalities. So, the point (2, 6) is not in this region.

iii The point (3, 3) is on the boundary line $y = x$. As this is a solid line, it is included in the region defined by all three inequalities. So, the point (3, 3) is included in this region.

EXERCISE 14C

C

1 **a** Draw the line $x = 2$ (as a solid line). **b** Shade the region defined by $x \leqslant 2$.

2 **a** Draw the line $y = -3$ (as a dashed line). **b** Shade the region defined by $y > -3$.

3 **a** Draw the line $x = -2$ (as a solid line).

b Draw the line $x = 1$ (as a solid line) on the same grid.

c Shade the region defined by $-2 \leqslant x \leqslant 1$.

4 **a** Draw the line $y = -1$ (as a dashed line).

b Draw the line $y = 4$ (as a solid line) on the same grid.

c Shade the region defined by $-1 < y \leqslant 4$.

B

5 **a** On the same grid, draw the regions defined by these inequalities.

i $-3 \leqslant x \leqslant 6$ **ii** $-4 < y \leqslant 5$

b Are the following points in the region defined by both inequalities?

i (2, 2) **ii** (1, 5) **iii** (–2, –4)

6 **a** Draw the line $y = 2x - 1$ (as a dashed line).

b Shade the region defined by $y < 2x - 1$.

7 **a** Draw the line $3x - 4y = 12$ (as a solid line).

b Shade the region defined by $3x - 4y \leqslant 12$.

8 **a** Draw the line $y = \frac{1}{2}x + 3$ (as a solid line).

b Shade the region defined by $y \geqslant \frac{1}{2}x + 3$.

> **HINTS AND TIPS**
>
> In exams it is always made clear which region is to be labelled or shaded. Make sure you do as the question asks, and label or shade as required, otherwise you could lose a mark.

9 Shade the region defined by $y < -3$.

10 **a** Draw the line $y = 3x - 4$ (as a solid line).

b Draw the line $x + y = 10$ (as a solid line) on the same diagram.

c Shade the diagram so that the region defined by $y \geqslant 3x - 4$ is left *unshaded*.

d Shade the diagram so that the region defined by $x + y \leqslant 10$ is left *unshaded*.

e Are the following points in the region defined by both inequalities?

i (2, 1) **ii** (2, 2) **iii** (2, 3)

11 **a** Draw the line $y = x$ (as a solid line).

b Draw the line $2x + 5y = 10$ (as a solid line) on the same diagram.

c Draw the line $2x + y = 6$ (as a dashed line) on the same diagram.

d Shade the diagram so that the region defined by $y \geqslant x$ is left *unshaded*.

e Shade the diagram so that the region defined by $2x + 5y \geqslant 10$ is left *unshaded*.

f Shade the diagram so that the region defined by $2x + y < 6$ is left *unshaded*.

g Are the following points in the region defined by these inequalities?

i (1, 1) **ii** (2, 2) **iii** (1, 3)

12 **a** On the same grid, draw the regions defined by the following inequalities. (Shade the diagram so that the overlapping region is left blank.)

i $y > x - 3$ **ii** $3y + 4x \leqslant 24$ **iii** $x \geqslant 2$

b Are the following points in the region defined by all three inequalities?

i (1, 1) **ii** (2, 2) **iii** (3, 3) **iv** (4, 4)

AU 13 The graph shows three points (1, 2), (1, 3) and (2, 3).

Write down three inequalities that between them surround these three grid intersection points and *no others*.

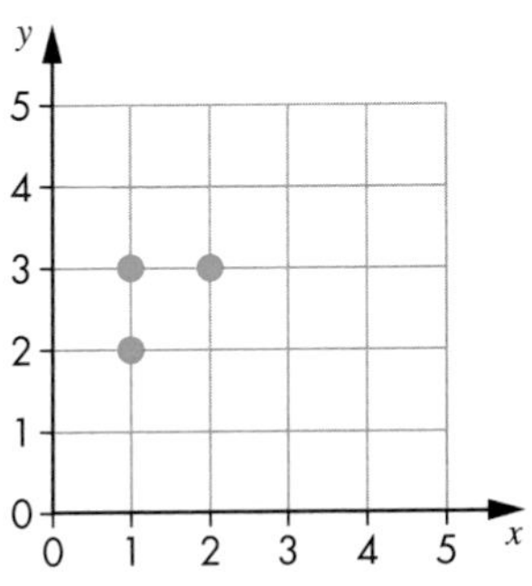

PS 14 If $x + y > 40$, which of the following may be true (M), must be false (F) or must be true (T)?

a $x > 40$ **b** $x + y \leqslant 20$ **c** $x - y = 10$

d $x \leqslant 5$ **e** $x + y = 40$ **f** $y > 40 - x$

g $y = 2x$ **h** $x + y \geqslant 39$

AU 15 Explain how you would find which side of the line represents the inequality $y < x + 2$.

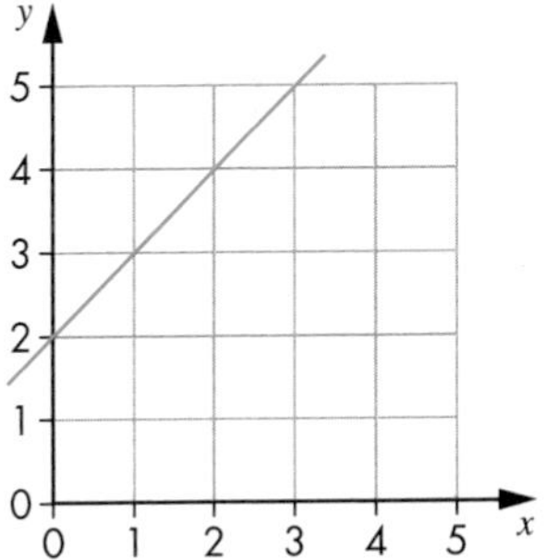

AU 16 The region marked R is the overlap of the inequalities:
the inequality $y < x + 2$.

$x + y \geqslant 3$ $y \leqslant \frac{1}{2}x + 3$ $y \geqslant 5x - 15$

a For which point in the region R is the value of the function $2x - y$ the greatest ?

b For which point in the region R is the value of the function $x - 3y$ the least?

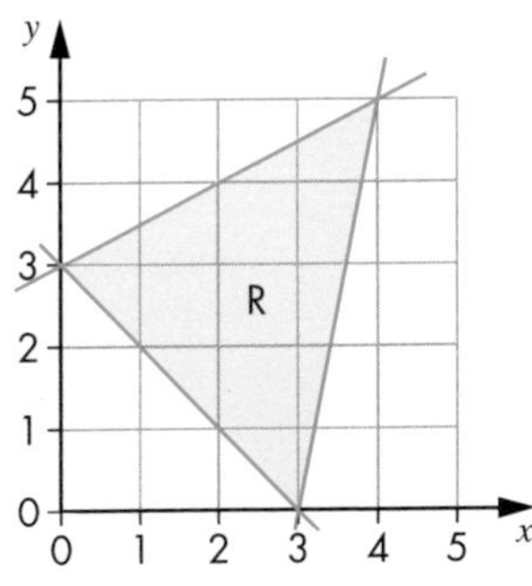

GRADE BOOSTER

C You can solve inequalities such as $3x + 2 < 5$ and represent the solution on a number line

B You can represent a region that satisfies a linear inequality graphically, and solve more complex linear inequalities

B You can represent a region that simultaneously satisfies more than one linear inequality graphically

What you should know now

- How to solve simple inequalities
- How to create algebraic inequalities from verbal statements
- How to represent linear inequalities on a graph
- How to depict a region satisfying more than one linear inequality

1 Solve the inequality:

$5x + 3 \leqslant 10$ *(2 marks)*

AQA, June 2006, Paper 2 Higher, Question 1

2 **a** Solve the inequality:

$3(x - 2) \leqslant 9$ *(3 marks)*

b The inequality $x \leqslant 3$ is shown on the number line below.

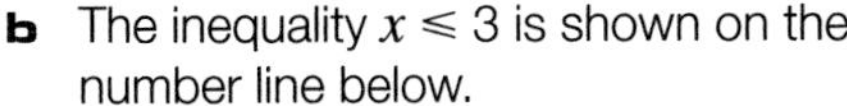

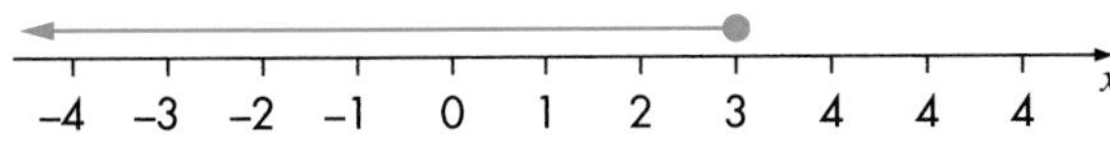

Draw another inequality on the number line so that only the following integers satisfy

{–2, –1, 0, 1, 2, 3} *(1 mark)*

AQA, November 2006, Paper 2 Higher, Question 4

3 **a** Solve the inequality:

$2x + 3 \geqslant 4x + 5$ *(2 marks)*

b Which inequality is represented by the shaded region? *(1 mark)*

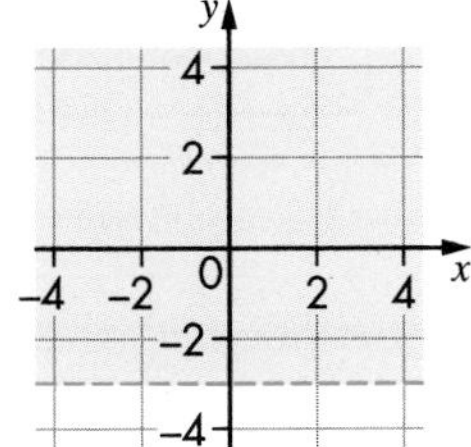

c The line $2x - 3y = 12$ is drawn on the grid:

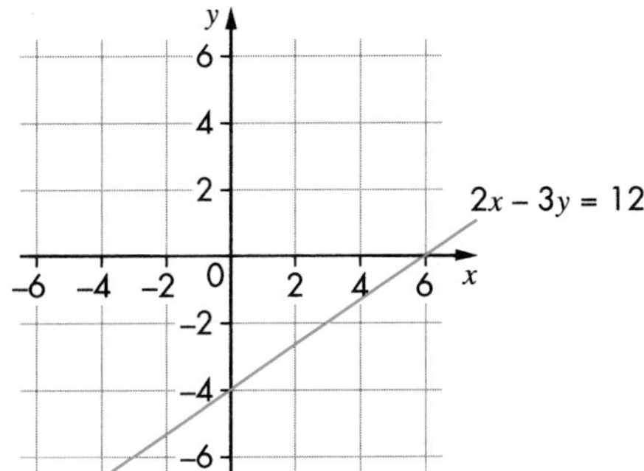

Shade the side of the line that represents

$2x - 3y \leqslant 12$.

Explain how you know which side to shade. *(1 mark)*

AQA, June 2008, Paper 2 Higher, Question 15

4 **a** Which of these inequalities is shown shaded on the grid below?

$y > 2 \quad y \geqslant 2 \quad x > 2 \quad x \geqslant 2$ *(1 mark)*

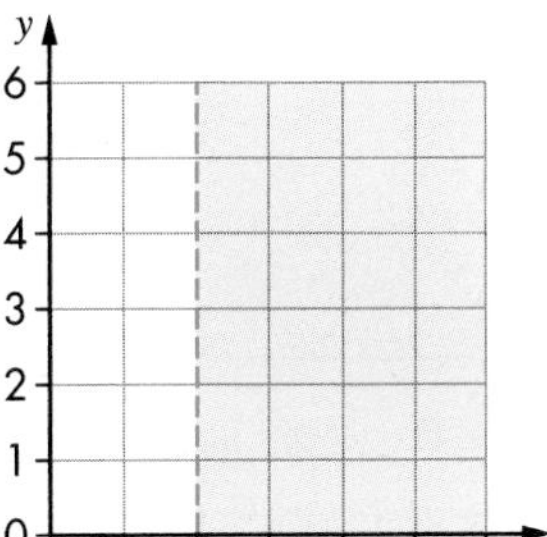

b On a grid like the one above, draw lines to find the region satisfied by the three inequalities:

$y > 2$

$y < x + 1$

$x + y < 5$

Label the region with the letter R. *(3 marks)*

AQA, November 2007, Paper 2 Higher, Question 12

5 Match each of the shaded regions to one of these inequalities.

A $y \leqslant -x + 2$ **D** $y \geqslant 2x - 4$

B $y \leqslant x + 2$ **E** $y \leqslant 2x - 4$

C $y \geqslant -2x + 4$ *(4 marks)*

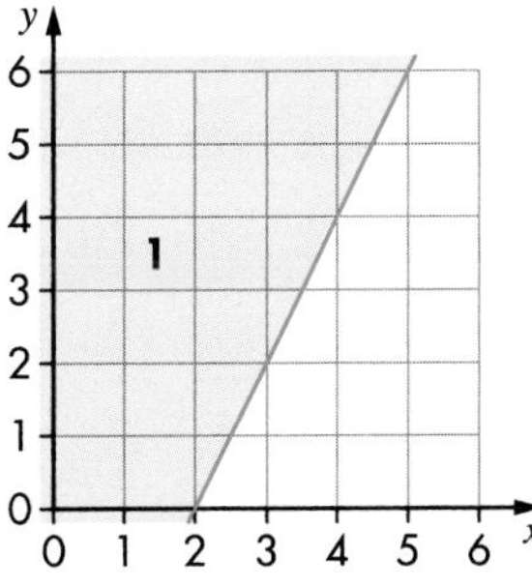

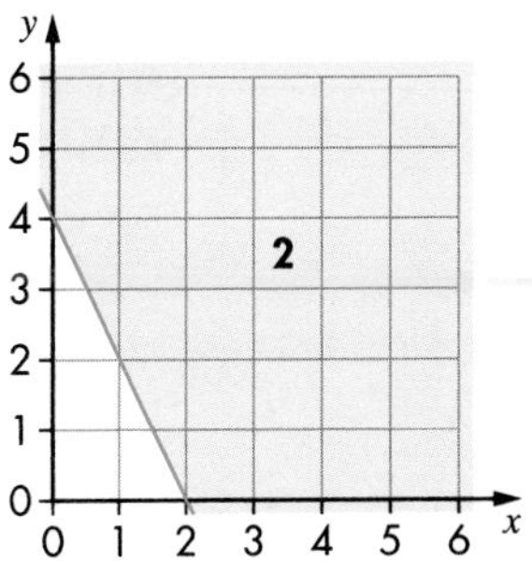

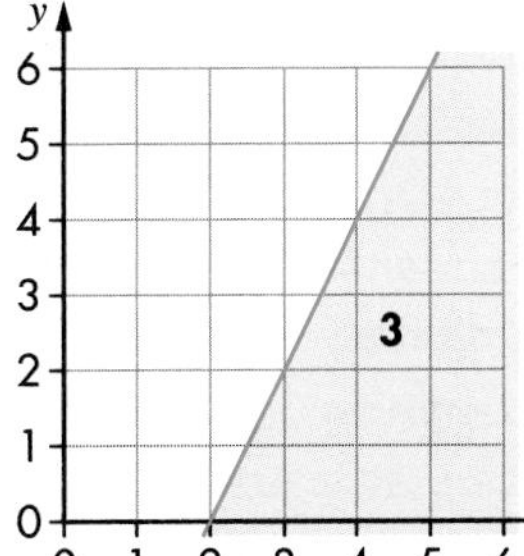

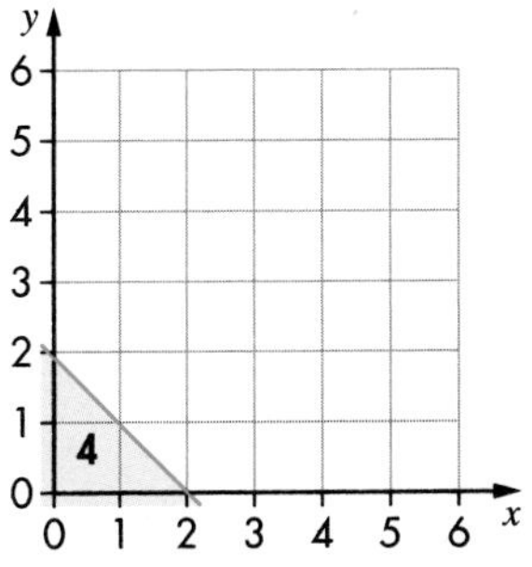

AQA, June 2006, Paper 1 Higher, Question 8

Worked Examination Questions

1 **a** On the number lines show these inequalities.

i $-2 \leqslant n < 4$

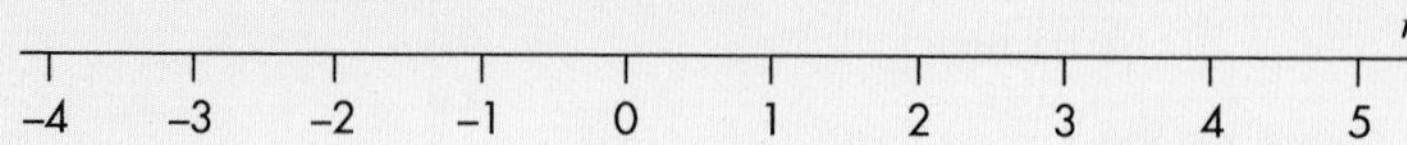

ii $n < 2$

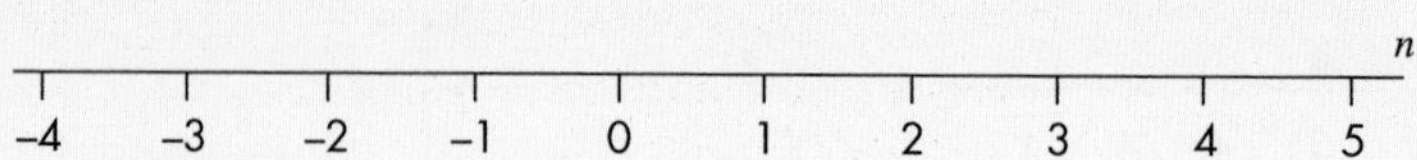

b n is an integer. Find the values of n that satisfy both inequalities in part **a**.

c Solve these inequalities.

i $3x + 8 > 2$

ii $3(x - 4) \leqslant \frac{1}{2}(x + 1)$

1 a i

ii

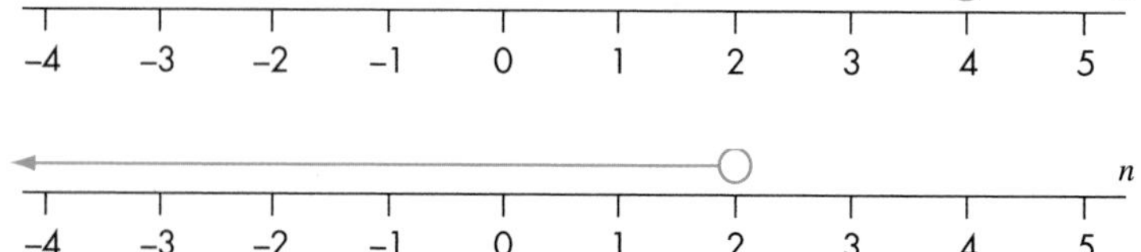

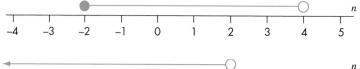

Remember that a strict inequality has an open circle to show the boundary and an inclusive inequality has a solid circle to show the boundary. These get 1 mark each.

b $\{-2, -1, 0, 1\}$

The integers that satisfy both inequalities are in the overlap of both lines. This gets 1 mark.

c i $3x + 8 > 2$

$3x > -6$

$x > -2$

As when solving an equation do the same thing to both sides. First subtract 8, then divide by 3. This gets 1 mark for method and 1 mark for accuracy.

ii $3(x - 4) \leqslant \frac{1}{2}(x + 1)$

$6(x - 4) \leqslant x + 1$

$6x - 24 < x + 1$

$5x < 25$

$x < 5$

First multiply by 2 to get rid of the fraction, then expand the brackets. This gets 1 mark for method. Then collect all the x terms on the left-hand side and the number terms on the right-hand side. This gets 1 mark for method.
Then simplify and divide by 5.
This gets 1 mark for accuracy.

Total: 7 marks

FM **2** A school uses two coach firms, Excel and Storm, to take students home from school. An Excel coach holds 40 students and a Storm coach holds 50 students. 1500 students need to be taken home by coach. If E Excel coaches and S Storm coaches are used, explain why:

$4E + 5S \geqslant 150$

2 E Excel coaches take $40E$ and S Storm coaches take $50S$ students. Together they take $40E + 50S$ students.

Write down the number of students and the total carried by each company's coaches.
This gets 1 mark.

There are 1500 students to use the coaches, so $40E + 50S$ must be at least 1500.

$40E + 50S \geqslant 1500$, then cancel by 10.

Explain that this must be at least the total number of students to be carried, and that the equation will cancel by 10.
This gets 1 mark for method and 1 mark for accuracy.

Total: 3 marks

Worked Examination Questions

PS **3** A bookshelf holds P paperback and H hardback books. The bookshelf can hold a total of 400 books. Which of the following may be true?

a $P + H < 300$ **b** $P \geqslant H$ **c** $P + H > 500$

3 $P + H < 300$ and $P \geqslant H$.

Both of these inequalities could be true. The bookshelf doesn't have to be full and there could be more paperbacks than hardbacks. The final inequality cannot be true as there can only be a maximum of 400 books.
These get 1 mark each.

Total: 2 marks

EQ **4** The region R is shown shaded below.

Write down three inequalities which together describe the shaded region.

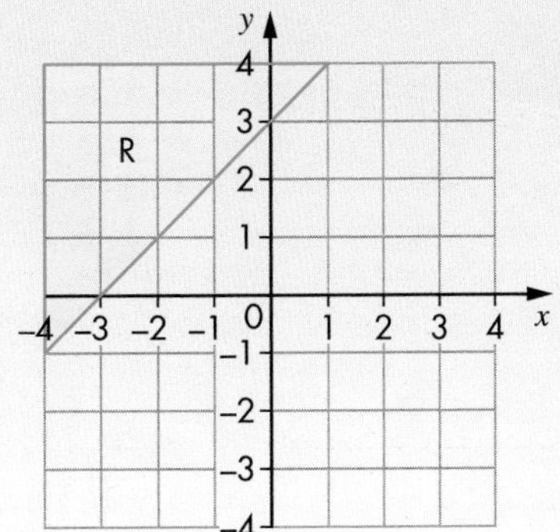

4 $y \leqslant 4, x \geqslant -4$ and $y \geqslant x + 3$

Work out the equation of each boundary line and then decide if points off the line are greater or less than the boundary.
These get 1 mark each.

Total: 3 marks

14 Functional Maths
Linear programming

Linear programming is a mathematical method that uses two-dimensional inequalities. It takes into account maximum and minimum values, and constraints to find the optimum solution to a problem. It is often used by shops to work out stock levels, and reduce cost to increase profit.

Getting started

A boy goes to the fair with £6.00 in his pocket. He only likes rides on the big wheel and eating hot-dogs. A big wheel ride costs £1.50 and a hot-dog costs £2.00. He has W big wheel rides and D hot-dogs.

a Explain why:
   i $W \leq 4$
   ii $D \leq 3$
   iii $3W + 4D \leq 12$

b If he cannot eat more than two hot-dogs before feeling full, write down an inequality that must be true.

c Which of these combinations of big wheel rides and hot-dogs are possible if they obey all of the above conditions?
   i two big wheel rides and one hot-dog
   ii three big wheel rides and two hot-dogs
   iii two big wheel rides and two hot-dogs
   iv one big wheel ride and one hot-dog

Your task

A shop stocks only sofas and beds.

A sofa takes up 3 m^2 of floor area and is worth £500. A bed takes up 4 m^2 of floor area and is worth £300.

The shop has 48 m^2 of floor space for stock.

The shop stocks at least 3 sofas and 2 beds at any one time. The insurance policy will allow a total of only £6000 of stock to be in the shop at any one time.

The shop stocks x beds and y sofas.

Use this information to investigate the number of sofas and beds the shop should stock.

Extension

Give some limiting factors of your own and display them diagrammatically.

Answers to Chapter 1

Quick check

1 **a** 468 **b** 366 **c** 54 **d** 300 **e** 102 **f** 95

2 **a** 3841 **b** 41 **c** 625

3 **a** 17 **b** 25 **c** 5

1.1 Solving real-life problems

Exercise 1A

1 **a** 6000
b 5 cans cost £1.95, so 6 cans cost £1.95.
32 = 5 × 6 + 2. Cost is £10.53.

2 **a** 288
b 16

3 **a** 38
b Coach price for adults = £8, coach price for juniors = £4, money for coaches raised by tickets = £12 400, cost of coaches = £12 160, profit = £240

4 £34.80

5 (18.81...) Kirsty can buy 18 models.

6 (7.58...) Eunice must work for 8 weeks.

7 £8.40 per year, 70p per copy

8 £450

9 15

10 3 weeks

11 £248.75

12 Gavin pays 2296.25 − 1840 = £456.25

1.2 Multiplication and division with decimals

Exercise 1B

1 **a** 0.028 **b** 0.09 **c** 0.192 **d** 3.0264 **e** 7.134 **f** 50.96 **g** 3.0625 **h** 46.512

2 **a** 35, 35.04, 0.04 **b** 16, 18.24, 2.24 **c** 60, 59.67, 0.33 **d** 180, 172.86, 7.14 **e** 12, 12.18, 0.18 **f** 24, 26.016, 2.016 **g** 40, 40.664, 0.664 **h** 140, 140.58, 0.58

3 **a** 572 **b** **i** 5.72 **ii** 1.43 **iii** 22.88

4 **a** Incorrect as should end in the digit 2
b Incorrect since 9 × 5 = 45, so answer must be less than 45

5 26.66 ÷ 3.1 (answer 8.6) since approximately 27 ÷ 3 = 9

6 **a** 18 **b** 140 **c** 1.4 **d** 12 **e** 21.3 **f** 6.9 **g** 2790 **h** 12.1 **i** 18.9

7 **a** 280 **b** 12 **c** 0.18 **d** 450 **e** 0.62 **f** 380 **g** 0.26 **h** 240 **i** 12

8 750

9 300

10 **a** 27 **b** **i** 27 **ii** 0.027 **iii** 0.27

11 £54.20

12 Mark bought a DVD, some jeans and a pen.

1.3 Approximation of calculations

Exercise 1C

1 **a** 50 000 **b** 60 000 **c** 30 000 **d** 90 000 **e** 90 000 **f** 0.5 **g** 0.3 **h** 0.006 **i** 0.05 **j** 0.0009 **k** 10 **l** 90 **m** 90 **n** 200 **o** 1000

2 **a** 56 000 **b** 27 000 **c** 80 000 **d** 31 000 **e** 14 000 **f** 1.7 **g** 4.1 **h** 2.7 **i** 8.0 **j** 42 **k** 0.80 **l** 0.46 **m** 0.066 **n** 1.0 **o** 0.0098

3 **a** 60 000 **b** 5300 **c** 89.7 **d** 110 **e** 9 **f** 1.1 **g** 0.3 **h** 0.7 **i** 0.4 **j** 0.8 **k** 0.2 **l** 0.7

4 **a** 65, 74 **b** 95, 149 **c** 950, 1499

5 Any correct multiplication such as 200 × 6 000, 1000 × 1200 etc.

6 Elsecar 750, 849, Hoyland 1150, 1249, Barnsley 164 500, 165 499

7 15, 16 or 17

8 1, because there could be 450 then 449

9 Donte has rounded to 2 significant figures or nearest 10 000

Exercise 1D

1 **a** 60 000 **b** 120 000 **c** 10 000 **d** 15 **e** 140 **f** 100 **g** 200 **h** 0.028 **i** 0.09 **j** 400 **k** 8000 **l** 0.16 **m** 45 **n** 0.08 **o** 0.25 **p** 4 000 000 **q** 360 000

2 **a** 5 **b** 50 **c** 25 **d** 600 **e** 3000 **f** 5000 **g** 2000 **h** 2000 **i** 400 **j** 8000 **k** 4 000 000 **l** 3 200 000

3 **a** 54 400 **b** 16 000

4 30 × 90 000 = 2 700 000
600 × 8000 = 4 800 000
5000 × 4000 = 20 000 000
200 000 × 700 = 140 000 000

5 1400 million

Exercise 1E

1 **a** 35 000 **b** 15 000 **c** 960 **d** 5 **e** 1200 **f** 500
2 **a** 39 700 **b** 17 000 **c** 933 **d** 4.44 **e** 1130 **f** 550
3 **a** 4000 **b** 10 **c** 1 **d** 20 **e** 3 **f** 18
4 **a** 4190 **b** 8.79 **c** 1.01 **d** 20.7 **e** 3.07 **f** 18.5
5 **a** £3000 **b** £2000 **c** £1500 **d** £700
6 **a** £15 000 **b** £18 000 **c** £17 500
7 £20 000
8 8p
9 $1000
10 **a** 40 miles per hour **b** 10 gallons **c** £70
11 **a** 80 000 **b** 2000 **c** 1000 **d** 30 000 **e** 5000 **f** 200 000 **g** 75 **h** 140 **i** 100 **j** 3000
12 **a** 86 900 **b** 1760 **c** 1030 **d** 29 100 **e** 3930 **f** 237 000 **g** 84.8 **h** 163 **i** 96.9 **j** 2440
13 Approximately 500
14 1000 or 1200
15 400 or 500
16 **a** **i** 27.571 428 57 **ii** 27.6
b **i** 16.896 516 39 **ii** 16.9
c **i** 704.419 889 5 **ii** 704

Exercise 1F

1 **a** 1.74 m **b** 6 minutes **c** 240 g
d 83°C **e** 35 000 people
f 15 miles **g** 14 m^2

2 82°F, 5km, 110 min, 43 000 people, 6.2 seconds, 67th, 1788, 15 practice walks, 5 seconds

The answers will depend on the approximations made. Your answers should be to the same order as these.

3 40
4 300 miles
5 40 × £20 = £800
6 40 minutes
7 60 stamps
8 270 fans
9 80 000 kg (80 tonnes)
10 22.5° C − 18.2° C = 4.3 Celsius degrees
11 149 000 000 ÷ 300 000 = 496.66 ≈ 500 seconds
12 Macau's population density is approximately 710 000 times the population density of Greenland.

Examination questions

1 6 weeks
2 17 boxes
3 13
4 **a** 30.946 944 26
b 30.95
5 **a** 3.586 440 678
b 3.59
6 4200
7 Briony

Answers to Chapter 2

Quick check

1 **a** $\frac{2}{5}$ **b** $\frac{3}{8}$ **c** $\frac{3}{7}$

2

Fraction	Percentage	Decimal
$\frac{3}{4}$	75%	0.75
$\frac{2}{5}$	40%	0.4
$\frac{11}{20}$	55%	0.55

3 **a** £23 **b** £4.60 **c** 23p

2.1 One quantity as a fraction of another

Exercise 2A

1 **a** $\frac{1}{3}$ **b** $\frac{1}{5}$ **c** $\frac{2}{5}$ **d** $\frac{5}{24}$ **e** $\frac{2}{5}$
f $\frac{1}{6}$ **g** $\frac{2}{7}$ **h** $\frac{1}{3}$
2 $\frac{3}{5}$
3 $\frac{12}{31}$
4 20 weeks.
5 Jon saves $\frac{30}{90} = \frac{1}{3}$

Matt saves $\frac{35}{100}$, which is greater than $\frac{1}{3}$, so Matt saves the greater proportion of his earnings.

6 $\frac{13}{20} = \frac{65}{100}$, $\frac{16}{25} = \frac{64}{100}$, so first mark is better.
7 $\frac{1}{8}$
8 $\frac{5}{12}$
9 $\frac{1}{5}$
10 $\frac{3}{20}$
11 $\frac{3}{10}$
12 32 or 36

2.2 Adding and subtracting fractions

Exercise 2B

1 **a** $\frac{8}{15}$ **b** $\frac{7}{12}$ **c** $\frac{3}{10}$ **d** $\frac{11}{12}$ **e** $\frac{1}{10}$ **f** $\frac{1}{8}$
g $\frac{1}{12}$ **h** $\frac{1}{3}$ **i** $\frac{7}{9}$ **j** $\frac{5}{8}$ **k** $\frac{3}{8}$ **l** $\frac{1}{15}$

2 **a** $3\frac{31}{45}$ **b** $4\frac{47}{60}$ **c** $\frac{41}{72}$ **d** $\frac{29}{48}$ **e** $1\frac{43}{48}$ **f** $1\frac{109}{120}$
g $1\frac{23}{30}$ **h** $1\frac{31}{84}$

3 $\frac{1}{20}$

4 **a** $\frac{1}{6}$ **b** 30

5 No, one eighth is left, which is 12.5 cl, so enough for one cup but not two cups.

6 260

7 Three-quarters of 68

8 He has added the numerators and added the denominators instead of using a common denominator. Correct answer is $3\frac{7}{12}$.

9 Possible answer: The denominators are 4 and 5. I first find a common denominator. The lowest common denominator is 20 because 4 and 5 are both factors of 20. So I am changing the fractions to twentieths. One-quarter is the same as five-twentieths (multiplying numerator and denominator by 5). Two-fifths is the same as eight-twentieths (multiplying numerator and denominator by 4). Five-twentieths plus eight-twentieths = thirteen-twentieths.

10 £51

11 10 minutes

2.3 Increasing and decreasing quantities by a percentage

Exercise 2C

1 **a** 1.1 **b** 1.03 **c** 1.2 **d** 1.07 **e** 1.12

2 **a** £62.40 **b** 12.96 kg **c** 472.5 g **d** 599.5 m
e £38.08 **f** £90 **g** 391 kg **h** 824.1 cm
i 253.5 g **j** £143.50 **k** 736 m **l** £30.24

3 £29 425 – 7% pay rise

4 1 690 200

5 **a** Bob: £17 325, Anne: £18 165, Jean: £20 475, Brian: £26 565
b 5% of different amounts is not a fixed amount. The more pay to start with, the more the increase (5%) will be.

6 £411.95

7 193 800

8 575 g

9 918

10 60

11 TV: £287.88, microwave: £84.60, CD: £135.13, stereo: £34.66

12 £10

13 **c** Both same as $1.05 \times 1.03 = 1.03 \times 1.05$

14 **d** Shop A as $1.04 \times 1.04 = 1.0816$, so an 8.16% increase.

15 £540.96

16 Calculate the VAT on certain amounts, and $\frac{1}{6}$ of that amount.

Show the error grows as the amount increases. After £600 the error is greater than £5, so the method works to within £5 with prices up to £600.

Exercise 2D

1 **a** 0.92 **b** 0.85 **c** 0.75 **d** 0.91 **e** 0.88

2 **a** £9.40 **b** 23 kg **c** 212.4 g **d** 339.5 m
e £4.90 **f** 39.6 m **g** 731 m **h** 83.52 g
i 360 cm **j** 117 min **k** 81.7 kg **l** £37.70

3 £5525

4 **a** 52.8 kg **b** 66 kg **c** 45.76 kg

5 Mr Speed: £176, Mrs Speed: £297.50, James: £341, John: £562.50

6 448

7 705

8 £18 975

9 **a** 66.5 mph **b** 73.5 mph

10 No, as the total is £101. She will save £20.20, which is less than the £25 it would cost to join the club.

11 **a** 524.8 units
b Less gas since 18% of the smaller amount of 524.8 units (94.464 units) is less than 18% of 640 units (115.2 units). I used 619.264 units.

12 TV £222.31, DVD player £169.20

13 10% off £50 is £45; 10% off £45 is £40.50; 20% off £50 is £40

14 £765

15 $1.10 \times 0.9 = 0.99$ (99%)

16 Offer A gives 360 grams for £1.40, i.e. 0.388 pence per gram. Offer B gives 300 grams for £1.12, i.e 0.373 pence per gram, so Offer B is the better offer.
Or Offer A is 360 for 1.40 = 2.6 g/p, offer B is 300 for 1.12 = 2.7 g/p, so offer B is better.

2.4 Expressing one quantity as a percentage of another

Exercise 2E

1 **a** 25% **b** 60.6% **c** 46.3% **d** 12.5%
e 41.7% **f** 60% **g** 20.8% **h** 10%
i 1.9% **j** 8.3% **k** 45.5% **l** 10.5%

2 32%

3 6.5%

4 33.7%

5 **a** 49.2% **b** 64.5% **c** 10.6%

6 17.9%

7 4.9%

8 90.5%

9 **a** Brit Com: 20.9%, USA: 26.5%, France: 10.3%, Other 42.3%
b Total 100%, all imports

10 Stacey had the greater percentage increase.
Stacey: $(20 - 14) \times 100 \div 14 = 42.9\%$
Calum: $(17 - 12) \times 100 \div 12 = 41.7\%$

11 Yes, as 38 out of 46 is over 80% (82.6%)

2.5 Compound interest and repeated percentage change

Exercise 2F

1 **a** **i** 10.5 g
ii 11.03 g
iii 12.16 g
iv 14.07 g
b 9 days
2 12 years
3 **a** £14 272.27 **b** 20 years
4 **a** **i** 2550
ii 2168
iii 1331
b 7 years
5 **a** £6800 **b** £5440 **c** £3481.60
6 **a** **i** 1.9 million litres
ii 1.6 million litres
iii 1.2 million litres
b 10th August
7 **a** **i** 51 980
ii 84 752
iii 138 186
b 2021
8 **a** 21 years **b** 21 years
9 3 years
10 30 years
11 $1.1 \times 1.1 = 1.21$ (21% increase)
12 Bradley Bank account is worth £1032, Monastery Building Society account is worth £1031.30, so Bradley Bank by 70p
13 4 months: fish weighs $3 \times 1.1^4 = 4.3923$ kg; crab weighs $6 \times 0.9^4 = 3.9366$ kg
14 4 weeks
15 20

2.6 Reverse percentage (working out the original quantity)

Exercise 2G

1 **a** 800 g **b** 250 m **c** 60 cm
d £3075 **e** £200 **f** £400
2 80
3 T shirt £8.40, Tights £1.20, Shorts £5.20, Sweater £10.74, Trainers £24.80, Boots £32.40
4 £833.33
5 £300
6 240
7 £350
8 4750 blue bottles
9 £22
10 **a** £1600
b With 10% cut each year he earns $£1440 \times 12 + £1296 \times 12 = £17280 + £15552 = £32832$
With immediate 14% cut he earns $£1376 \times 24 = £33024$, so correct decision
11 **a** 30% **b** 15%
12 Less by $\frac{1}{4}$%
13 £900
14 Calculate the pre-VAT price for certain amounts, and $\frac{5}{6}$ of that amount. Show the error grows as the amount increases. Up to £280 the error is less than £5.
15 £1250
16 £1250
17 Baz has assumed that 291.2 is 100% instead of 112%. He rounded his wrong answer to the correct answer of £260.

2.7 Ratio

Exercise 2H

1 $\frac{7}{10}$
2 $\frac{2}{5}$
3 **a** $\frac{2}{5}$ **b** $\frac{3}{5}$
4 **a** $\frac{7}{10}$ **b** $\frac{3}{10}$
5 Amy $\frac{3}{5}$, Katie $\frac{2}{5}$
6 **a** Fruit crush $\frac{5}{32}$, lemonade $\frac{27}{32}$
b The second recipe.
7 $13\frac{1}{2}$ litres
8 **a** $\frac{1}{2}$ **b** $\frac{7}{20}$ **c** $\frac{3}{20}$
9 James $\frac{1}{2}$, John $\frac{3}{10}$, Joseph $\frac{1}{5}$
10 Sugar $\frac{5}{22}$, flour $\frac{3}{11}$, margarine $\frac{2}{11}$, fruit $\frac{7}{22}$
11 3 : 1
12 $\frac{1}{7}$
13 1 : 1 : 1

Exercise 2I

1 **a** 160 g : 240 g
b 80 kg : 200 kg
c 150 : 350
d 950 m : 50 m
e 175 min : 125 min
f £20 : £30 : £50
g £36 : £60 : £144
h 50 g : 250 g : 300 g
2 **a** 175 **b** 30%
3 **a** 40% **b** 300 kg
4 21 horses
5 **a** No, Yes, No, No, Yes
b Possible answers: W26, H30; W31, H38; W33, H37
6 **a** 1 : 400000 **b** 1 : 125000
c 1 : 250000 **d** 1 : 25000
e 1 : 20000 **f** 1 : 40000
7 **a** 1 : 1000000 **b** 47 km
c 0.8 cm
8 **a** 1 : 250000 **b** 2 km
c 4.8 cm
9 **a** 1 : 20000 **b** 0.54 km
c 40 cm
10 **a** 4 : 3 **b** 90 miles
c Both arrive at the same time.
11 0.4 metres
12 **a** 1 : 1.6 **b** 1 : 3.25
c 1 : 1.125 **d** 1 : 1.44
e 1 : 5.4 **f** 1 : 1.5
g 1 : 4.8 **h** 1 : 42
i 1 : 1.25

Exercise 2J

1 **a** 3 : 2
b 32
c 80
2 **a** 100
b 160
3 0.4 litres
4 102
5 1000 g
6 Jamie has 1.75 pints, so he has enough.
7 8100
8 5.5 litres
9 **a** 14 min
b 75 min ($1\frac{1}{4}$ h)
10 **a** 11 pages
b 32%
11 Kevin £2040, John £2720
12 C, F, T, T
13 51
14 100
15 40cc
16 **a** 160 cans
b 48 cans
17 **a** Lemonade 20 litres, ginger 0.5 litres
b This one, in part **a** there are 50 parts in the ratio 40 : 9 : 1, so ginger is $\frac{1}{50}$ of total amount; in part **b** there are 13 parts in the ratio 10 : 2 : 1, so ginger is $\frac{1}{13}$ of total amount. $\frac{1}{13} > \frac{1}{50}$
18 225 kg
19 54

Examination questions

1 £332.80
2 **a** 48.1 seconds
b **i** 44.1 seconds
ii Di (40.23 seconds)
iii Di
3 £141
4 £2200 per month
5 £220
6 $\frac{9}{40}$
7 $4\frac{1}{12}$ pints
8 2 tins
9 **a** $\frac{312}{77}, \frac{54}{17}, \frac{22}{7}, \frac{221}{71}$
b $\frac{22}{7}$
10 Yes, investment will be worth £4008.46
11 8% decrease
12 Estimate: 80% (78.4%)
13 **a** No, only enough for 6 days:
$5 \div \frac{4}{5} = 6\frac{1}{4}$ or $5 \div \frac{2}{5} = 12.5$,
so $12\frac{1}{2}$ meals
b $2\frac{2}{3}$
14 £7375.53
15 194.6%
16 **a** 90%
b £152 000
17 **a** 18 adults, 108 children
b 1 : 4
18 4 more red balls
19 Yes, $100 \times 0.96^9 = 69.3$ kg
20 392 500 square kilometres
21 Jill is correct $0.4 \times 0.75 = 0.3$, so 30% of the original price is equal to 70% off.
22 Not correct, since $0.64^5 = 0.107$, lost 100% − 10.7% = 89.3% of its original contents
23 20%
24 60 men (and 50 women)

Answers to Chapter 3

Quick check

1 **a** 7 **b** 6 **c** 8 **d** 6

3.1 Averages

Exercise 3A

1 Mode
2 Three possible answers: 12, 14, 14, 16, 18, 20, 24; or 12, 14, 14, 16, 18, 22, 24; or 12, 14, 14, 16, 20, 22, 24
3 53
4 **a** Median (mean could be unduly influenced by results of very able and/or very poor candidates)
b Median (mean could be unduly influenced by pocket money of students with very rich or generous parents)
c Mode (numerical value of shoe sizes irrelevant, just want most common size)
d Median (mean could be distorted by one or two extremely short or tall performers)
e Mode (the only way to get an 'average' of non-numerical values)
f Median (mean could be unduly influenced by very low weights of premature babies)
5 The mean is 31.5 which rounds up to 32, so the statement is correct (though the mode and median are 31).
6 **a** **i** £20 000 **ii** £28 000 **iii** £34 000
b A 6% rise would increase the mean salary to £36 040, a £1500 pay increase would produce a mean of £35 500.
7 **a** Median **b** Mode **c** Mean
8 Tom – mean, David – median, Mohamed – mode
9 11.6
10 42.7 kg
11 24
12 **a** Possible answer: 1, 6, 6, 6, 6
b Possible answer: 2, 5, 5, 6, 7
13 Boss chose the mean while worker chose the mode.

3.2 Frequency tables

Exercise 3B

1 a i 7 ii 6 iii 6.4
b i 8 ii 8.5 iii 8.2
2 a 668 b 1.9 c 0 d 328
3 a 2.2, 1.7, 1.3 b Better dental care
4 a 50 b 2 c 2.8
5 a Roger 5, Brian 4 b Roger 3, Brian 8
c Roger 5.4, Brian 4.5 d Roger 5, Brian 4
e Roger, smaller range f Brian, better mean
6 a 40 b 7 c 3 d 2
e 2.5 f 2.5 g 2.4
7 a 2 b 1.9 c 49%
8 5
9 The total frequency could be an even number where the two middle numbers have an odd difference.
10 a 34
b $x + 80 + 3y + 104 = 266$, so $x + 3y = 266 - 184 = 82$
c $x = 10$, $y = 24$
d 2.5
11 The mean for 2009 = 396 ÷ 12 = 33, Range = 38

3.3 Grouped data

Exercise 3C

1 a i $30 < x \leqslant 40$ ii 29.5
b i $0 < y \leqslant 100$ ii 158.3
c i $5 < z \leqslant 10$ ii 9.43
d i 7–9 ii 8.41
2 a $100\text{ g} < w \leqslant 120\text{ g}$ b 10.86 kg c 108.6 g
3 a $175 < h \leqslant 200$ b 31%
c 193.3 hours d No the mean was under 200.
4 a Yes, average distance is 11.7 miles per day.
b Because shorter runs will be done faster which will affect the average
c Yes, because the shortest could be 1 mile, the longest 25 miles
5 24
6 Soundbuy; average increases are Soundbuy 17.7p, Springfields 18.7p, Setco 18.2p
7 a 160 b 52.6 minutes
c Modal group d 65%
8 The first 5 and the 10 are the wrong way round.
9 Find the midpoint of each group, multiply that by the frequency and add those products. Divide that total by the total frequency.
10 a Yes, as total in first two columns is 50, so median is between 39 and 40
b He could be correct, as the biggest possible range is $69 - 20 = 49$, and the lowest is $60 - 29 = 31$.

3.4 Frequency diagrams

Exercise 3D

1 a 36
b Pie charts with these angles: 50°, 50°, 80°, 60°, 60°, 40°, 20°
c Check students' bar charts
d Bar chart, because easier to make comparisons
2 a Pie charts with these angles: 124°, 132°, 76°, 28°
b Split of total data seen at a glance
3 a 55° b 22 c 33%
4 a Pie charts with these angles:
Strings: 36°, 118°, 126°, 72°, 8°
b Brass: 82°, 118°, 98°, 39°, 23°
Overall, the brass candidates did better, as a smaller proportion got the lowest grade. A higher proportion of strings candidates scored the top two grades.
5 The sector for 'Don't know' has an angle of $360° - (80° + 90° + 150°) = 40°$, as a fraction of the whole circle, the 'Don't know' sector is $\frac{40}{360} = \frac{1}{9}$, or as a percentage, 11%
6 Identify the possible ways in which students might come to school and, on the morning in question, use a tally chart to record how each arrives.

Exercise 3E

1 a

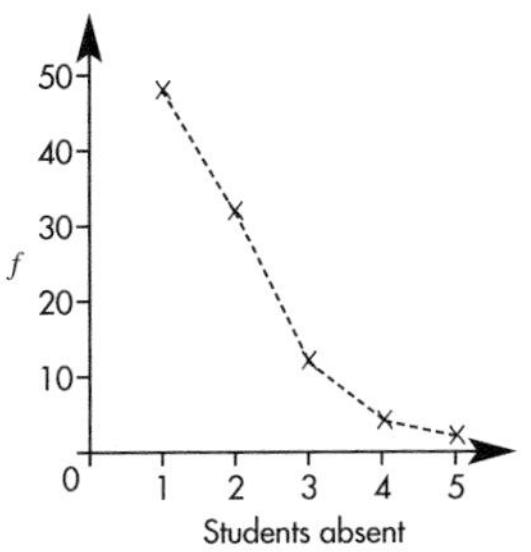

b 1.7

2 a

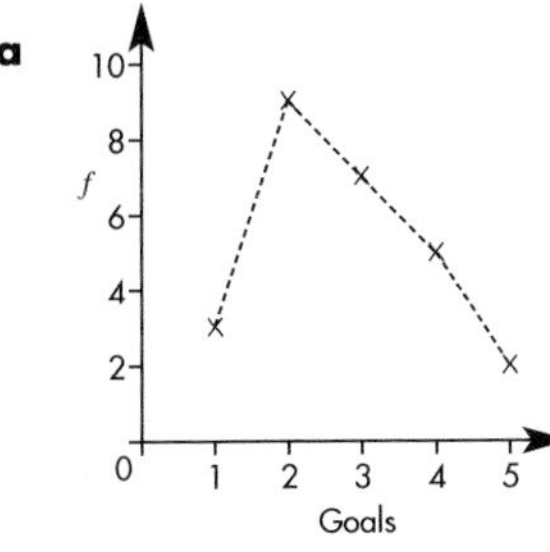

b 2.8

3 a i 17, 13, 6, 3, 1 ii £1.45
b i

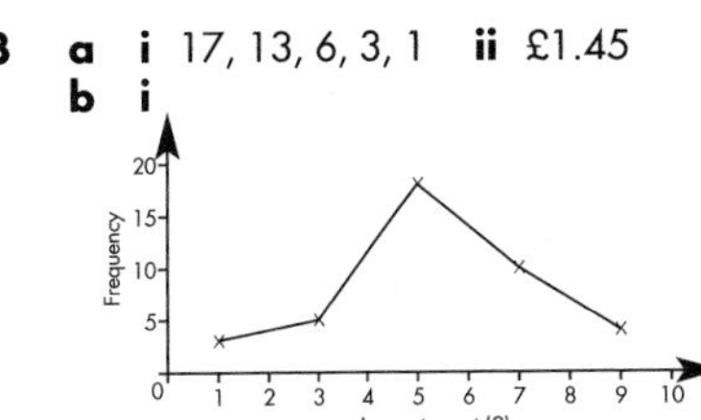

ii £5.35
c Much higher mean. Early morning, people just want a paper or a few sweets. Later people are buying food for the day.

Exercise 3E (continued)

4 a

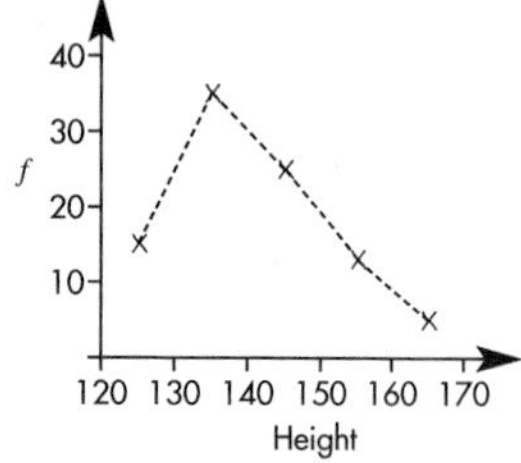

b

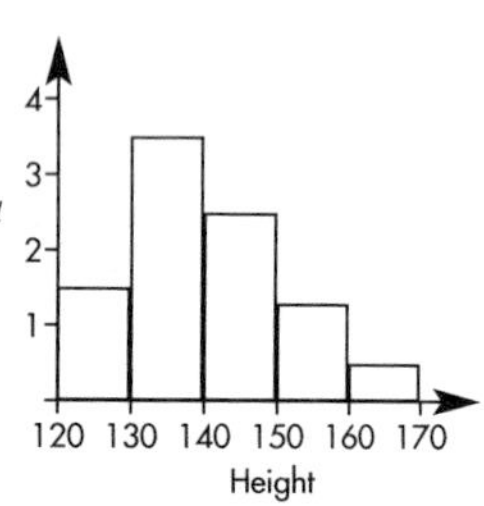

c 140.4 cm

5 a

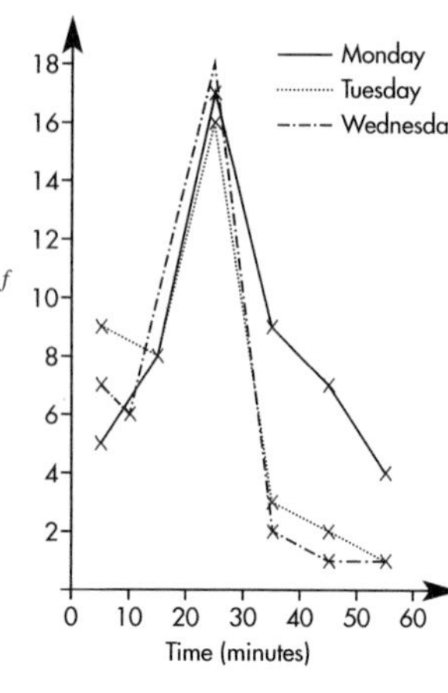

b Monday 28.4 min, Tuesday 20.9 min, Wednesday 21.3 min

c There are more patients on a Monday, and so longer waiting times, as the surgery is closed during the weekend.

6 a

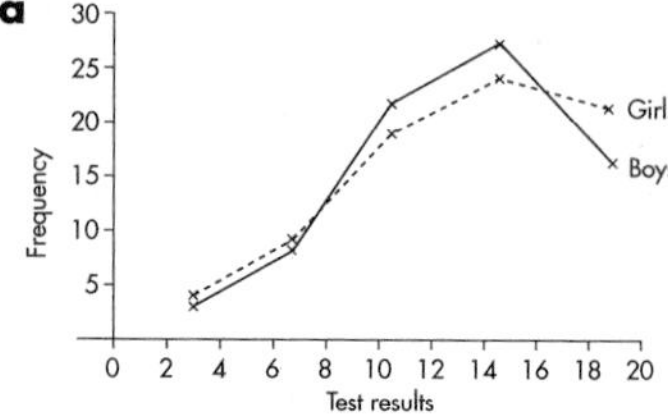

b Boys 12.9, girls 13.1, and so the girls did slightly better than the boys.

7 2.17 hours

8 That is the middle value of the time group 0 to 1 minute. It would be very unusual for most of them to be exactly in the middle at 30 seconds.

3.5 Histograms with bars of unequal width

Exercise 3F

1 The respective frequency densities on which each histogram should be based are:
a 2.5, 6.5, 6, 2, 1, 1.5 **b** 4, 27, 15, 3
c 17, 18, 12, 6.67 **d** 0.4, 1.2, 2.8, 1 **e** 9, 21, 13.5, 9

2 a

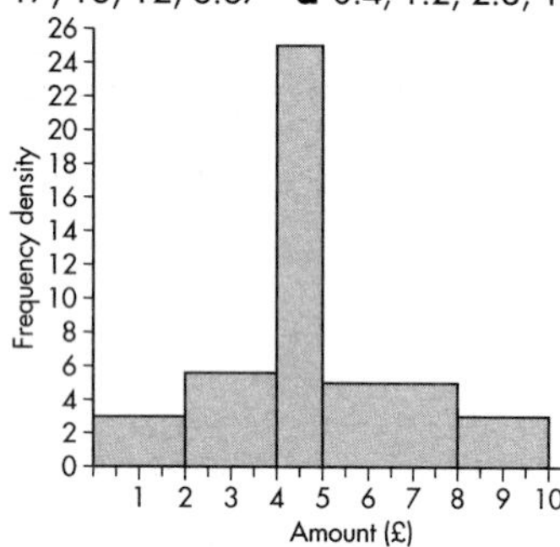

b

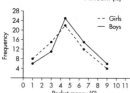

Frequency
Girls
Boys
Pocket money (£)

c Girls £4.36, boys £4.81. Boys get more pocket money than girls do.

3

Frequency density (000)
1940 1950 1960 1970 1980 1990 2000 2001
Year

4 a 775 **b** 400

5 Divide the frequency of the class interval by the width of the class interval.

6 a i

Age, y (years)	$9 < y \leq 10$	$10 < y \leq 12$	$12 < y \leq 14$	$14 < y \leq 17$	$17 < y \leq 19$	$19 < y \leq 20$
Frequency	4	12	8	9	5	1

ii 10–12 **iii** 13 **iv** 11, 16, 5 **v** 13.4

b i

Temperature, t (°C)	$10 < t \leq 11$	$11 < t \leq 12$	$12 < t \leq 14$	$14 < t \leq 16$	$16 < t \leq 19$	$19 < t \leq 21$
Frequency	15	15	50	40	45	15

ii 12–14°C **iii** 14.5°C **iv** 12°C, 17°C, 5°C **v** 14.8°C

c **i**

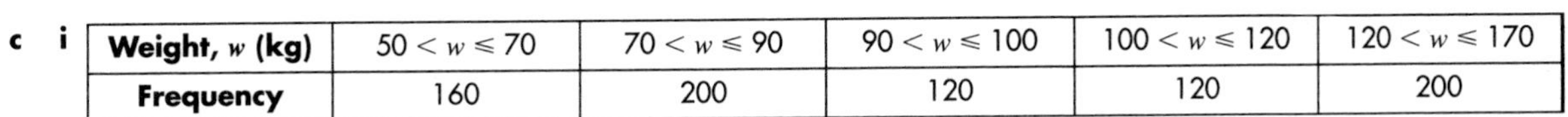

Weight, w (kg)	$50 < w \leqslant 70$	$70 < w \leqslant 90$	$90 < w \leqslant 100$	$100 < w \leqslant 120$	$120 < w \leqslant 170$
Frequency	160	200	120	120	200

ii 70–90 kg and 120–170 kg **iii** 93.33 kg **iv** 74 kg, 120 kg, 46 kg **v** 99.0 kg

7 **a** 7.33 hours **b** 8.44 hours **c** 7 hours

8 **a**

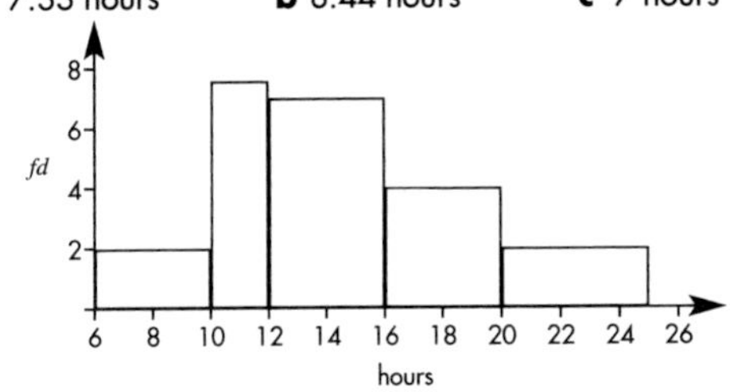

b 14.2 kg **c** 14.7 kg **d** 33 plants

9 **a**

Speed, v (mph)	$0 < v \leqslant 40$	$40 < v \leqslant 50$	$50 < v \leqslant 60$	$60 < v \leqslant 70$	$70 < v \leqslant 80$	$80 < v \leqslant 100$
Frequency	80	10	40	110	60	60

b 360 **c** 64.5 mph **d** 59.2 mph

10 **a** 102 **b** 35 **c** 104 **d** 75

11 0.45

3.6 Surveys

Exercise 3G

1–5 Check students' answers and designs, which will vary.

6 **a** Possible answer: Question – Which of the following foods would you normally eat for your main meal of the day?

Name	Sex	Chips	Beef burgers	Vegetables	Pizza	Fish

b Yes, as a greater proportion of girls ate healthy food

7 Possible answer: Question – What kind of tariff do you use on your mobile phone?

Name	Pay as you go		Contract	
	200 or over free texts	Under 200 free texts	200 or over free texts	Under 200 free texts

(Any sheet in which choices that can distinguish one from the other have to be made will be accepted.)

8 Possible answers: shop names, year of student, tally space, frequency

3.7 Questionnaires

Exercise 3H

1 **a** It is a leading question, and no option to disagree with the statement.
b Unbiased, and the responses do not overlap.

2 **a** Responses overlap.
b Provide options: up to £2, more than £2 and up to £5, more than £5 and up to £10, more than £10.

3–6 Check students' questionnaires.

7 **a** This is a leading question with no possibility of showing disagreement.
b This is a clear direct question that has an answer, and good responses as only one selection can be made.
c Check students' questions.

8 Possible questionnaire: Do you have a back problem?
☐ Yes ☐ No
Tick the diagram/text that best illustrates/describes how you sit.
☐ shoulders back awkwardly, curved spine
☐ slumped, straining lower back
☐ caved chest, pressure on spine
☐ balanced, head and spine aligned

9 The groups overlap, and the 'less than £15' is also in the 'less than £25'.

3.8 The data-handling cycle

Exercise 3I

1 **a** secondary data **b** primary data
c primary or secondary **d** primary or secondary
e primary data **f** primary data

2 Students' answers will vary

3 For example, Kath may carry out a survey among her friends or class-mates.

3.9 Other uses of statistics

Exercise 3J

1 Price 78p, 80.3p, 84.2p, 85p, 87.4p, 93.6p
2 **a** £1 = $1.88
b Greatest drop was from June to July.
c There is no trend in the data.
3 **a** 9.7 million **b** 4.5 years
c 12 million **d** 10 million
4 £74.73
5 General cost of living in 2009 dropped to 98% of the costs in 2008.
6 **a** Holiday month
b **i** 140 thousand
ii 207 thousand (an answer of 200–210 thousand over the 3 months is acceptable)

3.10 Sampling

Exercise 3K

1–4 Check students' answers as they will vary.
5 **a** How many times, on average, do you visit a fast-food outlet in a week?
Never 1 or 2 times
3 or 4 times More than 4 times
b

	Boys	Girls
Y9	11	8
Y10	10	11
Y11	10	10

6 555
7 Find the approximate proportion of men and women, girls and boys, then decide on a sample size. Work out the proportion of men in the whole group and find that proportion of the sample size to give the number of men in the sample. Similarly work out the number of women, boys and girls.
8 **a** There are many possible correct answers. Below are two examples.
How far from Meadowhall do you live?
☐ Less than 5 miles
☐ Between 5 and 10 miles inclusive
☐ More than 10 miles
When you visit Meadowhall, approximately how much do you usually spend?
☐ £50 or less
☐ Between £50 and £100
☐ £100 or more
b Y7 $= 143 \times \frac{100}{670} = 21$ Y10 $= 131 \times \frac{100}{670} = 20$
Y8 $= 132 \times \frac{100}{670} = 20$ Y11 $= 108 \times \frac{100}{670} = 16$
Y9 $= 156 \times \frac{100}{670} = 23$
9 **a** There are many more girls than boys.
b 20

Examination questions

1 **a** **i** 8 **ii** 23 **iii** 19
b There is no space for 0 hours and 6 hours appears in two groups.
2 **a** 1.7
b Which days of the week are you prepared to car share?
☐ None ☐ Mon ☐ Tues ☐ Wed ☐ Thu ☐ Fri
3 28.2 min
4 **a** 4060 ÷ 100
b **i** 125 **ii** 140.6 cm
c **i**

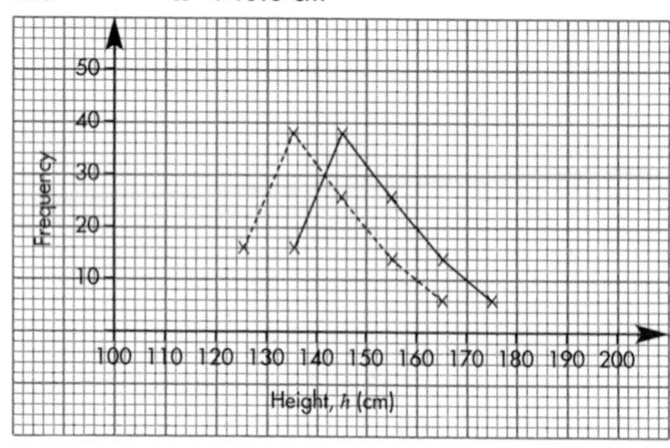

ii On average, the boys are about 10 cm taller than the girls. The range of the heights in both groups is the same, 40 cm.

5 **a**

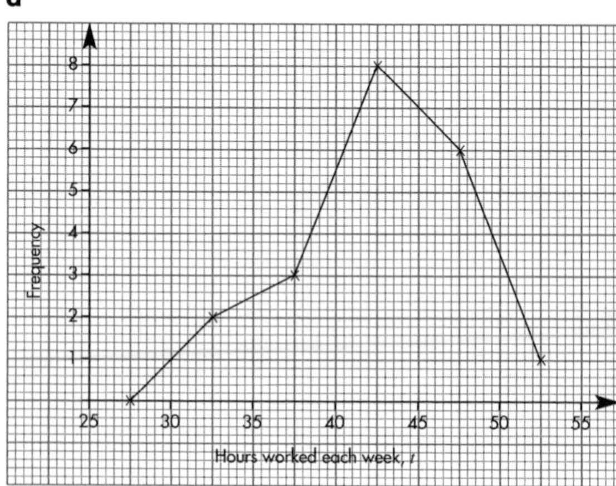

b 60
c It is what they thought and not what they measured.
6 **a** Level 5 **b** 3.2
c Because of all the zeros at the lower grades in German
7 Because over half the students have more than £10 pocket money, so the mean must be more than £10
8 £2.08
9 **a** 90% **b** £152 000
10 **a** 25 **b** 50 **c** 20 years
11 70

12 a

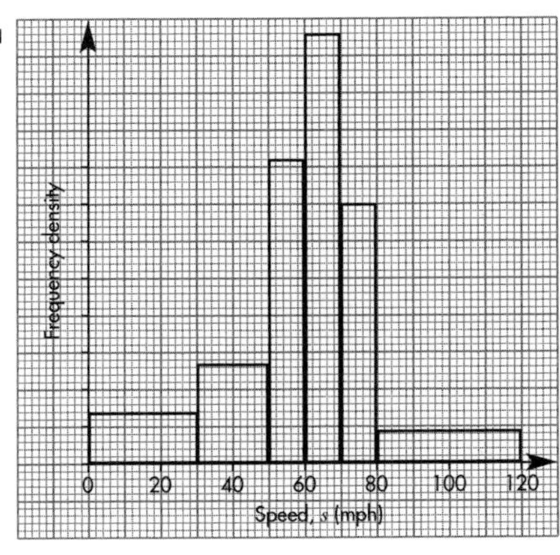

b 57

13 a

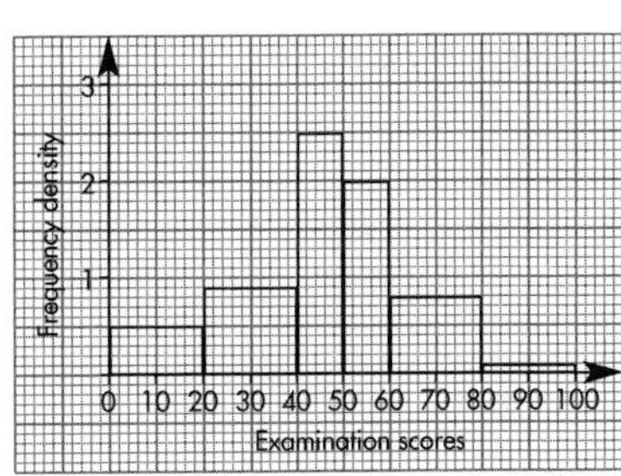

b 38

14 NUT 1040, ATL 680, NATFHE 280

15 12 − 9 = 3 more

16 Single 4, Couple 11, Family 15

Answers to Chapter 4

Quick check

1 29.0

4.1 Line graphs

Exercise 4A

1 a

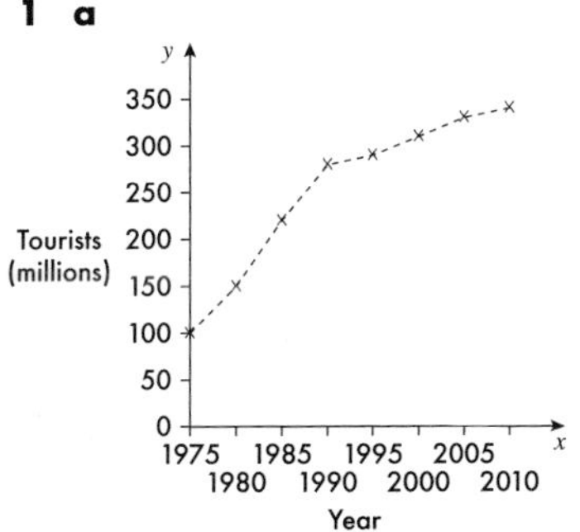

b About 328 million
c Between 1980 and 1985
d Rising living standards

2 a

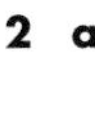

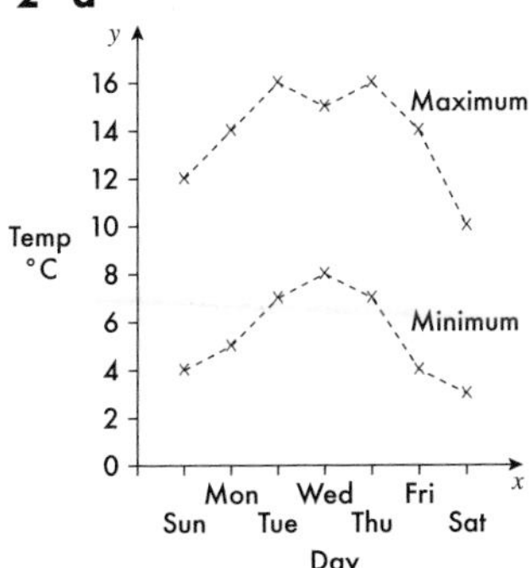

b Smallest difference Wednesday and Saturday (7°), greatest difference Friday (10°)

3 a

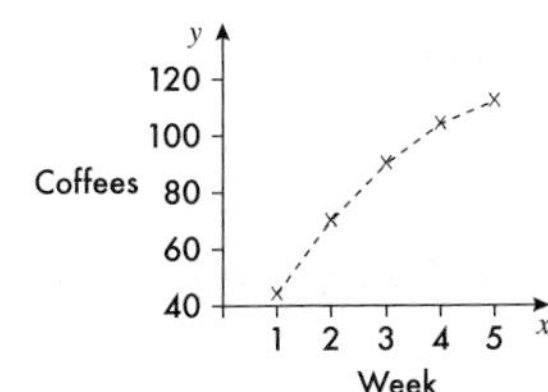

b 119
c The same people keep coming back and tell others, but new customers each week become more difficult to find.

4 Use a graph to estimate about 1040–1050 g.

5 All the temperatures were presumably higher than 20 °C.

4.2 Stem-and-leaf diagrams

Exercise 4B

1 a

2	8 9
3	4 5 6 8 8 9
4	1 1 3 3 3 8 8

b 43 cm **c** 39 cm **d** 20 cm

2 a

0	2 8 9 9 9
1	2 3 7 7 8
2	0 1 2 3

b 9 messages **c** 15 messages

3 a

0	7 8 9 9
1	0 2 3 4 5 8 8 9 9
2	0 3 4 4 6 8
3	1

key 2 | 3 = 23

b 18 **c** 24

4 The girls' heights are on the right, 15 | 3 means 153 cm tall. The boys' heights are on the left, 6 | 15 means 156 cm tall.

5 All the data start with a 5 and there are only two digits.

4.3 Scatter diagrams

Exercise 4C

1 **a** Positive correlation, reaction time increases with amount of alcohol drunk

b Negative correlation, you drink less alcohol as you get older

c No correlation, speed of cars on MI is not related to the temperature

d Weak, positive correlation, older people generally have more money saved in the bank

2 **a** and **b**

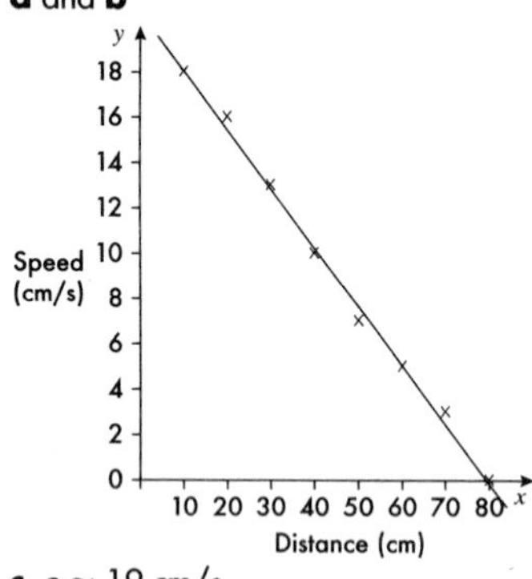

c c ≈ 19 cm/s

d ≈ 34 cm

3 **a** and **b**

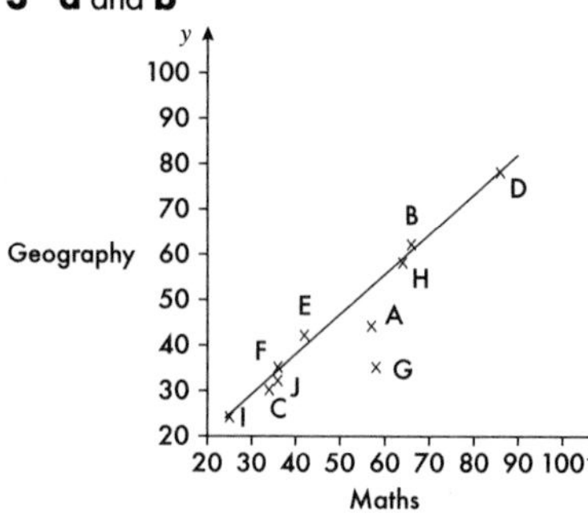

c Greta

d ≈ 70

e ≈ 70

4 **a**

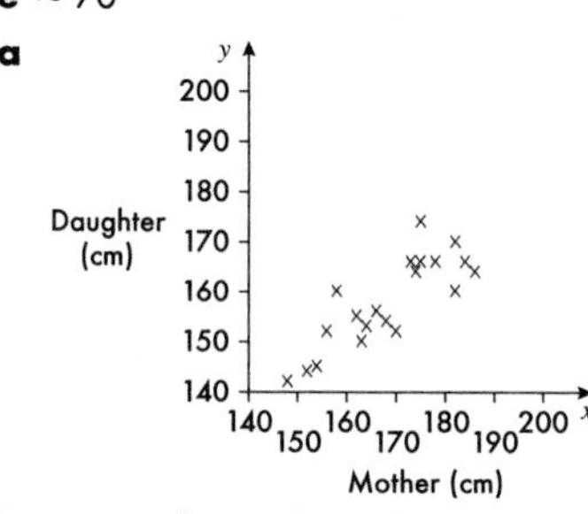

b Yes, usually good correlation

5 **a**

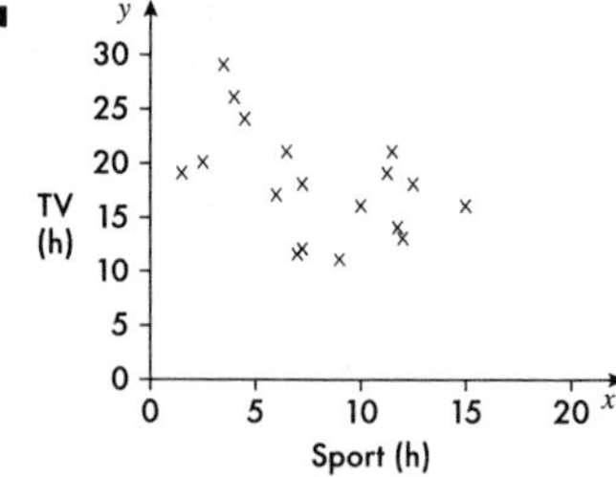

b Little correlation, so cannot draw a line of best fit

6 **a** and **b**

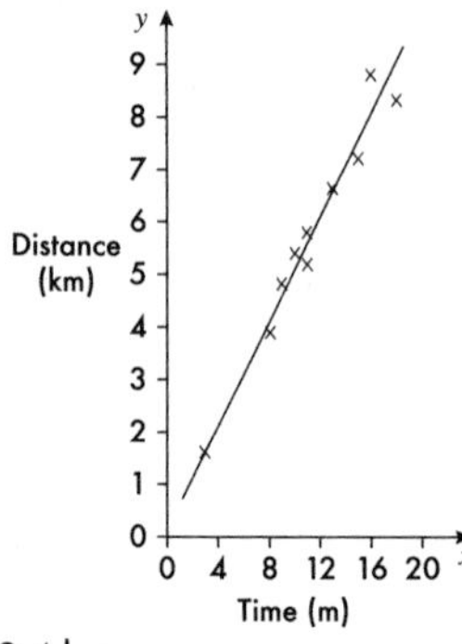

c About 2.4 km

d About 9 minutes

7 About 23 mph

8 Points showing a line of best fit sloping down from top left to bottom right

4.4 Cumulative frequency diagrams

Exercise 4D

1 **a** Cumulative frequency 1, 4, 10, 22, 25, 28, 30

b

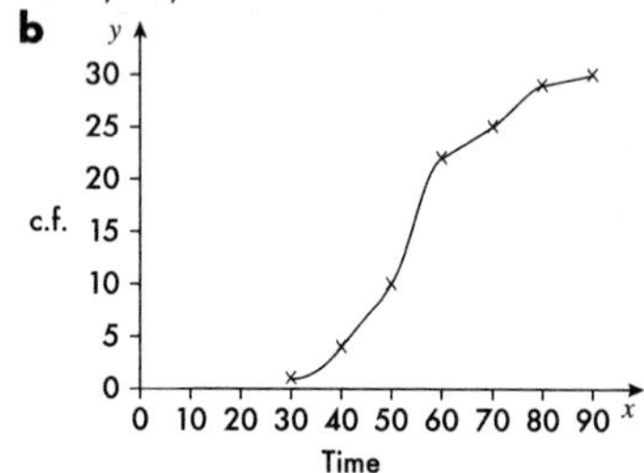

c 54 secs, 16 secs

2 **a** Cumulative frequency 1, 3, 5, 14, 31, 44, 47, 49, 50

b

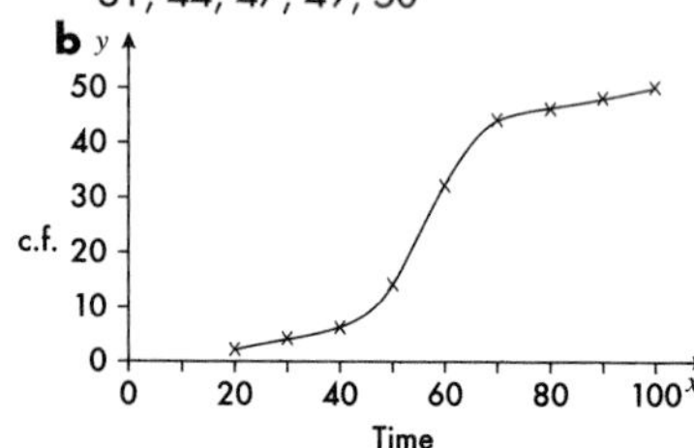

c 56 secs, 17 secs

d Pensioners, median closer to 60 secs

3 **a** Cumulative frequency 12, 30, 63, 113, 176, 250, 314, 349, 360

b

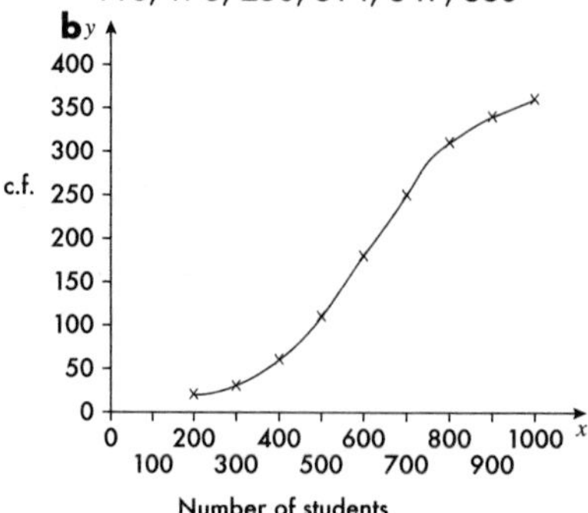

c 605 students, 280 students

d 46–47 schools

4 **a** Cumulative frequency 2, 5, 10, 16, 22, 31, 39, 45, 50

b

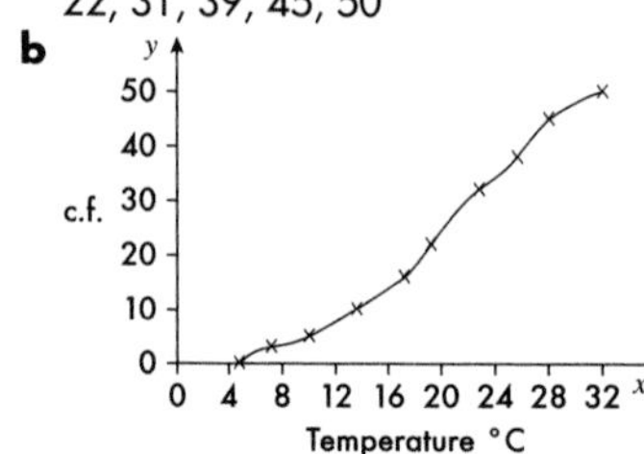

c 20.5 °C, 10 °C

5 **a**

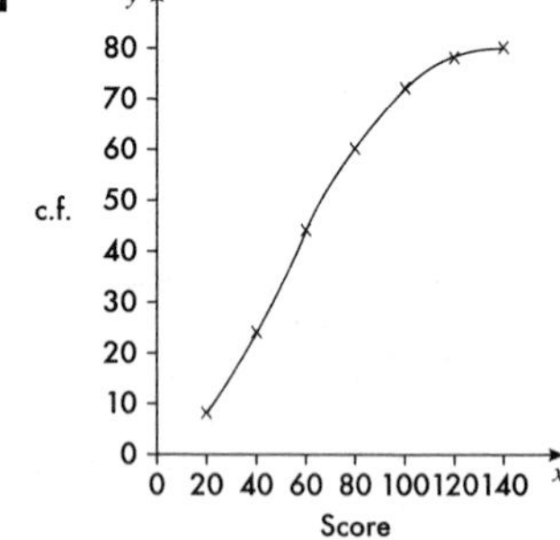

b 56, 43 **c** 17.5%

6 **a** Cumulative frequency 6, 16, 36, 64, 82, 93, 98, 100

b

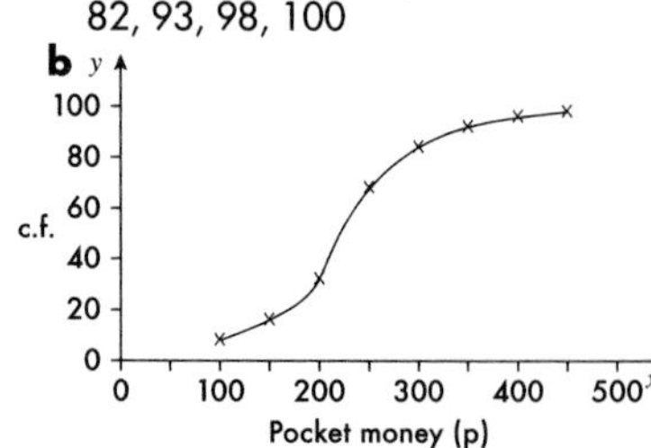

c 225p, 90p

7 **a** Paper A 66, Paper B 57
b Paper A 28, Paper B 18
c Paper B is the harder paper. It has a lower median and a lower upper quartile.
d **i** Paper A 43, Paper B 45
ii Paper A 78, Paper B 67

8 9.25 minutes (create a grouped frequency chart)
9 Find the top 10% on the cumulative frequency scale, read along to the graph and read down to the marks. The mark seen will be the minimum mark needed for this top grade.

4.5 Box plots

Exercise 4E

1 **a**

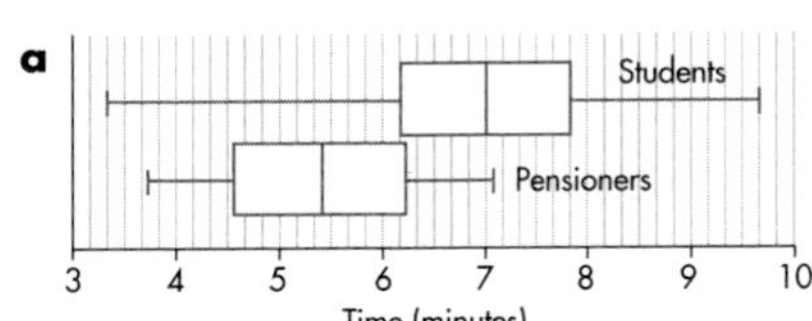

b Students are much slower than the pensioners. Both distributions have the same interquartile range, but students' median and upper quartiles are 1 minute, 35 seconds higher. The fastest person to complete the calculations was a student, but so was the slowest.

2 **a**

Rotherham
Dorset
200 400 600 800 1000 1200 1400 1600 1800 2000
Size (numbers of students)

b Schools are much larger in Rotherham than Dorset. The Dorset distribution is symmetrical, but the Rotherham distribution is negatively skewed – so most Rotherham schools are large.

3 **a** The resorts have similar median temperatures, but Resort B has a much wider temperature range, where the greatest extremes of temperature are recorded.
b Resort A is probably a better choice as the weather seems more consistent.

4 **a**

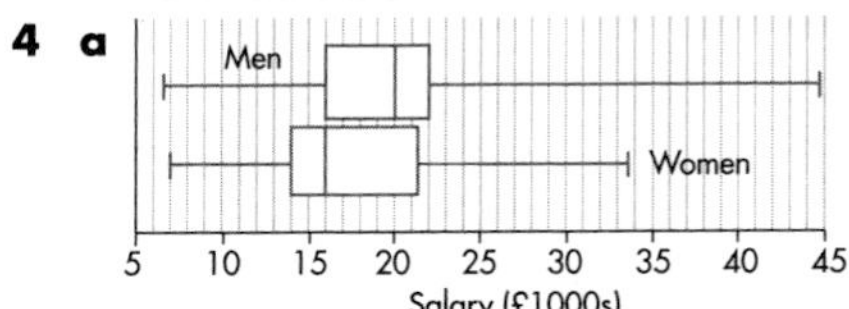

b Both distributions have a similar interquartile range, and there is little difference between the upper quartile values. Men have a wider range of salaries, but the higher men's median and the fact that the men's distribution is negatively skewed and the women's distribution is positively skewed indicates that men are better paid than women.

5 **a**

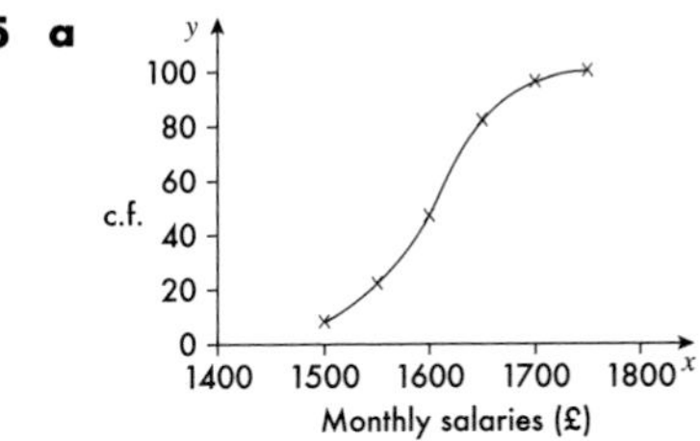

b £1605, £85
c **i**

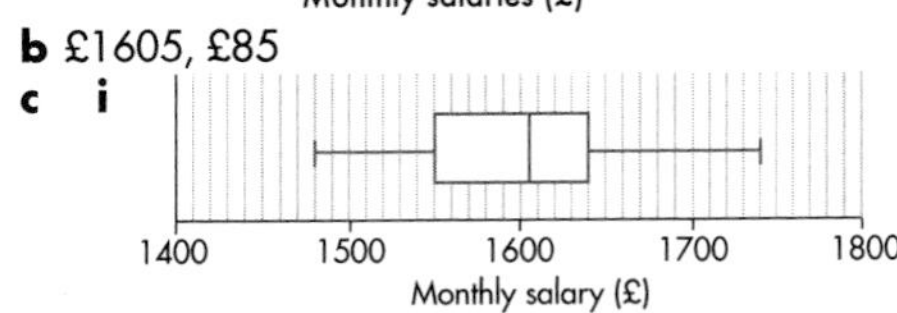

ii Negatively skewed

6 **a** **i** 24 min
ii 12 min
iii 42 min
b **i** 6 min
ii 17 min
iii 9 min
c Either doctor with a plausible reason, e.g. Dr Excel because his waiting times are always shorter than Dr Collins', or Dr Collins because he takes more time with each patient.

7 The girls have a mean 2.6 higher than the boys. (Create grouped frequencies using the four quartiles.)

8 Many possible answers but not including numerical values: 'Bude had a higher median than Torquay', 'Bude had a smaller interquartile range than Torquay', 'Bude had more sunshine on any one day'.

9 **a** Symmetric
b Negatively skewed
c Negatively skewed
d Symmetric
e Negatively skewed
f Positively skewed
g Negatively skewed
h Positively skewed
i Positively skewed
j Symmetric

10 A and X, B and Y, C and W, D and Z

Examination questions

1

6	5 7
7	0 0 2 6
8	0 2 4 5 7
9	1

6|7 represents 67 minutes

2 22.3 minutes

3 **a** Negative correlation
b **i** Check students' line of best fit.
ii 7
c He was a good typist.
d No, because the graph shows no further than 10 hours and the correlation could change beyond that point.

4 **a** and **c**

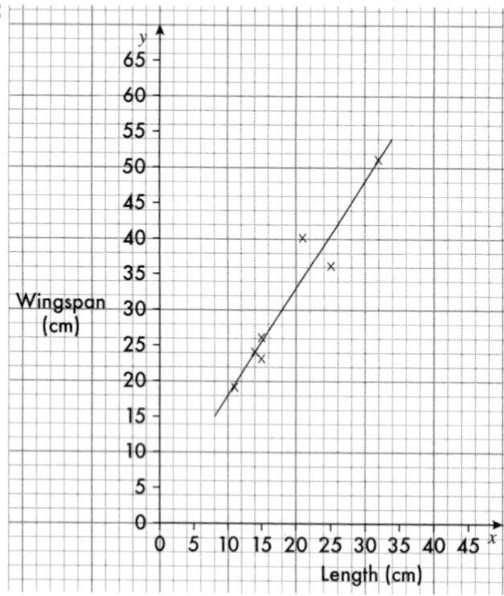

b Strong positive
d 32cm
e No data given is higher than a length of 32 cm and the correlation might not hold at 41 cm.

5 **a** and **b** Check students' scatter diagrams and lines of best fit.
c £7.20 **d** 820 pages

6 **a**

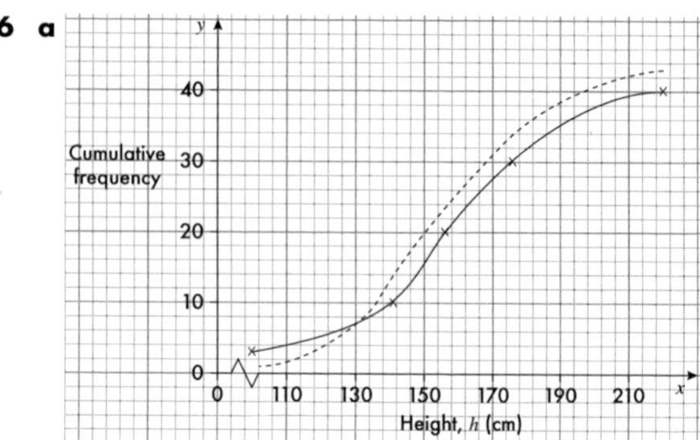

b 4

7 **a** 36 cm **b** 2.5 cm
c Men's neck measurements have a bigger IQR, men have a larger median neck measurement

8 **a**

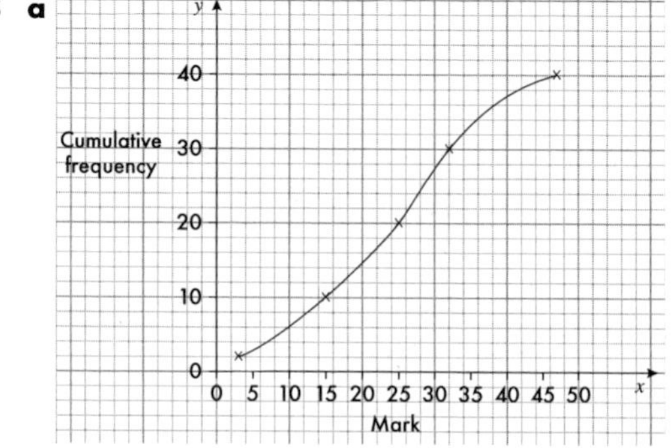

b 0.25

9 £3.06

10 Find the top 15% on the cumulative frequency scale, read along to the graph and read down to the marks. The mark seen will be the minimum mark needed for this top grade.

Answers to Chapter 5

Quick check

1 **a** Perhaps around 0.6 **b** Very close to 0.1 **c** Very close to 0 **d** 1 **e** 1

5.1 Experimental probability

Exercise 5A

1 **a** $\frac{1}{5}, \frac{2}{25}, \frac{1}{10}, \frac{21}{200}, \frac{37}{250}, \frac{163}{1000}, \frac{329}{2000}$
b 6 **c** 1
d $\frac{1}{6}$ **e** 1000

2 **a** $\frac{19}{200}, \frac{27}{200}, \frac{4}{25}, \frac{53}{200}, \frac{69}{200}$
b 40
c No, it is weighted towards the side with numbers 4 and 5

3 **a** 32 is too high, unlikely that 20 of the 50 throws between 50 and 100 were 5
b Yes, all frequencies fairly close to 100

4 **a** $\frac{1}{5}, \frac{1}{4}, \frac{38}{100}, \frac{21}{50}, \frac{77}{200}, \frac{1987}{5000}$
b 8

5 **a** 0.346, 0.326, 0.294, 0.305, 0.303, 0.306
b 0.231, 0.168, 0.190, 0.16, 0.202, 0.201
c Red 0.5, white 0.3, blue 0.2
d 1
e Red 10, white 6, blue 4

6 **a** Students' answers will vary.
b 20
c Answer depends on students' results
d Answer depends on answer to c

7 **a** 6
b and **c** Answer depends on students' results

8 **a** Caryl, most throws
b 0.43, 0.31, 0.17, 0.14
c Yes, it is more likely to give a 1 or 2

9 **a** Method B **b** B **c** C
d A **e** B **f** A
g B **h** B

10 **a** Not likely **b** Impossible
c Not likely **d** Certain
e Impossible **f** 50–50 chance
g 50–50 chance **h** Certain
i Quite likely

11 Thursday

12 The missing top numbers are 4 and 5; the two bottom numbers are likely to be close to 20.

13 Although you would expect the probability to be close to $\frac{1}{2}$, hence 500 heads, it is more likely that the number of heads is close to 500 rather than actually 500.

14 Roxy is correct, as the expected numbers are: 50, 12.5, 25, 12.5. Sam has not taken into account the fact that there are four red sectors.

5.2 Mutually exclusive and exhaustive events

Exercise 5B

1 **a** Yes **b** Yes **c** No
d Yes **e** Yes **f** Yes

2 Events **a** and **f**

3 $\frac{3}{5}$

4 **a** **i** $\frac{3}{10}$ **ii** $\frac{3}{10}$ **iii** $\frac{3}{10}$
b All except **iii**
c Event **iv**

5 **a** Jane/John, Jane/Jack, Jane/Anne, Jane/Dave, Dave/John, Dave/Jack, Dave/Anne, Anne/John, Anne/Jack, Jack/John
b **i** $\frac{1}{10}$ **ii** $\frac{3}{10}$
iii $\frac{3}{10}$ **iv** $\frac{7}{10}$
c All except **iii** **d** Event **ii**

6 **a** $\frac{3}{8}$ **b** $\frac{1}{8}$
c All except **ii**
d Outcomes overlap

7 $\frac{3}{20}$

8 $\frac{1}{75}$

9 Not mutually exclusive events

10 **a** **i** 0.25 **ii** 0.4 **iii** 0.7
b Events not mutually exclusive
c Man/woman, American man/American woman
d Man/woman

11 **a** **i** 0.95
ii 0.9 (assuming person chooses one or other)
iii 0.3
b Events not mutually exclusive
c Possible answer: pork and vegetarian

12 These are not mutually exclusive events.

5.3 Expectation

Exercise 5C

1 25

2 1000

3 **a** 260 **b** 40 **c** 130 **d** 10

4 5

5 **a** 150 **b** 100 **c** 250 **d** 0

6 **a** 167 **b** 833

7 1050

8 **a** Each score expected 10 times
b 3.5
c Find the average of the scores, which is 21 (1 + 2 + 3 + 4 + 5 + 6) divided by 6

9 **a** 0.111 **b** 40

10 281 days

11 Multiply the number of tomato plants by 0.003

12 400

5.4 Two-way tables

Exercise 5D

1 **a** 23 **b** 20% **c** $\frac{4}{25}$ **d** 480

2 **a** 10 **b** 7 **c** 14% **d** 15%

3 **a**

	1	**2**	**3**	**4**
5	6	7	8	9
6	7	8	9	10
7	8	9	10	11
8	9	10	11	12

b 4

c **i** $\frac{1}{4}$ **ii** $\frac{3}{16}$ **iii** $\frac{1}{4}$

4 **a** 16 **b** 16 **c** 73 **d** $\frac{51}{73}$

5 **a**

1	**2**	**3**	**4**	**5**	**6**
1	2	3	4	5	6
2	4	6	8	10	12

b 3 **c** $\frac{1}{4}$

6 **a** The greenhouse sunflowers are bigger on average.
b The garden sunflowers have a more consistent size (smaller range).

7 **a** 40%
b 45%
c No, as you don't know how much the people who get over £350 actually earn

8 Either Reyki because she had bigger tomatoes or Daniel because he had more tomatoes

9 $\frac{22}{36} = \frac{11}{18}$

10 **a**

Score of second spinner						
10	10	11	13	15	17	19
8	8	9	11	13	15	17
6	6	7	9	11	13	15
4	4	5	7	9	11	13
2	2	3	5	7	9	11
0	0	1	3	5	7	9
	0	**1**	**3**	**5**	**7**	**9**
	Score of first spinner					

b 9 or 11 **c** 0

d $\frac{15}{36} = \frac{5}{12}$ **e** $\frac{30}{36} = \frac{5}{6}$

5.5 Addition rules for events

Exercise 5E

1 **a** $\frac{1}{6}$ **b** $\frac{1}{6}$ **c** $\frac{1}{3}$

2 **a** $\frac{1}{4}$ **b** $\frac{1}{4}$ **c** $\frac{1}{2}$

3 **a** $\frac{1}{13}$ **b** $\frac{1}{13}$ **c** $\frac{2}{13}$

4 **a** $\frac{2}{11}$ **b** $\frac{4}{11}$ **c** $\frac{6}{11}$

5 **a** $\frac{1}{3}$ **b** $\frac{2}{5}$ **c** $\frac{11}{15}$
d $\frac{11}{15}$ **e** $\frac{1}{3}$

6 **a** 0.6 **b** 120

7 **a** 0.8 **b** 0.2

8 **a** 0.75 **b** 0.6 **c** 0.5 **d** 0.6
e **i** Cannot add P(red) and P(1) as events are not mutually exclusive
ii 0.75 (= 1 – P(blue))

9 **a** $\frac{17}{20}$ **b** $\frac{2}{5}$ **c** $\frac{3}{4}$

10 Probability cannot exceed 1, and probabilities cannot be summed in this way as events are not mutually exclusive.

11 **a** **i** 0.4 **ii** 0.5 **iii** 0.9
b 0.45
c 2 hours 12 minutes

12 $\frac{5}{52}$ or 0.096 to 3 decimal places

13 **a** $\frac{13}{20}$ as it cannot be square rooted
b $\frac{1}{9}$ as this gives a ratio of red to blue of 1 : 2

5.6 Combined events

Exercise 5F

1 **a** 7
b 2, 12
c $P(2) = \frac{1}{36}$, $P(3) = \frac{1}{18}$, $P(4) = \frac{1}{12}$,
$P(5) = \frac{1}{9}$, $P(6) = \frac{5}{36}$, $P(7) = \frac{1}{6}$,
$P(8) = \frac{5}{36}$, $P(9) = \frac{1}{9}$, $P(10) = \frac{1}{12}$,
$P(11) = \frac{1}{18}$, $P(12) = \frac{1}{36}$
d **i** $\frac{1}{12}$ **ii** $\frac{5}{9}$ **iii** $\frac{1}{2}$
iv $\frac{7}{36}$ **v** $\frac{5}{12}$ **vi** $\frac{5}{18}$

2 **a** $\frac{1}{12}$ **b** $\frac{11}{36}$ **c** $\frac{1}{6}$ **d** $\frac{5}{9}$

3 **a** $\frac{1}{36}$ **b** $\frac{11}{36}$ **c** $\frac{5}{18}$

4 **a** $\frac{5}{18}$ **b** $\frac{1}{6}$ **c** $\frac{1}{9}$
d 0 **e** $\frac{1}{2}$

5 **a** $\frac{1}{4}$ **b** $\frac{1}{2}$ **c** $\frac{3}{4}$ **d** $\frac{1}{4}$

6 **a** 6
b **i** $\frac{4}{25}$ **iii** $\frac{1}{5}$
ii $\frac{13}{25}$ **iv** $\frac{3}{5}$

7 **a** $\frac{1}{8}$ **b** $\frac{3}{8}$ **c** $\frac{7}{8}$ **d** $\frac{1}{8}$

8 **a** 16 **b** 32 **c** 1024 **d** 2^n

9 **a** $\frac{1}{12}$ **b** $\frac{1}{4}$ **c** $\frac{1}{6}$

10 **a**

	1	2	3	4	5	6
1	2	3	4	5	6	7
2	3	4	5	6	7	8
3	4	5	6	7	8	9
4	5	6	7	8	9	10
5	6	7	8	9	10	11
6	7	8	9	10	11	12

b $\frac{1}{18}$ **c** 18 **d** twice

11 0.5

12 You would need a 3D diagram or there would be too many different events to list.

5.7 Tree diagrams

Exercise 5G

1 a $\frac{1}{4}$ **b** $\frac{1}{2}$ **c** $\frac{3}{4}$

2 a $\frac{2}{13}$ **b** $\frac{11}{13}$

c i $\frac{1}{169}$ **ii** $\frac{25}{169}$

3 a $\frac{2}{3}$ **b** $\frac{1}{2}$

c

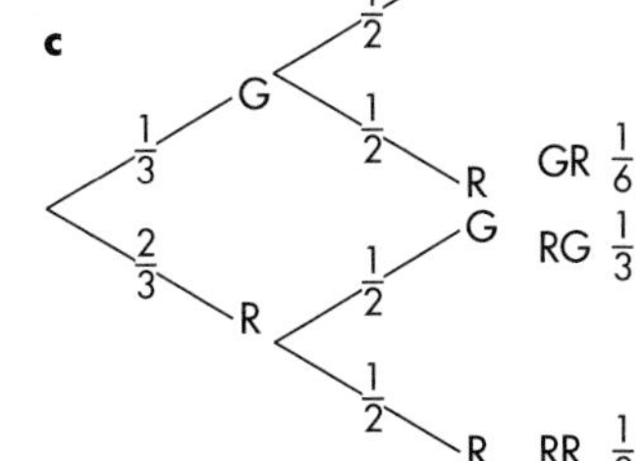

d i $\frac{1}{6}$ **ii** $\frac{1}{2}$ **iii** $\frac{5}{6}$

e 15 days

4 a $\frac{2}{5}$

b i $\frac{4}{25}$ **ii** $\frac{12}{25}$

5 a $\frac{1}{8}$ **b** $\frac{3}{8}$ **c** $\frac{7}{8}$

6 a 0.14 **b** 0.41 **c** 0.09

7 a $\frac{3}{5}$

b

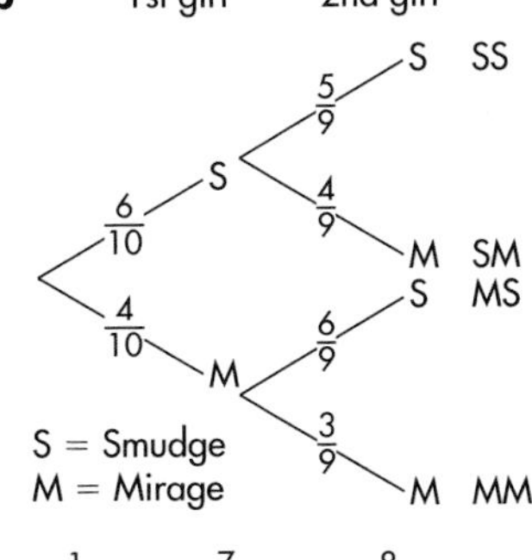

c i $\frac{1}{3}$ **ii** $\frac{7}{15}$ **iii** $\frac{8}{15}$

8 a 1 **b** 1

c

	$\frac{1}{4}$	$\frac{1}{4}$	$\frac{1}{10}$
$\frac{3}{5}$	$\frac{1}{3}$	$\frac{3}{5} \times \frac{1}{3}$	
	$\frac{2}{3}$	$\frac{3}{5} \times \frac{2}{3}$	$\frac{2}{5}$

9 0.036

10 It will help to show all the 27 different possible events and which ones give the three different coloured sweets, then the branches will help you to work out the chance of each.

5.8 Independent events 1

Exercise 5H

1 a $\frac{4}{9}$ **b** $\frac{4}{9}$

2 a $\frac{1}{169}$ **b** $\frac{2}{169}$

3 a $\frac{1}{4}$ **b** $\frac{1}{2}$

4 $\frac{1}{216}$

5 a $\frac{4}{25}$ **b** $\frac{12}{25}$

6 a 0.08 **b** 0.32 **c** 0.48

7 a 0.336 **b** 0.452 **c** 0.024

8 a 0.19 **b** 0.77 **c** 0.512

9 $(\frac{1}{6})^4 = 0.000\,77$

10 Check students' understanding

11 $\frac{1}{6}$ as each throw is independent of any previous throws.

Exercise 5I

1 a $\frac{125}{216}$ (0.579) **b** $\frac{91}{216}$ (0.421)

2 a $\frac{1}{16}$ **b** $\frac{15}{16}$

3 a 0.378 **b** 0.162 **c** 0.012 **d** 0.988

4 a $\frac{4}{25}$ **b** $\frac{9}{25}$ **c** $\frac{16}{25}$

5 a i $\frac{1}{216}$ (0.005)

ii $\frac{125}{216}$ (0.579)

iii $\frac{91}{216}$ (0.421)

b i $\frac{1}{1296}$ (0.000 77)

ii $\frac{625}{1296}$ (0.482)

iii $\frac{671}{1296}$ (0.518)

c i $\frac{1}{7776}$ (0.000 13)

ii $\frac{3125}{7776}$ (0.402)

iii $\frac{4651}{7776}$ (0.598)

d i $\frac{1}{6^n}$ **ii** $\frac{5^n}{6^n}$ **iii** $1 - \frac{5^n}{6^n}$

6 a $\frac{32}{243}$ (0.132) **b** $\frac{1}{243}$ (0.004)

c $\frac{242}{243}$ (0.996)

7 a $\frac{3}{8}$ **b** $\frac{1}{120}$ **c** $\frac{119}{120}$

8 a 0.65 **b** 0.4225 **c** 2 days **d** 0.116 **e** 0.884

9 $10 \times 0.6^9 \times 0.4 + 0.6^{10} = 0.046$

10 Here P(S) = probability of a sale on one day, then probability of at least one sale in week = $(1 - [1 - P(S)]^5$.

5.9 Independent events 2

Exercise 5J

1 **a** $\frac{27}{1000}$ **b** $\frac{189}{1000}$ **c** $\frac{441}{1000}$ **d** $\frac{343}{1000}$
2 **a** $\frac{1}{1296}$ (0.000 77) **b** $\frac{625}{1296}$ (0.482)
c $\frac{125}{324}$
3 **a** $\frac{1}{9}$ **b** $\frac{7}{18}$ **c** $\frac{7}{18}$
d $\frac{1}{9}$ **e** $\frac{8}{9}$
4 **a** 0.154 **b** 0.456
5 **a** 0.3024 **b** 0.4404
c 0.7428 (P(3 or 4))
6 **a** 0.9 **b** 0.6
c 0.54 **d** 0.216
7 **a** 0.6 **b** 0.6
c 0.432 **d** Independent events
8 **a** $\frac{1}{9}$ **b** $\frac{1}{9}$ **c** $\frac{7}{27}$ **d** $\frac{1}{27}$
9 **a** 0.126 **b** 0.4
c 0.42 **d** 0.054
10 **a** 0.42
b $0.75^2 \times 0.25 = 0.14$
c $0.75 \times 0.25 = 0.19$
d 0.25
11 0.8
12 He may already have a 10 or Jack or Queen or King in his hand, in which case the probability fraction will have a different numerator and, as he already has two cards, the denominator should be 50.

5.10 Conditional probability

Exercise 5K

1 **a** $\frac{1}{60}$ **b** 50
2 **a** $\frac{1}{6}$ **b** 0
c **i** $\frac{2}{3}$ **ii** $\frac{1}{3}$ **iii** 0
3 **a** **i** $\frac{3}{8}$ **ii** $\frac{5}{8}$
b **i** $\frac{5}{12}$ **ii** $\frac{7}{12}$
4 **a** **i** $\frac{5}{13}$ **ii** $\frac{8}{13}$
b **i** $\frac{15}{91}$ **ii** $\frac{4}{13}$
5 **a** **i** $\frac{1}{3}$ **ii** $\frac{2}{15}$
b $\frac{4}{15}$ **c** $\frac{1}{6}$ **d** 1
6 Both events are independent.
7 **a** $\frac{1}{120}$ **b** $\frac{7}{40}$ **c** $\frac{21}{40}$ **d** $\frac{7}{24}$
8 **a** $\frac{1}{9}$ **b** $\frac{2}{9}$ **c** $\frac{2}{3}$ **d** $\frac{7}{9}$
9 **a** 0.000 495 **b** 0.001 98
c 0.000 037 **d** 0.000 048
10 **a** 0.54 **b** 0.38 **c** 0.08 **d** 1
11 **a** RFC, FRC, CFC, CRC
b $\frac{1}{3}$
c $\frac{1}{3}$
d $\frac{1}{3}$
e Probability is the same regardless of which day he chooses
12 **a** 0.7 **b** 0.667 **c** 0.375
13 $\frac{1}{270725}$ or 0.000 003 694
14 Find P(B) and also P(W). Then find P(B) × P(B second) remembering numerator and denominator will each be one less, and P(W) × P(W second) again remembering the numerator and denominator will each be one less. Finally add together these probabilities.

Examination questions

1 The two possibilities, off or not, are not necessarily equally likely chances.
2 **a** 0.15 **b** 0.65
3 once
4 0.54
5 $\frac{5}{6}$
6 0.35
7 **a** 0.25
b $4 \times \frac{1}{4} \times \frac{14}{59} = 0.237$
c $24 \times \frac{1}{4} \times \frac{15}{59} \times \frac{15}{58} = 0.395$
8 **a** 120 **b** 121
9 0.246 or $\frac{602}{2450}$
10 $\frac{3}{8}$

Answers to Chapter 6

Quick check

1 **a** 6370 **b** 6400 **c** 6000

2 **a** 2.4 **b** 2.39

3 **a** 50 **b** 47.3

6.1 Limits of accuracy

Exercise 6A

1 **a** $6.5 \leqslant 7 < 7.5$ **b** $115 \leqslant 120 < 125$
c $3350 \leqslant 3400 < 3450$ **d** $49.5 \leqslant 50 < 50.5$
e $5.50 \leqslant 6 < 6.50$ **f** $16.75 \leqslant 16.8 < 16.85$
g $15.5 \leqslant 16 < 16.5$ **h** $14\,450 \leqslant 14\,500 < 14\,550$
i $54.5 \leqslant 55 < 55.5$ **j** $52.5 \leqslant 55 < 57.5$

2 **a** $5.5 \leqslant 6 < 6.5$ **b** $16.5 \leqslant 17 < 17.5$
c $31.5 \leqslant 32 < 32.5$ **d** $237.5 \leqslant 238 < 238.5$
e $7.25 \leqslant 7.3 < 7.35$ **f** $25.75 \leqslant 25.8 < 25.85$
g $3.35 \leqslant 3.4 < 3.45$ **h** $86.5 \leqslant 87 < 87.5$
i $4.225 \leqslant 4.23 < 4.235$ **j** $2.185 \leqslant 2.19 < 2.195$
k $12.665 \leqslant 12.67 < 12.675$ **l** $24.5 \leqslant 25 < 25.5$
m $35 \leqslant 40 < 45$ **n** $595 \leqslant 600 < 605$
o $25 \leqslant 30 < 35$ **p** $995 \leqslant 1000 < 1050$
q $3.95 \leqslant 4.0 < 4.05$ **r** $7.035 \leqslant 7.04 < 7.045$
s $11.95 \leqslant 12.0 < 12.05$ **t** $6.995 \leqslant 7.00 < 7.005$

3 **a** 7.5, 8.5 **b** 25.5, 26.5
c 24.5, 25.5 **d** 84.5, 85.5
e 2.395, 2.405 **f** 0.15, 0.25
g 0.055, 0.065 **h** 250 g, 350 g
i 0.65, 0.75 **j** 365.5, 366.5
k 165, 175 **l** 205, 215

4 There are 16 empty seats and the number getting on the bus is from 15 to 24 so it is possible if 15 or 16 get on.

5 C: The chain and distance are both any value between 29.5 and 30.5 metres, so there is no way of knowing if the chain is longer or shorter than the distance.

6 2 kg 450 grams

7 **a** 65.5 g **b** 64.5 g
c 2620 g **d** 2580 g

6.2 Problems involving limits of accuracy

Exercise 6B

1 Minimum 65 kg, maximum 75 kg

2 Minimum is 19, maximum is 20

3 **a** 12.5 kg **b** 20

4 3 years 364 days (Jack is on his fifth birthday; Jill is 9 years old tomorrow)

5 **a** $38.25\text{ cm}^2 \leqslant \text{area} < 52.25\text{ cm}^2$
b $37.1575\text{ cm}^2 \leqslant \text{area} < 38.4475\text{ cm}^2$
c $135.625\text{ cm}^2 \leqslant \text{area} < 145.225\text{ cm}^2$

6 **a** $5.5\text{ m} \leqslant \text{length} < 6.5\text{ m}$, $3.5\text{ m} \leqslant \text{width} < 4.5\text{ m}$
b 29.25 m^2
c 18 m

7 $79.75\text{ m}^2 \leqslant \text{area} < 100.75\text{ m}^2$

8 $216.125\text{ m}^3 \leqslant \text{volume} < 354.375\text{ m}^3$

9 12.5 metres

10 Yes, because they could be walking at 4.5 mph and 2.5 mph meaning that they would cover 4.5 miles + 2.5 miles = 7 miles in 1 hour

11 $20.9\text{ m} \leqslant \text{length} < 22.9\text{ m}$ (3 sf)

12 $15.0\text{ cm}^2 \leqslant \text{area} < 19.8\text{ cm}^2$ (3 sf)

13 **a** **i** $64.1\text{ cm}^3 \leqslant \text{volume} < 69.6\text{ cm}^3$ (3 sf)
ii £22 578 ⩽ price < £24 515 (nearest £)
b 23 643 ⩽ price < £23 661 (nearest £)
c Errors in length compounded by being used 3 times in **a**, but errors in weight only used once in **b**

14 **a** $14.65\text{ s} \leqslant \text{time} < 14.75\text{ s}$
b $99.5\text{ m} \leqslant \text{length} < 100.5\text{ m}$
c 6.86 m/s (3 sf)

15 **a** +1.25% (3 sf)
b +1.89% (3 sf)

16 $3.41\text{ cm} \leqslant \text{length} < 3.43\text{ cm}$ (3 sf)

17 $5.80\text{ cm} \leqslant \text{length} < 5.90\text{ cm}$ (3 sf)

18 $14\text{ s} \leqslant \text{time} < 30\text{ s}$

19 Cannot be certain as limits of accuracy for all three springs overlap:
Red: 12.5 newtons to 13.1 newtons
Green: 11.8 newtons to 13.2 newtons
Blue: 9.5 newtons to 12.9 newtons
For example, all tensions could be 12 newtons

Examination questions

1 **a** 1845 **b** 1854

2 215 miles

3 **a** 79.5 cm **b** 40.5 cm **c** 3260.25 cm^2

4 18.95 cm and 21.16 cm

5 7.25 metres

6 £23.57

7 1.36

8 5.63 cm

9 2.92

10 7.39 m/s

11 **a** 5.196 m **b** Yes

12 12.9 to 1 dp

13 56 749

14 100 000

15 Yes, at the most the total of the individual pieces is 9 kg 900 g; scales at airport would weigh this at most as 9.95 kg so does not exceed allowance

Answers to Chapter 7

Quick check

1 **a** 4427 **b** 36 **c** 36

2 Answers will vary

3 **a** 64 **b** 144 **c** 13

7.1 Multiples, factors, prime numbers, powers and roots

Exercise 7A

1 **a** 12 **b** 9 **c** 6 **d** 13 **e** 15 **f** 14 **g** 16 **h** 10 **i** 18 **j** 17 **k** 8 (or 16) **l** 21
2 4 packs of sausages and 5 packs of buns (or multiples of these)
3 24 seconds
4 30 seconds
5 12 minutes; Debbie will have run 4 laps; Fred will have run 3 laps.
6 $1 + 3 + 5 + 7 + 9 = 25$, $1 + 3 + 5 + 7 + 9 + 11 = 36$, $1 + 3 + 5 + 7 + 9 + 11 + 13 = 49$, $1 + 3 + 5 + 7 + 9 + 11 + 13 + 15 = 64$
7 **a** −2 **b** −5 **c** −7 **d** −1 **e** −9 **f** −11 **g** −12 **h** −20 **i** −30 **j** −13
8 **a** 1 **b** 3 **c** 4 **d** 2 **e** 10 **f** −2 **g** −1 **h** 20 **i** 40 **j** −4
9 **a** 1, 3, 6, 10, 15, 21, 28, 36, 45, 55, 66, 78, 91, 105
b Adding consecutive pairs gives you square numbers.
10

	Square number	Factor of 56
Cube number	64	8
Multiple of 7	49	28

11 **a** These numbers of dots can be arranged in a triangle pattern.
b 21, 28, 36, 45, 55
12 2, 3 and 12
13 **a** 1, 64, 729, 4096, 15 625
b 1, 8, 27, 64, 125
c $\sqrt{a^3} = a \times \sqrt{a}$
d Square numbers
14 **a** 0.2 **b** 0.5 **c** 0.6 **d** 0.9 **e** 1.2 **f** 0.8 **g** 1.1 **h** 1.5
15 The answers will depend on the approximations made. Your answers should be to the same order as these.
a 60 **b** 1500 **c** 180

7.2 Prime factors, LCM and HCF

Exercise 7B

1 **a** $84 = 2 \times 2 \times 3 \times 7$ **b** $100 = 2 \times 2 \times 5 \times 5$
c $180 = 2 \times 2 \times 3 \times 3 \times 5$ **d** $220 = 2 \times 2 \times 5 \times 11$
e $280 = 2 \times 2 \times 2 \times 5 \times 7$
f $128 = 2 \times 2 \times 2 \times 2 \times 2 \times 2 \times 2$
g $50 = 2 \times 5 \times 5$
2 **a** $84 = 2^2 \times 3 \times 7$ **b** $100 = 2^2 \times 5^2$
c $180 = 2^2 \times 3^2 \times 5$ **d** $220 = 2^2 \times 5 \times 11$
e $280 = 2^3 \times 5 \times 7$ **f** $128 = 2^7$
g $50 = 2 \times 5^2$
3 $1, 2, 3, 2^2, 5, 2 \times 3, 7, 2^3, 3^2, 2 \times 5, 11, 2^2 \times 3, 13, 2 \times 7, 3 \times 5, 2^4, 17, 2 \times 3^2, 19, 2^2 \times 5, 3 \times 7, 2 \times 11, 23, 2^3 \times 3, 5^2, 2 \times 13, 3^3, 2^2 \times 7, 29, 2 \times 3 \times 5, 31, 2^5, 3 \times 11, 2 \times 17, 5 \times 7, 2^2 \times 3^2, 37, 2 \times 19, 3 \times 13, 2^3 \times 5, 41, 2 \times 3 \times 7, 43, 2^2 \times 11, 3^3 \times 5, 2 \times 23, 47, 2^4 \times 3, 7^2, 2 \times 5^2$
4 **a** 2 is always the only prime factor
b 64, 128 **c** 81, 243, 729
d 256, 1024, 4096
e $3, 3^2, 3^3, 3^4, 3^5, 3^6, 4, 4^2, 4^3, 4^4, 4^5, 4^6$
5 **a** $2 \times 2 \times 3 \times 5$ **b** $2^2 \times 3 \times 5$
c $120 = 2^3 \times 3 \times 5$, $240 = 2^4 \times 3 \times 5$, $480 = 2^5 \times 3 \times 5$
6 **a** $7^2 \times 11^2 \times 13^2$ **b** $7^3 \times 11^3 \times 13^3$
c $7^{10} \times 11^{10} \times 13^{10}$
7 Because 3 is not a factor of 40 so it does not divide exactly

Exercise 7C

1 **a** 20 **b** 56 **c** 6 **d** 28 **e** 10 **f** 15 **g** 24 **h** 30
2 They are the two numbers multiplied together.
3 **a** 8 **b** 18 **c** 12 **d** 30
4 No. The numbers have a common factor. Multiplying them together would mean using this factor twice, thus increasing the size of the common multiple. It would not be the least common multiple.
5 **a** 168 **b** 105 **c** 84 **d** 84 **e** 96 **f** 54 **g** 75 **h** 144
6 3 packs of cheese slices and 4 packs of bread rolls
7 **a** 8 **b** 7 **c** 4 **d** 14 **e** 4 **f** 9 **g** 5 **h** 4 **i** 3 **j** 16 **k** 5 **l** 18
8 **a** ii and iii **b** iii
9 18 and 24

7.3 Negative numbers

Exercise 7D

1 **a** −15 **b** −14 **c** −24 **d** 6 **e** 14 **f** 2 **g** −2 **h** −8 **i** −4 **j** 3 **k** −24 **l** −10 **m** −18 **n** 16 **o** 36
2 **a** −9 **b** 16 **c** −3 **d** −32 **e** 18 **f** 18 **g** 6 **h** −4 **i** 20 **j** 16 **k** 8 **l** −48 **m** 13 **n** −13 **o** −8
3 **a** −2 **b** 30 **c** 15 **d** −27 **e** −7
4 **a** −9 **b** 3 **c** 1
5 **a** 16 **b** −2 **c** −12
6 $-1 \times 12, 1 \times -12, -2 \times 6, 2 \times -6, -3 \times 4, 3 \times -4,$
7 Any appropriate divisions
8 **a** −24 **b** 24 degrees **c** 3×-6
9 $13 \times -6, -15 \times 4, -72 \div 4, -56 \div -8$

Exercise 7E

1 **a** −4 **b** −6 **c** 4 **d** 45 **e** 6 **f** 6
2 **a** 38 **b** 24 **c** −3 **d** −6 **e** −1 **f** 2 **g** −25 **h** 25 **i** 0 **j** −20 **k** 4 **l** 0
3 **a** $(3 \times -4) + 1 = -11$ **b** $-6 \div (-2 + 1) = 6$ **c** $(-6 \div -2) + 1 = 4$ **d** $4 + (-4 \div 4) = 3$ **e** $(4 + -4) \div 4 = 0$ **f** $(16 - -4) \div 2 = 10$
4 **a** 49 **b** −1 **c** −5 **d** −12
5 **a** 40 **b** 1 **c** 78 **d** 4
6 Possible answer: $3 \times -4 \div 2$
7 Possible answer: $(2 - 4) \times (7 - 3)$
8 $(5 + 6) - (7 \div 8) \times 9$

Examination questions

1 **a** $2 \times 3 \times 7$
b 84
2 **a** 90 **b** 240 **c** 6
3 $2^3 \times 5$
4 Possible answer: 18 and 36 or 4 and 9
5 5 times
6 120
7 **a** $x = 5$
b $2 \times 3 \times 5 \times 5$
8 **a** $p = 2, q = 5$
b 10
9 **a** $a = 2, b = 5$ (or vice versa)
b There are two possible solutions, 1 and 6 or 2 and 3.

Answers to Chapter 8

Quick check

1 **a** $2x + 12$ **b** $4x - 12$ **c** $12x - 6$
2 **a** $5y$ **b** $4x - 3$ **c** $-x - 4$
3 **a** $6x$ **b** $8y^2$ **c** $2c^3$
4 **a** $x = 1$ **b** $x = 3$ **c** $x = 9$ **d** $x = 8$ **e** $x = 24$ **f** $x = 15$

8.1a Basic algebra: Substitution

Exercise 8A

1 **a** 13 **b** −3 **c** 5
2 **a** 2 **b** 8 **c** −10
3 **a** 6 **b** 3 **c** −2
4 **a** −7 **b** −10 **c** 6.5
5 **a** −4.8 **b** 48 **c** 32
6 **a** 1.4 **b** 1.4 **c** −0.4
7 **a** 13 **b** 74 **c** 17
8 **a** 75 **b** 22.5 **c** −135
9 **a** 2.5 **b** −20 **c** 2.5
10 **a** £4 **b** 13 km
c No, 5 miles is 8 km so fare would be £6.50
11 **a** $\frac{150}{n}$ **b** £925
12 **a** $2 \times 8 + 6 \times 11 - 3 \times 2 = 76$
b $5 \times 2 - 2 \times 11 + 3 \times 8 = 12$
13 **a** £477.90
b £117.90 still owed (debit)
14 **a** One odd one even value, different from each other.
b Any valid combination, e.g. $x = 1$, $y = 2$
15 Any values such that $2lw = bh$
16 **a** **i** Odd **ii** Odd **iii** Even **iv** Odd
b Any valid expression such as $xy + z$
17 **a** £20
b **i** −£40
ii Delivery cost will be zero.
c 40 miles
18 A expression, B formula, C identity, D equation
19 **a** First term is cost of petrol, each mile is a tenth of £0.98. Second term is the hire cost divided by the miles.
b 29.8p per mile

8.1b Basic algebra: Expansion

Exercise 8B

1 **a** $6 + 2m$ **b** $10 + 5l$ **c** $12 - 3y$
d $20 + 8k$ **e** $6 - 12f$ **f** $10 - 6w$
g $10k + 15m$ **h** $12d - 8n$ **i** $t^2 + 3t$
j $k^2 - 3k$ **k** $4t^2 - 4t$ **l** $8k - 2k^2$
m $8g^2 + 20g$ **n** $15h^2 - 10h$ **o** $y^3 + 5y$
p $h^4 + 7h$ **q** $k^3 - 5k$ **r** $3t^3 + 12t$
s $15d^3 - 3d^4$ **t** $6w^3 + 3tw$ **u** $15a^3 - 10ab$
v $12p^4 - 15mp$ **w** $12h^3 + 8h^2g$ **x** $8m^3 + 2m^4$

2 **a** $5(t - 1)$ and $5t - 5$
b Yes, as $5(t - 1)$ when $t = 4.50$ is $5 \times 3.50 = £17.50$.

3 He has worked out 3×5 as 8 instead of 15 and he has not multiplied the second term by 3. Answer should be $15x - 12$.

4 **a** $3(2y + 3)$
b $2(6z + 4)$ or $4(3z + 2)$

8.1c Basic algebra: Simplification

Exercise 8C

1 **a** $7t$ **b** $9d$ **c** $3e$
d $2t$ **e** $5t^2$ **f** $4y^2$
g $5ab$ **h** $3a^2d$

2 **a** $2x$ and $2y$ **b** a and $7b$

3 **a** $3x - 1 - x$ **b** $10x$
c 25 cm

4 **a** $22 + 5t$ **b** $21 + 19k$
c $22 + 2f$ **d** $14 + 3g$

5 **a** $2 + 2h$ **b** $9g + 5$
c $17k + 16$ **d** $6e + 20$

6 **a** $4m + 3p + 2mp$
b $3k + 4h + 5hk$
c $12r + 24p + 13pr$
d $19km + 20k - 6m$

7 **a** $9t^2 + 13t$ **b** $13y^2 + 5y$
c $10e^2 - 6e$ **d** $14k^2 - 3kp$

8 **a** $17ab + 12ac + 6bc$
b $18wy + 6ty - 8tw$
c $14mn - 15mp - 6np$
d $8r^3 - 6r^2$

9 **a** $5(f + 2s) + 2(2f + 3s) = 9f + 16s$
b $£(270f + 480s)$
c $£42\,450 - £30\,000 = £12\,450$

10 For x-coefficients, 3 and 1 or 1 and 4; for y-coefficients, 5 and 1 or 3 and 4 or 1 and 7

11 $5(3x + 2) - 3(2x - 1) = 9x + 13$

8.2 Factorisation

Exercise 8D

1 **a** $6(m + 2t)$ **b** $3(3t + p)$ **c** $4(2m + 3k)$
d $4(r + 2t)$ **e** $m(n + 3)$ **f** $g(5g + 3)$
g $2(2w - 3t)$ **h** $y(3y + 2)$ **i** $t(4t - 3)$
j $3m(m - p)$ **k** $3p(2p + 3t)$ **l** $2p(4t + 3m)$
m $4b(2a - c)$ **n** $5bc(b - 2)$ **o** $2b(4ac + 3de)$
p $2(2a^2 + 3a + 4)$ **q** $3b(2a + 3c + d)$ **r** $t(5t + 4 + a)$
s $3mt(2t - 1 + 3m)$ **t** $2ab(4b + 1 - 2a)$ **u** $5pt(2t + 3 + p)$

2 **a** Mary has taken out a common factor.
b Because the bracket adds up to £10.
c £30

3 **a**, **d**, **f** and **h** do not factorise.
b $m(5 + 2p)$
c $t(t - 7)$
e $2m(2m - 3p)$
g $a(4a - 5b)$
i $b(5a - 3bc)$

4 **a** Bernice
b Aidan has not taken out the largest possible common factor. Craig has taken m out of both terms but there isn't an m in the second term.

5 There are no common factors.

6 $4x^3 - 12x$, $2x - 6$

8.3 Solving linear equations

Exercise 8E

1 **a** 30 **b** 21 **c** 72 **d** 12
e 6 **f** $10\frac{1}{2}$ **g** -10 **h** 7
i 11 **j** 2 **k** 7 **l** $2\frac{4}{5}$
m 1 **n** $11\frac{1}{2}$ **o** $\frac{1}{5}$

2 Any valid equations

3 **a** Amanda
b First line: Betsy adds 4 instead of multiplying by 5.
Second line: Betsy adds 5 instead of multiplying by 5.
Fourth line: Betsy subtracts 2 instead of dividing by 2.

Exercise 8F

1 **a** 3 **b** 7 **c** 5 **d** 3
e 4 **f** 6 **g** 8 **h** 1
i $1\frac{1}{2}$ **j** $2\frac{1}{2}$ **k** $\frac{1}{2}$ **l** $1\frac{1}{5}$
m 2 **n** -2 **o** -1 **p** -2
q -2 **r** -1

2 Any values that work, e.g. $a = 2$, $b = 3$ and $c = 30$.

3 55

8.3c Solving linear equations: Variables on both sides

Exercise 8G

1 **a** $x = 2$ **b** $y = 1$ **c** $a = 7$ **d** $t = 4$ **e** $p = 2$ **f** $k = -1$ **g** $m = 3$ **h** $s = -2$

2 $3x - 2 = 2x + 5, x = 7$

3 **a** $d = 6$ **b** $x = 11$ **c** $y = 1$ **d** $h = 4$ **e** $b = 9$ **f** $c = 6$

4 $6x + 3 = 6x + 10$; $6x - 6x = 10 - 3$; $0 = 7$, which is obviously false. Both sides have $6x$, which cancels out.

5 $8x + 7 + x + 4 = 11x + 5 - x - 4$, $x = 10$

6 Check students' explanations.

8.4 Simultaneous equations

Exercise 8H

1 **a** $x = 4, y = 1$ **b** $x = 1, y = 4$ **c** $x = 3, y = 1$ **d** $x = 5, y = -2$ **e** $x = 7, y = 1$ **f** $x = 5, y = \frac{1}{2}$ **g** $x = 4\frac{1}{2}, y = 1\frac{1}{2}$ **h** $x = -2, y = 4$ **i** $x = 2\frac{1}{2}, y = -1\frac{1}{2}$ **j** $x = 2\frac{1}{4}, y = 6\frac{1}{2}$ **k** $x = 4, y = 3$ **l** $x = 5, y = 3$

2 **a** 3 is the first term. The next term is $3 \times a + b$, which equals 14.
b $14a + b = 47$ **c** $a = 3, b = 5$ **d** 146, 443

Exercise 8I

1 **a** $x = 2, y = -3$ **b** $x = 7, y = 3$ **c** $x = 4, y = 1$ **d** $x = 2, y = 5$ **e** $x = 4, y = -3$ **f** $x = 1, y = 7$ **g** $x = 2\frac{1}{2}, y = 1\frac{1}{2}$ **h** $x = -1, y = 2\frac{1}{2}$ **i** $x = 6, y = 3$ **j** $x = \frac{1}{2}, y = -\frac{3}{4}$ **k** $x = -1, y = 5$ **l** $x = 1\frac{1}{2}, y = \frac{3}{4}$ **m** $x = 1\frac{1}{2}, y = 6\frac{1}{2}$

2 **a** They are the same equation. Divide the first by 2 and it is the second, so they have an infinite number of solutions.
b Double the second equation to get $6x + 2y = 14$ and subtract to get $9 = 14$. The left-hand sides are the same if the second is doubled so they cannot have different values.

Exercise 8J

1 **a** $x = 5, y = 1$ **b** $x = 3, y = 8$ **c** $x = 9, y = 1$ **d** $x = 7, y = 3$ **e** $x = 4, y = 2$ **f** $x = 6, y = 5$ **g** $x = 3, y = -2$ **h** $x = 2, y = \frac{1}{2}$ **i** $x = -2, y = -3$ **j** $x = -1, y = 2\frac{1}{2}$ **k** $x = 2\frac{1}{2}, y = -\frac{1}{2}$ **l** $x = -1\frac{1}{2}, y = 4\frac{1}{2}$ **m** $x = -\frac{1}{2}, y = -6\frac{1}{2}$ **n** $x = 3\frac{1}{2}, y = 1\frac{1}{2}$ **o** $x = -2\frac{1}{2}, y = -3\frac{1}{2}$

2 (1, −2) is the solution to equations A and C; (−1, 3) is the solution to equations A and D; (2, 1) is the solution to B and C; (3, −3) is the solution to B and D.

3 Intersection points are (0, 6), (1, 3) and (2, 4). Area is 2 cm^2.

4 Intersection points are (0, 3), (6, 0) and (4, −1). Area is 6 cm^2.

8.5 Rearranging formulae

Exercise 8K

1 $k = \frac{T}{3}$

2 $y = X + 1$

3 $p = 3Q$

4 $r = \frac{A - 9}{4}$

5 $n = \frac{W + 1}{3}$

6 **a** $m = p - t$ **b** $t = p - m$

7 $m = gv$

8 $m = \sqrt{t}$

9 $r = \frac{C}{2\pi}$

10 $b = \frac{A}{h}$

11 $l = \frac{P - 2w}{2}$

12 $p = \sqrt{m - 2}$

13 **a** $-40 - 32 = -72$, $-72 \div 9 = -8$, $5 \times -8 = -40$
b $68 - 32 = 36$, $36 \div 9 = 4$, $4 \times 5 = 20$
c $F = \frac{9}{5}C + 32$

14 **a** $5x = 9y + 75$, $y = \frac{5x - 75}{9}$
b 25p

15 Average speeds: outward journey = 72 kph, return journey = 63 kph, taking 2 hours. He was held up for 15 minutes.

16 **a** $a = \frac{v - u}{t}$
b $t = \frac{v - u}{a}$

17 $d = \sqrt{\frac{4A}{\pi}}$

18 **a** $n = \frac{W - t}{3}$
b $t = W - 3n$

19 **a** $y = \frac{x + w}{5}$
b $w = 5y - x$

20 $p = \sqrt{\frac{k}{2}}$

21 **a** $t = u^2 - v$
b $u = \sqrt{v + t}$

22 **a** $m = k - n^2$
b $n = \sqrt{k - m}$

23 $r = \sqrt{\frac{T}{5}}$

24 **a** $w = K - 5n^2$
b $n = \sqrt{\frac{K - w}{5}}$

Examination questions

1 32
2 **a** **i** $y^2 + 4y - 5$
ii Odd × odd + 4 × odd − odd = odd + even − odd = even
b $2y(x - 3y)$
3 $x^2 + x - 12$
4 **a** Identity, (Formula), Equation, Expression
b Add any even number, multiply by any odd number
5 **a** 3.5 **b** 2.2 **c** 1.5
6 **a** **i** y^9
ii y^5
iii y^{14}
b **i** y^{14}
ii y^5
7 **a** 6 **b** $x = 2.25, y = -1.75$
8 **a** $5x(x + 4)$
b $(x - 7)(x + 7)$
c $5(x + 1)(x + 3)$
9 **a** 20
b $\frac{1}{3}$
c $2ab(3b - 1)$
d $(3x - 4)(x + 3)$
10 $x = 8, y = -2$
11 **a** $p^2 + pq + qp + q^2$
b $(2x + 3 + x - 1)^2 = (3x + 2)^2 = 9x^2 + 12x + 4$

Answers to Chapter 9

Quick check

1 **a** 0.6 **b** 0.44 **c** 0.375
2 **a** $\frac{17}{100}$ **b** $\frac{16}{25}$ **c** $\frac{429}{500}$
3 **a** $\frac{13}{15}$ **b** $\frac{9}{40}$
4 **a** 5 **b** 4

9.1 Powers (indices)

Exercise 9A

1 **a** 2^4 **b** 3^5 **c** 7^2 **d** 5^3
e 10^7 **f** 6^4 **g** 4^1 **h** 1^7
i 0.5^4 **j** 100^3
2 **a** 3 × 3 × 3 × 3
b 9 × 9 × 9
c 6 × 6
d 10 × 10 × 10 × 10 × 10
e 2 × 2 × 2 × 2 × 2 × 2 × 2 × 2 × 2 × 2
f 8
g 0.1 × 0.1 × 0.1
h 2.5 × 2.5
i 0.7 × 0.7 × 0.7
j 1000 × 1000
3 **a** 16 **b** 243
c 49 **d** 125
e 10 000 000 **f** 1296
g 4 **h** 1
i 0.0625 **j** 1 000 000
4 **a** 81 **b** 729
c 36 **d** 100 000
e 1024 **f** 8
g 0.001 **h** 6.25
i 0.343 **j** 1 000 000
5 125 m^3
6 **b** 10^2 **c** 2^3 **d** 5^2
7 **a** 1 **b** 4 **c** 1
d 1 **e** 1
8 Any power of 1 is equal to 1.
9 10^6
10 10^6
11 **a** 1 **b** −1 **c** 1
d 1 **e** −1
12 **a** 1 **b** −1 **c** −1
d 1 **e** 1
13 $2^{24}, 4^{12}, 8^8, 16^6$

Exercise 9B

1 **a** $\frac{1}{5}$ **b** $\frac{1}{6}$ **c** $\frac{1}{10}$ **d** $\frac{1}{3^2}$
e $\frac{1}{8}$ **f** $\frac{1}{9}$ **g** $\frac{1}{w^2}$ **h** $\frac{1}{t}$
i $\frac{1}{x^m}$ **j** $\frac{4}{m^3}$
2 **a** 3^{-2} **b** 5^{-1} **c** 10^{-3} **d** m^{-1}
e t^{-n}
3 **a** **i** 2^4
ii 2^{-1}
iii 2^{-4}
iv -2^3
b **i** 10^3
ii 10^{-1}
iii 10^{-2}
iv 10^6
c **i** 5^3
ii 5^{-1}
iii 5^{-2}
iv 5^{-4}
d **i** 3^2
ii 3^{-3}
iii 3^{-4}
iv -3^5
4 **a** $\frac{5}{x^3}$ **b** $\frac{6}{t}$ **c** $\frac{7}{m^2}$ **d** $\frac{4}{q^4}$
e $\frac{10}{y^5}$ **f** $\frac{1}{2x^3}$ **g** $\frac{1}{2m}$ **h** $\frac{3}{4t^4}$
i $\frac{4}{5y^3}$ **j** $\frac{7}{8x^5}$
5 **a** $7x^{-3}$ **b** $10p^{-1}$ **c** $5t^{-2}$
d $8m^{-5}$ **e** $3y^{-1}$
6 **a** **i** 25
ii $\frac{1}{125}$
iii $\frac{4}{5}$
b **i** 64
ii $\frac{1}{16}$
iii $\frac{5}{256}$
c **i** 8
ii $\frac{1}{32}$
iii $\frac{9}{2}$ or $4\frac{1}{2}$
d **i** 1000000
ii $\frac{1}{1000}$
iii $\frac{1}{4}$
7 24 (32 − 8)
8 $x = 8$ and $y = 4$ (or $x = y = 1$)
9 $\frac{1}{2097152}$
10 **a** x^{-5}, x^0, x^5 **b** x^5, x^0, x^{-5}
c x^5, x^{-5}, x^0

Exercise 9C

1 **a** 5^4 **b** 5^3 **c** 5^2 **d** 5^3 **e** 5^{-5}

2 **a** 6^3 **b** 6^0 **c** 6^6 **d** 6^{-7} **e** 6^2

3 **a** a^3 **b** a^5 **c** a^7 **d** a^4 **e** a^2 **f** a^1

4 **a** Any two values such that $x + y = 10$
b Any two values such that $x - y = 10$

5 **a** 4^6 **b** 4^{15} **c** 4^6 **d** 4^{-6} **e** 4^6 **f** 4^0

6 **a** $6a^5$ **b** $9a^2$ **c** $8a^6$ **d** $-6a^4$ **e** $8a^8$ **f** $-10a^{-3}$

7 **a** $3a$ **b** $4a^3$ **c** $3a^4$ **d** $6a^{-1}$ **e** $4a^7$ **f** $5a^{-4}$

8 **a** $8a^5b^4$ **b** $10a^3b$ **c** $30a^{-2}b^{-2}$ **d** $2ab^3$ **e** $8a^{-5}b^7$

9 **a** $3a^3b^2$ **b** $3a^2c^4$ **c** $8a^2b^2c^3$

10 **a** Possible answer: $6x^2 \times 2y^5$ and $3xy \times 4xy^4$
b Possible answer: $24x^2y^7 \div 2y^2$ and $12x^6y^8 \div x^4y^3$

11 12 ($a = 2$, $b = 1$, $c = 3$)

12 $1 = \frac{a^x}{a^x} = a^x \div a^x = a^{x-x} = a^0$

Exercise 9D

1 **a** 5 **b** 10 **c** 8 **d** 9 **e** 25 **f** 3 **g** 4 **h** 10 **i** 5 **j** 8 **k** 12 **l** 20 **m** 5 **n** 3 **o** 10 **p** 3 **q** 2 **r** 2 **s** 6 **t** 6 **u** $\frac{1}{4}$ **v** $\frac{1}{2}$ **w** $\frac{1}{3}$ **x** $\frac{1}{5}$ **y** $\frac{1}{10}$

2 **a** $\frac{5}{6}$ **b** $1\frac{2}{3}$ **c** $\frac{8}{9}$ **d** $1\frac{4}{5}$ **e** $\frac{5}{8}$ **f** $\frac{3}{5}$ **g** $\frac{1}{4}$ **h** $2\frac{1}{2}$ **i** $\frac{4}{5}$ **j** $1\frac{1}{7}$

3 $(x^{\frac{1}{n}})^n = x^{\frac{1}{n} \times n} = x^1 = x$, but
$(\sqrt[n]{x})^n = \sqrt[n]{x} \times \sqrt[n]{x} \ldots n$ times $= x$,
so $x^{\frac{1}{n}} = \sqrt[n]{x}$

4 $64^{-\frac{1}{2}} = \frac{1}{8}$, others are both $\frac{1}{2}$

5 Possible answer: The negative power gives the reciprocal, so $27^{-\frac{1}{3}} = \frac{1}{27^{\frac{1}{3}}}$ The power one-third means cube root, so you need the cube root of 27 which is 3, so $27^{\frac{1}{3}} = 3$ and $\frac{1}{27^{\frac{1}{3}}} = \frac{1}{3}$

6 Possible answers: $x = 1$ and $y = 1$, $x = 8$ and $y = \frac{1}{64}$

Exercise 9E

1 **a** 16 **b** 25 **c** 216 **d** 81

2 **a** $t^{\frac{2}{3}}$ **b** $m^{\frac{3}{4}}$ **c** $k^{\frac{2}{5}}$ **d** $x^{\frac{3}{2}}$

3 **a** 4 **b** 9 **c** 64 **d** 3125

4 **a** $\frac{1}{5}$ **b** $\frac{1}{6}$ **c** $\frac{1}{2}$ **d** $\frac{1}{3}$ **e** $\frac{1}{4}$ **f** $\frac{1}{2}$ **g** $\frac{1}{2}$ **h** $\frac{1}{3}$

5 **a** $\frac{1}{125}$ **b** $\frac{1}{216}$ **c** $\frac{1}{8}$ **d** $\frac{1}{27}$ **e** $\frac{1}{256}$ **f** $\frac{1}{4}$ **g** $\frac{1}{4}$ **h** $\frac{1}{9}$

6 **a** $\frac{1}{100000}$ **b** $\frac{1}{12}$ **c** $\frac{1}{25}$ **d** $\frac{1}{27}$ **e** $\frac{1}{32}$ **f** $\frac{1}{32}$ **g** $\frac{1}{81}$ **h** $\frac{1}{13}$

7 $8^{-\frac{2}{3}} = \frac{1}{4}$, others are both $\frac{1}{8}$

8 Possible answer: The negative power gives the reciprocal, so $27^{-\frac{2}{3}} = \frac{1}{27^{\frac{2}{3}}}$
The power one-third means cube root, so we need the cube root of 27 which is 3 and the power 2 means square, so $3^2 = 9$, so $27^{\frac{2}{3}} = 9$ and $\frac{1}{27^{\frac{2}{3}}} = \frac{1}{9}$

9.2 Standard form

Exercise 9F

1 **a** 31 **b** 310 **c** 3100 **d** 31 000

2 **a** 65 **b** 650 **c** 6500 **d** 65 000

3 **a** 0.31 **b** 0.031 **c** 0.0031 **d** 0.000 31

4 **a** 0.65 **b** 0.065 **c** 0.0065 **d** 0.000 65

5 **a** 250 **b** 34.5 **c** 4670 **d** 346 **e** 207.89 **f** 56 780 **g** 246 **h** 0.76 **i** 999 000 **j** 23 456 **k** 98 765.4 **l** 43 230 000 **m** 345.78 **n** 6000 **o** 56.7 **p** 560 045

6 **a** 0.025 **b** 0.345 **c** 0.004 67 **d** 3.46 **e** 0.207 89 **f** 0.056 78 **g** 0.0246 **h** 0.0076 **i** 0.000 000 999 **j** 2.3456 **k** 0.098 765 4 **l** 0.000 043 23 **m** 0.000 000 034 578 **n** 0.000 000 000 06 **o** 0.000 000 567 **p** 0.005 600 45

7 **a** 230 **b** 578 900 **c** 4790 **d** 57 000 000 **e** 216 **f** 10 500 **g** 0.000 32 **h** 9870

8 **a**, **b** and **c**

9 Power 24 means more digits in the answer.

10 6

Exercise 9G

1 **a** 0.31 **b** 0.031 **c** 0.0031 **d** 0.000 31

2 **a** 0.65 **b** 0.065 **c** 0.0065 **d** 0.000 65

3 **a** $9\,999\,999\,999 \times 10^{99}$
b $0.000\,000\,001 \times 10^{-99}$
(depending on number of digits displayed)

4 **a** 31 **b** 310 **c** 3100 **d** 31 000

5 **a** 65 **b** 650 **c** 6500 **d** 65 000

6 **a** 250 **b** 34.5 **c** 0.004 67 **d** 34.6 **e** 0.020 789 **f** 5678 **g** 246 **h** 7600 **i** 897 000 **j** 0.008 65 **k** 60 000 000 **l** 0.000 567

7 **a** 2.5×10^2 **b** 3.45×10^{-1} **c** 4.67×10^4 **d** 3.4×10^9 **e** 2.078×10^{10} **f** 5.678×10^{-4} **g** 2.46×10^3 **h** 7.6×10^{-2} **i** 7.6×10^{-4} **j** 9.99×10^{-1} **k** 2.3456×10^2 **l** $9.876\,54 \times 10^1$ **m** 6×10^{-4} **n** 5.67×10^{-3} **o** $5.600\,45 \times 10^1$

8 2.7797×10^4

9 $2.815\,81 \times 10^5$, 3×10^1, $1.382\,101 \times 10^6$

10 1.298×10^7, 2.997×10^9, 9.3×10^4

11 100

12 36 miles

Exercise 9H

1 **a** 5.67×10^3 **b** 6×10^2 **c** 3.46×10^{-1} **d** 7×10^{-4} **e** 5.6×10^2 **f** 6×10^5 **g** 7×10^3 **h** 1.6 **i** 2.3×10^7 **j** 3×10^{-6} **k** 2.56×10^6 **l** 4.8×10^2 **m** 1.12×10^2 **n** 6×10^{-1} **o** 2.8×10^6

2 **a** 1.08×10^8 **b** 4.8×10^6 **c** 1.2×10^9 **d** 1.08 **e** 6.4×10^2 **f** 1.2×10^1 **g** 2.88 **h** 2.5×10^7 **i** 8×10^{-6}

3 **a** 1.1×10^8 **b** 6.1×10^6 **c** 1.6×10^9 **d** 3.9×10^{-2} **e** 9.6×10^8 **f** 4.6×10^{-7} **g** 2.1×10^3 **h** 3.6×10^7 **i** 1.5×10^2 **j** 3.5×10^9 **k** 1.6×10^4

4 **a** 2.7×10 **b** 1.6×10^{-2} **c** 2×10^{-1} **d** 4×10^{-8} **e** 2×10^5 **f** 6×10^{-2} **g** 2×10^{-5} **h** 5×10^2 **i** 2×10

5 **a** 5.4×10 **b** 2.9×10^{-3} **c** 1.1 **d** 6.3×10^{-10} **e** 2.8×10^2 **f** 5.5×10^{-2} **g** 4.9×10^2 **h** 8.6×10^6

6 2×10^{13}, 1×10^{-10}, mass $= 2 \times 10^3$ g (2 kg)

7 **a** (2^{63}) 9.2×10^{18} grains **b** $2^{64} - 1 = 1.8 \times 10^{19}$

8 **a** 6×10^7 sq miles **b** 30%

9 1.5×10^7 sq miles

10 5×10^4

11 2.3×10^5

12 455070000 kg or 455070 tonnes

13 80000000 (80 million)

14 **a** 2.048×10^6 **b** 4.816×10^6

15 250

16 9.41×10^4

17 Any value from 1.00000001×10^8 to 1×10^9 (excluding 1×10^9), i.e. any value of the form $a \times 10^8$ where $1 \leqslant a < 10$

9.3 Rational numbers and reciprocals

Exercise 9I

1 **a** 0.5 **b** $0.\dot{3}$ **c** 0.25 **d** 0.2 **e** $0.1\dot{6}$ **f** $0.\dot{1}4285\dot{7}$ **g** 0.125 **h** $0.\dot{1}$ **i** 0.1 **j** $0.\dot{0}7692\dot{3}$

2 **a** $\frac{4}{7} = 0.5714285 \ldots$

$\frac{5}{7} = 0.7142857 \ldots$

$\frac{6}{7} = 0.8571428 \ldots$

2 **b** They all contain the same pattern of digits, starting at a different point in the pattern.

3 $0.\dot{1}$, $0.\dot{2}$, $0.\dot{3}$, etc. Digit in decimal fraction same as numerator.

4 $0.\dot{0}\dot{9}$, $0.\dot{1}\dot{8}$, $0.\dot{2}\dot{7}$, etc. Sum of digits in recurring pattern = 9. First digit is one less than numerator.

5 0.444 …, 0.454 …, 0.428 …, 0.409 …, 0.432 …, 0.461 …; $\frac{9}{22}, \frac{3}{7}, \frac{16}{37}, \frac{4}{9}, \frac{5}{11}, \frac{6}{13}$

6 $\frac{38}{120}, \frac{35}{120}, \frac{36}{120}, \frac{48}{120}, \frac{50}{120}$

$\frac{7}{24}, \frac{3}{10}, \frac{19}{60}, \frac{2}{5}, \frac{5}{12}$

7 **a** $\frac{1}{8}$ **b** $\frac{17}{50}$ **c** $\frac{29}{40}$ **d** $\frac{5}{16}$ **e** $\frac{89}{100}$ **f** $\frac{1}{20}$ **g** $2\frac{7}{20}$ **h** $\frac{7}{32}$

8 **a** $0.08\dot{3}$ **b** 0.0625 **c** 0.05 **d** 0.04 **e** 0.02

9 **a** $\frac{4}{3}$ **b** $\frac{6}{5}$ **c** $\frac{5}{2}$ **d** $\frac{10}{7}$ **e** $\frac{20}{11}$ **f** $\frac{15}{4}$

10 **a** 0.75, $1.\dot{3}$; $0.8\dot{3}$, 1.2; 0.4, 2.5; 0.7, $1.\dot{4}2857\dot{1}$; 0.55, $1.\dot{8}\dot{1}$; $0.2\dot{6}$, 3.75

b Not always true, e.g. reciprocal of 0.4 $(\frac{2}{5})$ is $\frac{5}{2} = 2.5$

11 $1 \div 0$ is infinite, so there is no finite answer.

12 **a** 10 **b** 2

c The reciprocal of a reciprocal is always the original number.

13 The reciprocal of x is greater than the reciprocal of y. For example, $2 < 10$, reciprocal of 2 is 0.5, reciprocal of 10 is 0.1, and $0.5 > 0.1$

14 Possible answer: $-\frac{1}{2} \times -2 = 1$, $-\frac{1}{3} \times -3 = 1$

15 **a** 24.24242 … **b** 24 **c** $\frac{24}{99} = \frac{8}{33}$

16 **a** $\frac{8}{9}$ **b** $\frac{34}{99}$ **c** $\frac{5}{11}$ **d** $\frac{21}{37}$ **e** $\frac{4}{9}$ **f** $\frac{2}{45}$ **g** $\frac{13}{90}$ **h** $\frac{1}{22}$ **i** $2\frac{7}{9}$ **j** $7\frac{7}{11}$ **k** $3\frac{1}{3}$ **l** $2\frac{2}{33}$

17 **a** true **b** true **c** recurring

18 **a** $\frac{9}{9}$ **b** $\frac{45}{90} = \frac{1}{2} = 0.5$

9.4 Surds

Exercise 9J

1 **a** $\sqrt{6}$ **b** $\sqrt{15}$ **c** 2 **d** 4 **e** $2\sqrt{10}$ **f** 3 **g** $2\sqrt{3}$ **h** $\sqrt{21}$ **i** $\sqrt{14}$ **j** 6 **k** 6 **l** $\sqrt{30}$

2 **a** 2 **b** $\sqrt{5}$ **c** $\sqrt{6}$ **d** $\sqrt{3}$ **e** $\sqrt{5}$ **f** 1 **g** $\sqrt{3}$ **h** $\sqrt{7}$ **i** 2 **j** $\sqrt{6}$ **k** 1 **l** 3

3 **a** $2\sqrt{3}$ **b** 15 **c** $4\sqrt{2}$ **d** $4\sqrt{3}$ **e** $8\sqrt{5}$ **f** $3\sqrt{3}$ **g** 24 **h** $3\sqrt{7}$ **i** $2\sqrt{7}$ **j** $6\sqrt{5}$ **k** $6\sqrt{3}$ **l** 30

4 **a** $\sqrt{3}$ **b** 1 **c** $2\sqrt{2}$ **d** $\sqrt{2}$ **e** $\sqrt{5}$ **f** $\sqrt{3}$ **g** $\sqrt{2}$ **h** $\sqrt{7}$ **i** $\sqrt{7}$ **j** $2\sqrt{3}$ **k** $2\sqrt{3}$ **l** 1

5 **a** a **b** 1 **c** $\sqrt{a}$

6 **a** $3\sqrt{2}$ **b** $2\sqrt{6}$ **c** $2\sqrt{3}$ **d** $5\sqrt{2}$ **e** $2\sqrt{2}$ **f** $3\sqrt{3}$ **g** $4\sqrt{3}$ **h** $5\sqrt{3}$ **i** $3\sqrt{5}$ **j** $3\sqrt{7}$ **k** $4\sqrt{2}$ **l** $10\sqrt{2}$ **m** $10\sqrt{10}$ **n** $5\sqrt{10}$ **o** $7\sqrt{2}$ **p** $9\sqrt{3}$

7 **a** 36 **b** $16\sqrt{30}$ **c** 54 **d** 32 **e** $48\sqrt{6}$ **f** $48\sqrt{6}$ **g** $18\sqrt{15}$ **h** 84 **i** 64 **j** 100 **k** 50 **l** 56

8 **a** $20\sqrt{6}$ **b** $6\sqrt{15}$ **c** 24 **d** 16 **e** $12\sqrt{10}$ **f** 18 **g** $20\sqrt{3}$ **h** $10\sqrt{21}$ **i** $6\sqrt{14}$ **j** 36 **k** 24 **l** $12\sqrt{30}$

9 **a** 6 **b** $3\sqrt{5}$ **c** $6\sqrt{6}$ **d** $2\sqrt{3}$ **e** $4\sqrt{5}$ **f** 5 **g** $7\sqrt{3}$ **h** $2\sqrt{7}$ **i** 6 **j** $2\sqrt{7}$ **k** 5 **l** 24

10 **a** $2\sqrt{3}$ **b** 4 **c** $6\sqrt{2}$ **d** $4\sqrt{2}$ **e** $6\sqrt{5}$ **f** $24\sqrt{3}$ **g** $3\sqrt{2}$ **h** $\sqrt{7}$ **i** $10\sqrt{7}$ **j** $8\sqrt{3}$ **k** $10\sqrt{3}$ **l** 6

11 **a** abc **b** $\frac{a}{c}$ **c** $c\sqrt{b}$

12 **a** 20 **b** 24 **c** 10 **d** 24 **e** 3 **f** 6

13 **a** $\frac{3}{4}$ **b** $8\frac{1}{3}$ **c** $\frac{5}{16}$ **d** 12 **e** 2

14 **a** False **b** False

15 Possible answer: $\sqrt{3} \times 2\sqrt{3}$ (= 6)

Exercise 9K

1 Expand the brackets each time.

2 **a** $2\sqrt{3} - 3$ **b** $3\sqrt{2} - 8$ **c** $10 + 4\sqrt{5}$
d $12\sqrt{7} - 42$ **e** $15\sqrt{2} - 24$ **f** $9 - \sqrt{3}$

3 **a** $2\sqrt{3}$ **b** $1 + \sqrt{5}$ **c** $-1 - \sqrt{2}$
d $\sqrt{7} - 30$ **e** -41 **f** $7 + 3\sqrt{6}$
g $9 + 4\sqrt{5}$ **h** $3 - 2\sqrt{2}$ **i** $11 + 6\sqrt{2}$

4 **a** $3\sqrt{2}$ cm **b** $2\sqrt{3}$ cm **c** $2\sqrt{10}$ cm

5 **a** $\sqrt{3} - 1$ cm^2 **b** $2\sqrt{5} + 5\sqrt{2}$ cm^2 **c** $2\sqrt{3} + 18$ cm^2

6 **a** $\frac{\sqrt{3}}{3}$ **b** $\frac{\sqrt{2}}{2}$ **c** $\frac{\sqrt{5}}{5}$ **d** $\frac{\sqrt{3}}{6}$ **e** $\sqrt{3}$ **f** $\frac{5\sqrt{2}}{2}$
g $\frac{3}{2}$ **h** $\frac{5\sqrt{2}}{2}$ **i** $\frac{\sqrt{21}}{3}$ **j** $\frac{\sqrt{2}+2}{2}$ **k** $\frac{2\sqrt{3}-3}{3}$
l $\frac{5\sqrt{3}+6}{3}$

7 **a** **i** 1 **ii** -4 **iii** 2
iv 17 **v** -44
b They become whole numbers. Difference of two squares makes the 'middle terms' (and surds) disappear.

8 **a** Possible answer: $\sqrt{2}$ and $\sqrt{2}$ or $\sqrt{2}$ and $\sqrt{8}$
b Possible answer: $\sqrt{2}$ and $\sqrt{3}$

9 **a** Possible answer: $\sqrt{2}$ and $\sqrt{2}$ or $\sqrt{8}$ and $\sqrt{2}$
b Possible answer: $\sqrt{3}$ and $\sqrt{2}$

10 Possible answer: $80^2 = 6400$, so $80 = \sqrt{6400}$ and $10\sqrt{70} = \sqrt{7000}$
Since $6400 < 7000$, there is not enough cable.

11 $9 + 6\sqrt{2} + 2 - (1 - 2\sqrt{8} + 8) = 11 - 9 + 6\sqrt{2} + 4\sqrt{2}$
$= 2 + 10\sqrt{2}$

12 $x^2 - y^2 = (1 + \sqrt{2})^2 - (1 - \sqrt{8})^2 =$
$1 + 2\sqrt{2} + 2 - (1 - 2\sqrt{8} + 8) =$
$3 - 9 + 2\sqrt{2} + 4\sqrt{2} = -6 + 6\sqrt{2}$
$(x + y)(x - y) = (2 - \sqrt{2})(3\sqrt{2}) = 6\sqrt{2} - 6$

Examination questions

1 **a** 169
b 14^2 must have units digit 6 or $14^2 = 196$

2 **a** 8^9 **b** w^4
c Answer should be $12x^6$; he has added rather than multiplied the numbers, and $x = x^1$, so powers should add up to 6.
d $3y^4z^2$

3 5.9×10^9 km

4 **a** $3ab^2$ **b** $81x^{12}y^8$

5 $\frac{8}{15}$

6 **a** 2.994×10^{-23} **b** 3.34×10^{22}

7 $\frac{4}{55}$

8 $x = 5\sqrt{2}$

9 **a** Check students' proofs.
b $\frac{41}{110}$

10 **a** **i** $\sqrt{20} = \sqrt{4 \times 5} = \sqrt{4} \times \sqrt{5} = 2\sqrt{5}$
ii $12 + 4\sqrt{5}$
b $(\sqrt{3})^2 + (2 + \sqrt{5})^2 = 3 + 4 + 4\sqrt{5} + 5$
$= 12 + 4\sqrt{5}$
$= (\sqrt{2} + \sqrt{10})^2$
Therefore triangle is right-angled.

11 $2\sqrt{3}$ cm

12 **a** **i** $\sqrt{32} = \sqrt{16 \times 2} = \sqrt{16} \times \sqrt{2}$ **ii** $14 + 4\sqrt{6}$
b $2^2 + (2 + \sqrt{6})^2 = 4 + 4 + 4\sqrt{6} + 6$
$= 14 + 4\sqrt{6}$
$= (\sqrt{2} + \sqrt{12})^2$

Answers to Chapter 10

Quick check

1 **a** $-3x$ **b** $2x$ **c** $-3x$ **d** $6m^2$ **e** $-6x^2$ **f** $-12p^2$ 2 **a** -6 **b** $-\frac{1}{2}$ **c** $\frac{2}{3}$

10.1 Expanding brackets

Exercise 10A

1 $x^2 + 5x + 6$
2 $t^2 + 7t + 12$
3 $w^2 + 4w + 3$
4 $m^2 + 6m + 5$
5 $k^2 + 8k + 15$
6 $a^2 + 5a + 4$
7 $x^2 + 2x - 8$
8 $t^2 + 2t - 15$
9 $w^2 + 2w - 3$
10 $f^2 - f - 6$
11 $g^2 - 3g - 4$
12 $y^2 + y - 12$
13 $x^2 + x - 12$
14 $p^2 - p - 2$
15 $k^2 - 2k - 8$
16 $y^2 + 3y - 10$
17 $t^2 + t - 12$
18 $x^2 - 9$
19 $t^2 - 25$
20 $m^2 - 16$
21 $t^2 - 4$
22 $y^2 - 64$
23 $p^2 - 1$
24 $25 - x^2$
25 $49 - g^2$
26 $x^2 - 36$
27 $(x + 2)$ and $(x + 3)$
28 **a** B: $1 \times (x - 2)$
C: 1×2
D: $2 \times (x - 1)$
b $(x - 2) + 2 + 2(x - 1)$
$= 3x - 2$
c Area A $=$
$(x - 1)(x - 2)$
$=$ area of square minus areas (B + C + D)
$= x^2 - (3x - 2)$
$= x^2 - 3x + 2$
29 **a** $x^2 - 9$
b **i** 9991
ii 39991

Exercise 10B

1 $6x^2 + 11x + 3$
2 $12y^2 + 17y + 6$
3 $6t^2 + 17t + 5$
4 $8t^2 + 2t - 3$
5 $10m^2 - 11m - 6$
6 $12k^2 - 11k - 15$
7 $6p^2 + 11p - 10$
8 $10w^2 + 19w + 6$
9 $6a^2 - 7a - 3$
10 $8r^2 - 10r + 3$
11 $15g^2 - 16g + 4$
12 $12d^2 + 5d - 2$
13 $8p^2 + 26p + 15$
14 $6t^2 + 7t + 2$
15 $6p^2 + 11p + 4$
16 $6 - 7t - 10t^2$
17 $12 + n - 6n^2$
18 $6f^2 - 5f - 6$
19 $12 + 7q - 10q^2$
20 $3 - 7p - 6p^2$
21 $4 + 10t - 6t^2$
22 **a** $x^2 + 2x + 1$
b $x^2 - 2x + 1$
c $x^2 - 1$
d $p + q = (x + 1 + x - 1) = 2x$
$(p + q)^2 = (2x)^2 = 4x^2$
$p^2 + 2pq + q^2 = x^2 + 2x + 1 + 2(x^2 - 1) + x^2 - 2x + 1$
$= 4x^2 + 2x - 2x + 2 - 2 = 4x^2$
23 **a** $(3x - 2)(2x + 1) = 6x^2 - x - 2$, $(2x - 1)(2x - 1) = 4x^2 - 4x + 1$, $(6x - 3)(x + 1) = 6x^2 + 3x - 3$, $(3x + 2)(2x + 1) = 6x^2 + 7x + 2$
b Multiply the x terms to match the x^2 term and/or multiply the constant terms to get the constant term in the answer.

Exercise 10C

1 $4x^2 - 1$
2 $9t^2 - 4$
3 $25y^2 - 9$
4 $16m^2 - 9$
5 $4k^2 - 9$
6 $16h^2 - 1$
7 $4 - 9x^2$
8 $25 - 4t^2$
9 $36 - 25y^2$
10 $a^2 - b^2$
11 $9t^2 - k^2$
12 $4m^2 - 9p^2$
13 $25k^2 - g^2$
14 $a^2b^2 - c^2d^2$
15 $a^4 - b^4$
16 **a** $a^2 - b^2$
b Dimensions: $a + b$ by $a - b$; Area: $a^2 - b^2$
c Areas are the same, so $a^2 - b^2 = (a + b) \times (a - b)$
17 First shaded area is $(2k)^2 - 1^2 = 4k^2 - 1$
Second shaded area is $(2k + 1)(2k - 1) = 4k^2 - 1$

Exercise 10D

1 $x^2 + 10x + 25$
2 $m^2 + 8m + 16$
3 $t^2 + 12t + 36$
4 $p^2 + 6p + 9$
5 $m^2 - 6m + 9$
6 $t^2 - 10t + 25$
7 $m^2 - 8m + 16$
8 $k^2 - 14k + 49$
9 $9x^2 + 6x + 1$
10 $16t^2 + 24t + 9$
11 $25y^2 + 20y + 4$
12 $4m^2 + 12m + 9$
13 $16t^2 - 24t + 9$
14 $9x^2 - 12x + 4$
15 $25t^2 - 20t + 4$
16 $25r^2 - 60r + 36$
17 $x^2 + 2xy + y^2$
18 $m^2 - 2mn + n^2$
19 $4t^2 + 4ty + y^2$
20 $m^2 - 6mn + 9n^2$
21 $x^2 + 4x$
22 $x^2 - 10x$
23 $x^2 + 12x$
24 $x^2 - 4x$
25 **a** Bernice has just squared the first term and the second term. She hasn't written down the brackets twice.
b Pete has written down the brackets twice but has worked out $(3x)^2$ as $3x^2$ and not $9x^2$.
c $9x^2 + 6x + 1$
26 Whole square is $(2x)^2 = 4x^2$.
Three areas are $2x - 1$, $2x - 1$ and 1.
$4x^2 - (2x - 1 + 2x - 1 + 1) = 4x^2 - (4x - 1) = 4x^2 - 4x + 1$

10.2 Quadratic factorisation

Exercise 10E

1 $(x + 2)(x + 3)$
2 $(t + 1)(t + 4)$
3 $(m + 2)(m + 5)$
4 $(k + 4)(k + 6)$
5 $(p + 2)(p + 12)$
6 $(r + 3)(r + 6)$
7 $(w + 2)(w + 9)$
8 $(x + 3)(x + 4)$
9 $(a + 2)(a + 6)$
10 $(k + 3)(k + 7)$
11 $(f + 1)(f + 21)$
12 $(b + 8)(b + 12)$
13 $(t - 2)(t - 3)$
14 $(d - 4)(d - 1)$
15 $(g - 2)(g - 5)$
16 $(x - 3)(x - 12)$
17 $(c - 2)(c - 16)$
18 $(t - 4)(t - 9)$
19 $(y - 4)(y - 12)$
20 $(j - 6)(j - 8)$
21 $(p - 3)(p - 5)$
22 $(y + 6)(y - 1)$
23 $(t + 4)(t - 2)$
24 $(x + 5)(x - 2)$
25 $(m + 2)(m - 6)$
26 $(r + 1)(r - 7)$
27 $(n + 3)(n - 6)$
28 $(m + 4)(m - 11)$
29 $(w + 4)(w - 6)$
30 $(t + 9)(t - 10)$
31 $(h + 8)(h - 9)$
32 $(t + 7)(t - 9)$
33 $(d + 1)^2$
34 $(y + 10)^2$
35 $(t - 4)^2$
36 $(m - 9)^2$
37 $(x - 12)^2$
38 $(d + 3)(d - 4)$
39 $(t + 4)(t - 5)$
40 $(q + 7)(q - 8)$
41 $(x + 2)(x + 3)$, giving areas of $2x$ and $3x$, or $(x + 1)(x + 6)$, giving areas of x and $6x$.
42 **a** $x^2 + (a + b)x + ab$
b **i** $p + q = 7$
ii $pq = 12$
c 7 can only be 1×7 and $1 + 7 \neq 12$

Exercise 10F

1 $(x + 3)(x - 3)$
2 $(t + 5)(t - 5)$
3 $(m + 4)(m - 4)$
4 $(3 + x)(3 - x)$
5 $(7 + t)(7 - t)$
6 $(k + 10)(k - 10)$
7 $(2 + y)(2 - y)$
8 $(x + 8)(x - 8)$
9 $(t + 9)(t - 9)$
10 **a** x^2
b **i** $(x - 2)$ **ii** $(x + 2)$
iii x^2 **iv** 4
c $A + B - C = x^2 - 4$, which is the area of D, which is $(x + 2)(x - 2)$.
11 **a** $x^2 + 4x + 4 - (x^2 + 2x + 1) = 2x + 3$
b $(a + b)(a - b)$
c $(x + 2 + x + 1)(x + 2 - x - 1) = (2x + 3)(1) = 2x + 3$
d The answers are the same.
e $(x + 1 + x - 1)(x + 1 - x + 1) = (2x)(2) = 4x$
12 $(x + y)(x - y)$
13 $(x + 2y)(x - 2y)$
14 $(x + 3y)(x - 3y)$
15 $(3x + 1)(3x - 1)$
16 $(4x + 3)(4x - 3)$
17 $(5x + 8)(5x - 8)$
18 $(2x + 3y)(2x - 3y)$
19 $(3t + 2w)(3t - 2w)$
20 $(4y + 5x)(4y - 5x)$

Exercise 10G

1 $(2x + 1)(x + 2)$
2 $(7x + 1)(x + 1)$
3 $(4x + 7)(x - 1)$
4 $(3t + 2)(8t + 1)$
5 $(3t + 1)(5t - 1)$
6 $(4x - 1)^2$
7 $3(y + 7)(2y - 3)$
8 $4(y + 6)(y - 4)$
9 $(2x + 3)(4x - 1)$
10 $(2t + 1)(3t + 5)$
11 $(x - 6)(3x + 2)$
12 $(x - 5)(7x - 2)$
13 $4x + 1$ and $3x + 2$
14 **a** All the terms in the quadratic have a common factor of 6.
b $6(x + 2)(x + 3)$. This has the highest common factor taken out.

10.3 Solving quadratic equations by factorisation

Exercise 10H

1 −2, −5
2 −3, −1
3 −6, −4
4 −3, 2
5 −1, 3
6 −4, 5
7 1, −2
8 2, −5
9 7, −4
10 3, 2
11 1, 5
12 4, 3
13 −4, −1
14 −9, −2
15 2, 4
16 3, 5
17 −2, 5
18 −3, 5
19 −6, 2
20 −6, 3
21 −1, 2
22 −2
23 −5
24 4
25 −2, −6
26 7
27 **a** $x(x - 3) = 550$, $x^2 - 3x - 550 = 0$
b $(x - 25)(x + 22) = 0$, $x = 25$
28 $x(x + 40) = 48\,000$, $x^2 + 40x - 48\,000 = 0$, $(x + 240)(x - 200) = 0$ Fence is $2 \times 200 + 2 \times 240 = 880$ m.
29 −6, −4
30 2, 16
31 −6, 4
32 −9, 6
33 −10, 3
34 −4, 11
35 −8, 9
36 8, 9
37 1
38 Mario was correct. Sylvan did not make it into a standard quadratic and only factorised the x terms. She also incorrectly solved the equation $x - 3 = 4$.

Exercise 10I

1 **a** $\frac{1}{3}, -3$ **b** $1\frac{1}{3}, -\frac{1}{2}$
c $-\frac{1}{5}, 2$ **d** $-2\frac{1}{2}, 3\frac{1}{2}$
e $-\frac{1}{6}, -\frac{1}{3}$ **f** $\frac{2}{3}, 4$
g $\frac{1}{2}, -3$ **h** $\frac{5}{2}, -\frac{7}{6}$
i $-1\frac{2}{3}, 1\frac{2}{5}$ **j** $1\frac{3}{4}, 1\frac{2}{7}$
k $\frac{2}{3}, \frac{1}{8}$ **l** $\pm\frac{1}{4}$
m $-2\frac{1}{4}, 0$ **n** $\pm 1\frac{2}{5}$
o $-\frac{1}{3}, 3$

2 **a** 7, −6 **b** $-2\frac{1}{2}, 1\frac{1}{2}$
c 7, −6 **d** $-1, \frac{11}{13}$
e 3, −2 **f** $-\frac{2}{5}, \frac{1}{2}$
g $-\frac{1}{3}, -\frac{1}{2}$ **h** $\frac{1}{5}, -2$
i 4 **j** $-2, \frac{1}{8}$
k $-\frac{1}{3}, 0$ **l** ± 5
m $-1\frac{2}{3}$ **n** $\pm 3\frac{1}{2}$
o $-2\frac{1}{2}, 3$

3 **a** Both only have one solution: $x = 1$.
b B is a linear equation, but A and C are quadratic equations.

4 **a** $(5x - 1)^2 = (2x + 3)^2 + (x + 1)^2$, when expanded and collected into the general quadratics, gives the required equation.
b $(10x + 3)(2x - 3)$, $x = 1.5$; area $= 7.5$ cm^2.

10.4 Solving a quadratic equation by completing the square

Exercise 10J

1 **a** $(x + 2)^2 - 4$ **b** $(x + 7)^2 - 49$ **c** $(x - 3)^2 - 9$
d $(x + 3)^2 - 9$ **e** $(x - 2)^2 - 4$ **f** $(x - 5)^2 - 25$
g $(x + 10)^2 - 100$ **h** $(x + 5)^2 - 25$ **i** $(x + 4)^2 - 16$
j $(x - 1)^2 - 1$ **k** $(x + 1)^2 - 1$

2 **a** $(x + 2)^2 - 5$ **b** $(x + 7)^2 - 54$ **c** $(x - 3)^2 - 6$
d $(x + 3)^2 - 2$ **e** $(x - 2)^2 - 5$ **f** $(x + 3)^2 - 6$
g $(x - 5)^2 - 30$ **h** $(x + 10)^2 - 101$ **i** $(x + 4)^2 - 22$
j $(x + 1)^2 - 2$ **k** $(x - 1)^2 - 8$ **l** $(x + 1)^2 - 10$

3 **a** $-2 \pm \sqrt{5}$ **b** $-7 \pm 3\sqrt{6}$ **c** $3 \pm \sqrt{6}$
d $-3 \pm \sqrt{2}$ **e** $2 \pm \sqrt{5}$ **f** $-3 \pm \sqrt{6}$
g $5 \pm \sqrt{30}$ **h** $-10 \pm \sqrt{101}$ **i** $-4 \pm \sqrt{22}$
j $-1 \pm \sqrt{2}$ **k** $1 \pm 2\sqrt{2}$ **l** $-1 \pm \sqrt{10}$

4 **a** 1.45, −3.45 **b** 5.32, −1.32 **c** −4.16, 2.16
5 Check or correct proof.
6 $p = -14$, $q = -3$
7 **a** 3rd, 1st, 4th and 2nd – in that order
b Rewrite $x^2 - 4x - 3 = 0$ as $(x - 2)^2 - 7 = 0$, take −7 over the equals sign, square root both sides, take −2 over the equals sign
c **i** $x = -3 \pm \sqrt{2}$ **ii** $x = 2 \pm \sqrt{7}$
8 H, C, B, E, D, J, A, F, G, I

Examination questions

1 **a** **i** $(y - 2)(y - 3)$ **ii** $y = 2, y = 3$
b $\frac{x + 3}{4}$ **c** $16m^{12}p^4$
2 **a** $a = 4, b = -21$
b $x = 0.58$ or -8.58 (2 dp)
3 $x = \frac{a - bc^2}{c^2}$ or $x = \frac{a}{c^2} - b$
4 **a** $(2n + 3)(n + 3)$
b $299 = 13 \times 23$; let $n = 10$; $299 = 2n^2 + 9n + 9 = (2n + 3)(n + 3) = (2 \times 10 + 3)(10 + 3) = 23 \times 13$
5 **a** $2(4p - 3)$ **b** $r(r + 6)$ **c** s^6
6 $x = 6, x = -5\frac{1}{3}$
7 **a** $x^2(x^3 - 4)$
b **i** $(x - 5)(x + 2)$ **ii** $x = 5, x = -2$
8 $6p^2 - 17pq + 5q^2$
9 **a** $a^2 - b^2$
b **i** $(x - 18)(x - 2)$
ii $x = 18, x = 2$
10 **a** $\frac{1}{2}(25 - 2x)$
b $\frac{1}{2}x(25 - 2x) = 38$, $25x - 2x^2 = 76$, $2x^2 - 25x + 76 = 0$
c 7.28 cm (width is 5.22 cm)
11 **a** $a = 5, b = 15$
b Minimum is 15, when $x = -5$.
12 $3(x + 2y)(x - 2y)$
13 **a** $(2n + 3)(n + 1)$
b 11×23; let $n = 10$; $253 = 2n^2 + 5n + 3 = (2n + 3)(n + 1) = (2 \times 10 + 3)(10 + 1) = 23 \times 11$
14 $x = 1.74$ or -5.74
15 **a** $a = 3, b = -12$
b $x = -3 \pm 2\sqrt{3}$
16 **a** $(x - 2)(x - 6)$
b $y = 1$ or $y = 5$

Answers to Chapter 11

Quick check

1 A (3, 0), B (1, 4), C (4, 5)

2 **a** 18 **b** 265

11.1 Straight-line distance–time graphs

Exercise 11A

1 **a** **i** 2 h **ii** 3 h **iii** 5 h
b **i** 40 km/h **ii** 120 km/h **iii** 40 km/h
c 6.30 am

2 **a** **i** 125 km **ii** 125 km/h
b **i** Between 2 pm and 3 pm **ii** About $12\frac{1}{2}$ km/h

3 **a** 30 km **b** 40 km **c** 100 km/h

4 **a** **i** 263 m/min (3 sf) **ii** 15.8 km/h (3 sf)
b **i** 500 m/min
c Paul by 1 minute

5 **a** Patrick ran quickly at first, then had a slow middle section but he won the race with a final sprint. Araf ran steadily all the way and came second. Sean set off the slowest, speeded up towards the end but still came third.
b **i** 1.67 m/s **ii** 6 km/h

6 There are three methods for doing this question. This table shows the first, which is writing down the distances covered each hour.

Time	9am	9:30	10:00	10:30	11:00	11:30	12:00	12:30
Walker	0	3	6	9	12	15	18	21
Cyclist	0	0	0	0	7.5	15	22.5	30

The second method is algebra:

Walker takes T hours until overtaken, so $T = \frac{D}{6}$; Cyclist takes $T - 1.5$ to overtake, so $T - 1.5 = \frac{D}{15}$.

Rearranging gives $15T - 22.5 = 6T$, $9T = 22.5$, $T = 2.5$.

The third method is a graph:

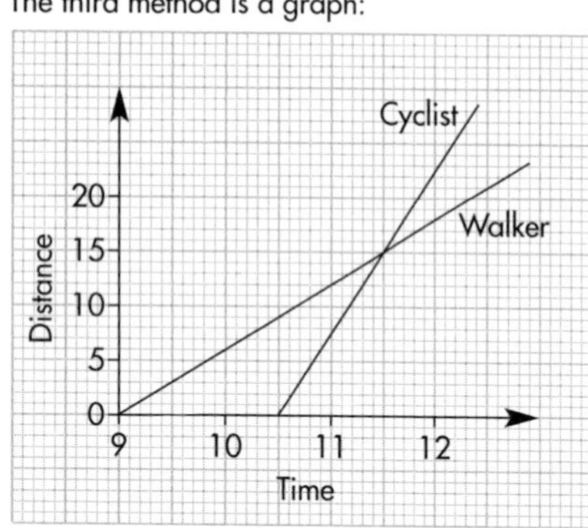

All methods give the same answer of 11:30 when the cyclist overtakes the walker.

7 **a** **i** Because it stopped several times **ii** Ravinder
b Ravinder at 3.58 pm, Sue at 4.20 pm, Michael at 4.35 pm
c **i** 24 km/h **ii** 20.5 km/h **iii** 5

Exercise 11B

1 **a** 39.2°C **b** Day 4 and 5, steepest line
c Day 8 and 9, steepest line
d **i** Day 5 **ii** 4
e 37° C

2 **a** $\frac{15}{2}$ **b** $\frac{25}{8}$ **c** $\frac{15}{16}$ **d** $\frac{2}{25}$
e $\frac{6}{35}$ **f** $\frac{1}{2}$ **g** $-\frac{4}{5}$

3 **a** $2\frac{1}{2}$ km/h **b** 3.75 m/s **c** $2\frac{1}{2}$ km/h

4 **a** AB: 30 km/h, BC: 6 km/h, CD: 0 km/h, DE: 36 km/h (in opposite direction)
b FG: 4 m/s, GH: 16 m/s, HI: 2 m/s (in opposite direction), IJ: 16 m/s (in opposite direction)

5 Rob has misread the scales. The gradient is actually 2. The line is $y = 2x + 2$ when $x = 10$, $y = 22$.

6 **a** 4 m **b** 1 m
c **i** $\frac{4}{3}$ m **ii** 3 m

11.2 Other types of graphs

Exercise 11C

1 **a** Graph C
b Any container with a regular horizontal cross-section

2 **a**

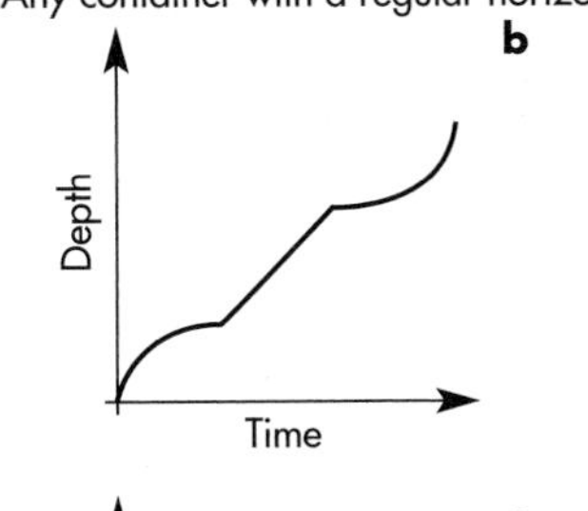

b

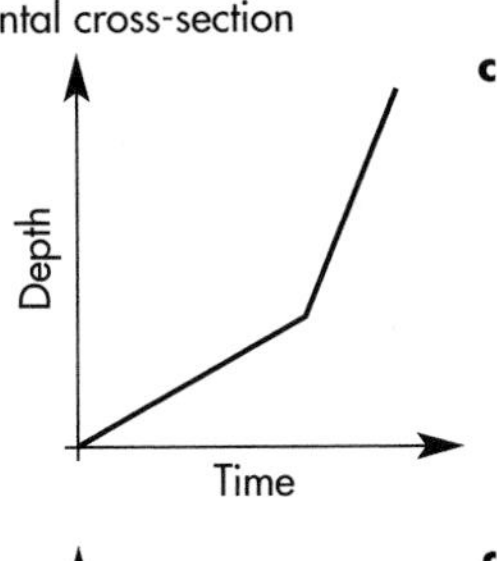

c

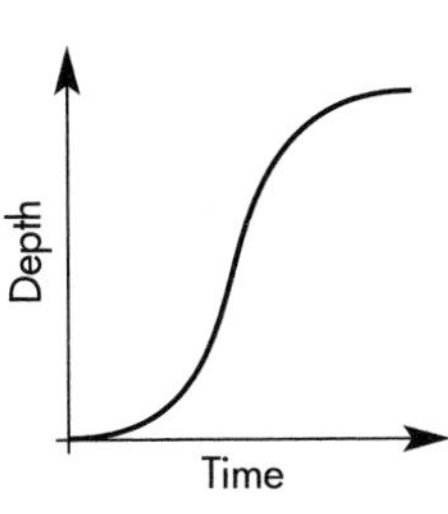

d

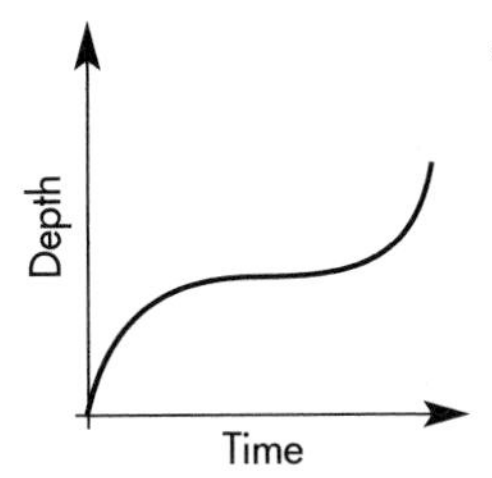

e

Depth
Time

f

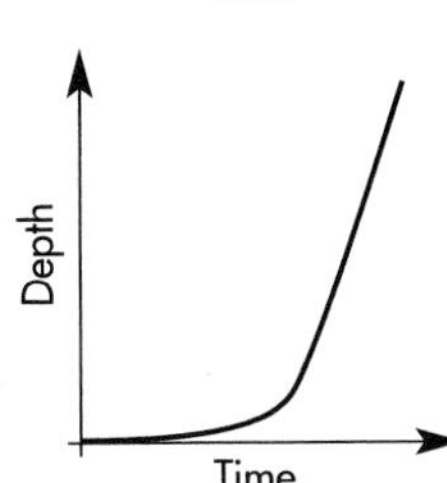

3

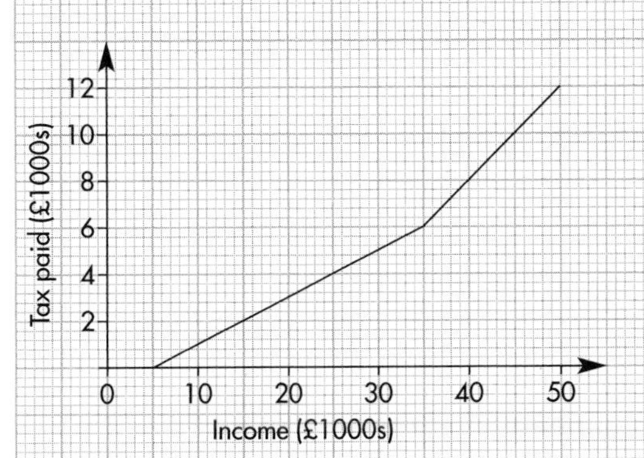

Examination questions

1 **a**

Distance from home (km)
0 1 2 3 4 5 6 7 8 9 10 11 12 13
10:00 10:30 11:00 11:30 12:00 12:30 13:00 13:30 14:00
Time

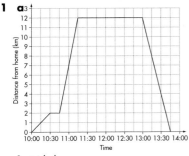

b 16 kph

2 **a** 150 miles
b 10 minutes
c 50 mph

3 68 mph

4 20 kilometres per litre

5 **a** Grant
b 93 seconds
c 65m/min
d **i** Mark
ii Steeper line

6 **a**

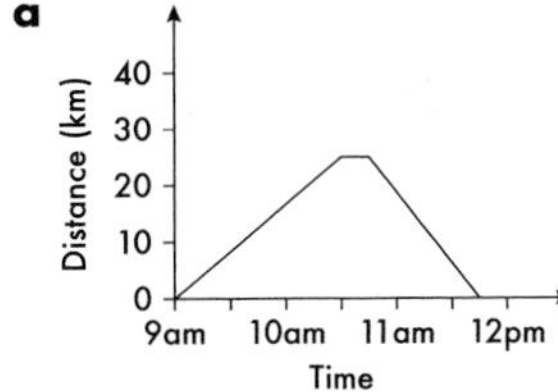

b 25 kph

Answers to Chapter 12

Quick check

1 **a** 13 **b**

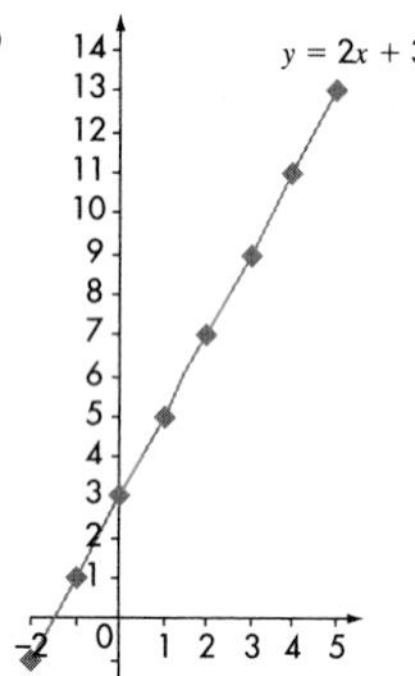

12.1 Linear graphs

Exercise 12A

1 $y = 3x + 4$

2 $y = 2x - 5$

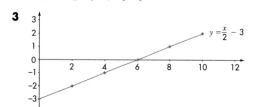

3 $y = \frac{x}{2} - 3$

4

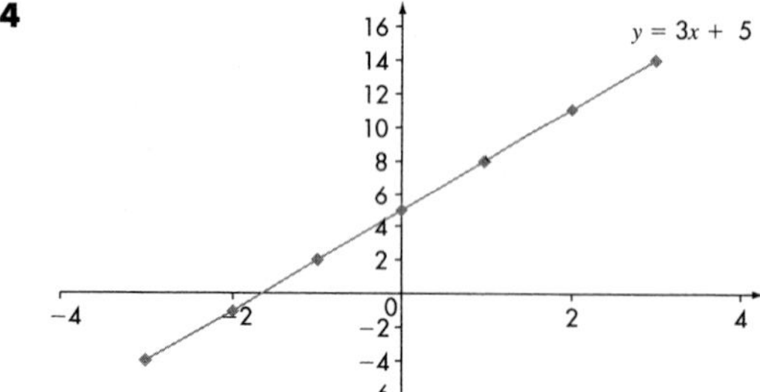

5

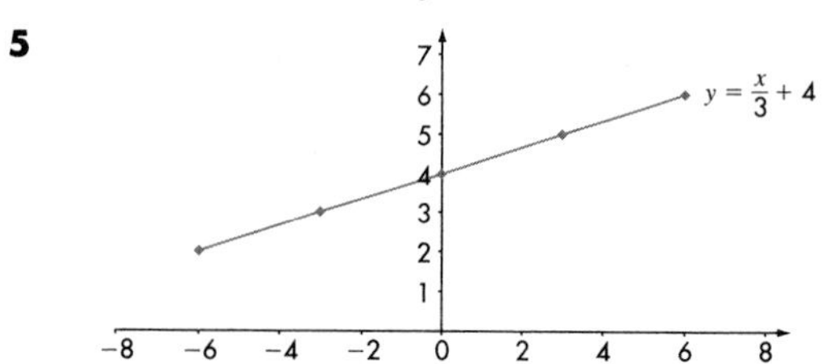

6 **a**

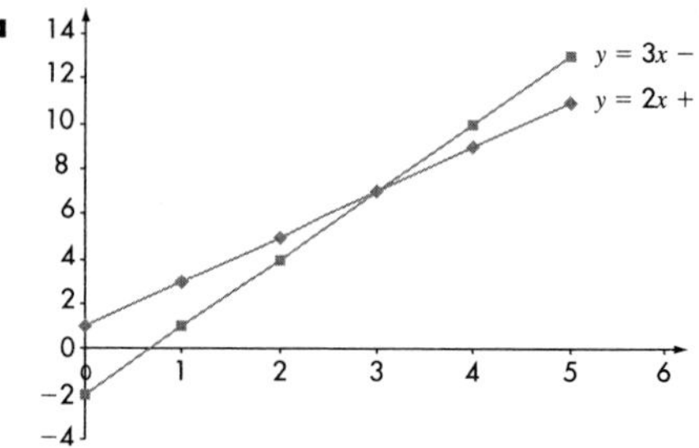

b (3, 7)

7 **a**

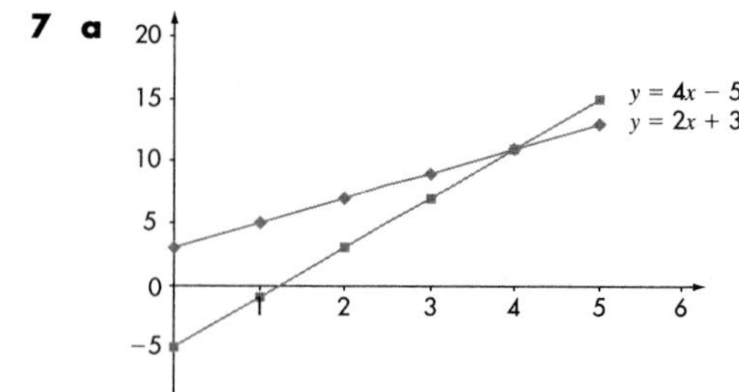

b (4, 11)

8 **a**

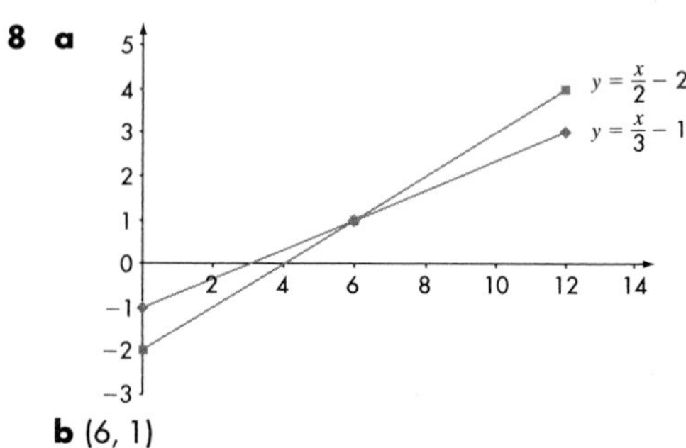

b (6, 1)

9 **a**

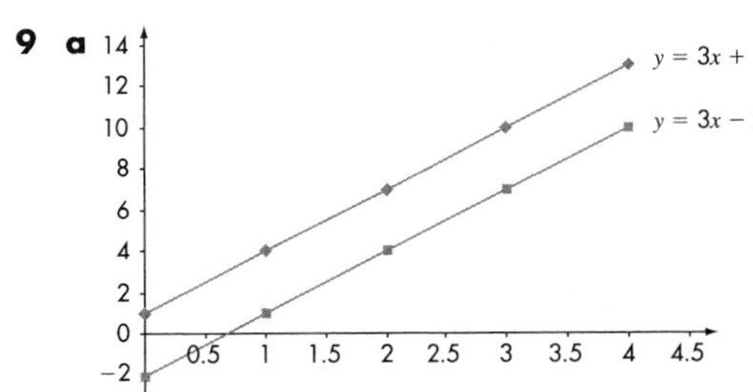

b No, because the lines are parallel

10

x	0	1	2	3	4	5
y	5	4	3	2	1	0

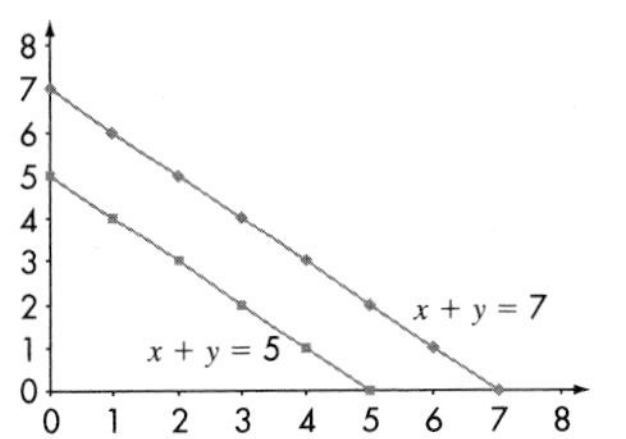

11 **a**

Ian
John

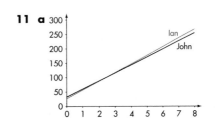

b Ian, as Ian only charges £85, whilst John charges £90 for a 2-house job.

12 **a**

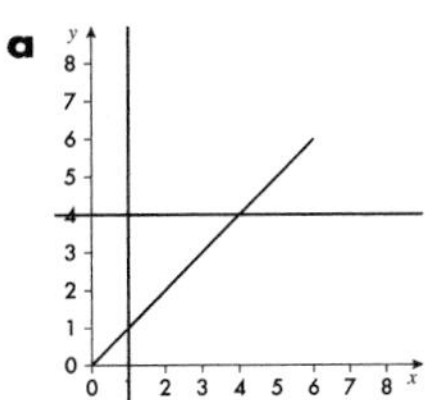

b 4.5 units squared

13

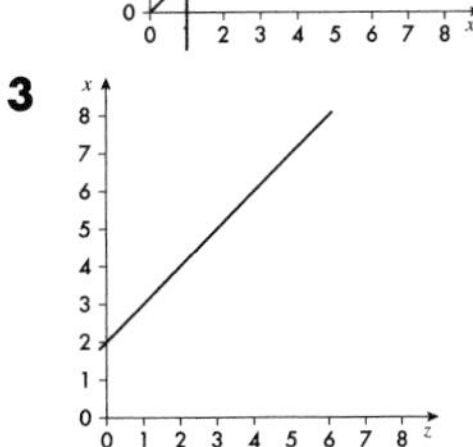

Exercise 12B

1 **a** 2 **b** $\frac{1}{3}$ **c** −3 **d** 1 **e** −2
f $-\frac{1}{3}$ **g** 5 **h** −5 **i** $\frac{1}{5}$ **j** $-\frac{3}{4}$

2

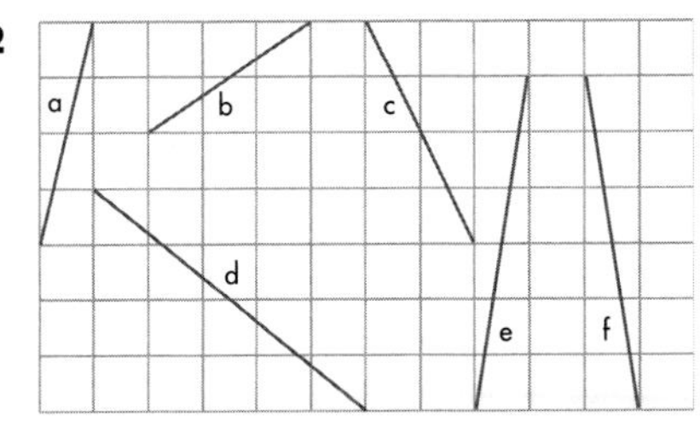

3 **a** 1
b −1. They are perpendicular and symmetrical about the axes.

4 **a** Approx. 320 feet in half a mile (2640 feet), so gradient is about 0.12.
b **i** Because the line on the graph has the steepest gradient.
ii Approximately 550 feet in half a mile so gradient is about −0.21
c BM. Approximately 1200 foot of climbing in 6.3 miles ≈ 190 feet of ascent on average

5 **a** 0.5 **b** 0.4 **c** 0.2 **d** 0.1 **e** 0

6 **a** $1\frac{2}{3}$ **b** 2 **c** $3\frac{1}{3}$ **d** 10 **e** ∞

7 Raisa has misread the scales. The second line has four times the gradient (2.4) of the first (0.6).

8 6 : 4, 8 : 5, 5 : 3, 11 : 6, 2 : 1, 5 : 2

12.2 Drawing graphs by the gradient-intercept method

Exercise 12C

1 **a, b, c, d**

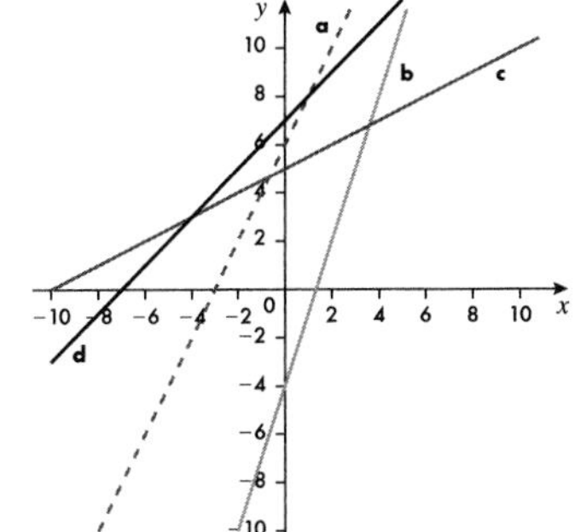

e, f, g, h

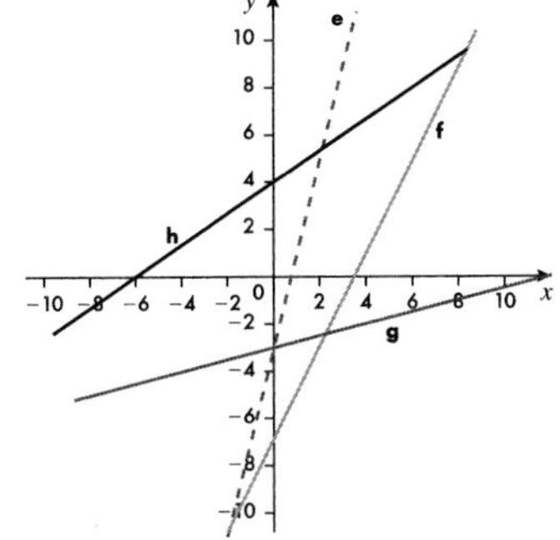

i, j, k, l

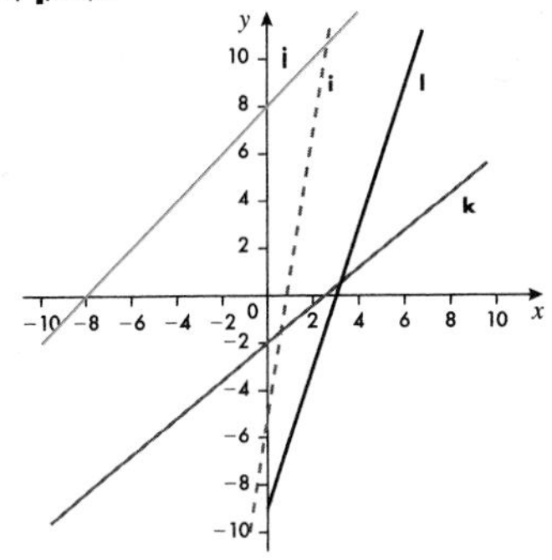

2 a

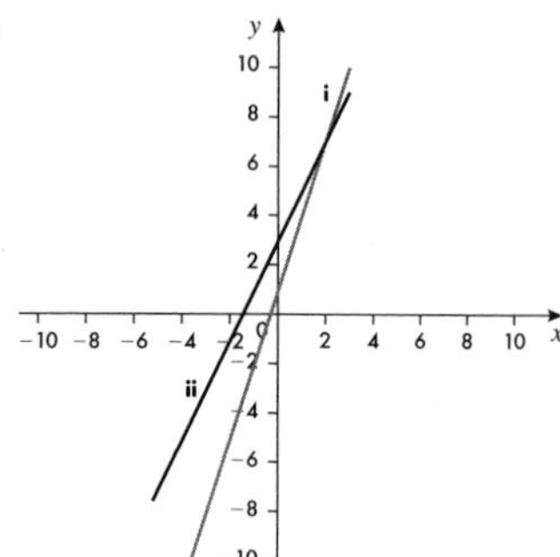

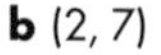

b (2, 7)

3 a

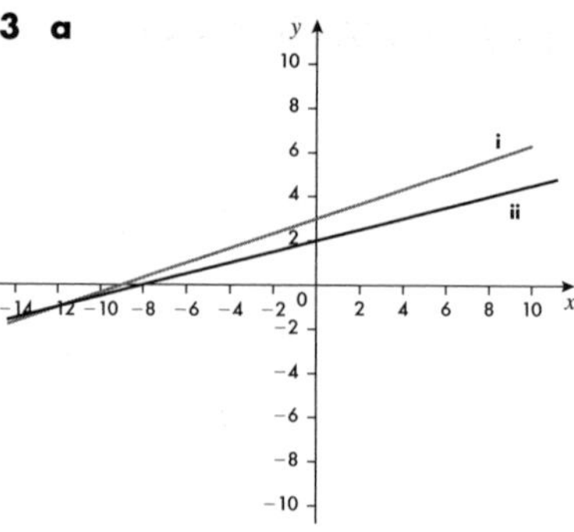

b (−12, −1)

4 a

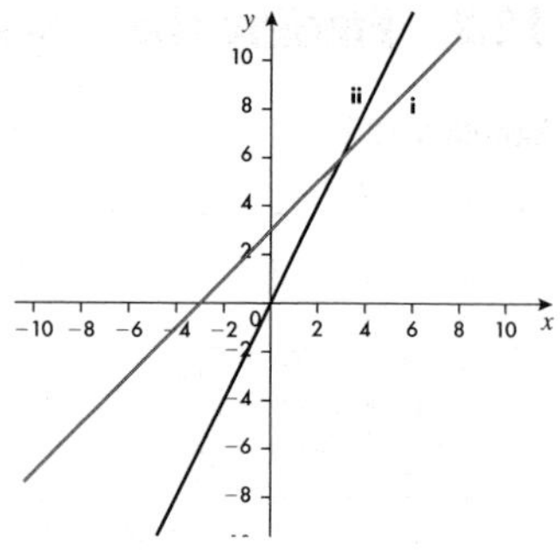

b (3, 6)

5 **a** They have the same gradient (3).
b They intercept the y-axis at the same point (0, −2).
c (−1, −4)

6 **a** −2 **b** $\frac{1}{2}$ **c** 90°
d Negative reciprocal **e** $-\frac{1}{3}$

Exercise 12D

1 a, b, c, d

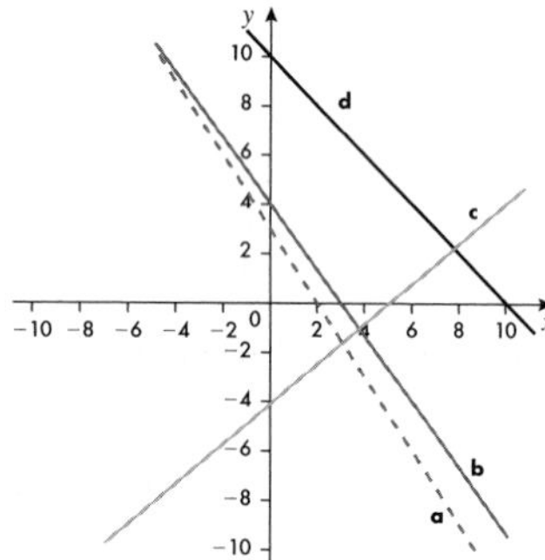

e, f, g, h

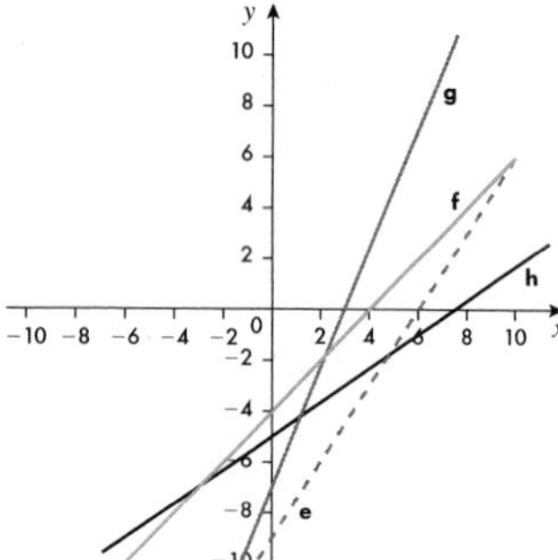

i, j, k, l

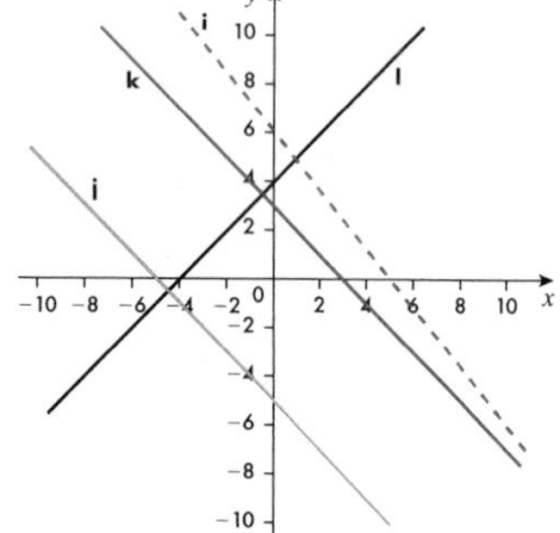

2 a

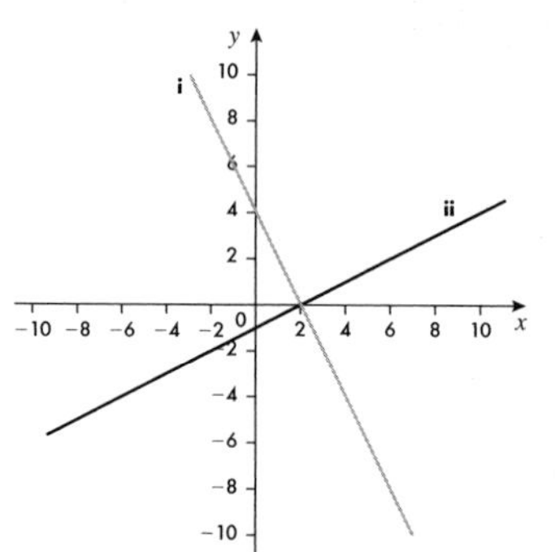

b (2, 0)

3 a

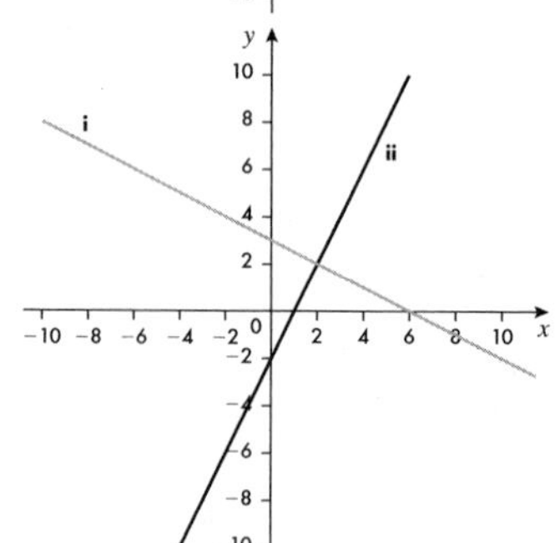

b (2, 2)

4 a

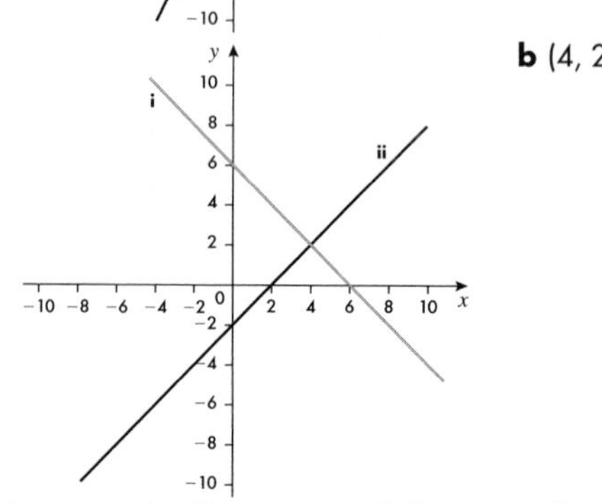

b (4, 2)

5 **a** Intersect at (6, 0) **b** Intersect at (0, −3)
c Parallel **d** $-2x + 9y = 18$

6 **a** **i** $x = 3$ **ii** $x - y = 4$ **iii** $y = -3$
iv $x + y = -4$ **v** $x = -3$ **vi** $y = x + 4$
b **i** −3 **ii** $\frac{1}{3}$ **iii** $-\frac{1}{3}$

12.3 Finding the equation of a line from its graph

Exercise 12E

1 **a** $y = \frac{4}{3}x - 2$ or $3y = 4x - 6$ **b** $y = x + 1$
c $y = 2x - 3$ **d** $2y = x + 6$
e $y = x$ **f** $y = 2x$

2 **a** **i** $y = 2x + 1$, $y = -2x + 1$
ii Reflection in y-axis (and $y = 1$)
iii Different sign
b **i** $5y = 2x - 5$, $5y = -2x - 5$
ii Reflection in y-axis (and $y = -1$)
iii Different sign
c **i** $y = x + 1$, $y = -x + 1$
ii Reflection in y-axis (and $y = 1$)
iii Different sign

3 **a** x-coordinates go from $2 \to 1 \to 0$ and y-coordinates go from $5 \to 3 \to 1$.
b x-step between the points is 1 and y-step is 2.
c $y = 3x + 2$

4 **a** $y = -2x + 1$
b $2y = -x$
c $y = -x + 1$
d $5y = -2x - 5$
e $y = -\frac{3}{2}x - 3$ or $2y = -3x - 6$

5 **a** **i** $2y = -x + 1$, $y = -2x + 1$
ii Reflection in $x = y$
iii Reciprocal of each other
b **i** $2y = 5x + 5$, $5y = 2x - 5$
ii Reflection in $x = y$
iii Reciprocal of each other
c **i** $y = 2$, $x = 2$
ii Reflection in $x = y$
iii Reciprocal of each other (reciprocal of zero is infinity)

12.4 Uses of graphs

Exercise 12F

1 **a** 32° F
b $\frac{9}{5}$ (Take gradient at C = 10° and 30°)
c $F = \frac{9}{5}C + 32$

2 **a** 0.07 (Take gradient at U = 0 and 500)
b £10
c C = £(10 + 0.07U) or Charge = £10 + 7p/unit

3 **a** $1900 – $1400 = $500
b **i** $7500 **ii** £3788

4

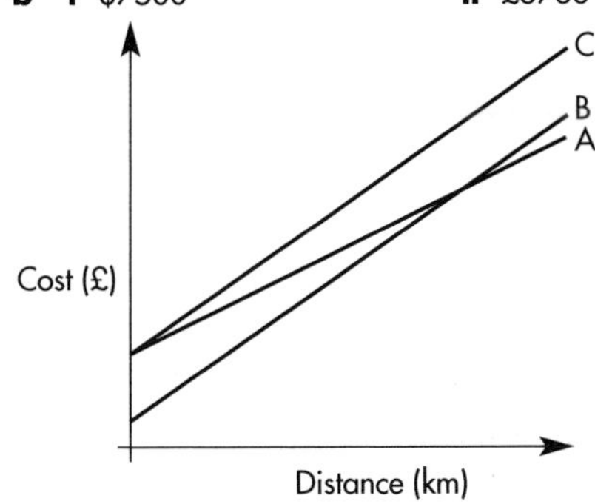

5 $y = 2x + 15$ $0 < x \leqslant 5$
$y = x + 20$ $5 < x \leqslant 12$
$y = \frac{1}{2}x + 26$ $12 < x \leqslant 25$

6 **a** $\frac{5}{2}$ (Take gradient at D = 0 and 40)
b £20
c $C = £(20 + \frac{5D}{2})$ or Charge = £20 + £2.50/day

7 **a** $\frac{1}{2}$ (Take gradient at N = 0 and 500)
b £50
c $C = £(50 + \frac{N}{2})$ or £50 + 50p/person

8 **a** $\frac{1}{10}$
b 24.5 cm
c 0.1 cm or 1 mm
d $L = 24.5 + \frac{W}{10}$ or Length = 24.5 + 1 mm/kg

Exercise 12G

1 (4, 1)
2 (2, 3)
3 (3, 10)
4 (5, 5)
5 (1, 5)
6 (3, 16)
7 (−2, 6)
8 (−6, −9)
9 (1, −1)
10 (2, 6)
11 (2, 8)
12 $(7\frac{1}{2}, 3\frac{1}{2})$
13 $x + 2y = 9.5$, $2x + y = 8.5$
Graphs intersect at (2.5, 3.5), so a cheesecake costs £2.50 and a gâteau costs £3.50.
14 **a** P and R
b R and S
c P and Q
d Q and S
e $(-\frac{2}{5}, -\frac{3}{5})$
15 (0, 0), (−3, 3), (−3, −3), (−3, 2), (−2, 2), (2, 2)

12.5 Parallel and perpendicular lines

Exercise 12H

1 **a** Line parallel to the original, intersecting the charge axis at a higher point
b Line passing through the same intersecting point on the charge axis, with a steeper gradient

2 **a** Line A does not pass through (0, 1).
b Line C is perpendicular to the other two.
c (i)

3 **a** $-\frac{1}{2}$ **b** $\frac{1}{3}$ **c** $-\frac{1}{5}$ **d** 1 **e** −2 **f** −4
g 3 **h** $\frac{3}{2}$ **i** $-\frac{2}{3}$ **j** $-\frac{1}{10}$ **k** $\frac{1}{6}$ **l** $-\frac{3}{4}$

4 **a** $y = -\frac{1}{2}x - 1$ **b** $y = \frac{1}{3}x + 1$ **c** $y = -x + 2$
d $y = x + 2$ **e** $y = -2x + 3$ **f** $y = -4x - 3$
g $y = 3x$ **h** $y = 1.5x - 5$

5 **a** $y = 4x + 1$ **b** $y = \frac{1}{2}x - 2$ **c** $y = -x + 3$

6 **a** $y = -\frac{1}{3}x - 1$ **b** $y = 3x + 5$ **c** $y = -x + 1$

7 **a** $y = -x + 14$ **b** $y = x + 2$

8 $y = 2x + 6$

9 $y = -\frac{1}{4}x + 2$

10 **a** (0, −20) **b** $y = -\frac{1}{5}x + 6$ **c** $y = 5x - 20$

11 $y = -\frac{1}{2}x + 5$

12 **a** $y = 3x - 6$
b Bisector of AB is $y = -2x + 9$, bisector of AC is $y = \frac{1}{2}x + \frac{3}{2}$, solving these equations shows the lines intersect at (3, 3).
c (3, 3) lies on $y = 3x - 6$ because $(3 \times 3) - 6 = 3$

13 $y = 2x + \frac{9}{2}$

Examination questions

1 **a**

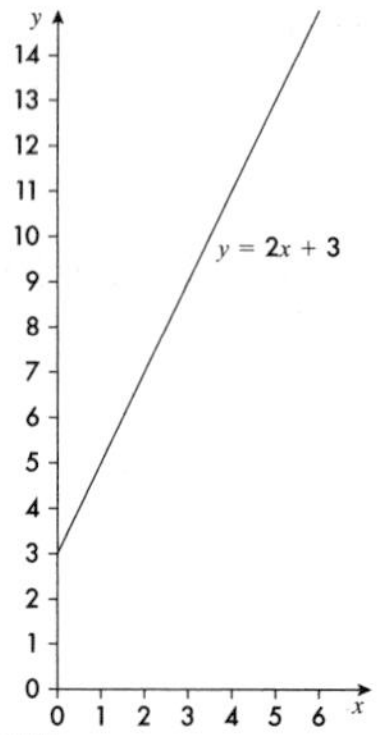

$y = 2x + 3$

b 1.75

2

$y = 3x + 1$
b $y = x + 1$
a $y = 1$

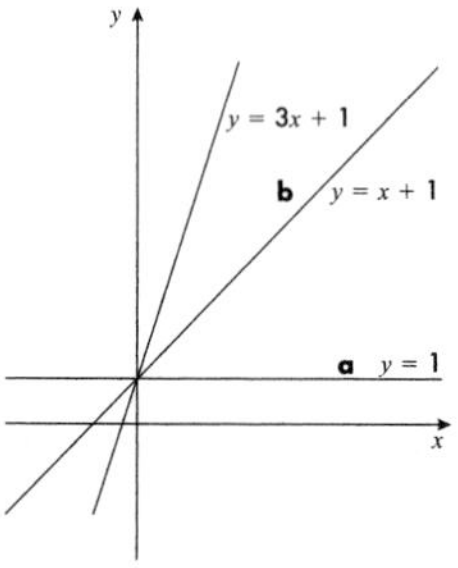

3 **a** $y = -3x + 9$
b −9
c $\frac{1}{3}$

4 **a** i and iv
b ii and v
c iv and vi

5 $y = -2x + 5$

6 $3y = 9 - 5x$

7 $2y = 10 - x$

8 $y = 3x + 3$

9 $y = 16 - 2x$

10 (2, 1)

Answers to Chapter 13

Quick check

1 **a** 17, 20, 23 **b** 49, 64, 81

2 **a** 1 **b** 4 **c** 7

3 **a** $2(x + 3)$ **b** $x(x - 1)$ **c** $2x(5x + 1)$

4 **a** $x^2 + 8x + 12$ **b** $2x^2 - 5x - 3$ **c** $x^2 - 4x + 4$

5 **a** $x = 3 - 2y$ **b** $x = 4 + 3y$ **c** $x = 4y - 3$

13.1 Number sequences

Exercise 13A

1 **a** 21, 34: add previous 2 terms
b 49, 64: next square number
c 47, 76: add previous 2 terms
2 15, 21, 28, 36
3 61, 91, 127
4 $\frac{1}{2}, \frac{3}{5}, \frac{2}{3}, \frac{5}{7}, \frac{3}{4}$
5 **a** 6, 10, 15, 21, 28
b It is the sums of the natural numbers, or the numbers in Pascal's triangle or the triangular numbers.
6 **a** 2, 6, 24, 720 **b** 69!
7 X. There are 351 (1 + 2 + ... + 25 + 26) letters from A to Z. 3 × 351 = 1053. 1053 − 26 = 1027, 1027 − 25 = 1002, so, as Z and Y are eliminated, the 1000th letter must be X.
8 364: Daily totals are 1, 3, 6, 10, 15, 21, 28, 36, 45, 55, 66, 78 (these are the triangular numbers). Cumulative totals are: 1, 4, 10, 20, 35, 56, 84, 120, 165, 220, 286, 364.
9 29 and 41
10 No, because in the first sequence, the terms are always one less than in the 2nd sequence
11 $4n - 2 = 3n + 7$ rearranges as $4n - 3n = 7 + 2$, so $n = 9$

13.2 Finding the nth term of a linear sequence

Exercise 13B

1 **a** 13, 15, $2n + 1$ **b** 25, 29, $4n + 1$ **c** 33, 38, $5n + 3$
d 32, 38, $6n - 4$ **e** 20, 23, $3n + 2$ **f** 37, 44, $7n - 5$
g 21, 25, $4n - 3$ **h** 23, 27, $4n - 1$ **i** 17, 20, $3n - 1$
j 42, 52, $10n - 8$ **k** 24, 28, $4n + 4$ **l** 29, 34, $5n - 1$
2 **a** $3n + 1$, 151 **b** $2n + 5$, 105 **c** $5n - 2$, 248
d $4n - 3$, 197 **e** $8n - 6$, 394 **f** $n + 4$, 54
g $5n + 1$, 251 **h** $8n - 5$, 395 **i** $3n - 2$, 148
j $3n + 18$, 168 **k** $7n + 5$, 355 **l** $8n - 7$, 393
3 **a** 33rd **b** 30th **c** 100th = 499
4 **a** **i** $4n + 1$ **ii** 401 **iii** 101, 25th
b **i** $2n + 1$ **ii** 201 **iii** 99 or 101, 49th and 50th
c **i** $3n + 1$ **ii** 301 **iii** 100, 33rd
d **i** $2n + 6$ **ii** 206 **iii** 100, 47th
e **i** $4n + 5$ **ii** 405 **iii** 101, 24th
f **i** $5n + 1$ **ii** 501 **iii** 101, 20th
g **i** $3n - 3$ **ii** 297 **iii** 99, 34th
h **i** $6n - 4$ **ii** 596 **iii** 98, 17th
i **i** $8n - 1$ **ii** 799 **iii** 103, 13th
j **i** $2n + 23$ **ii** 223 **iii** 99 or 101, 38th and 39th
5 **a** $\frac{2n+1}{3n+1}$
b Getting closer to $\frac{2}{3}$ $(0.\dot{6})$
c **i** 0.667 774 (6dp) **ii** 0.666 778 (6dp)
d 0.666 678 (6dp), 0.666 667 (6dp)
6 **a** $\frac{4n-1}{5n+1}$
b Getting closer to $\frac{4}{5}$ (0.8)
c **i** 0.796 407 (6dp) **ii** 0.799 640 (6dp)
d 0.799 964 (6dp), 0.799 9996 (7dp)
7 **a** £305 **b** £600 **c** 3 **d** 5
8 **a** $\frac{3}{4}, \frac{5}{7}, \frac{7}{10}$
b **i** 0.666 666 7778 **ii** $\frac{2}{3}$
c for n, $\frac{2n-1}{3n-1} \approx \frac{2n}{3n} = \frac{2}{3}$
9 **a** $8n + 2$ **b** $8n + 1$ **c** $8n$ **d** £8
10 **a** Sequence goes up in 2s; first term is 2 + 29
b $n + 108$
c Because it ends up as $2n \div n$
d 79th

13.3 Special sequences

Exercise 13C

1 **a** 64, 128, 256, 512, 1024
b **i** $2n - 1$ **ii** $2n + 1$ **iii** 3×2^n
2 **a** The number of zeros equals the power.
b 6
c **i** $10^n - 1$ **ii** 2×10^n
3 **a** Even,

+	Odd	Even
Odd	Even	Odd
Even	Odd	Even

b Odd,

×	Odd	Even
Odd	Odd	Even
Even	Even	Even

4 **a** $1 + 3 + 5 + 7 = 16 = 4^2$, $1 + 3 + 5 + 7 + 9 = 25 = 5^2$
b **i** 100 **ii** 56
5 **a** 28, 36, 45, 55, 66
b **i** 210 **ii** 5050
c You get the square numbers.
6 **a** Even **b** Odd **c** Odd
d Odd **e** Odd **f** Odd
g Even **h** Odd **i** Odd
7 **a** Odd or even **b** Odd or even **c** Odd or even
d Odd **e** Odd or even **f** Even
8 **a** **i** Odd **ii** Even **iii** Even
b Any valid answer, e.g. $x(y + z)$
9 11th triangular number is 66, 18th triangle number is 171
10 **a** 36, 49, 64, 81, 100
b **i** $n^2 + 1$ **ii** $2n^2$ **iii** $n^2 - 1$

13.4 General rules from given patterns

Exercise 13D

1 **a** 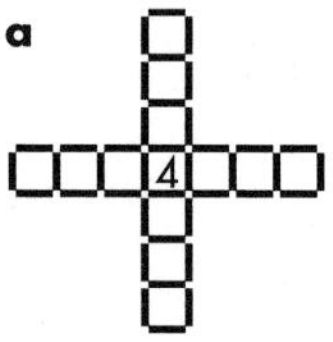

b $4n - 3$
c 97
d 50th diagram

2 **a** 
b $2n + 1$
c 121
d 49th set

3 **a** 18 **b** $4n + 2$ **c** 12

4 **a** **i** 24 **ii** $5n - 1$ **iii** 224
b 25

5 **a** **i** 20 cm **ii** $(3n + 2)$ cm **iii** 152 cm
b 332

6 **a** **i** 20 **ii** 162
b 79.8 km

7 **a** **i** 14 **ii** $3n + 2$ **iii** 41
b 66

8 **a** **i** 5 **ii** n **iii** 18
b 20 tins

9 **a** 2^n
b **i** $100 \times 2^{n-1}$ ml **ii** 1600 ml

10 The nth term is $(\frac{3}{4})^n$, so as n gets very large, the unshaded area gets smaller and smaller and eventually it will be zero; so the shaded area will eventually cover the triangle.

11 Yes, as the number of matches is 12, 21, 30, 39, … which is $9n + 3$; so he will need $9 \times 20 + 3 = 183$ matches for the 20th step and he has $5 \times 42 = 210$ matches.

12 **a** 20 **b** 120

13.5 Changing the subject of a formula

Exercise 13E

1 $-8y$

2 $-\frac{x}{8}$

3 $\frac{b + 5c}{4}$

4 $\frac{b(q + p)}{q - p}$

5 $\frac{a(q - p)}{q + p}$

6 $\frac{A}{\pi(2h + k)}$

7 $\frac{u}{\sqrt{(1 - a)}}$

8 $\frac{3 + st}{2 + s}$

9 $\frac{6 + st}{2 + s}$

10 $\frac{2R - 3}{R - 1}$

11 **a** $\frac{P}{\pi + 2k}$
b $\sqrt{\frac{2A}{\pi + \sqrt{(k^2 - 1)}}}$

12 $\frac{100A}{100 + RY}$

13 **a** $b = \frac{Ra}{a - R}$
b $a = \frac{Rb}{b - R}$

14 **a** $\frac{2 + 2y}{y - 1}$
b $y - 1 = \frac{4}{x - 2}$, $(x - 2)(y - 1) = 4$, $x - 2 = \frac{4}{y - 1}$, $x = 2 + \frac{4}{y - 1}$
c $y = 1 + \frac{4}{x - 2} = \frac{x - 2 + 4}{x - 2} = \frac{x + 2}{x - 2}$
$x = \frac{2x + 2y}{y - 1}$
d Same formulae as in **a**

15 **a** Cannot factorise the expression
b $\frac{3V}{r^2(2r + 3h)}$
c Yes, $\sqrt[3]{\frac{3V}{5\pi}}$

16 $x = \frac{2W - 2zy}{z + y}$

17 $x = \frac{1 - 3y}{2y - 5}$

The first number at the top of the answer is the constant term on the top of the original. The coefficient of y at the top of the answer is the negative constant term on the bottom of the original. The coefficient of y at the bottom of the answer the coefficient of x on the bottom of the original. The constant term on the bottom is negative the coefficient of x on the top of the original.

18 **a** $b^2 = c^2 + a^2 - 2ac \cos B$
b $\cos C = \frac{a^2 + b^2 - c^2}{2ab}$

13.6 Algebraic fractions

Exercise 13F

1 **a** $\frac{5x}{6}$
b $\frac{19x}{20}$
c $\frac{23x}{20}$
d $\frac{3x + 2y}{6}$
e $\frac{x^2y + 8}{4x}$
f $\frac{5x + 7}{6}$
g $\frac{7x + 3}{4}$
h $\frac{13x + 5}{15}$
i $\frac{3x + 1}{4}$
j $\frac{5x - 10}{4}$

2 **a** $\frac{x}{6}$
b $\frac{11x}{20}$
c $\frac{7x}{20}$
d $\frac{3x - 2y}{6}$
e $\frac{xy^2 - 8}{4y}$
f $\frac{x - 1}{6}$
g $\frac{x + 1}{4}$
h $\frac{-7x - 5}{15}$
i $\frac{x - 1}{4}$
j $\frac{2 - 3x}{4}$

3 **a** 3
b 6
c 2
d 5
e 0.75
f 3

4 **a** $\frac{x^2}{6}$
b $\frac{3xy}{14}$
c $\frac{8}{3}$
d $\frac{2xy}{3}$
e $\frac{x^2 - 2x}{10}$
f $\frac{1}{6}$
g $\frac{6x^2 + 5x + 1}{8}$
h $\frac{2x^2 + x}{15}$
i $\frac{2x - 4}{x - 3}$
j $\frac{1}{2x}$

5 **a** $\frac{3}{2}$
b $\frac{x}{y}$
c $\frac{8}{3}$
d $\frac{2xy}{3}$
e $\frac{5x}{2x - 4}$
f $\frac{2x^2 - 12x + 18}{75}$
g 1

h $\frac{1}{4x+2}$
i $\frac{x^2-5x+6}{48}$
j $\frac{1}{2x}$

6 **a** x
b $\frac{x}{2}$
c $\frac{3x^2}{16}$
d 3

e $\frac{17x+1}{10}$
f $\frac{13x+9}{10}$
g $\frac{3x^2-5x-2}{10}$
h $\frac{x+3}{2}$
i $\frac{2}{3}$
j $\frac{2x^2-6y^2}{9}$

7 All parts: students' own working

8 First, he did not factorise and just cancelled the x^2s. Then he cancelled 2 and 6 with the wrong signs. Then he said two minuses make a plus when adding, which is not true.

9 $\frac{2x^2+x-3}{4x^2-9}$

10 **a** 3, −1.5
b 4, −1.25
c 3, −2.5
d 0, 1

11 **a** $\frac{x-1}{2x+1}$
b $\frac{2x+1}{x+3}$
c $\frac{2x-1}{3x-2}$
d $\frac{x+1}{x-1}$
e $\frac{2x+5}{4x-1}$

13.7 Linear and non-linear simultaneous equations

Exercise 13G

1 **a** (5, −1)
b (4, 1)
c (8, −1)

2 **a** (1, 2) and (−2, −1)
b (−4, 1) and (−2, 2)

3 **a** (3, 4) and (4, 3)
b (0, 3) and (−3, 0)
c (3, 2) and (−2, 3)

4 **a** (2, 5) and (−2, −3)
b (−1, −2) and (4, 3)
c (3, 3) and (1, −1)

5 **a** (−3, −3), (1, 1)
b (3, −2), (−2, 3)
c (−2, −1), (1, 2)
d (2, −1), (3, 1)
e (−2, 1), (3, 6)
f (1, −4), (4, 2)
g (4, 5), (−5, −4)

6 **a** (1, 0)
b **iii** as the straight line just touches the curve

7 **a** (−2, 1)
b **i** (2, 1)
ii (−2, −1)
iii (2, −1)

8 **a** (2, 4)
b (1, 0)
c The line is a tangent to the curve.

13.8 Algebraic proof

Exercise 13H

1 **a** Odd, yes
b $(2n+1)+2m=2(n+m)+1$, which is odd.

2 Check students' proofs.

3 **a** 3, 5, 8, 13, 21, 34, 55
b $3a+5b$, $5a+8b$, $8a+13b$, $13a+21b$, $21a+34b$
c $(8a+13b)-(2a+3b)=6a+10b=2(3a+5b)$

4 Check students' answers.

5 **a** **i** 10
b–d Check students' proofs.

6–15 Check students' proofs.

Exercise 13I

1–7 Check students' proofs.

8 $(2x+1)^2-(x-1)^2=4x^2+4x+1-(x^2-2x+1)$
$=4x^2+4x+1-x^2+2x-1=3x^2+6x=3x(x+2)$
$=(2x+1+x-1)(2x-1-(x-1))$

9 **a** $10^2=100$, $1+8+27+64=100$
b $(\frac{1}{2}n(n+1))^2=\frac{1}{4}n^2(n+1)^2$

Examination questions

1 **a** 5
b $\frac{1}{2}$

Working to be shown

2 **a** $5n-1$
b 1.4, 1.5, 1.57 …

3 $u=\frac{2s-vt}{t}$

4 7.25

5 11

6 **a** $x=\frac{a-bc^2}{c^2}$ **b** $p=-10$, $q=-8$

7 $x=\frac{a^2+ab}{a-b}$

8 **a** $2(2a-5)(2a+5)$
b $\frac{2x-5}{2x+1}$

9 0 and $\frac{1}{6}$

10 $a=\frac{2(A-bh)}{b+h}$

11 $x=\frac{1}{y}+2$ or $\frac{1+2y}{y}$

12 $\frac{2x+3}{x+6}$

13 **a** $x^2+(x+4)^2=26$, $x^2+x^2+8x+16=26$, $2x^2+8x-10=0$
b (−5, −1), (1, 5)

14 (5, 1) and (−3, −3)

Answers to Chapter 14

Quick check

1 **a** 8 **b** 10

2 **a**

b

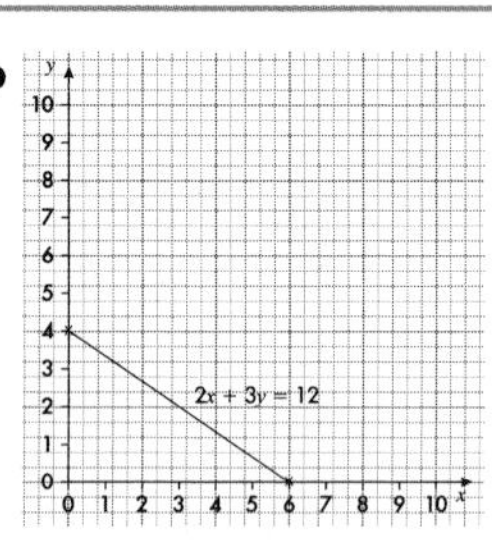

14.1 Solving inequalities

Exercise 14A

1 **a** $x < 3$ **b** $t > 8$ **c** $p \geqslant 10$ **d** $x < 5$
e $y \leqslant 3$ **f** $t > 5$ **g** $x < 6$ **h** $y \leqslant 15$
i $t \geqslant 18$ **j** $x < 7$ **k** $x \leqslant 3$ **l** $t \geqslant 5$

2 **a** 8 **b** 6 **c** 16 **d** 3 **e** 7

3 **a** 11 **b** 16 **c** 16

4 $2x + 3 < 20$, $x < 8.50$, so the most each could cost is £8.49

5 **a** Because $3 + 4 = 7$, which is less than the third side of length 8
b $x + x + 2 > 10$, $2x + 2 > 10$, $2x > 8$, $x > 4$, so smallest value of x is 5

6 **a** $x = 6$ and $x < 3$ scores -1 (nothing in common), $x < 3$ and $x > 0$ scores $+1$ (1 in common for example), $x > 0$ and $x = 2$ scores $+1$ (2 in common), $x = 2$ and $x \geqslant 4$ scores -1 (nothing in common), so we get $-1 + 1 + 1 - 1 = 0$
b $x > 0$ and $x = 6$ scores $+1$ (6 in common), $x = 6$ and $x \geqslant 4$ scores $+1$ (6 in common), $x \geqslant 4$ and $x = 2$ scores -1 (nothing in common), $x = 2$ and $x < 3$ scores $+1$ (2 in common). $+1 + 1 - 1 + 1 = 2$
c Any acceptable combination, e.g. $x = 2$, $x < 3$, $x > 0$, $x \geqslant 4$, $x = 6$

7 **a** $x \geqslant -6$ **b** $t \leqslant \frac{8}{3}$ **c** $y \leqslant 4$
d $x \geqslant -2$ **e** $w \leqslant 5.5$ **f** $x \leqslant \frac{14}{5}$

8 **a** $x \leqslant 2$ **b** $x > 38$ **c** $x < 6\frac{1}{2}$
d $x \geqslant 7$ **e** $t > 15$ **f** $y \leqslant \frac{7}{5}$

9 **a** $3 < x < 6$ **b** $2 < x < 5$ **c** $-1 < x \leqslant 3$
d $1 \leqslant x < 4$ **e** $2 \leqslant x < 4$ **f** $0 \leqslant x \leqslant 5$

Exercise 14B

1 **a** $x > 1$
b $x \leqslant 3$
c $x < 2$
d $x \geqslant -1$
e $x \leqslant -1$
f $x \geqslant 1$

2 **a** **b** **c** **d** **e** **f** **g** **h**

3 **a** $x \geqslant 4$
b $x < -2$
c $x \geqslant 3.5$
d $x < -1$
e $x < 1.5$
f $x \leqslant -2$
g $x > 50$
h $x \geqslant -6$

4 **a** Because 3 apples plus the chocolate bar cost more that £1.20: $x > 22$
b Because 2 apples plus the chocolate bar left Max with at least 16p change: $x \leqslant 25$
c

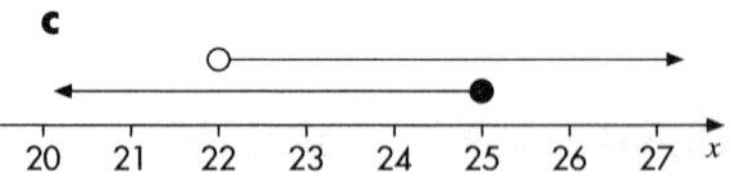

d Apples could cost 23p, 24p or 25p.

5 Any two inequalities that overlap only on the integers -1, 0, 1 and 2 – for example, $x \geqslant -1$ and $x < 3$

6 1 and 4

7 **a** $x > 2$
b $x \geqslant 6$
c $x \leqslant -1$

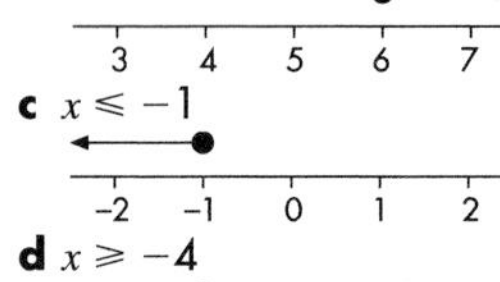

d $x \geqslant -4$

14.2 Graphical inequalities

Exercise 14C

1

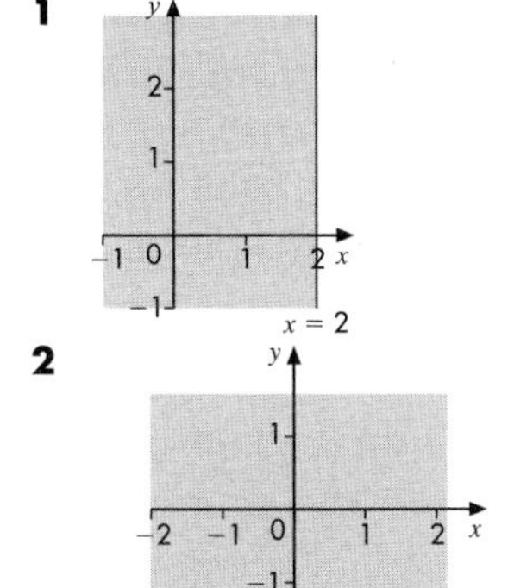

2

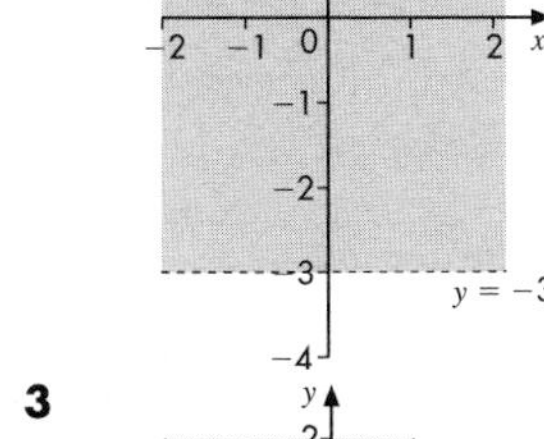

3

4

5 a

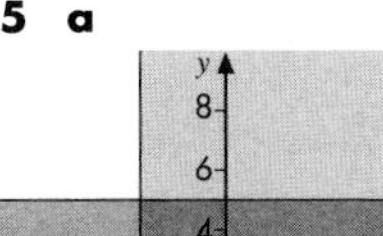

b **i** Yes **ii** Yes **iii** No

6

7

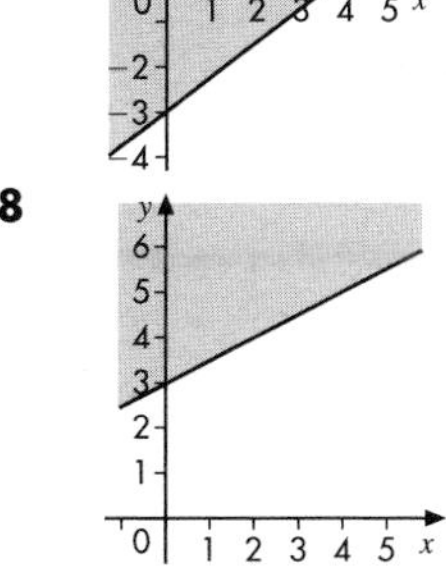

8

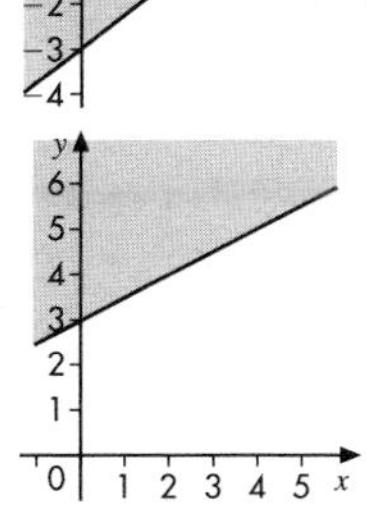

9

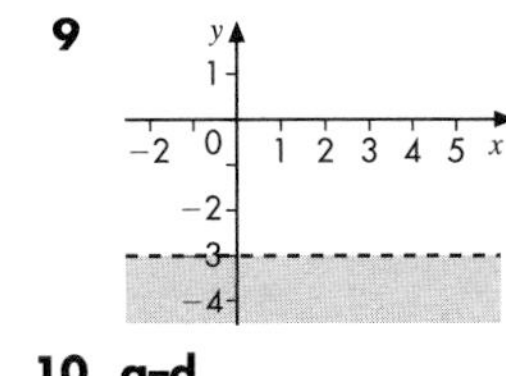

10 a–d

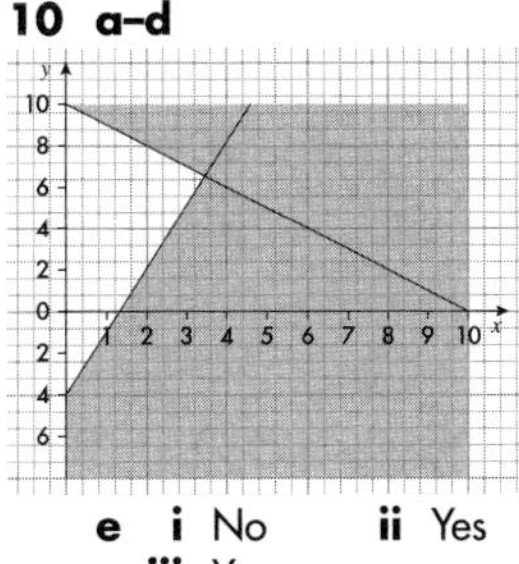

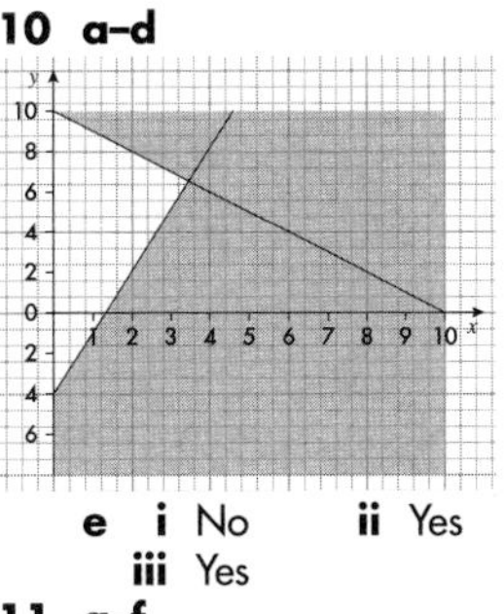

e **i** No **ii** Yes **iii** Yes

11 a–f

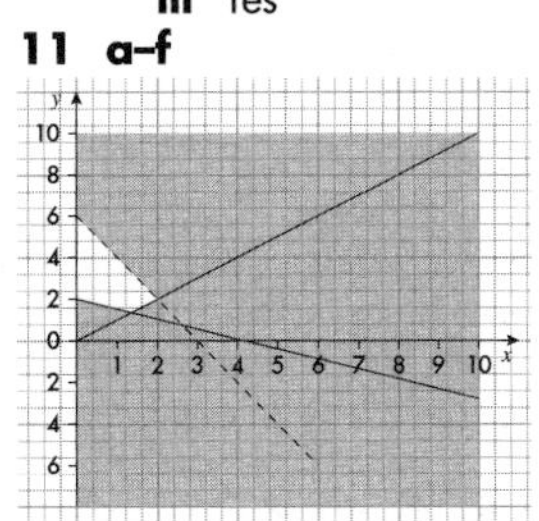

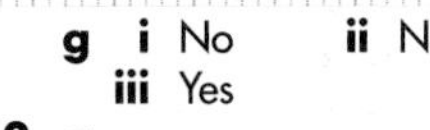

g **i** No **ii** No **iii** Yes

12 a

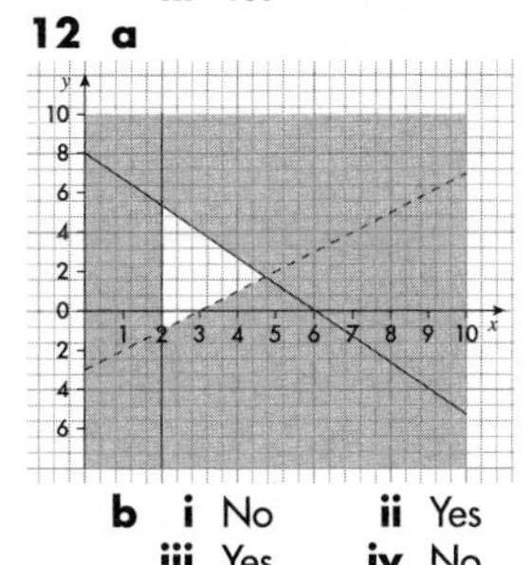

b **i** No **ii** Yes **iii** Yes **iv** No

13 For example, $x \geqslant 1$, $y \leqslant 3$ and $y \geqslant x + 1$. There are many other valid answers.

14 May be true: a, c, d, g
Must be false: b, e
Must be true: f, h

15 Test a point such as the origin (0, 0), so $0 < 0 + 2$, which is true. So the side that includes the origin is the required side.

16 **a** (3, 0) **b** (4, 5)

Examination questions

1 $x \leqslant 1.4$

2 **a** $x \leqslant 5$ **b** A line with a solid circle from -2 to 3

3 **a** $x \leqslant -1$ **b** $y > -3$
c Top side shaded; test a point such as the origin $0 \leqslant 12$

4 **a** $x > 2$
b

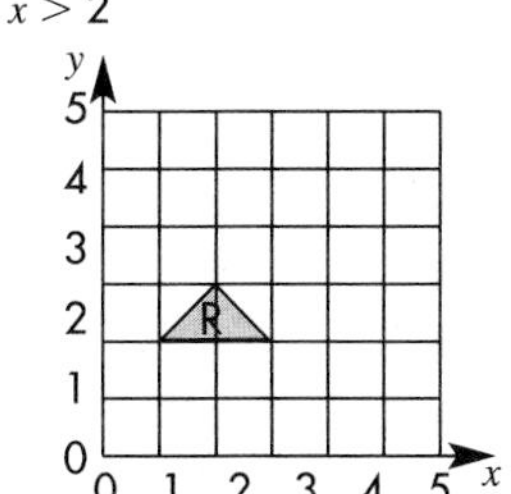

5 Region 1 is graph D, Region 2 is graph C, Region 3 is graph E, region 4 is graph A.

and In solving probability problems, if two events occur, A and B, the probability of them both occurring is P(A) × P(B).

annual rate The annual rate of interest is the percentage interest received or charged for one year.

approximate An inexact value that is accurate enough for the current situation.

average speed A single value that represents the speed achieved during a journey. The speed of the whole journey if it had been completed at constant speed.

axis (plural: axes) A fixed line used for reference, along or from which distances or angles are measured. A pair of coordinate axes is shown.

balance the coefficients The first step to solving simultaneous equations is to make the coefficients of one of the variables the same. This is called balancing the coefficients.

boundary When drawing a graph of an inequality first consider the equality. This line forms the limit or boundary of the inequality. When a strict inequality is stated ($<$ or $>$), the boundary line should be drawn as a dashed line to show that it is not included in the range of values. When $\leqslant$ or $\geqslant$ are used, the boundary line should be drawn as a solid line to show that the boundary is included.

box plot Or box-and-whisker plot. This is a way of displaying data for comparison. It requires five pieces of data; lowest value, the lower quartile (Q1), the median (Q2), the upper quartile (Q3), and the highest value.

brackets The symbols '(' and ')' which are used to separate part of an expression. This may be for clarity or to indicate a part to be worked out individually. When a number and/or value is placed immediately before an expression or value inside a pair of brackets, the two are to be multiplied together. For example, $6a(5b + c) = 30ab + 6ac$.

cancel A fraction can be simplified to an equivalent fraction by dividing the numerator and denominator by a common factor. This is called cancelling.

check Calculations can be checked by carrying out the inverse operation. Solutions to equations can be checked by substituting values of the variable(s).

class interval The size or spread of the measurement defining a class. For example, heights could be grouped in 1 cm or 10 cm class intervals.

coefficient The number in front of an unknown quantity (the letter) in an algebraic term. For example, in $8x$, 8 is the coefficient of x.

column method (or traditional method) A method of calculating a 'long multiplication' by multiplying the number by the value of each digit of the multiplier and displaying the results in columns before adding them together to find the result.

combined events Two or more events (independent or mutually exclusive) that may occur during a trial.

common factor A common factor is a factor that is common to two or more numbers. (See also *factor*, *highest common factor* and *lowest common factor*.)

common unit Express two or more quantities in the same unit, for the purpose of comparison or use in calculations. For example, if one time is given in hours and another in days, they need to be converted to a 'common unit' before they can be compared or used in a calculation.

completing the square A method of solving quadratic equations which involves rewriting the equation: $x^2 + px + q$ in the form $(x + a)^2 + b$.

compound interest Instead of interest being calculated once at the end of the term, it is calculated annually (or monthly or daily) and added to the principal (initial amount) before the next period starts. This has the effect of increasing the amount of interest earned or owed above that calculated by using simple interest.

conditional probability This describes the situation when the probability of an event is dependent upon the outcome of another event. For example, the probability of the colour of a second ball drawn from a bag is conditional to the colour of the first ball drawn from the bag — if the first ball is not replaced.

consecutive Next to each other. For example, Monday and Tuesday are consecutive days, 7 and 8 are consecutive numbers.

constant term A term in an algebraic expression that does not change because it does not contain a variable, the number term. For example, in $6x^2 + 5x + 7$, 7 is the constant term.

continuous data Data that can be measured rather than counted, such as weight and height. It can have an infinite number of values within a range.

cover-up method To plot a straight line graph, only two points need to be known. (Finding a third point acts as a check.) The easiest points to find are those when $x = 0$ and $y = 0$. By covering over the x and y terms, you can easily see what the associated values of y and x are.

cross-multiply A method for taking the denominator from one side of an equals sign to the numerator on the other side of the equals sign. You are actually multiplying both sides of the equation by the denominator, but it cancels out on the original side. (Take care that you multiply all the terms by the denominator.)

cube roots The original number that was raised to the power of three (see also *cubes*). For example, the cube root of 8 is 2 (because 2 × 2 × 2 = 8).

cubes 1. A 3-D shape with six identical square faces.
2. The result of raising a number to the power of three. For example, 'two cubed' is written: 2^3, which is 2 × 2 × 2 = 8.

cumulative frequency Can be found by adding each frequency to the sum of all preceding frequencies.

cumulative frequency diagram A graph where the value of the variable is plotted against the total frequency so far. The last plot will show the total frequency.

data collection sheet A form or table that is used for recording data collected during a survey.

decimal place Every digit in a number has a place value (hundreds, tens, ones, etc.). The places after (to the right of) the decimal point have place values of tenths, hundredths, etc. These place values are called the decimal places.

decimal point A dot which is placed between the units and tenths column in a decimal number. Each column which is to the right of the decimal point is a decimal place.

denominator The number under the line in a fraction. It tells you the denomination, name or family of the fraction. For example, a denominator of 3 tells that you are thinking about thirds; the whole thing has been divided into three parts.

difference The result of the subtraction of two numbers; the amount by which one number is greater than another number.

difference of two squares The result $a^2 - b^2 = (a - b)(a + b)$ is called the difference of two squares.

discrete data Data that is counted, rather than measured, such as favourite colour or a measurement that occurs in integer values, such as a number of days. It can only have specific values within a range.

dispersion Another name for the interquartile range.

distance The separation (usually along a straight line) of two points.

distance–time graph A graph showing the variation of the distance of an object from a given point during an interval of time. Usually, time is measured along the horizontal axis, and distance is measured up the vertical axis.

do the same to both sides To keep an equation balanced, you must do the same thing to both sides. If you add something to one side, you must add the same thing to the other side. If you double one side, you must double the other side, etc. If you are manipulating a fraction, you must do the same thing to the numerator and the denominator to keep the value of fraction unchanged. However you can only multiply or divide the numbers. Adding or subtracting will alter the value of the fraction.

either One or the other.

eliminate To get rid of.

equation A number sentence where one side is equal to the other. An equation always contains an equals sign (=).

equivalent fraction An equivalent fraction is a fraction that can be cancelled down to the same value, such as: $\frac{10}{20} = \frac{5}{20} = \frac{1}{2}$.

estimated mean A mean value obtained from a frequency chart or table of values where data is gathered in classes.

estimation The value of an estimate.

even Integers that have 2 as a factor. Even numbers are multiples of 2: i.e. 2, 4, 6, 8, …

exact values An alternative name for surds.

exhaustive events The events giving all possible outcomes of a trial, so that their probabilities add up to 1.

expand Make bigger. Expanding brackets means you must multiply the terms inside a bracket by the number or letters outside. This will take more room to write, so you have 'expanded' the expression.

expectation This is when you know the probability of an event, and you can predict how many times you would expect that event to happen in a certain number of trials.

experimental probability The probability found by a series of trials or experiment. It will be an estimate of the 'true' probability.

expression Collection of symbols representing a number. These can include numbers, variables (x, y, etc.), operations (+, ×, etc.), functions (squaring, cosine, etc.), but there will be no equals sign (=).

factor A whole number that divides exactly into a given number. For example, factors of 30 are 1, 2, 3, 5, 6, 10, 15 and 30. Or, a number or term that divides exactly into an algebraic expression.

factorisation (noun) Finding one or more factors of a given number or expression. (verb: factorise)

final amount The amount after working out, for example, the percentage.

formula (plural: formulae) An equation that enables you to convert or find a measurement from another known measurement or measurements. For example, the conversion formula from the Fahrenheit scale of temperature to the more common Celsius scale is $\frac{C}{5} = \frac{F-32}{9}$ where C is the temperature on the Celsius scale and F is the temperature on the Fahrenheit scale.

fraction A fraction means 'part of something'. To give a fraction a name, such as 'fifths' we divide the whole amount into equal parts (in this case five equal parts). A 'proper' fraction represents an amount less than one. (The numerator is smaller than the denominator.) Any two numbers or expressions can be written as a fraction, i.e. they are written as a numerator and denominator. (See also *numerator* and *denominator*.)

frequency density The vertical axis of a histogram. Frequency density = Frequency of class interval ÷ width of class interval.

frequency polygon A line graph drawn from the information given in a frequency table.

frequency table A table showing values (or classes of values) of a variable alongside the number of times each one has occurred.

gradient How steep a hill or the line of a graph is. The steeper the slope, the larger the value of the gradient. A horizontal line has a gradient of zero.

gradient-intercept The point at which the gradient of a curve or line crosses an axis.

grid method (or box method) A method of calculating a 'long multiplication' by arranging the value of each digit in a grid and multiplying them all separately before adding them together to find the result.

group Information of the same kind.

grouped data Data from a survey that is grouped into classes.

highest common factor (HCF) When all the factors of two or more numbers are found, some numbers will have factors in common (the same factors). For example, 6 has the factors 1, 2, 3 and 6. 9 has the factors 1, 3, and 9. They both have the factors 1 and 3. (1 and 3 are common factors.) The greatest of these is 3, so 3 is the highest common factor (HCF).

highest value The largest value in a range of values.

histogram A diagram, similar to a bar chart, but where quantities are represented by rectangles of different, appropriate areas.

hypothesis A theory or idea.

identity An identity is similar to an equation, but is true for all values of the variable(s). Instead of the usual equals (=) sign, ≡ is used. For example, $2x \equiv 7x - 5x$.

included A point is included in a region on a graph if it satisfies certain criteria. A boundary is included if it is defined by an equality (=) or a 'weak' inequality (⩽ or ⩾). (See also *strict inequality*.)

inclusive inequality Inequality in which the boundary value is included, such as $x \leqslant 5$, $y \geqslant 10$.

independent events Two events are independent if the occurrence of one has no influence on the occurrence of the other. For example, getting a Head when tossing a coin has no influence over scoring a 2 with a dice. Missing a bus and getting to school on time are not independent events.

index (plural: indices) A power or exponent. For example, in the expression 3^4, 4 is the index, power or exponent.

index notation A way of writing numbers (particularly factors) using indices. For example, 2700 = 2 × 2 × 3 × 3 × 3 × 5 × 5. This is written more efficiently as $2^2 \times 3^3 \times 5^2$.

indices (See *index*.)

inequality An inequality is a relation that shows that two numbers or quantities are or may be unequal. The symbols <, ⩽, ⩾, > are used. The symbols ⩽ and ⩾ include the possibility of equality.

integer A whole number. Integers include all the positive whole numbers, negative whole numbers and zero.

intercept The point where a line or graph crosses an axis.

interquartile range The difference between the values of the lower and upper quartiles.

leading question A question in a survey that is likely to encourage the interviewee to answer in certain way. For example, "Do you care about animals?" is unlikely to get a 'no' answer.

least common multiple (LCM) Also known as lowest common multiple (LCM). Every number has an infinite number of multiples. Two (or more) numbers might have some multiples in common (the same multiples). The smallest of these is called the lowest common multiple. For example, 6 has multiples of 6, 12, 18, 24, 30, 36, etc. 9 has multiples of 9, 18, 27, 36, 45, etc. They both have multiples of 18 and 36, 18 is the LCM.

like terms Terms in algebra that are the same apart from their numerical coefficients. For example: $2ax^2$ and $5ax^2$ are a pair of like terms but $5x^2y$ and $7xy^2$ are not. Like terms can be combined by adding together their numerical coefficients so $2ax2 + 5ax^2 = 7ax^2$.

limits of accuracy No measurement is entirely accurate. The accuracy depends on the tool used to measure it. The value of every measurement will be rounded to within certain limits. For example, you can probably measure with a ruler to the nearest half-centimetre. Any measurement you take could be inaccurate by up to half a centimetre. This is your limit of accuracy. (See also *lower bound* and *upper bound*.)

line graphs A graph constructed by joining a number of points together.

line of best fit When data from an experiment or survey is plotted on graph paper, the points may not lie in an exact straight line or smooth curve. You can draw a line of best fit by looking at all the points and deciding where the line should go. Ideally, there should be as many points above the line as there are below it.

linear Forming a line.

linear graphs A straight-line graph from an equation such as $y = 3x + 4$.

long division A method of division involving division by numbers with a large number of digits.

long multiplication A multiplication involving numbers with a large number of digits.

lower bound The lower limit of a measurement. (See also *limits of accuracy*.)

lower quartile The value of the item at one-quarter of the total frequency. It is the $\frac{n}{4}$th value. (See also *upper quartile*.)

lowest common denominator The lowest common multiple (LCM) of all the denominators. (See also *denominator*.)

lowest value The smallest value in a range of values.

margin of error Conclusions made from surveys and polls cannot be entirely accurate because, for example, the statistician can only interview a sample of people. The margin of error tells us how confident they are about the accuracy of their conclusion.

maximum The greatest value of something. The turning point or point at which the graph of a parabola $y = -ax^2 + bx + c$ is at its highest.

mean The mean value of a sample of values is the sum of all the values divided by the number of values in the sample. The mean is often called the average, although there are three different concepts associated with 'average': mean, mode and median.

measure of location Alternative name for 'average'.

median The middle value of a sample of data that is arranged in order. For example, the sample 3, 2, 6, 2, 2, 3, 7, 4 may be arranged in order as follows 2, 2, 2, 3, 3, 4, 6, 7. The median is the fourth value, which is 3. If there is an even number of values the median is the mean of the two middle values, for example, 2, 3, 6, 7, 8, 9, has a median of $(6 + 7) \div 2 = 6.5$.

minimum The smallest value of something. The turning point or the point at which the graph of a parabola $y = ax^2 + bx + c$ is at its lowest.

modal class If data is arranged in classes, the mode will be a class rather than a specific value. It is called the modal class.

modal group Information that is grouped in the same way.

mode The value that occurs most often in a sample. For example, the mode of the sample: 2, 2, 3, 3, 3, 3, 4, 5, 5, is 3.

multiple The multiples of a number are found by the multiplication of the number by each of 1, 2, 3, ... For example, the multiples of 10 are 10, 20, 30, 40, ...

multiplier The number used to multiply by.

mutually exclusive If the occurrence of a certain event means that another event cannot occur, the two events are mutually exclusive. For example, if you miss a bus you cannot also catch the bus.

national census The national census has been held every 10 years since 1841. Everybody in the UK has to be registered and modern censuses ask for information about things such as housing, work and certain possessions.

negative (in maths) Something less than zero. The opposite of positive. (See also *positive*.)

negative correlation If the effect of increasing one measurement is to decrease another, they are said to show negative correlation. For example, the time taken for a certain journey will have negative correlation with the speed of the vehicle. The slope of the line of best fit has a negative gradient.

negative reciprocal The reciprocal multiplied by –1. The gradients of perpendicular lines are the negative reciprocal of each other.

no correlation If the points on a scatter graph are random and do not appear to form a straight line, the two measurements show no correlation (or link, or relationship). One does not affect the other.

non-linear An expression or equation that does not form a straight line. The highest power of x, is greater than 1.

***n*th term** The general term in a sequence. The formula for the nth term describes the rule used to get any term. For example, in the number sequence 1, 3, 5, 7, 9, 11, 13, … the nth term is $2n - 1$.

number line A continuous line on which all the numbers (whole numbers and fractions; can also include negative numbers) can be shown by points at distances from zero.

odd (numbers) When referring to number sequences, odd numbers occur frequently and are useful to know, for example: 1, 3, 5, 7, 9, 11, …

or In solving probability problems, if two events occur, A or B, the probability of either of them occurring is P(A) + P(B).

order
1. Arranged according to a rule. For example, ascending order.
2. The sequence of carrying out arithmetic operations.
3. Approximate size. If a result is expected to be in the order of 500, we know it will not be 3 or 7 million.

ordered (data) Data or results arranged in ascending or descending order.

origin The point (0, 0) on Cartesian coordinate axes.

original amount The amount you start with. The amount before an increase or decrease is applied to it.

parallel Lines that are the same distance apart and will not meet.

pattern This could be geometric, where pictures or colours are arranged according to a rule, such as using symmetry. Or it could be numerical where numbers are generated according to an arithmetic rule.

percentage A number written as a fraction with 100 parts. Instead of writing /100 we use the symbol %. So $\frac{50}{100}$ is written as 50%.

percentage change Instead of stating an actual amount by which something has changed you give the percentage change. For example, if the mass of a sack of potatoes decreases from 50 kg to 49 kg, the actual change is 1 kg and the percentage change is 2%.

percentage decrease If an actual amount decreases, the percentage change will be a percentage decrease.

percentage increase If an actual amount increases, the percentage change will be a percentage increase.

percentage loss If an amount of money decreases, the percentage change will be a percentage loss.

percentage profit If an amount of money increases, the percentage change will be a percentage profit.

perpendicular At right angles to. Two perpendicular lines are at right angles to each other. A line or plane can also be perpendicular to another plane.

pie chart A chart that represents data as slices of a whole 'pie' or circle. The circle is divided into sections. The number of degrees in the angle at the centre of each section represents the frequency.

poll A collection of data gathered from a survey of a group of people. An election is a poll because each person records their wish for the outcome of the election. 'Public opinion' is gathered in polls where people state their preferences or ideas.

population All the members of a particular group. The population could be people or specific outcomes of an event.

positive (in maths) Something greater than zero. The opposite of negative (See also *positive gradient* and *negative*.)

positive correlation If the effect of increasing one measurement is to increase another, they are said to show positive correlation. For example, the time taken for a journey in a certain vehicle will have positive correlation with the distance covered. The slope of the line of best fit has a positive gradient. (See also *negative correlation*.)

power When a number or expression is multiplied by itself, the power is how many 'lots' are multiplied together, for example, $2^3 = 2 \times 2 \times 2$ (Note that it is not the number of times that 2 is multiplied by itself; it is one more than the number of times it is multiplied by itself.) The name given to the symbol to indicate this, such as 2. (See also *square* and *cube*.)

powers of 2 All the numbers that can be written as $2n$; 1, 2, 4, 8 …

powers of 10 All the numbers that can be written as $10n$; 1, 10, 100 …

primary data In data collection, primary data is data that you collect yourself. You control it, in terms of accuracy and amount.

prime factor A factor of a number that is also a prime number. (See also *prime number*.)

prime factor tree A diagram showing all the prime factors of a number. (See also *prime number*.)

prime number A number whose only factors are 1 and itself. 1 is not a prime number. 2 is the only even prime number.

principal The original amount deposited in, or borrowed from, a bank.

probability space diagram A diagram or table showing all the possible outcomes of an event.

problem A method of reasoning to solve a problem.

product The result of multiplying two or more numbers or expressions together.

product of prime factors The result of multiplying two or more prime factors together.

proof The highest level in an algebraic proof; an argument that establishes a fact about numbers or geometry for all cases. Showing that the fact is true for specific cases is a demonstration. (See also *show* and *verify*.)

quadratic expression An expression involving an x^2 term.

quantity A measurable amount of something which can be written as a number or a number with appropriate units. For example, the capacity of a bottle.

quartile One of four equal parts, formed when data is divided.

questionnaire A list of questions distributed to people so statistical information can be collected.

random Haphazard. A random number is one chosen without following a rule. Choosing items from a bag without looking means they are chosen at random; every item has an equal chance of being chosen.

ratio The ratio of A to B is a number found by dividing A by B. It is written as A : B. For example, the ratio of 1 m to 1 cm is written as 1 m : 1 cm = 100 : 1. Notice that the two quantities must both be in the same units if they are to be compared in this way.

rationalise To make into a ratio. Removing a surd from a denominator (by multiplying the numerator and denominator by that surd) is called rationalising the denominator.

rational number A rational number is a number that can be written as a fraction, for example, $\frac{1}{4}$ or $\frac{10}{3}$.

raw data Data in the form it was collected. It hasn't been ordered or arranged in any way.

rearrange (See *rearrangement*.)

rearrangement To change the arrangement of something. An equation can be rearranged using the rules of algebra to help you solve it. Data can be rearranged to help you analyse it.

reciprocal The reciprocal of any number is 1 divided by the number. The effect of finding the reciprocal of a fraction is to turn it upside down. The reciprocal of 3 is $\frac{1}{3}$, the reciprocal of $\frac{1}{4}$ is 4, the reciprocal of $\frac{10}{3}$ is $\frac{3}{10}$.

recurring decimal A decimal number that repeats forever with a repeating pattern of digits, for example $3.\dot{3}$.

region An area on a graph defined by certain rules or parameters.

relative frequency Also known as experimental probability. It is the ratio of the number of successful events to the number of trials. It is an estimate for the theoretical probability.

retail price index (RPI) A measure of the variation in the prices of retail goods and other items.

round To approximate a number so that it is accurate enough for some specific purpose. The rounded number may be used to make arithmetic easier or may be less precise than the unrounded number.

rule An alternative name for a formula.

sample The part of a population that is considered for statistical analysis. The act of taking a sample within a population is called sampling. There are two factors that need to be considered when sampling from a population:

1. The size of the sample. The sample must be large enough for the results of a statistical analysis to have any significance.
2. The way in which the sampling is done. The sample should be representative of the population.

sample space diagram (See *probability space diagram.*)

scale A scale on a diagram shows the scale factor used to make the drawing. The axes on a graph or chart will use a scale depending on the space available to display the data. For example, each division on the axis may represent 1, 2, 5, 10 or 100, etc. units.

scatter diagram A diagram of points plotted of pairs of values of two types of data. The points may fall randomly or they may show some kind of correlation.

secondary data In data collection, secondary data is data that has been collected by someone else. You have to rely on other souces for accuracy. (See also *primary data.*)

sector A region of a circle, like a slice of a pie, bounded by an arc and two radii.

sequence An ordered set of numbers that follow a rule to give the next term.

show The middle level in an algebraic proof. You are required to show that both sides of the result are the same algebraically. (See also *proof* and *verify.*)

significant figures The significance of a particular digit in a number is concerned with its relative size in the number. The first (or most) significant figure is the left-most, non-zero digit; its size and place value tell you the approximate value of the complete number. The least significant figure is the right-most digit; it tells you a small detail about the complete number. For example, if we write 78.09 to 3 significant figures we would use the rules of rounding and write 78.1.

simplest form A fraction cancelled down so it cannot be simplified any further. Or, an expression where the arithmetic is completed so that it cannot be simplified any further.

simplification To make an equation or expression easier to work with or understand by combining like terms or cancelling down. For example, $4a - 2a + 5b + 2b = 2a + 7b$ or $\frac{12}{18} = \frac{2}{3}$.

simultaneous equations Two or more equations that are true at the same time.

social statistics Information about the condition and circumstances of people. For example, data about health and employment.

solution The result of solving a mathematical problem. Solutions are often given in equation form.

solve Finding the value or values of a variable (x) that satisfy the given equation or problem.

speed How fast something moves.

square
1. A polygon with four equal sides and all the interior angles equal to 90°.
2. The result of multiplying a number by itself. For example, 52 or 5 squared is equal to $5 \times 5 = 25$.

square roots The square of a square root of number gives you the number. The square root of 9 (or $\sqrt{9}$) is 3, $3 \times 3 = 32 = 9$.

squares Or square numbers. Numbers where an array of dots form a square. Numbers obtained by squaring the whole numbers. For example, 1, 4, 9, 16, 25, … are square numbers.

standard form Also called standard index form. Standard form is a way of writing very large and very small numbers using powers of 10. A number is written as a value between 1 and 10 multiplied by a power of 10. That is, $a \times 10^n$ where $1 \leqslant a < 10$, and n is a whole number.

standard index form (See *standard form.*)

strategy A plan for solving a problem.

stratified Used in terms of sampling, for example, the population is divided into categories. The sample is then made up of members from these categories in the same proportions as they are in the population. The required sample from each category is chosen at random.

strict inequality An inequality, $<$ or $>$, that does not allow for equality. (See also *included.*)

subject The subject of a formula is the letter on its own on one side of the equals sign. For example, t is the subject of this formula: $t = 3f + 7$.

substitute When a letter in an equation, expression or formula is replaced by a number, we have substituted the number for the letter. For example, if $a = b + 2x$, and we know $b = 9$ and $x = 6$, we can write $a = 9 + 2 \times 6$. So $a = 9 + 12 = 17$.

surd A number written as $\sqrt{x}$. For example, $\sqrt{7}$.

survey A questionnaire or interview held to find data for statistical analysis.

term 1. A part of an expression, equation or formula. Terms are separated by + and – signs.
2. Each number in a sequence or arrangement in a pattern.

terminating decimal A terminating decimal can be written exactly. $\frac{33}{100}$ can be written as 0.33, but $\frac{3}{10}$ is 0.3333… (or $0.\dot{3}$) with the 3s recurring forever.

term-to-term Referred to when working out a sequence of numbers that has a rule. For example, a pattern in which each term (apart from the first) is derived from the term before it is a term-to-term sequence.

time How long something takes. Time is measured in days, hours, seconds, etc.

time series A sequence of measurements taken over a certain time.

transpose To rearrange a formula.

tree diagram A diagram to show all the possible outcomes of combined events.

trends A collection data can be analysed (for example, by drawing a time graph) so that any trend or pattern, such as falling profits, may be discovered.

trials An experiment to discover an approximation to the probability of the outcome of an event will consist of many trials where the event takes place and the outcome is recorded.

triangle numbers Numbers where an array of dots forms a triangle: 1, 3, 6, 10, 15, 21, 28, etc.

triangular numbers Numbers that can be represented by an array of dots that form a triangle/can make triangular patterns. 1, 3, 6, 10, 15, 21, 28, etc.

two-way tables A table that links two variables. One is listed in the column headers and the other in the row headers; the combination of the variables is shown in the body of the table.

upper bound The higher limit of a measurement. (See also *limits of accuracy*.)

upper quartile The value of the item at three-quarters of the total frequency. It is the $\frac{3n}{10}$th value.

unbiased Being given an equal chance; no discrimination.

unitary method A method of calculation where the value for item is found before finding the value for several items.

unordered (data) (See *raw data*.)

variable A quantity that can have many values. These values may be discrete or continuous. They are often represented by x and y in an expression.

verify The first of the three levels in an algebraic proof. Each step must be shown clearly and at this level you need to substitute numbers into the result to show how it works. (See also *proof* and *show*.)

$y = mx + c$ The general equation of a straight line. m is the gradient and c is the y-intercept.

INDEX

William Collins' dream of knowledge for all began with the publication of his first book in 1819. A self-educated mill worker, he not only enriched millions of lives, but also founded a flourishing publishing house. Today, staying true to this spirit, Collins books are packed with inspiration, innovation and practical expertise. They place you at the centre of a world of possibility and give you exactly what you need to explore it.

Collins. Freedom to teach.

Published by Collins
An imprint of HarperCollins*Publishers*
77 – 85 Fulham Palace Road
Hammersmith
London
W6 8JB

Browse the complete Collins catalogue at
www.collinseducation.com

10 9 8 7 6 5 4 3 2

ISBN-13 978-0-00-734010-1

Kevin Evans, Keith Gordon, Trevor Senior, Brian Speed and Chris Pearce assert their moral rights to be identified as the authors of this work.

British Library Cataloguing in Publication Data

A Catalogue record for this publication is available from the British Library.

Commissioned by Katie Sergeant
Project managed by Priya Govindan
Edited and proofread by Joan Miller, Karen Westall and Brian Asbury
Indexing by Esther Burd
Answers checked by Amanda Dickson
Cover design by Angela English
Content design by Nigel Jordan
Typesetting by Jordan Publishing Design
Functional maths and problem-solving pages by EMC Design and Jerry Fowler
Production by Arjen Jansen
Printed and bound by L.E.G.O. S.p.A. Italy

AQA has checked that the content and level of this publication are appropriate for its GCSE Mathematics (4360) specification.

Acknowledgements

The publishers have sought permission from AQA to reproduce questions from past GCSE Mathematics papers.

The publishers wish to thank the following for permission to reproduce photographs. Every effort has been made to trace copyright holders and to obtain their permission for the use of copyright material. The publishers will gladly receive any information enabling them to rectify any error or omission at the first opportunity.

p.6 © iStockphoto.com/claudiobaba, © iStockphoto.com/tejerophotography, © iStockphoto.com/choja, © iStockphoto.com/Viktor_Kitaykin, © iStockphoto.com/sjlocke, © iStockphoto.com/Joas, © iStockphoto.com/nullplus, © iStockphoto.com/lisafx; p.24 © BG Jazzboo (Dr); p.25 © C Angelo Gilardelli (Dr), © BR Scott Karcich (Dr), © BL Petar Neychev (Dr); p.26 © iStockphoto.com/eugeph, © iStockphoto.com/compassandcamera, © iStockphoto.com/weareadventurers, © iStockphoto.com/eyecrave, © iStockphoto.com/digitalskillet; p.58 © BG Stanko07 (Dr), A/W Jerry Fowler; p.59 © C R. Eko Bintoro (Dr), © BL Dariusz Kopestynski (Dr), © BR Weareadventurers (iS); p.60 © iStockphoto.com/romkaz; p.112–113 © SpatzPhoto/Alamy; p.114 © Christopher Small, Lamont Doherty Earth Observatory, Columbia University NYC USA, www.LDEO.columbia.edu/~small; p.144–145 © iStockphoto.com/Roob (main image), © iStockphoto.com/johnwoodcock (map); p.146 © iStockphoto.com/Lisegagne; p.196 © BG Olivier Meerson (Dr), A/W Jerry Fowler; p.197 A/W Jerry Fowler; p.198 A/W Jerry Fowler; p.212–213 ©BG Julian Addington-barker (Dr), ©TL Olena Mykhaylova (Dr); p.214 © iStockphoto.com/René Mansi/iStockphoto.com; p.232–233 © iStockphoto.com/shoobydoooo (main); © iStockphoto.com/ARTPUPPY (small), © iStockphoto.com/Daxi (small); p.264 ©BG Peter Garbet (iS); p.265 ©TL Iztok Grilic (iS), ©TC Chritine Glade (iS), ©TR Anastasia Pelikh (iS); p.266 © iStockphoto.com/Christian Anthony; p.298 © BG Skutvik (Dr), © TR Harland & Wolff, A/W Jerry Fowler; p.299 © TL Tebnad (Dr); p.300 © iStockphoto.com/Karimhesham, © iStockphoto.com/Berenike; p.324 ©BG Slallison (Dr), A/W Jerry Fowler; p.325 © TR Panagiotis Risvas (Dr), © CR Konstantin Sutyagin (Dr); p.342-343 © Catherine Karnow/Corbis; p.376 © BG D (Dr), A/W Jerry Fowler; p.377 © TL Alexandr Mitiuc (Dr), A/W Jerry Fowler; p.378 © iStockphoto.com/Derek Dammann, © iStockphoto.com/Rick Szczechowski; p.418 © BG Sculpies (iS), © BL James Mcquarrie (Dr); p.419 © BL Andrey Konovalikov (Dr), © BC Christian Delbert (Dr); p.420 © iStockphoto.com/narvikk, © iStockphoto.com/Goktug Gurellier; p.436–437 © IKEA Systems B.V., © Daniel PG.

With thanks to Samantha Burns, Claire Beckett, Andy Edmonds, Anton Bush (Gloucester High School for Girls), Matthew Pennington (Wirral Grammar School for Girls), James Toyer (The Buckingham School), Gordon Starkey (Brockhill Park Performing Arts College), Laura Radford and Alan Rees (Wolfreton School) and Mark Foster (Sedgefield Community College).

NOTES

NOTES

NOTES

NOTES

NOTES

NOTES

NOTES